S0-DHX-435

Introduction to Properties of Materials

UNIVERSITY SERIES IN BASIC ENGINEERING

REED-HILL, ROBERT E.—Physical Metallurgy Principles

ROSENTHAL, DANIEL, AND ROBERT M. ASIMOW—Introduction to Properties of Materials, Second Edition

HAGERTY, WILLIAM W., AND HAROLD J. PLASS, JR.—Engineering Mechanics

CHOU, PEI CHI, AND NICHOLAS PAGANO—Elasticity: Tensor, Dyadic, and Engineering Approaches

Introduction to Properties of Materials

Second Edition

Daniel Rosenthal

Senior Professor, Harvey Mudd College

(*formerly Professor of Engineering, University of California, Los Angeles*)

Robert M. Asimow

Professor of Engineering, University of Maryland

Van Nostrand Reinhold Company

New York/Cincinnati/Toronto/London/Melbourne

Van Nostrand Reinhold Company Regional Offices:
New York Cincinnati Chicago Millbrae Dallas

Van Nostrand Reinhold Company International Offices:
London Toronto Melbourne

Library of Congress Catalog Card Number 79-152327

Manufactured in the United States of America

Published by Van Nostrand Reinhold Company
450 West 33rd Street, New York, N.Y. 10001

Published simultaneously in Canada by
Van Nostrand Reinhold Ltd.

10 9 8 7 6 5 4 3 2 1

To Lucy and Adele

PREFACE

The reader familiar with the first edition of this book may have good cause to wonder why the second edition has been increased in size by more than one-third. If alloys, ceramics, and polymers are being given such prominent place in this edition, he may ask, why were they omitted from the previous edition? Yet the omission was not due to oversight. The publisher, more aware of current demands of engineering schools than the author, pressed hard for their inclusion. What kept the author from complying was not that these topics lacked relevance, but that they did not fit in the "plot." At least not in the traditional presentation based on formal, macroscopic thermodynamics; and the author could conceive of no other at that time. It was only when a statistical approach, compatible with the level of preparation of the students, was finally worked out that processes such as allotropy, phase transformation, and diffusivity fell in line with the properties of materials considered in Part II of the book.

The senior author has been fortunate in securing the expert co-authorship of Professor Robert M. Asimow for the demanding task of writing Chapters 18 and 21. And so Part III was conjured up, not surprisingly, with the help of the same two powerful genies: the principles of configurational and statistical stabilities that guided the author through Parts I and II.

Allotropy—phase transformation of homogeneous systems—is the subject of Chapter 17, which begins Part III. Particular attention is paid to the role of temperature in promoting more open and often more symmetrical configurations based on statistical stability. However, the role of pressure is also emphasized, especially in connection with recent work on phase transformations under high pressure.

Phase transformations of heterogeneous systems is alluded to in Chapter 17, but it is given its deserved prominence in the treatment of *alloys* in Chapter 18. The interplay between configurational and statistical stabilities comes to the fore in depicting simplified binary phase diagrams. The prediction of properties based on these diagrams is thereby greatly facilitated, as is the understanding of the ensuing structural changes produced by heat treatment. Without minimizing the importance of phase diagrams, the exceptional role of *coordinated polyhedra*, so brilliantly developed by Linus Pauling in his classical work on the nature of the chemical bond, is taken full advantage of in discussing *ceramics* (Chapter 19). This role is particularly well-exemplified in the knotty alpha-beta quartz transformation—a subject generally avoided in textbooks because of its seeming complexity. Nor can the role of coordinated polyhedra be ignored when dealing with the short-range and long-range aggregations in ceramics, leading as it does to crystalline, amorphous, and mixed states of aggregation and exemplified by whitewares, glasses, and cement.

The constant interplay between configurational and statistical stabilities which occurs in the short-range vs. long-range arrangement of molecules in ceramics is also found in *polymers* (Chapter 20), thereby offering a natural transition from ceramic to polymeric materials: fibers, elastomers, and plastics. An engineering approach to the most efficient utilization of these properties is seen in the *composite materials* with the polymeric matrix bonding high strength filaments into a flexible and resistant unit. And so the probing into the nature of things which had begun with a single atom in Chapter 1 ends in Chapter 20 with a glimpse into the most intricate and complex patterns of atoms which nature and man have contrived to pack into one giant molecule: the polymeric chain, an ultimate product of interplay between the configurational and statistical stabilities. A further step in this interplay takes us out of the field of engineering materials into the realm of living organisms.

Yet the task is not finished. It is not enough to produce materials to the desired specification; it is also necessary to anticipate their performance in a given environment. The final chapter addresses itself to this important practical question.

The inclusion of Part III in the Second Edition has understandably increased the list of persons to whom we owe thanks and gratitude for help and advice. We would like to single out Dr. W. J. Knapp and Dr. W. J. Bailey to whom we are deeply indebted for guidance in the less familiar fields of materials, the former in the field of ceramics, the latter in the field of polymers. If this guidance has not borne the desired fruits, the blame for the shortcomings rests on the authors alone. Our thanks are due also to Mrs. Mildred Hudson for her patient typing and retyping of the manuscript.

Daniel Rosenthal
Robert M. Asimow

CONTENTS

4 Determination of Structure of Solids

PART II
GENERAL PROPERTIES OF MATERIALS

5 Definition and Subdivision of Material Properties

6 Mechanical Properties: Elasticity

7 Properties Related to Elasticity: 1 Specific Surface Energy

SUMMARY OF SYMBOLS, UNITS, AND NOMENCLATURE

As far as possible the symbols, units, and abbreviations recommended by the International Union of Pure and Applied Physics were adopted (see *Physics Today*, **15**, 6, June 1962, pp. 21–30). As a rule the MKSQ system of units is used, except where other systems, CGS or English, are more convenient. Quantities are rounded off to three significant figures. Unless there is duplication, the symbols appear in the same order as in the text.

List of Abbreviations

ampere	amp	erg	(spell out)
ampere-turn	amp-turn	gram	g
angstrom	Å	joule	J
atmosphere	atm	kilogram	kg
calorie	cal	kilowatt-hour	kWh
centi (prefix)	c	meter	m
centimeter	cm	milli (prefix)	m
centipoise	cP	mole	(spell out)
coulomb	Q	newton	N
debye	(spell out)	ohm	(spell out)
decibel	db	poise	P
degree	deg or °	pounds per square inch	lb/in.^{2}
degrees Celsius, degrees centigrade	°C	rhe	(spell out)
degrees Kelvin	°K	second	sec
dyne	dyn	stoke	(spell out)
electromotive force	emf	volt	V
electron volt	eV	watt	W
electrostatic unit	esu	weber	Wb

Fundamental Units and Quantities

1 Å	one angstrom $= 10^{-10}$ m $= 10^{-8}$ cm
e	electric charge of the electron $= -4.80 \times 10^{-10}$ CGS esu $= -1.60 \times 10^{-19}$ Q
k	Boltzmann's gas constant $= 1.38 \times 10^{-23}$ J/deg

m	rest mass of electron = 9.11×10^{-31} kg
h	Planck's constant = 6.62×10^{-34} J sec
N_A	Avogadro's number = 6.02×10^{23} atoms or molecules per mole
N_0	number of molecules of a gas at standard conditions (atmospheric pressure and 273°K) = $2.69 \times 10^{25}/m^3$
ε_0	dielectric constant in vacuum (conversion factor) = 8.85×10^{-12} Q^2 $sec^2/(kg\ m^3)$
1 debye	unit of molecular dipole moment = 3.33×10^{-30} Qm
$\hat{\mu}_0$	magnetic permeability in vacuum (conversion factor) = 1.25×10^{-6} kg m/Q^2
1 Bohr magneton	unit of atomic magnetic dipole = 9.27×10^{-24} Q m^2/sec
1 eV	one electron volt = 1.60×10^{-19} J
$\boldsymbol{L}$	Lorenz number = 2.45×10^{-8} $(V/deg)^2$

Symbols and Units

Structure of Matter

(Chapters 1–4)

M	mass per mole [g/mole]
N_A	Avogadro's number (*see* Fundamental Units and Quantities)
ρ	density [g/cm^3] or [kg/m^3]
a	edge of unit cell [Å]
V	volume [cm^3] or [m^3]
n	number of atoms per pattern or per unit cell
t_m	melting point [°C]
T_m	melting point [°K]
t_{cr}	critical temperature of undercooling [°C]
T_{cr}	critical temperature of undercooling [°K]
λ	wavelength [Å]
d	interplanar distance [Å]
Δd	increment of d
(hkl)	indices of a family of crystallographic planes
$\{hkl\}$	indices of families (hkl) of the same form
$[uvw]$	indices of crystallographic direction
$\langle uvw \rangle$	indices of directions $[uvw]$ of the same form

Mechanical Properties

(Chapters 5–12)

e	charge of the electron in CGS esu units (*see* Fundamental Units and Quantities)
f	force [dyn]

also f	coefficient of friction [number]
f_{max}	cohesive force per ion [dyn]
r	distance of closest approach [cm]
also r	radius
Δr	increment of r
r_0	equilibrium distance of closest approach [cm]
r_1	interionic distance at f_{max} [Å]
k	r_1/r_0
e_A	charge of an anion [CGS esu units]
e_C	charge of a cation [CGS esu units]
z	valency [number]
m	repulsion exponent [number]
also m	mass of a molecule [g]
F	force [dyn]
S	cross-sectional area [cm^2]
also S	reverse fatigue strength [dyn/cm^2] or [lb/in.^{2}]
l	length [cm]
Δl	increase of length
K	spring constant [dyn/cm]
σ	axial stress [dyn/cm^2] or [N/M^2] or [lb/in.^{2}]
σ_{max}	cohesive strength [dyn/cm^2]
ε	axial strain [number]
ε_t	transverse strain [number]
ε_v	volumetric strain [number]
σ_0	conventional axial stress [dyn/cm^2] or [lb/in.^{2}]
E	Young's modulus of elasticity [dyn/cm^2] or [lb/in.^{2}]
$\mu = \varepsilon_t/\varepsilon$	Poisson's ratio [number]
E_0	Modulus of elasticity for $\mu = 0$
τ	shear stress [dyn/cm^2] or [lb/in.^{2}]
τ_{cr}	critical shear stress [dyn/cm^2]
γ	shear strain [number]
also γ	surface tension [dyn/cm]
G	shear modulus of elasticity [dyn/cm^2] or [lb/in.^{2}]
G_u	unrelaxed shear modulus
G_r	relaxed shear modulus
B	bulk modulus of elasticity [dyn/cm^2] or [lb/in.^{2}]
v	volume [cm^3]
also v	velocity [cm/sec]
W	work or energy [ergs] or [in. lb]
W'	work or energy per unit volume [erg/cm^3] or [in.lb/in.^{3}]
W'_e	elastic energy per unit volume [ergs/cm^3] or [in.lb/in.^{3}]
u	energy per unit mass [J/kg]
w	work per ion [ergs]
ω	specific surface energy [ergs/cm^2]

p	pressure [dyn/cm^2] or [lb/in.^{2}]
Δp	pressure increment
δ	density [g/cm^3]
also δ	period of thermal vibration [sec]
g	acceleration of gravity [cm sec^{-2}]
P	force or load [dyn]
c	length of Griffith crack [cm]
t	thickness [cm]
also t	time [sec]
b	breadth [cm]
T	force [dyn]
s	shear displacement
Y.S.	yield stress [dyn/cm^2] or [lb/in.^{2}]
0.2% Y.S.	yield stress at 0.2% permanent strain
T.S.	tensile strength [dyn/cm^2] or [lb/in.^{2}]
N	number of cycles in fatigue
M	mean stress [dyn/cm^2] or [lb/in.^{2}]
v	$1/\delta$ frequency of thermal vibrations per second
Δv	velocity increment
a_0	side of a cubical volume assigned to a molecule [Å] or [cm]
$\dot{\gamma}$	shear strain rate, per second, $= d\gamma/dt$
η	viscosity [dyn sec/cm^2]
1 P	one poise = 1 dyn sec/cm^2
1 cP	one centipoise = 1/100 P
$\phi = 1/\eta$	coefficient of fluidity [cm^2/dyn sec]
1 rhe	1 cm^2/dyn cm
η/ρ	kinematic viscosity [cm^2/sec]
1 stoke	1 cm^2/sec
1 centistoke	1/100 stoke
R	radius [cm]
θ	relaxation time [sec] ($= \eta/G$)
T	temperature [°K] or [°C]
T_f	melting point [°K] or [°C]
Q	rate of flow [cm^3/sec]

Electrical and Thermal Properties

(Chapters 13–16)

e	electric charge of the electron (*see* Fundamental Units and Quantities)
k	Boltzmann's gas constant (*see* Fundamental Units and Quantities)

T	absolute temperature [°K]
T_0	273°K
N, N'	number of molecules per m^3, also number of valence electrons per m^3
N_0	N at standard conditions (*see* Fundamental Units and Quantities)
M	molar mass [kg/mole]
ρ	density [kg/m^3]
f	force [N]
$\boldsymbol{q}, \boldsymbol{q}'$	electric charges [Q]
$\boldsymbol{E}$	electric field strength [N/Q.]
$\boldsymbol{E}_1$	local field strength [N/Q.]
$\boldsymbol{\varepsilon}_0$	dielectric constant in vacuum (*see* Fundamental Units and Quantities)
$\boldsymbol{V}$	electric potential [V] or [J/Q]
$\Delta \boldsymbol{V}$	potential difference
$\boldsymbol{\varepsilon}$	dielectric constant or permittivity [Q^2 sec^2/(kg m^3)], generally listed as $\boldsymbol{\varepsilon}/\boldsymbol{\varepsilon}_0$
Z, n	atomic number of an element
d	distance between centroids of charges [Å] or [m]
R	radius of atom [Å] or [m]
$\boldsymbol{\mu}, \boldsymbol{\mu}_p$	molecular dipole moment [Q m]
β	fraction [number]
also β	(fraction of $\boldsymbol{\mu}_p N$), $\beta = \boldsymbol{E}\boldsymbol{\mu}_p/3kT$ [number]
1 debye	unit of molecular dipole moment (*see* Fundamental Units and Quantities)
$\boldsymbol{P}$	electric polarization, or electric dipole per unit volume [Qm/m^3]
A, A'	cross-sectional area [m^2]
also A	constant
l	distance [m]
$\boldsymbol{D}$	electrical charge density [Q/m^2]
$\boldsymbol{\chi}$	electrical susceptibility [number] $= (\boldsymbol{\varepsilon} - \boldsymbol{\varepsilon}_0)/\boldsymbol{\varepsilon}_0$
W	work [J]
$\boldsymbol{\alpha}$	total polarizability [Q^2 sec^2/kg]
$\boldsymbol{\alpha}_e$	electronic polarizability [Q^2 sec^2/kg]
$\boldsymbol{\alpha}_i$	ionic polarizability [Q^2 sec^2/kg]
$\boldsymbol{\alpha}_0$	orientation polarizability [Q^2 sec^2/kg] $= \boldsymbol{\mu}_p^2/3kT$
F, F_1, F_2	force [N]
z	valency [number]
r	distance or radius [m]
r_0	equilibrium distance [Å] or [m]
Δr	increment of distance
m	repulsion exponent [number]

also m	rest mass of the electron (*see* Fundamental Units and Quantities)
$\sqcap_i$	molar ionic polarization [m^3/mole]
$\sqcap_1 \rho/M$	ionic molar polarizability, per unit volume
$\boldsymbol{d}$	piezoelectric modulus [m/V]
$\boldsymbol{g}$	voltage output coefficient $\left[\frac{V/m}{N/m^2}\right]$
W	energy [J]
u	energy per unit mass [J/kg]
h	Planck's constant (*see* Fundamental Units and Quantities)
also h	height [m]
b	breadth [m]
$\boldsymbol{I}, \boldsymbol{i}\, \boldsymbol{i}'$	electric current [Q/sec]
T	torque [Nm]
$\boldsymbol{m}, \boldsymbol{m}_i, \boldsymbol{m}_d, \boldsymbol{m}'$	magnetic moment [Qm^2/sec]
$\boldsymbol{B}$	magnetic induction [Wb/m^2] or [kg/Q sec]
$\boldsymbol{B}_S$	magnetic induction at saturation
1 Wb	one weber = 1 V sec
$\boldsymbol{H}$	magnetic field intensity [amp-turns/m] or [Q/(m sec)]
$\hat{\mu}$	magnetic permeability [kg m/Q^2]
$\hat{\mu}_0$	magnetic permeability in vacuum (*see* Fundamental Units and Quantities)
$\boldsymbol{M}, \boldsymbol{M}_d$	magnetization, or magnetic moment per unit volume [Q/(sec m)]
$\boldsymbol{M}^*$	magnetization of a long solenoid [Q/(sec m)]
$\boldsymbol{M}_S$	saturation magnetization [Q/(sec m)]
$\boldsymbol{M}_0$	ultimate magnetization at absolute zero [Q/(sec m)]
1 $\boldsymbol{m}_B$	Bohr magneton (*see* Fundamental Units and Quantities)
$\boldsymbol{m}_p$	permanent magnetic dipole [Q m^2/sec]
$\chi_m = (\hat{\mu} - \hat{\mu}_0)/\hat{\mu}_0$	magnetic susceptibility [number]
χ_m/N	molecular magnetic susceptibility [m^3/molecule]
$\chi_m N_A/N$	molar magnetic susceptibility [m^3/mole]
χ_m/ρ	specific magnetic susceptibility [m^3/kg]
a_H	radius of Bohr's hydrogen atom
ν	frequency, per second
v	velocity [m/sec]
λ	wavelength [m] or [Å]
also λ, λ'	mean free path [m] or [Å]
C	constant in Curie's law [°K]
C_m	$\chi_m T/N$ – material constant [m^3 °K]
C_M	$\chi_m N_A T/N$ – material constant [m^3 °K/mole]
C_ρ	$\chi_m T/\rho$ – material constant [m^3 °K/kg]
$\boldsymbol{\Phi}$	magnetic flux, webers or [kg m^3/(Q sec)]

Φ	induced emf $\left(= \frac{d\Phi}{dt} = \text{volt}\right)$
θ	Curie point [°K]
s	$\boldsymbol{M}_s/\boldsymbol{M}_0$
ϕ	T/θ
T_c	Néel point [°K]
v_c	drift velocity [m/sec]
t_c	mean free time [sec]
L	length [m]
$\boldsymbol{R}$	electrical resistance, ohms or [kg m/(Q² sec)]
1 ohm	1 kg m/(Q² sec)
$\boldsymbol{\rho}$	electrical resistivity [ohm m]
$\boldsymbol{\rho}_e$	conduction electron resistivity
$\boldsymbol{\rho}_h$	hole resistivity
$\boldsymbol{\sigma}$	electrical conductivity [(ohm m)$^{-1}$]
$\boldsymbol{\sigma}_i$	intrinsic semiconductivity [(ohm m)$^{-1}$]
$\boldsymbol{\sigma}_e$	extrinsic semiconductivity [(ohm m)$^{-1}$]
α_T	thermal coefficient of resistivity, per degree
$\boldsymbol{J}$	current density [amperes per unit area] or [Q/(sec m²)]
m_e	variable mass of electron [kg]
m_h	"mass" of the hole [kg]
t_e, t_h	collision times [sec]
n_e	number of conducting electrons per unit volume [m^{-3}]
n_h	number of holes per unit volume [m^{-3}]
K, K', K_1	dissociation coefficients
1 eV	one electron volt (*see* Fundamental Units and Quantities)
E_g	energy gap [eV]
E_i	ionization energy [eV]
N_D	number of donors per unit volume [m^{-3}]
N_A	number of acceptors per unit volume [m^{-3}]
$\dot{Q}$, $\dot{Q}'$	heat flow or rate of heat transfer [watts, W]
κ	thermal conductivity [W/m deg (Kelvin or centigrade)]
κ_e	thermal conductivity due to free charge carriers
κ_1	thermal conductivity due to lattice vibration
$\boldsymbol{L}$	Lorenz number (*see* Fundamental Units and Quantities)
c	velocity of sound [m/sec]
S	thermal emf coefficient or thermoelectric power [V/deg]
$\boldsymbol{V}_t$	thermal emf
w_i, w_i'	thermal inflow energy per electron or molecule [J]
w_e, w_e'	thermal outflow energy per electron or molecule [J]
$\dot{W}$, $\dot{W}_i$, $\dot{W}_e$	thermal energy, thermal inflow energy, and thermal outflow energy, respectively, per unit time [W]

N	number of electrons passing through a given cross-sectional area in unit time [$\sec^{-1}$]

Alloys, Ceramics, and Polymers

(Chapters 17–20)

W'	work of deformation per unit volume
p	pressure
W'_v	work of deformation per unit volume in three directions
H'_p and H'_o	heats of fusion per unit volume under external pressure p and under no pressure, respectively
T_f	temperature of fusion
v_m	volume per mole
H_f	heat of fusion per mole
c	composition
f	fraction of unmixed arrangements
c_A, c_B	concentrations of components A and B
N	number of atoms in a given volume
N_A, N_B	number of atoms A and B, $N_A + N_B = N$
p_A, p_B	partial pressures of components A and B
V	volume occupied by mixture of atoms A and B
V_A, V_B	volume occupied by atoms A and B, $V_A + V_B = V$
S	area
W	work of deformation
W_A, W_B	works of unmixing of gases A and B, $W_A + W_B = W$
a, b	diameters of atoms
ε_n	strain of the nth hexagon
$(b - a)/a$	size factor
u	strain energy per unit volume
B	bulk modulus of elasticity
u_i	fraction of strain energy, u depending on concentration
α	coefficient
$\langle B \rangle$, $\langle a \rangle$	average values of B and a
(w/o)	weight percent
(a/o)	atomic percent
a_0	lattice parameter
N	number of atoms
N_x^o	number of solute atoms per unit area transported in the x direction
ν	frequency
φ, φ', φ''	fraction
c_a, c_b	concentration
a_0	distance

J	N_x^o/N – flux
D	diffusivity
a_0	lattice parameter
r_c, r_a	radius of cation and anion, respectively
N, N_i	number
f	fractional charge
z, z'	valence
n	coordination number
s	z/n bond strength
$\hat{\varepsilon}_e$	electric polarizability
$\hat{\mu}_e$	magnetic permeability
v	velocity
n	index of refraction
w/c	water cement ratio
w_b/c	chemically bond water cement ratio
w_a/c	adsorbed water cement ratio
w_e/c	capillary water cement ratio
a/c	aggregate cement ratio

The Effect of Environment on Materials

(Chapter 21)

E, E^o, E_T	voltage
a, b	number
n, n_c	number
e	charge of electron
G	free energy
c_A, c_B, c_D, c_H	concentration
F	Faraday constant
J, J_a, J_c	number of moles leaving the electrodes per unit area and time
I	electric current
A, A_c	area
R, R_e, R_i, R_j	electric resistance
D	diffusivity
y, x	distance
V	voltage
V_{ox}, V_{met}	volume
ρ	density
M	molar or atomic mass
K	constant
t	time
Z	number of equivalents

κ	conductivity
E_p, E_n	energy
m	neutron mass
L_d	mean free path
σ_d	displacement cross section
N_a	number of atoms per unit volume

I / THE STRUCTURE OF MATTER

"Atoms are eternal, absolutely simple; they are all alike in quality but different in shape, order and position." **Democritus,** c. 460–357 B.C.

1/ AGGREGATION OF ATOMS

Most of this chapter is a review of topics learned in general chemistry. The emphasis here, however, is slightly different. We will be concerned with the conditions under which atoms aggregate rather than with the methods and chemical reactions that bring about these aggregations. The concept of stability will be given special attention.

1-1 Why Aggregation. A modern cosmogonist elaborating on the creation of the Universe might be tempted to recast the first sentence of Genesis: "In the beginning there were neutrons, protons, and electrons." The modern engineer will do well to leave this step of design to others. If he wants to make new materials, his chances of success are much greater if he starts directly with atoms, which are the first step of aggregation of the elementary particles: neutrons, protons, and electrons.

This maxim follows from the teachings of general chemistry. It is found that the elements listed in the periodic table are the stable ones and are probably the only stable aggregations of elementary particles available for his use. With a few notable exceptions, such as fuels and explosives, the materials in which the engineer is mostly interested are those that are, or can be made, stable under operating conditions. It would make little sense ensuring the stability of an entire structure when the building blocks themselves are bound to disintegrate in the process like a heap of unfired bricks. The engineer has no choice but to use atoms as nature has provided them. The same is not true of the next step in the building process—the aggregation of atoms into more complex structures. As we shall see, several competing factors are involved in this process, and those used by nature are not the only ones capable of imparting stability to the atomic structure under operating conditions. The study of these factors and their relative importance in the building of naturally occurring structures can therefore provide useful clues for synthesis of new structures.

1-2 Properties of the Atom. It will suffice for our purpose to recall that the atom consists of (a) *protons* (positively charged particles) and *neutrons* (uncharged particles about 1% heavier and approximately equal in number) concentrated in a small volume (*nucleus*) of a linear size 10^{-14} m, and (b) *electrons* (negatively charged particles with a mass roughly 2000 times smaller than that of either protons or neutrons) revolving about the nucleus at distances of the order of 10^{-10} m from the nucleus.

It follows from this description that the nucleus is always positively charged. The magnitude of this charge, expressed in multiples of the charge of the electron (with changed sign), is called the atomic number. It also follows that in a neutral atom (in which the negative charge of the electrons neutralizes the positive charge of the nucleus) the number of electrons is equal to the atomic number. This circumstance makes the atomic number a far more important characteristic of the atom in problems of aggregation than its mass, since it is the electrons and not the nucleus that are here the governing factor.[1] The periodic table of elements is arranged accordingly in the order of increasing atomic numbers: 1 for hydrogen, 2 for helium, 3 for lithium, etc., up to 92 for uranium, and beyond.

The periodicity of chemical properties, after the number of electrons has increased by 8, is the most significant characteristic of the first 16 elements following helium, Table 1-1. Thus argon (Ar), atomic number 18, has the same properties as neon (Ne), atomic number 10, and helium (He), atomic number 2. It is the same with chlorine (Cl), atomic number 17, and fluorine (F), atomic number 9, or with sodium (Na), atomic number 11, and lithium (Li), atomic number 3. Since He, Ne, and Ar are inert elements—with no tendency to form stable associations (compounds) with other elements—

TABLE 1-1 PERIODIC TABLE OF THE FIRST 18 ELEMENTS

Period		I	II	III	IV	V	VI	VII	VIII
1	Element Electrons	H 1							He 2
2	Element Electrons	Li 2 + 1	Be 2 + 2	B 2 + 3	C 2 + 4	N 2 + 5	O 2 + 6	F 2 + 7	Ne 2 + 8 = 10
3	Element Electrons	Na 10 + 1	Mg 10 + 2	Al 10 + 3	Si 10 + 4	P 10 + 5	S 10 + 6	Cl 10 + 7	Ar 10 + 8 = 18

we conclude that the configurations of 2, 2 + 8 = 10 electrons, 2 + 8 + 8 = 18 electrons, are particularly stable. This stability is characterized by the resistance the electrons offer to being removed from the atom. Thus it has been found that to remove any of the two electrons from He (i.e., to convert He to an ion, He^+) requires about 4.5 times as much work as to remove the next, third, electron from Li. Similarly, to remove any of the eight additional electrons of Ne requires more than four times as much work as to remove the next, eleventh, electron of Na, and so on. Note however,

[1] We recall for the sake of completeness that two elements having the same atomic number (the same number of protons), but different masses (different number of neutrons), are called *isotopes* (from Greek *isos*, meaning the same, and *topos*, meaning place), because they occupy the same place in the periodic table.

that any of the additional eight electrons of Ne is held somewhat less tightly than any of the two electrons of He. It is the same with the next additional eight electrons of Ar compared to the eight previously considered electrons of Ne. Here the ratio is 1 to 1.35 in favor of Ne.

We conclude that, although an octet of electrons represents in the inert elements a particularly stable configuration compared to that of the neighboring atoms, each additional octet is somewhat less tightly held than the previous ones. We picture this situation as though the first two electrons were closer to the nucleus than the next eight, and these, in turn, closer than the succeeding eight. This, according to present views, is true on the average but not at any particular instant. We also say, using the description of the older atom model, the Bohr atom, that the first pair of electrons and each of the succeeding octets fill the first, second, and third shell, respectively. Once a shell is filled, each additional electron moves to the next outer shell. Thus Na following Ne puts the next, eleventh, electron in the third shell. We saw that this electron, being alone in the shell, is not held particularly tightly. The bond is strengthened, however, when the shell receives a second occupant, and so on, until the shell is filled again with eight electrons.

We summarize these findings by saying that each period in the periodic table corresponds to the formation of a new outer shell, with one electron for Group I, two for Group II, etc., up to eight electrons for Group VIII, at which stage the outer shell and the period are closed. We know that the chemical properties of atoms, in particular their valences, are generally governed by the number of electrons in the outer shell. Hence their name of valence electrons. As an example, Fig. 1-1 shows the schematic structure

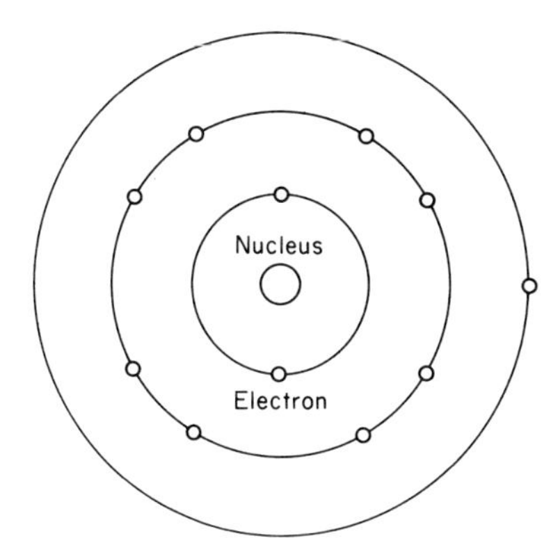

FIG. 1-1 Structure of sodium atom—simplified Bohr model

of Na, with one valence electron in the outer shell. However, this general picture requires amendment in regard to transition elements. We shall come to this point later in connection with magnetic properties, Chapter 14.

1-3 Inert Elements. We are now in a better position to describe the modes of aggregation of atoms found in various elements at room temperature. The governing principle here is the attainment of the greatest stability of aggregation. That is, among the various modes of aggregation, that mode will prevail which requires the greatest amount of work for removing any of the electrons from the whole.

To explain our point of view we shall begin with inert elements, Group VIII, Table 1-1. We pointed out previously that the formation of octets confers great stability to each individual atom of these elements. The question arises whether the stability of the atoms will be increased if, say, two of them are kept close together. We can rephrase this question by asking whether any of the atoms of, say, Ne will strengthen the hold on its own electrons by having an additional electron in close vicinity. The computation made for room temperature and above shows that the answer is no. This follows from the argument that the eleventh electron is not being held tightly even in Na, where the nucleus has a stronger hold on the electrons because of an added positive charge. Lacking this support, the eleventh electron and any additional electrons will be repelled. We shall see later (Section 1-8) that a small electrostatic attraction (molecular bonding) is nevertheless possible between atoms but at a much lower temperature. At room temperature the thermal agitation is much too strong to allow such a weak bond to be stable.

In conclusion, the most stable aggregation of inert elements at room temperature is that of isolated atoms, or of a monoatomic gas.

1-4 Covalent Bonding. The above is not true of the neighboring elements of Group VII, whose atoms lack one valence electron to fill the shell. By acquiring the missing electron, the shell would have been more stable, but the nucleus has not got the necessary extra proton to keep permanently an additional electron. A way out of this difficulty could be found by sharing the coveted electron with a neighbor. The latter, however, could lay a similar claim to one of the electrons of the former. When two such competing tendencies exist, the solution insuring the greatest stability for both nuclei is obtained by a compromise—both "seventh" electrons are shared. By being held close to the two nuclei, these electrons must necessarily remain between them most of the time. They also remain close to each other by virtue of the mutual attraction exercised by their magnetic fields. (This point will be considered further in Chapter 14.) On both counts, a strong bond develops between the two atoms; this is the *covalent* bond of the chemists which is directed from one nucleus to the other and which resists any attempt to separate them into individual atoms. This explains the type of structures found in the elements of Group VII—the building block here is the diatomic molecule, not the atom, Fig. 1-2. The attraction between molecules is, of course, weak, since each of them now represents a stable configuration of electrons. Thus chlorine is a diatomic gas at room temperature, and although iodine is a solid, it sublimes readily into a diatomic gas, an indication that the solid is rather unstable.

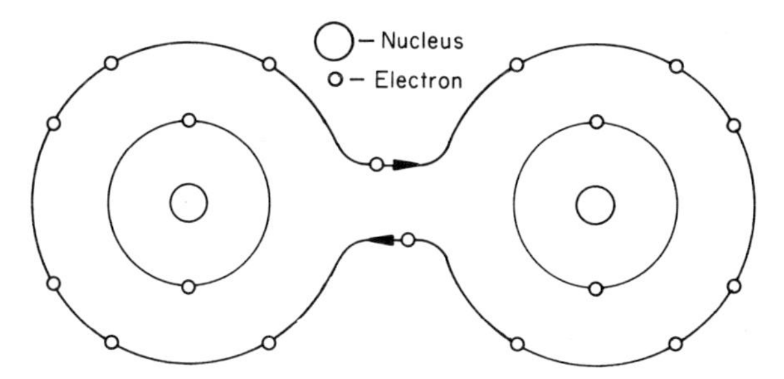

FIG. 1-2 Aggregation of atoms in fluorine (schematic) by sharing one pair of electrons—diatomic molecule

This process of sharing of electron pairs is also the basic mechanism of aggregations prevailing among the elements of Groups VI, V, and IV.

The atom of Group VI lacks two valence electrons to fill the shell. Accordingly, it forms two covalent bonds, one with a neighbor from the left and one with a neighbor from the right. Since each of the neighbors does the same, a long chain of atoms is built with the covalent bond between them acting as the connecting link. The chain is not straight. It turns out that the electrons that each atom assigns to the formation of the two bonds, even though on the same shell, have a preferred direction of motion with respect to each other. The bonds, too, acquire directional properties and have a definite angle, the bond angle, between them. This angle can be determined from the analysis of crystal structure (e.g., by X-rays, as explained in Chapter 4). Its value for sulfur (S), selenium (Se), and tellurium (Te)—all in Group VI—is close to 90°, being 106°, 105°, and 102°, respectively. The magnitude of the angle is the only restriction to which these bonds are subjected. After two links have been formed between three atoms, the third link (with the fourth atom) does not have to—and in general does not—lie in the plane formed by the first two. The thermal motion of the atom will tend as a rule to keep it out of this plane. The same is true, of course, of each successive link. As a result, the chain will coil in a sort of a spiral. This is readily recognized in the structure of Te, Fig. 1-3. Coiled structures of similar nature will be encountered later, the most outstanding example being rubber. Here, too, the coiling is due to the nonalignment of single covalent bonds, the only difference being that the bonds link identical hydrocarbon molecules rather than identical atoms. The ease with which these structures can be coiled and uncoiled is manifest in the high elasticity of rubber.

It is clear from the foregoing that when the atom lacks three instead of two electrons to fill the outer shell, it will tend to build three covalent bonds by pairing each of its own three electrons with a corresponding electron of its three close neighbors. Since the same is true of each of the neighbors, and of the neighbors of these neighbors, and so on, a two-dimensional *layer* of

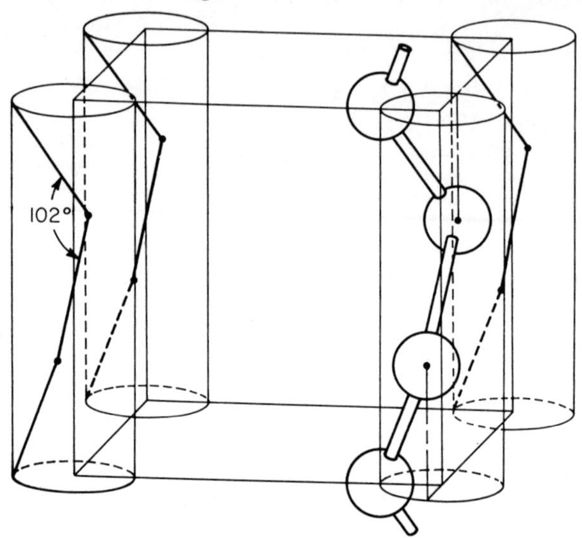

FIG. 1-3 Aggregation of atoms in tellurium (schematic) by sharing two pairs of electrons—chain molecule

atoms results. If all atoms of the layer lie on the same plane, they would form a honeycomb structure, as shown by the dotted lines in Fig. 1-4. Actually a structure of this kind will be encountered later (e.g., graphite and

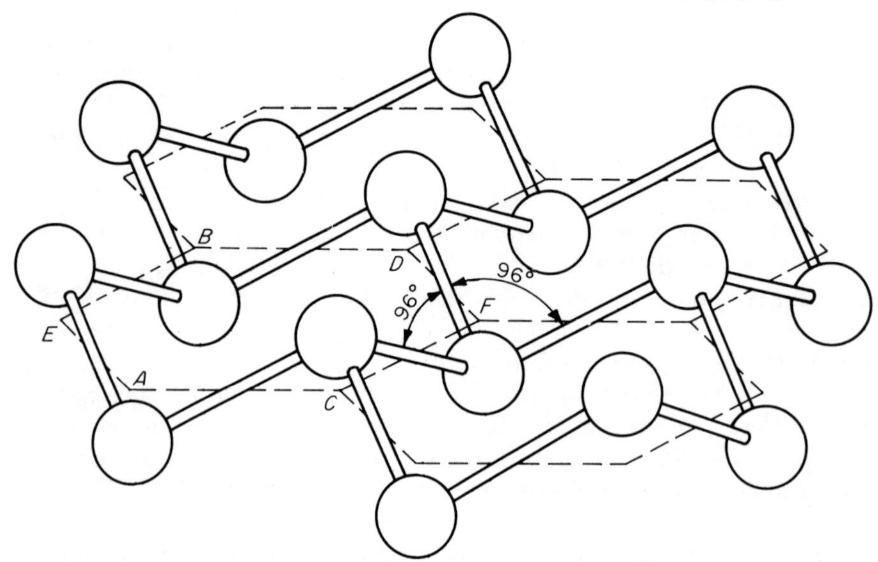

FIG. 1-4 Aggregation of atoms in antimony (schematic) by sharing three pairs of electrons—layer molecule

silicates), but here, as in the case of S, Se, and Te, the bonds acquire a definite orientation with respect to each other, and for the same reasons; the three bonding electrons in the atom have a preferred direction of motion. The resulting bonding angles are even closer to 90° than those of Group VI elements, being 97° for arsenic (As), 96° for antimony (Sb), and 94° for bismuth (Bi). In other words, the three bonds stand almost at right angles to each other with the atom forming the apex of a regular pyramid. We can account for such a configuration by folding the hexagon along the diagonals AB and CD and placing the points A, B, and F on one plane and points E, C, and D on another. This makes the layer look like a sheet of corrugated metal. The layer is as basic to the structure of elements of Group V as the chain is to the structure of elements of Group VI. However, the corrugations cannot be as easily flattened out as the chains can be uncoiled, because the electrons resist any attempt to change the bond angles between them. The layer structures, therefore, lack the high elasticity of rubber.

Before turning to the important type of bonding of Group IV, we will observe that covalent bonding alone is not sufficient to build three-dimensional solids out of the elements of the groups considered so far. We shall see below that indeed other types of bonding intervene to aggregate the diatomic molecules of Group VII, the chains of Group VI, and the layers of Group V into larger structures. This is not true for Group IV. Here the covalent bonds alone suffice to build a three-dimensional aggregate of atoms of great stability. The reason is twofold:

1. All four valence electrons contribute to the covalent bonding.
2. The four covalent bonds making equal solid angles between them place the four neighboring atoms at the corners of a regular tetrahedron, Fig. 1-5.

The building unit is therefore a three-dimensional cell, and its growth can proceed unimpeded in all three directions merely by extending the mechanism of bonding to each neighbor. The resulting structure is characteristic of diamond, but it is also found in other elements of Group IV: silicon (Si), germanium (Ge), and the nonmetallic variety of tin (Sn). Unlike the elements of the previous groups of the periodic table, these elements build their solids directly from atoms without using intermediate aggregations of atoms (molecules) as building blocks. In fact, the whole solid can be considered as one single giant molecule.

The diamond structure with its four covalent bonds is as typical of the solid state as the horse with its four legs is typical of the terrestrial animal. Both convey the image of perfection and stability.[2]

[2] The great hardness of diamond is certainly more due to its structure than to the chemical nature of the carbon. This has been proved recently by building a new mineral called *borazon* out of boron (B) and nitrogen (N). The atoms of B and N can provide together the four pairs of valence electrons needed to form the four covalent bonds. They do not combine in this fashion under natural conditions but they can under high temperature and pressure. The resulting compound has a diamond structure and a hardness comparable to that of diamond.

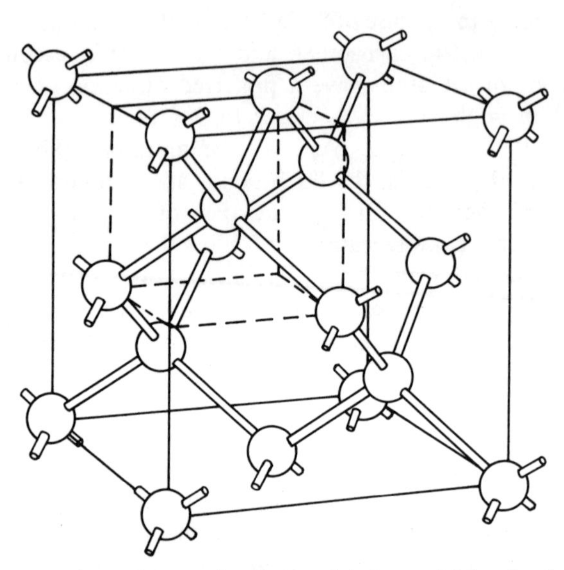

Fig. 1-5 Aggregation of atoms in diamond (schematic) by sharing four pairs of electrons—three-dimensional (giant) molecule. (From William Shockley, *Electrons and Holes in Semiconductors*, Van Nostrand, Princeton, N.J., 1950, by permission)

1-5 Metallic Bonding. The simple concept of covalent bonding comes to grief when we turn to the elements of Groups III, II, and I. To insure the stability of structure in accordance with this concept, five, six, and seven covalent bonds are required, respectively, for which, however, there are only three, two, and one pair of electrons available. The stability of structure must therefore be achieved differently. We find that the valence electrons here are free to move about all the atoms instead of commuting between close neighbors. It is as though by throwing their valence electrons in common pool and becoming positive ions (with closed electron shells), the atoms have a better chance to rebuild a more stable shell by catching more electrons. At the same time, they must surround themselves with more neighbors to neutralize the excess negative charge. The result is a characteristic compaction of the spherical ions which takes two forms: the hexagonal close-packed and the face-centered cubic.

To explain the difference between these two modes of aggregation we resort to a model. We picture the atoms as hard spheres (e.g., ping pong balls)—an analogy generally applicable to ions with closed shells. There is only one way they can then be stacked in two layers one above the other so that each ball touches all its closest neighbors. This stacking is illustrated in the exploded views of Figs. 1-6 and 1-7 by layers 1 and 2. When it comes to the next layer, two possibilities exist: Either the configuration of the first layer is repeated, as in the exploded view of Fig. 1-6, or the third layer is obtained by turning the second 60° about the axis OO', as shown in Fig. 1-7b. In both cases the third layer is in close contact with the underlying one. So are the fourth, fifth, etc., by reproducing the configuration of either the first

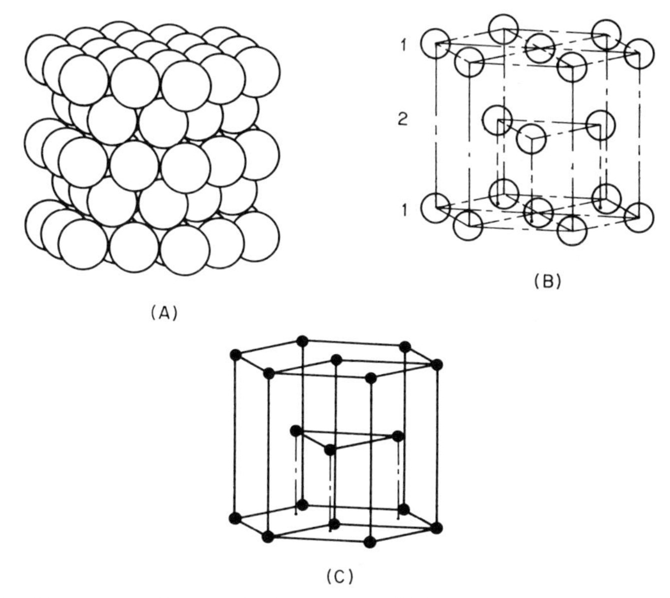

FIG. 1-6 Hexagonal close-packed structure: (a) hexagonal packing; (b) exploded view; (c) hexagonal unit cell

or the second layer at random. However, the kinds of repetitions that prevail in nature on a large scale are found to be ordered, and only two exist:

(a) 1–2–1–2–, etc., as in Fig. 1-6, or
(b) 1–2–3–1–2–3–, etc., as in Fig. 1-7

The first mode of aggregation when enough balls are packed around those shown in Fig. 1-6b leads to the structure depicted in Fig. 1-6a. The same structure can alternatively be built by stacking *hexagonal unit cells* drawn in Fig. 1-6c with the balls reduced to points. Hence the name *hexagonal close-packed* structure (HCP).

Similarly, when enough balls are packed around those shown in Fig. 1-7, a structure depicted in Fig. 1-7a is obtained. The same structure can alternatively be built by stacking *cubic unit cells* shown in Fig. 1-7c with the balls reduced to points.[3] Hence the name *face-centered cubic* structure (FCC).[4]

It can be found by the analysis of crystal structure (described in Chapter 2) that these are the only two close-packed arrangements of atoms which can alternatively be reproduced by a repeated stacking of *identical* unit cells and

[3] In Fig. 1-7a the front half of the cube has been removed to display the close packing on planes such as 1–1–1 passing through the face diagonals.

[4] Also face-centered cubic lattice; see Chapter 2.

therefore the only ones in which the *regularity* of the unit cell is preserved on a large scale. Since these arrangements are also found to be favored by

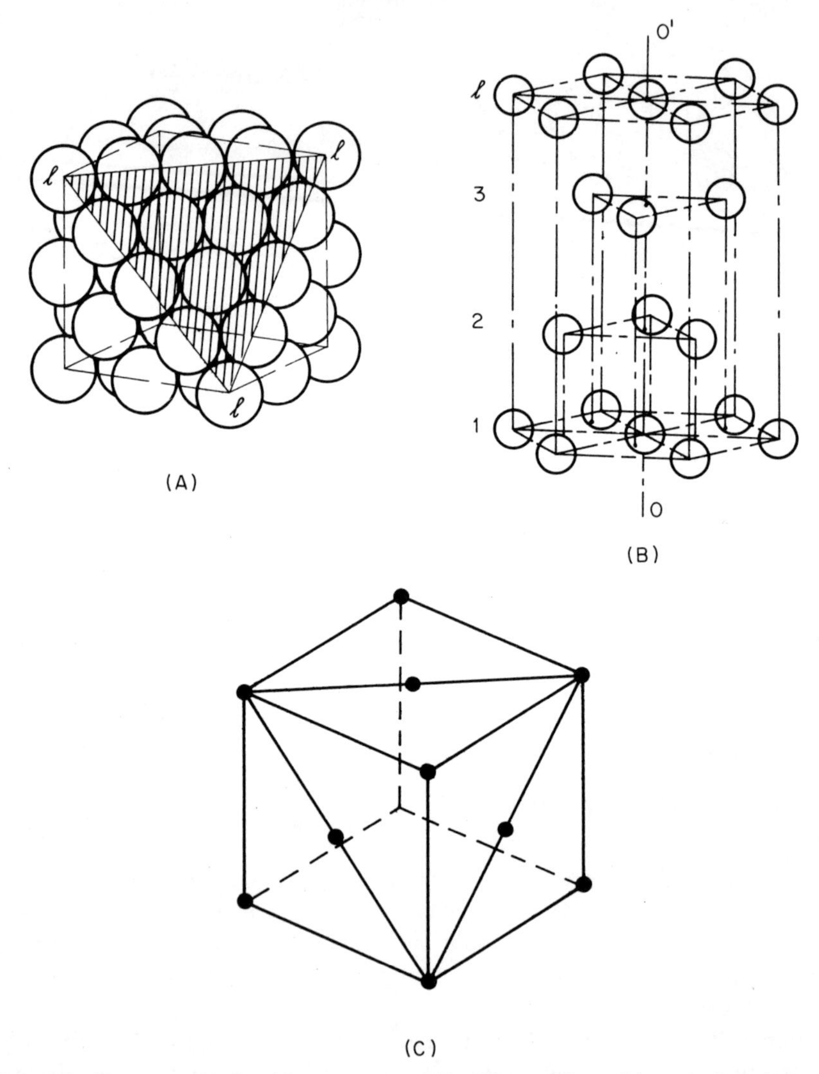

FIG. 1-7 Face-centered cubic structure: (a) cubic packing; (b) exploded view of densest layers; (c) face-centered cubic unit cell

nature, we conclude they are the most stable. Thus, regularity of configuration on a large scale is an important element of stability.[5]

In addition to the hexagonal close-packed and the face-centered cubic

[5] We shall see in Chapter 3 that local disorder or imperfections do exist in real solids on the atomic scale. Among them are *stacking faults*, a disorderly stacking of close-packed layers.

structure, a frequently encountered type of aggregation of the elements of Groups I, II, III—particularly among transition elements—is that based on the body-centered cubic unit cell, Fig. 1-8.

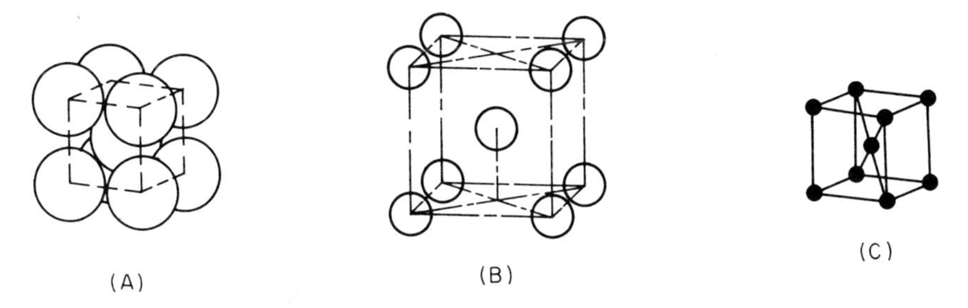

FIG. 1-8 Body-centered cubic structure: (a) body-centered aggregation; (b) exploded view; (c) body-centered cubic unit cell

The freedom with which the valence electrons can move about the atoms in the elements of these three groups accounts for their good electrical conductivity. This will be explained in more detail in Chapter 15. Since good electrical conductivity is characteristic of metals, the type of covalent bonding based on the motion of free electrons is also called *metallic bonding*.

Characteristically, metallic bonding can be found among heavy elements, such as lead (Pb), antimony (Sb), and bismuth (Bi), belonging to other groups of the periodic table. Apparently the valence electrons are here so loosely attached to individual atoms that common sharing increases the stability of the aggregate. A close-packed structure is not uncommon in these elements. Thus Pb has a regular face-centered cubic structure.

1-6 Multiple Bonds. Oxygen and nitrogen form diatomic molecules, but oxygen lacks two electrons to fill its shell and nitrogen lacks three. It is known that these molecules are considerably more stable than those built by the elements of Group VII (considerably more work is required to separate the two atoms). We infer that the atoms of oxygen and nitrogen are held together by more than one covalent bond. The situation with oxygen is rather complicated, because the extra bonds must also account for the magnetic properties of the molecules, but the three bonds of nitrogen are strictly covalent. Nitrogen is a good example of the way nature selects and maintains the types of aggregations that ensure maximum stability. It turns out that if nitrogen were to build layer structures according to the rule of three missing electrons, the stability of the three bonds attaching the atom to its three neighbors (that is, the work necessary to remove the atom from the layer) would be considerably smaller than that of the triple bond holding only two atoms together but at a much shorter distance in a diatomic molecule. The converse is true for the heavier elements selenium and antimony, which cannot be brought together as close as two atoms of nitrogen.

In many instances, however, the situation is not so clear cut. The two modifications of carbon—diamond and graphite—are a good case in point. There are indications that graphite is the more stable one, which may account for its greater abundance. Diamond has been already described as a structure formed by four single covalent bonds. The structure of graphite is shown in Fig. 1-9. It is a layer structure in which each atom has three instead of

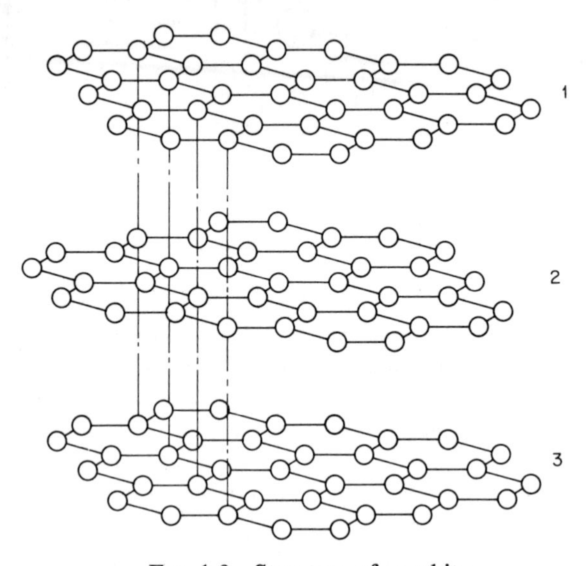

FIG. 1-9 Structure of graphite

four close neighbors. Yet the difference with a typical layer structure of Group V is considerable. First, the layers are flat instead of being corrugated, and second, the distance between the close neighbors is smaller than in diamond. This situation is very similar to that encountered with aromatic molecules (benzene, toluene, etc.). It is ascribed to the fact that the fourth pair of electrons, instead of forming an independent covalent bond, contributes to the strengthening of the three other covalent bonds in equal measure, thus forming the so-called *resonating bond.* There is reason to believe that a bond resonating between three covalent bonds contributes more to the energy of each of them than one-third of the single bond energy.

This would explain why it is more difficult to remove one atom of carbon from a layer of graphite than from the three-dimensional framework of diamond, despite the fact that one is very soft and the other very hard. We shall come to this point once more in dealing with the weak, van der Waals, bonding.

1-7 Ionic Bonding. The greater abundance of compounds in the earth's crust, mostly in the form of minerals rather than elements, can be taken as a good indication that the former are more stable than the latter under atmospheric conditions. Compounds, which are aggregates of unlike atoms, are formed as a rule by a process of transfer of one or more electrons from the less needy—less electronegative—element to the more needy—more electronegative—one. The electrostatic attraction which develops between the loser (the positive ion or *cation*) and the gainer (the negative ion or *anion*) is called *ionic* bonding. By getting rid of all its valence electrons, the loser reverts to the more stable configuration of the inert gas. The gainer builds up to this configuration by getting hold of all missing valence electrons.

The degree of stability which characterizes the ionic bond of a compound can be best illustrated by comparison with the covalent bonds of its components. For example, the work necessary to separate $Li^{+}F^{-}$ into neutral atoms of lithium and fluorine is almost four times as great as that necessary to break the covalent bond of F and six times as great as the work necessary to break the (weaker) metallic bond of Li. The competing advantage of the ionic bonding in the building of the earth's crust can thus be readily understood. It should not be inferred, however, that ionic bonding is the only type of bonding occurring between unlike atoms.

The dielectric behavior of diatomic molecules (halides) discussed in Chapter 13 suggests that the valence electrons of the cation do not go all the way to the anion but stop short of the shell they are supposed to close. This configuration amounts to producing a partly directed (covalent) bond between the cation and anion.

Likewise the modes of aggregation between unlike atoms can often be interpreted in terms of covalent as well as ionic bonds.

We find here again a situation similar to that encountered in a multiple versus a single covalent bond. When the strengths of two types of bonds become comparable, a more stable configuration is obtained through a compromise: the valence electrons are neither shared equally between unlike atoms nor are they confined to a closed shell, but they gravitate somewhere between these two extremes, forming a *partially* ionic bond.

It should come to us as no surprise that this hybrid condition is the rule rather than the exception among unlike atoms. A similar *hybridization* exists between ionic and metallic bonding, particularly among compounds of strong metals and weak metalloids such as nickel arsenate (NiAs).

1-8 Molecular Bonding. The types of aggregations considered above involved only atoms. These aggregations can rightly be called molecules: diatomic, one-dimensional chains, two-dimensional layers, and finally, giant three-dimensional frameworks. Only the latter type produces solids. All elements and compounds, nevertheless, even inert monoatomic gases, can be solidified given a sufficiently low temperature to reduce the thermal agitation of atoms. We conclude that between molecules, too, there must exist a certain type of bonding to allow the isolated independent units to bunch into three-dimensional frameworks. This type of bonding in gases was anticipated and studied by the Dutch physicist van der Waals at the end of the last century; hence the alternative name, *van der Waals bonding*. To understand how this bonding is brought about, it is best to consider the simplest case of inert gases. To a first degree of approximation, valid for all but the very low temperatures (e.g., above 63.8°K for argon), the atoms of inert gases have no need of each other, because they have a perfectly stable configuration by themselves. However, when thermal agitation subsides enough to keep a pair of atoms sufficiently close to each other and for a sufficiently long time, the electrons of the outer shells repulse each other and thus come under the influence of the positively charged nuclei of the partner. A weak, short-range attraction then takes place which holds them together, Fig. 1-10. Because of

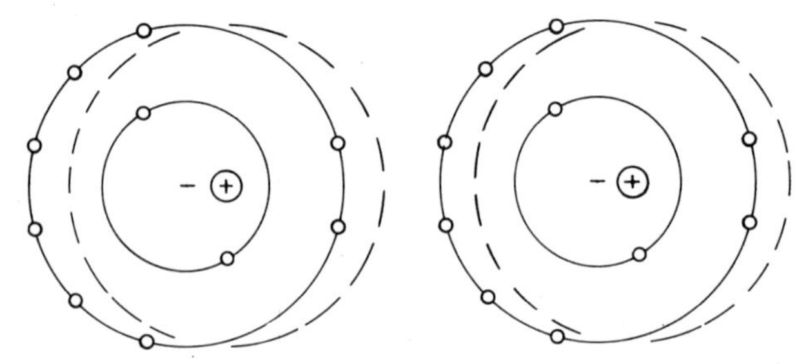

FIG. 1-10 Molecular bonding between two atoms of neon (schematic)

the rotational symmetry of the outer shell, the location of the partner is immaterial. When several partners surround the atom, the compromise between the competing tendencies operates again to produce a sort of rotating contact (resonating bond) of greater stability. This explains the close-packed configuration of solid inert gases. The reason molecular bonding is weak and operates only at short range is discussed in Chapter 6. Molecular bonds predominate among organic materials, which as a rule comprise long chains of identical units of smaller molecules, but they also bind together, somewhat loosely to be sure, the layers of structures such as graphite, Fig. 1-9. In the particular case of graphite, the distance between the layers is so large compared to the size of the atom that the bonding is exceedingly weak. This explains the ease with which the layers can glide one over the other, causing apparently the lubricating action of graphite.[6] Since molecular bonding depends on the charge of the nucleus, the heavier the element, the stronger is the bond. This explains why it is easier to solidify the heavy xenon (at 161°K) than the light helium (only at 0.8°K). It also explains why, among the elements of Group V, antimony is harder than arsenic. In fact, the layers of the former are held so strongly together that it is no longer possible to attribute it to the molecular bonding. It is also of interest to note that antimony as well as bismuth exhibit clearly metallic properties, thus implying

[6] For a more complete explanation see Problem 11-3.

the existence of free electrons. Perhaps, here too the now familiar phenomenon of resonance between molecular and metallic bonding operates to produce greater stability.

1-9 Summary. The aggregation of atoms is governed by the tendency of valence electrons to build stable octets. This is the reason for the *absence* of strong bonds between atoms of inert elements of Group VIII and presence of *strong* primary bonds between atoms of all other elements.

There are three kinds of primary bonds: (a) *covalent*—between atoms of elements of Groups VII, VI, V, and IV, (b) *metallic*—between atoms of elements of Groups III, II, and I, and (c) *ionic*—between unlike atoms.

Diatomic, chain, layer, and three-dimensional (giant) molecules as a rule are the result of simple covalent bonding in Groups VII, VI, V, and IV, respectively. *Multiple* bonding accounts for the exceptions from the above rule. Close-packed aggregations (HCP and FCC) are characteristic of the metallic bonding.

There is, however, a competition between these various bondings, resulting often in a compromise as an answer to greater stability. Compromises of this nature give rise to *resonating* bonding, as between simple and multiple bonds, covalent and ionic bonds, and ionic and metallic bonds.

There is, finally, a weak secondary bond between atoms of inert elements, between molecules of the Groups VII, VI, and V, and between molecules of unlike atoms. This bonding is called *molecular*, or *van der Waals*, bonding.

Molecular bonding can compete or cooperate with primary bonds in the process of building three-dimensional frameworks, or *solids*.

The existence of two or more alternative aggregations (e.g., diamond and graphite) of the same atom or molecule suggests that competition between various types of bonding can result in two or more almost equally stable configurations. By varying the external conditions, the engineer can often tip the balance in favor of the type of bonding most suitable to his practical needs (for example, borazon and natural boron nitride; see footnote, p. 9).

References

ELEMENTARY

1. L. Pauling, *General Chemistry*, Freeman, San Francisco, 1948.
2. W. L. Bragg, *Concerning the Nature of Things*, Dover, New York, 1954.
3. J. P. Frankel, *Principles of the Properties of Materials*, McGraw-Hill, New York, 1957.

ADVANCED

1. L. Pauling, *The Nature of the Chemical Bond*, Cornell, Ithaca, N.Y., 1948.
2. W. H. Bragg and W. L. Bragg, *The Crystalline State*, Bell & Sons, London, 1949.

Problems

1-1 To remove the second electron from sodium almost nine times as much work is required as to remove the first electron from the outer shell. What is the reason?

1-2 To remove the valence electron from rubidium, 20% less work is required than to remove the valence electron from sodium. Offer an explanation for the slight decrease of work.

1-3 What kind of structure would nitrogen build if the neighboring atoms were held by one covalent bond instead of three?

1-4 Carbon atoms in diamond are said to be tetrahedrally surrounded by their neighbors. Sketch the corresponding tetrahedra within the cube of Fig. 1-5.

1-5 Show by a sketch that by rotating the atoms of Fig. 1-3 an isolated chain can be coiled up more tightly or uncoiled in a flat chain, yet the angles between the bonds will be preserved.

1-6 Explain why most of the heavy elements at the bottom of the periodic table exhibit metallic properties?

1-7 Graphite is a much better conductor of electricity than diamond. Offer an explanation.

1-8 Natural boron nitride (BN) builds a layer structure similar to graphite. Man-made borazon probably builds a structure similar to diamond. Sketch both types of structure with the positions of B and N in each of them.

1-9 The distance between the nuclei of lithium and fluorine in Li^+F^- is 1.96 Å (1 Å $= 10^{-10}$ m). The distance between two lithium atoms in the solid metal of Li is about 3.0 Å. What conclusion can you draw from these data regarding the strength of bonds in both types of aggregation?

2 / CRYSTAL STRUCTURE

In solids, the concept of regularity is almost inseparable from the concept of stability considered in Chapter 1. We shall use the concept of regularity to define the crystal structure and those elements of the latter that play a prominent role in the behavior of solids.

2-1 Crystals and Solid State. The regular arrangement of atoms is characteristic not only of the solid elements described in Chapter 1 but of the solid state in general. With the exception of glasses, all solids possess a structure that can be described in terms of a framework, or *lattice*, built by the repetition of a certain pattern of atoms or molecules in all three directions. The detail of the pattern here is of no importance. It may consist of one atom or a cluster of atoms. The important thing is its repetition at regular intervals. The structure produced by the process of repetition is called a crystal. In order to describe some of the important properties of crystalline solids (such as plasticity in metal crystals, Chapter 9), it is necessary to define three essential elements of crystal structure: (1) the crystallographic direction, (2) the crystallographic plane, and (3) the unit cell.

2-2 Crystallographic Direction. To simplify the description, suppose the pattern is reduced to a single atom. This means that a regular array of atoms exists in space as shown in Fig. 2-1. Without loss of generality and with

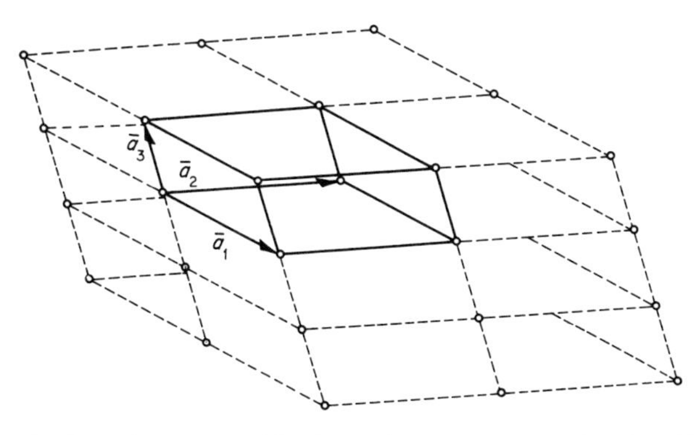

FIG. 2-1 Regular array of lattice points in space and unit cell $a_1a_2a_3$

much greater ease of visualization, we can replace this three-dimensional array by a two-dimensional one, Fig. 2-2. We see that the position of each atom can be obtained by taking any position, such as O, for origin and performing a certain number of translations, say n_1, in the direction OA and

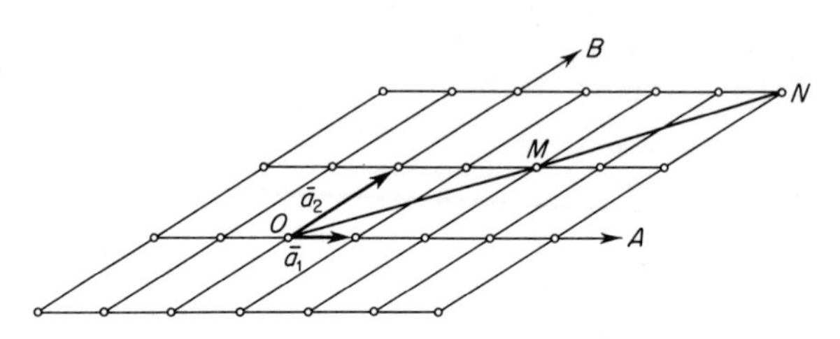

FIG. 2-2 Crystallographic direction in a plane lattice

another number of translations, n_2, in the direction OB. The unit translations $\bar{a}_1$ and $\bar{a}_2$ need not be of the same length. A point M, called a *lattice point*, is thus reached. This point, however—as well as any other—can also be reached by a single translation $\overline{OM}$ from the origin. The line OM defines a crystallographic direction. Since the origin O is arbitrary, the crystallographic direction is defined more generally by a line joining any two points of the lattice. Crystallographic directions have the following characteristics:

1. If we extend the intercept between two lattice points so that the extension is equal to the intercept, another lattice point will be reached, and by repeating the operation, as many lattice points can be included as we wish, until the boundary of the crystal is reached.
2. The same crystallographic direction is defined by any line drawn parallel to the first one through a lattice point that has not been included in the operation of extension described in property 1.
3. All these lines constitute the same *family of crystallographic directions*. Since any lattice point not yet accounted for can serve as an origin for a line of the family, we can alternatively say that a family of crystallographic directions must *include all points of the lattice*.

These properties are more or less self-evident and are a consequence of the regularity of the array of the lattice points.

In particular, property 1 follows from the fact that any vector such as OM can be written as a sum of two vectors built from the unit translations $\bar{a}_1$ and $\bar{a}_2$ as follows:

$$\overline{OM} = n_1\bar{a}_1 + n_2\bar{a}_2 \tag{2-1}$$

If we extend the line by an amount equal to the intercept OM, a point N will be reached such that

$$\overline{MN} = n_1\bar{a}_1 + n_2\bar{a}_2 \tag{2-2}$$

Hence, by definition, N is a point of the lattice, and so on.

Obviously, there is an almost unlimited number of families of crystallographic directions, because a crystallographic direction is defined by either Eq. (2-1) or (2-2), and n_1 and n_2 can be any pair of integers (including negative numbers).

An important concept that will be used subsequently (Chapter 9, *Plasticity*) is the *densest* crystallographic direction—that containing the smallest intercept between lattice points. Inspection of Fig. 2-2 shows that OA is the densest direction. It is also easy to see that the denser the direction the more distant are the *lines of the same family* from each other.

This is so because in a given volume the number of lattice points is fixed. The more of them that lie on a certain line (i.e., the denser the crystallographic direction), the fewer lines are needed to cover the same number of lattice points. Since all these lines are parallel to each other, the existence of fewer lines in the same volume means they are farther apart.

Our illustration refers to what obviously is a two-dimensional lattice. However, the reasoning and conclusions remain the same for a three-dimensional one. In particular, to prove property 1, it is only necessary to add another term to Eq. (2-1) representing the translation in the third direction. Thus, if $\bar{a}_3$ is the unit translation and n_3 the number of translations in this direction, then

$$\overline{OM} = n_1\bar{a}_1 + n_2\bar{a}_2 + n_3\bar{a}_3 \tag{2-3}$$

To return to the important concept of the densest direction, consider rigid spheres in contact. If they are all aligned, they will obviously form such a direction. In the close-packed aggregation of atoms, Figs. 1-6 and 1-7, this direction is aligned with the side of the hexagon in the HCP structure and with the face diagonal in the FCC structure. In the body-centered cube, Fig. 1-8, the densest direction—that in which the spheres also touch each other—is aligned with the cube diagonal. Often, but not always, aggregations of atoms in the solid state can be adequately depicted by a model of rigid spheres which touch each other in the densest direction. It should therefore-fore come to us as no surprise that in the diamond structure, Fig. 1-5, the densest directions are those which are aligned with the covalent bonds. The distance between the atoms in the densest direction is called (quite properly) the distance of *closest approach*.

2-3 Crystallographic Plane. The concept of crystallographic plane follows directly from that of crystallographic direction. Any two intersecting lines belonging to two different families of crystallographic directions define a *crystallographic plane*. There is obviously another crystallographic plane parallel to the first, and on the whole as many planes as the number of intersecting lines of the two families of crystallographic directions. All these planes belong to the same *family of crystallographic planes*. One such family of crystallographic planes is represented in Fig. 2-3. The two sets of crystallographic directions used for generating the planes of this family are also shown. It is clear from the drawing that we could use other crystallographic directions, such as *BC* and *BD*, for generating the same family of planes. In Fig. 2-3 another family of planes is generated by two other sets of crystallographic directions, and so on. There is practically an infinite variety of

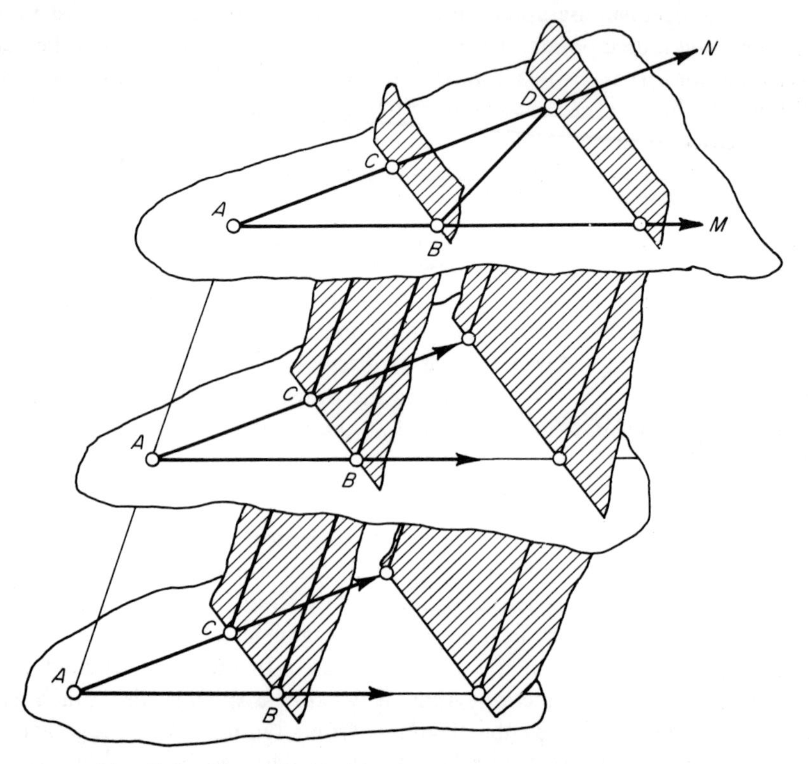

FIG. 2-3 Crystallographic planes and families of planes

families of crystallographic planes in the space lattice. They share several properties with the families of crystallographic directions, namely,

1. Through any lattice point located outside a given crystallographic plane, it is always possible to draw another (parallel) plane of the same family. Therefore, a family of crystallographic planes *must include all points of the space lattice.*

2. Among the various families of crystallographic planes in a given space lattice there is one family (and sometimes several) whose planes are the densest, i.e., containing the greatest number of lattice points per unit area. These planes obviously also contain the densest crystallographic direction or directions (if there are more than one).

3. The denser the crystallographic plane, the greater is its distance from the neighboring plane of the same family.

The proof is similar to that given in connection with the families of crystallographic directions. It can be worded as follows: The number of lattice points is fixed in a given volume. Therefore, the more lattice points in a certain plane, the less planes of the same family are needed to cover the fixed number of lattice points. However, all planes of the same family are parallel and equidistant. Hence, the fewer the planes, the farther apart they are. By the same argument, the distances separating the densest planes are the largest.

Figure 2-4 depicts families of the densest crystallographic planes for the three now familiar modes of aggregation of metallic elements: HCP, FCC,

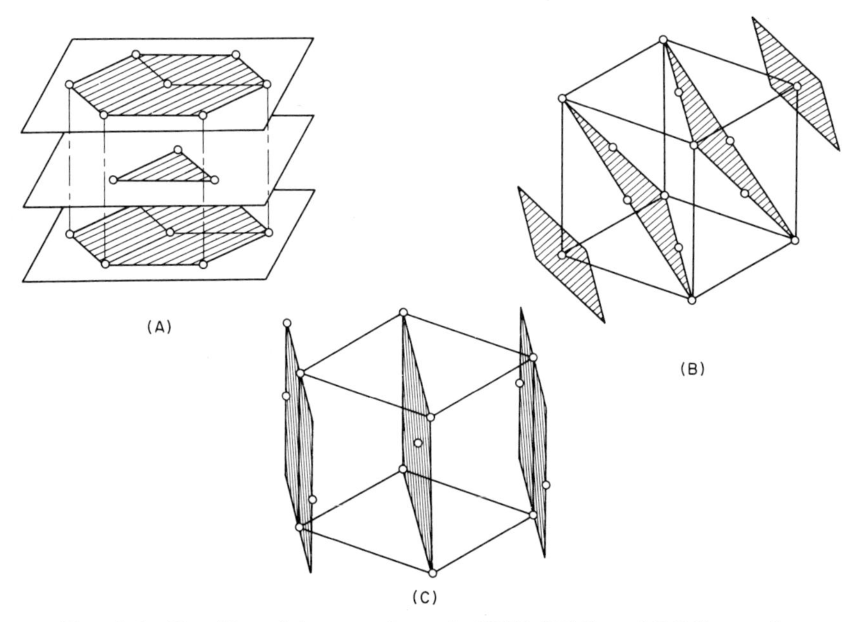

FIG. 2-4 Families of densest planes in HCP, FCC, and BCC crystals

and BCC. It may be seen that in the last two modes of aggregation there are also other differently oriented families of densest crystallographic planes.

2-4 Unit Cell. We have mentioned previously that the aggregation of atoms in the solid state can be described as a cluster of atoms (a pattern)—often reduced to a single atom—grouped identically about each point of a regular three-dimensional space lattice. To make the description complete, we also specify three unit non-coplanar vectors, $\bar{a}_1\ \bar{a}_2\ \bar{a}_3$, which represent the magnitude and direction of displacements necessary to bring one lattice point into coincidence with others by repeated translations. Two alternative descriptions also have been given: one in terms of a family of crystallographic directions, the other in terms of a family of crystallographic planes. None is as convenient and informative as that based on the concept of a *unit cell* defined below.

In the simplest case, the unit consists of a parallelepiped built on the three translation vectors, $\bar{a}_1\,\bar{a}_2\,\bar{a}_3$, Fig. 2-1. These form the edges of the unit cell with lattice points at its corners. Using such a structural element as a building stone, we can erect the entire crystalline framework like a wall of bricks simply by stacking the unit cells above and beside the others. Note that no additional information is necessary to identify the crystal. It is all contained in the small volume of the unit cell. The process of stacking the unit cells merely increases the size of the crystal but adds nothing to our knowledge about its nature.

At first there still seems to be some arbitrariness left, since the unit cell itself can be arbitrarily chosen. This is seen in Fig. 2-5, where the same crystalline structure as that of Fig. 2-1 has been built by means of a different unit cell, $c_1\,c_2\,c_3$. A little bit of reflection will show that this is not so. Picking another unit cell amounts to selecting another set of translation vectors, $\bar{c}_1\,\bar{c}_2\,\bar{c}_3$. However, the new translation vectors can be expressed in terms of the previous set of translation vectors by means of Eq. (2-3). For example,

$$\bar{c}_1 = \bar{a}_1 + \bar{a}_3$$

Thus changing translation vectors in the space lattice is like changing the coordinate system in analytical geometry. The information has not changed. It still refers to the same geometrical figure, but the algebraic form is different. If we press this analogy a little further, we shall find that we can also make a unique choice of the unit cell. Take, for example, the equation of an ellipse. We can express it in any system of Cartesian coordinates, but if we align the coordinates x and y with the major and minor axes, the algebraic expression contains only x^2 and y^2, showing that the ellipse is symmetrical about the major and minor axes.

It is the same with the choice of the unit cell. For each type of crystal structure, the crystallographer picks the particular kind of unit cell that reveals directly the symmetry of the crystal and thus gives the greatest number of clues on its properties. On that basis, the unit cell of Fig. 2-5 is preferable to that of Fig. 2-1 because it is a cube, and in the cube the three translations, $\bar{c}_1\,\bar{c}_2\,\bar{c}_3$, are not only equal but interchangeable. That is, the properties of the crystal in these three directions must also be the same—information that can be put to good use.

It is also for this reason that we prefer to describe one of the close-packed aggregations by means of the more complex face-centered cube, Fig. 1-7, rather than the more primitive cell of Fig. 2-6. The same holds for the other close-packed aggregation. Here the more complex hexagonal prism is preferable to the more simple four-sided prism, Fig. 2-7. The use of the body-centered cube, Fig. 1-8, has a similar justification.

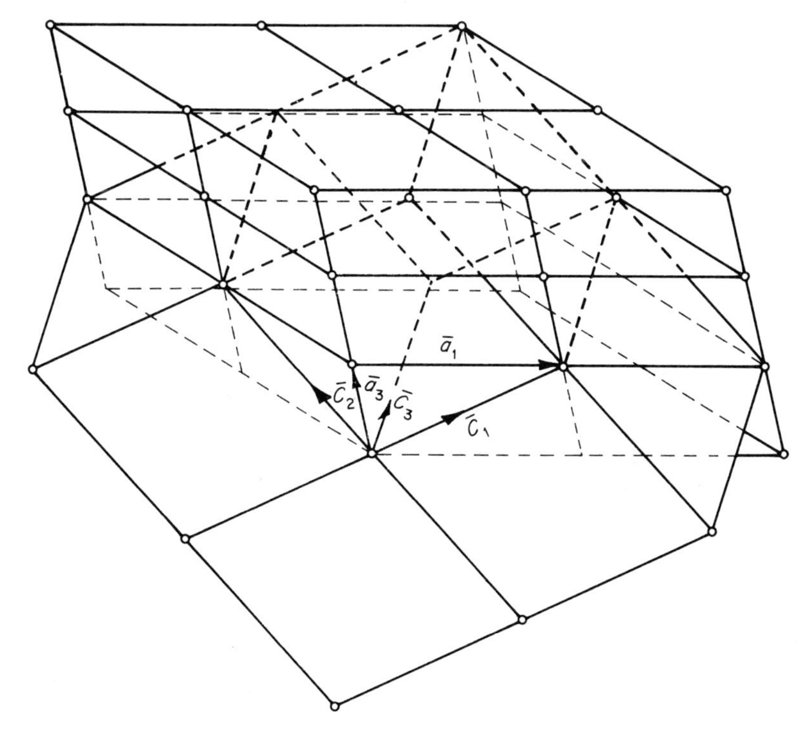

FIG. 2-5 Regular array of lattice points of Fig. 2-1 built from a unit cell $c_1\ c_2\ c_3$

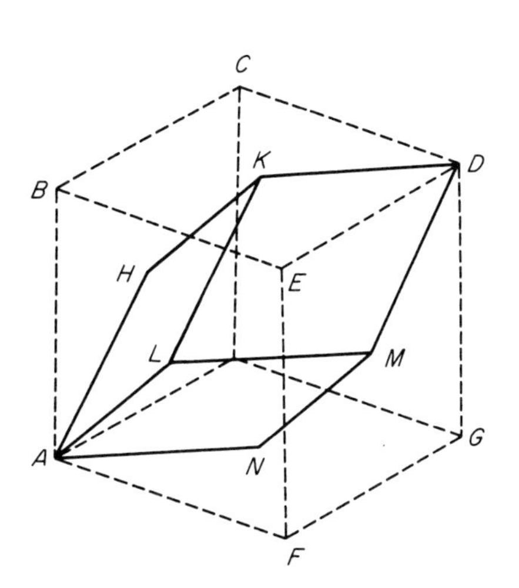

FIG. 2-6 Primitive cell $AHKD\ldots$ and compound cell $ABCD\ldots$ of a face-centered cubic lattice

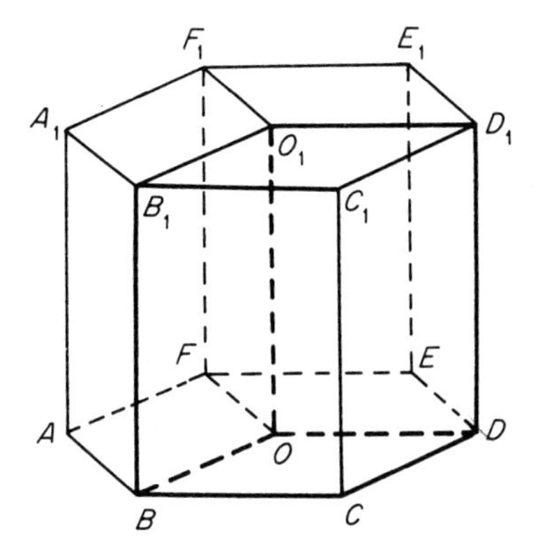

FIG. 2-7 Primitive cell $O_1D_1C_1B_1B\ldots$ and compound cell $A_1F_1E_1D_1C_1B_1B\ldots$ of a hexagonal lattice

The three types of unit cells mentioned—face-centered cube, body-centered cube, and hexagonal prism—are called *compound cells* to differentiate them from the *primitive cells* of Figs. 2-6 and 2-7 into which they can be decomposed.

Another way of looking at a compound cell is to consider it as a primitive cell with a more complicated pattern (e.g., a cluster of atoms instead of one atom per cell). This raises the question of how many atoms there are in a unit cell. What is really meant by this question is how many atoms per unit cell are needed to build the whole crystal. Let us begin with a two-dimensional lattice where both visualization and computation are simpler and let us restrict the discussion to a primitive cell in the form of a parallelogram, Fig. 2-2, with one atom at each corner. To build the first cell, four atoms are needed, but for each consecutive cell of the first row, two atoms suffice. The first cell of each successive row requires two atoms, but all the rest of the cells can be built by adding only one atom. Thus we have the following tabulation:

Row	*Number of Cells*	*Number of Atoms*
1st	N	$2(N - 1) + 4 = 2N + 2$
2nd	N	$2 + N - 1 = N + 1$
M-th	N	$2 + N - 1 = N + 1$
Total	NM	$MN + N + M + 1$

Hence the number of atoms per cell is

$$\frac{MN + N + M + 1}{MN} = 1 + \frac{1}{M} + \frac{1}{N} + \frac{1}{MN}$$

In ordinary crystals, both N and M (the number of atoms in a row and the number of rows) are of the order of 10^8. Thus $1/M$ and $1/N$ (let alone $1/MN$) are negligibly small compared to unity, and the number of atoms per cell is simply one.

It is easy to see that in a three-dimensional space lattice, built on a primitive cell with atoms only at the corners, there is likewise only one atom per cell. This can be shown in another way. Each atom of the corner of a cell in the interior of the crystal is shared by eight neighbors. Hence each corner contributes only $\frac{1}{8}$ of the atom to each cell. Since there are eight corners, the total contribution is $8 \times \frac{1}{8} = 1$ atom, as previously computed. The situation on the free surface of the crystal is different, but the number of atoms on the faces of the crystal is so small compared to the total number that this difference can be neglected (the difference per cell is again 10^{-8} compared to one).

The above argument can be generalized. In a body-centered cube, the atom in the center of the cube is shared by none of the neighbors; hence the number of atoms per unit cell is two (the pattern consists of two atoms).

In the face-centered cube, the atoms in the center of each face are shared by two contiguous cells, hence the number of atoms per cell is $8 \times \frac{1}{8} + 6 \times \frac{1}{2} = 4$ (the pattern consists of four atoms). By the same argument, the hexagonal close-packed unit cell has a pattern of six atoms.

We have thus come to distinguish between two important concepts: the unit cell and the pattern. The former builds the framework for which the latter provides the content. Together they produce the crystal structure, or in short, the *structure* of the solid. Table 2-1 summarizes the important characteristics of structure of some common metals.

The unit cell and the pattern are closely related. If the pattern possesses a certain symmetry, it imposes this symmetry on the unit cell (and the entire lattice).[1] Thus the tetrahedral arrangement of the four atoms in the pattern, Fig. 2-8, and the diagonal arrangement of the two atoms in the pattern,

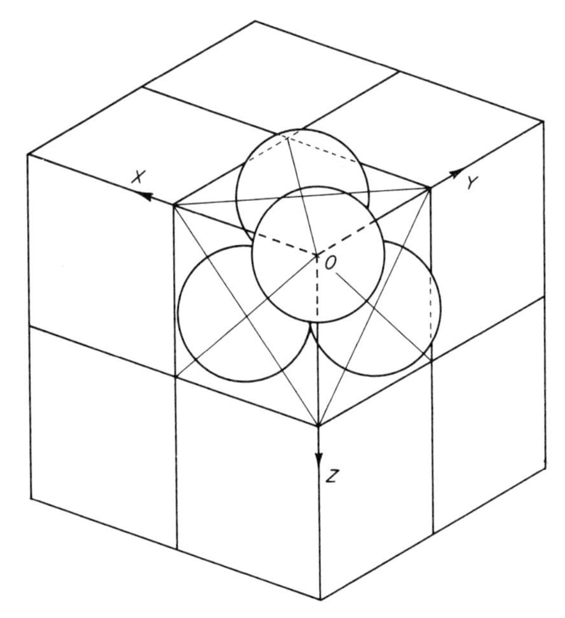

FIG. 2-8 Face-centered cubic cell viewed as a primitive cell with a pattern of four atoms

Fig. 2-9, both impose the symmetry of the cube on the lattice. That is, in both cases the axes x, y, and z can be interchanged by rotation without altering the figure. Similarly, the stacking of the six atoms in the pattern, Fig. 2-10, leads to the symmetry of the hexagon for the lattice. (Note: If only four of them were stacked about O, they would lead to cubic symmetry.)

Although the determination of the crystal lattice (by means of X-rays, for example; see Chapter 4) is a straightforward, though sometimes tedious

[1] But not vice versa. The lattice can, and in general will, possess additional elements of symmetry.

TABLE 2-1 CHARACTERISTICS OF CRYSTAL STRUCTURE OF SOME COMMON METALS

Metal	*Structure*	a* (Å)	h† (Å)	*Atoms per cell*	*Closest approach* (Å)	*Densest Plane*
Al	FCC	4.0490	—		2.862	Octahedral
Cu	FCC	3.6153	—		2.556	(through three
Ni	FCC	3.5238	—	4	2.491	face diagonals
Pb	FCC	4.9495	—		3.499	—densest directions)
Fe	BCC	2.8664	—		2.481	Dodecahedral
Cr	BCC	2.8845	—	2	2.498	(through two
W	BCC	3.1648	—		2.739	cube diagonals —densest directions)
Mg	HCP	3.2092	5.2103		3.196	Base of hexa-
Ti	HCP	2.9504	4.6833	6	2.890	gonal prism
Zn	HCP	2.664	4.945		2.664	

* Edge of cube or side of hexagon, room temperature.
† Height of hexagon, room temperature.
Source: C. S. Barret, *Structure of Metals*, McGraw-Hill, New York, 1952.

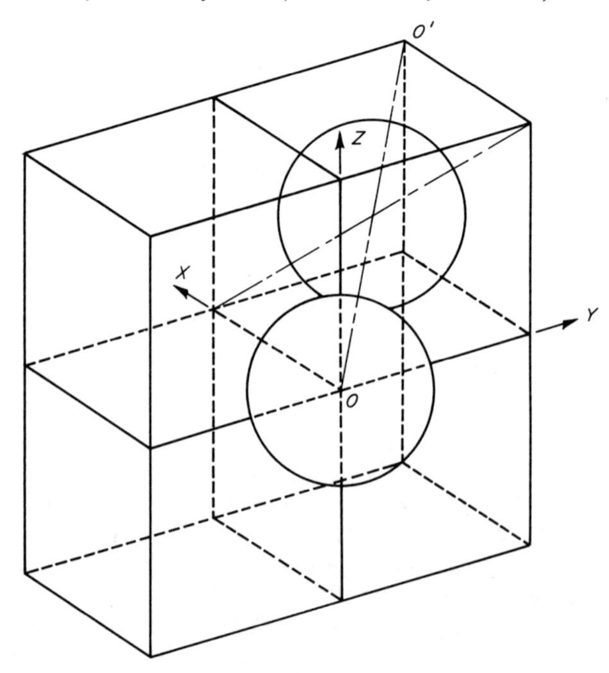

FIG. 2-9 Body-centered cubic cell viewed as a primitive cell with a pattern of two atoms

procedure, unravelling the pattern often requires a great deal of guesswork. The latter can be speeded up by the use of a computer, but any additional information concerning the symmetry of the pattern reduces the labor considerably. Additional information also helps us to understand and anticipate the properties of the crystal based on symmetry.

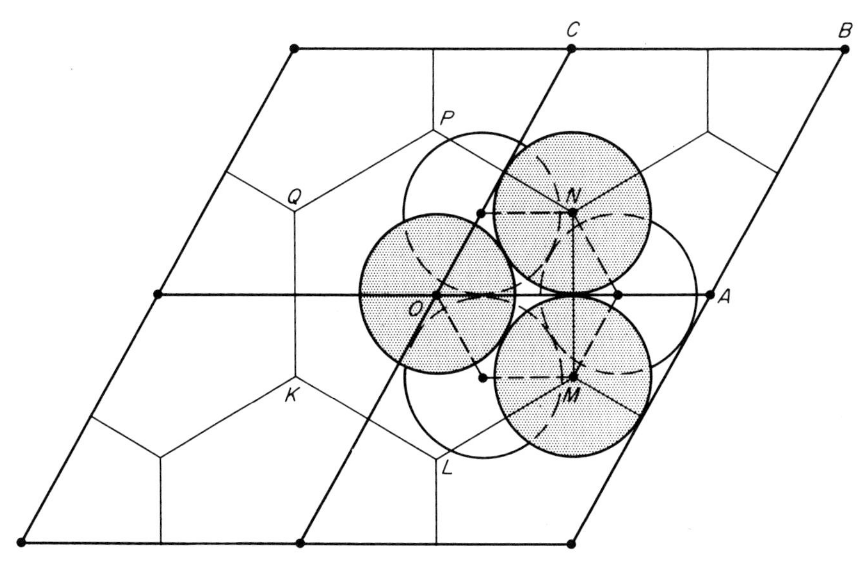

FIG. 2-10 A close-packed pattern of three atoms (shaded) superimposed on three other atoms and based on the cell *OABC* of a hexagonal lattice. The same pattern can alternatively be placed on the hexagonal cell *KLMNPQ*, as shown in Fig. 1-6

To see why, consider, for example, a simple cubic lattice. Its existence implies that the properties in the three cube directions, Ox, Oy, Oz, are the same, nothing more. To get additional information, we must consider the pattern. From the pattern of Fig. 2-9 we infer that any property measured in the direction OO' must be the same as that measured in the opposite direction $O'O$. This is so because the pattern itself looks the same both ways (after all lattice points in Fig. 2-9 have been occupied). However, if the second atom of the pattern were not in the center of the cell and were much smaller than the first (as in zincblende, ZnS), then viewed from O the pattern would not look the same as from O', Fig. 2-11. The properties might also differ when measured both ways. For example, in ZnS the plus charge will be closer when viewed from O to O' than from O' to O. This circumstance accounts for the particular electric behavior (piezoelectricity) of ZnS, discussed in Chapter 13.

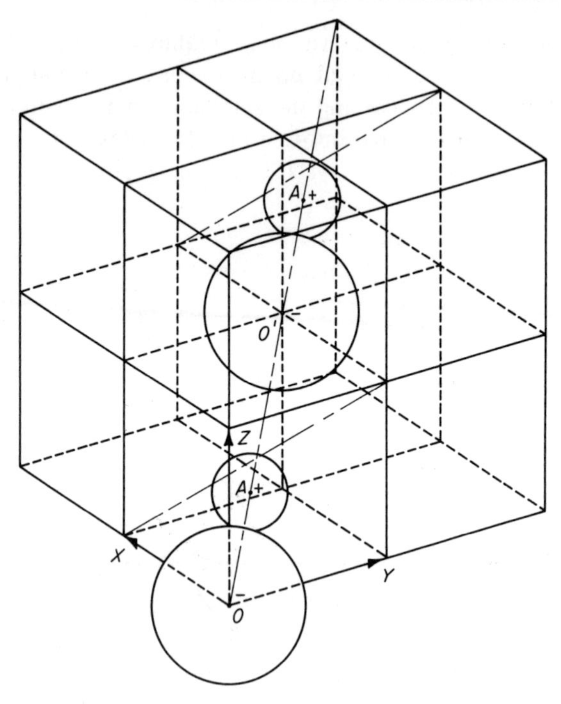

FIG. 2-11 Pattern of two unequal atoms (ions) in a cubic cell

2-5 Computation of Number of Atoms in the Pattern. To unravel the pattern, it is first necessary to find out how many atoms it contains. This information can often be conveniently obtained from the knowledge of the mass of the unit cell. We shall make this computation for the simple case of an element—in which all atoms are alike—to show how the macroscopic (bulk) and microscopic (atomic) properties of matter are related.

Consider, for example, a cubic crystal. Let

n = number of atoms in the pattern
M = mass of the element per mole
N_A = 6.02×10^{23}, Avogadro's number: number of atoms per mole
ρ = density
a = edge of the unit cell

We can express the mass of the unit cell in two ways: (1) Mass of unit cell = total mass of the atoms it contains = nM/N_A; (2) Mass of unit cell = volume × density = $a^3\rho$. Equating (1) to (2) yields

$$\rho a^3 = nM/N_A \tag{2-4}$$

and, more generally, for a non-cubic unit cell of volume V,

$$\rho V = nM/N_A \tag{2-5}$$

from which n can be determined.

Examples.

1. Copper: $M = 63.54$ g/mole, $\rho = 8.97$ g/cm^3, $a = 3.608$ Å $= 3.608 \times 10^{-8}$ cm. Substitution in Eq. (2-4) gives $n = 4$.
2. Silicon: $M = 28.09$ g/mole, $\rho = 2.42$ g/cm^3, $a = 5.4282$ Å. Substitution in Eq. (2-4) gives $n = 8$.

Note. Any one of the five quantities can be computed from Eq. (2-4) or (2-5) if the other four are known. Since all of them can also be determined from other measurements (including n), Eqs. (2-4) and (2-5) can be used to improve the accuracy of measurements of one of them, such as N_A.

2-6 SUMMARY. The structure of the majority of solids is *regular*. It can be described in terms of a three-dimensional lattice obtained by *repeated* translations of any of its elements: lattice points, crystallographic directions, crystallographic planes and unit cell.

Of these, the unit cell contains in its small volume all the information for the growth of the crystal by repetition. It also contains the pattern—the number and arrangement of atoms around the lattice points.

The symmetry of the unit cell and the lattice depends on the symmetry of the pattern. However, only the latter provides the clue to the properties based on symmetry.

The number of atoms in the pattern of an element can be obtained from the formula

$$\rho V = nM/N_A$$

where n is the number of atoms in the pattern, M is the mass of the element per mole, N_A is Avogadro's number, ρ is the density, and V is the volume of the unit cell.

References

ELEMENTARY

1. W. L. Bragg, *Concerning the Nature of Things*, Dover, New York, 1954.

ADVANCED

1. W. H. Bragg and W. L. Bragg, *The Crystalline State*, Bell & Sons, London, 1949.
2. C. S. Barret, *Structure of Metals*, McGraw-Hill, New York, 1953.

Problems

2-1 Draw a two-dimensional (plane) lattice with two different translation vectors $\bar{a}_1$ and $\bar{a}_2$. Draw four crystallographic directions: $O\overline{M}_1 = 3\bar{a}_1 + 4\bar{a}_2$; $O\overline{M}_2 = 3\bar{a}_1 - 4\bar{a}_2$; $O\overline{M}_3 = -3\bar{a}_1 + 4\bar{a}_2$; $O\overline{M}_4 = 4\bar{a}_1 + 3\bar{a}_1$.

2-2 In the two-dimensional lattice of Problem 2-1, draw two different primitive cells and derive the relationships between the unit translations $\bar{a}_1$ and $\bar{a}_2$ (in one) and $\bar{c}_1$ and $\bar{c}_2$ (in the other).

2-3 Compute the distance between two neighboring densest directions of the same family in the FCC, BCC, and hexagonal lattices.

2-4 Prove that the areas of two primitive cells in a two-dimensional (plane) lattice are equal. (Hint: Both have only one lattice point.)

2-5 Show that in the HCP structure there are six atoms (pattern) per one compound cell and two atoms (pattern) per one primitive cell of the hexagonal lattice. (Note: We say HCP structure, not lattice, because it implies a pattern.)

2-6 Compute the height of the unit cell of zinc and magnesium from the distances of closest approach and compare the results with the values reported in Table 2-1. Offer an explanation for discrepancy, if any.

2-7 Compute the density of chromium from the data of Table 2-1 and compare the result with the reported value of density (e.g., in *Handbook of Chemistry and Physics*, Chemical Rubber Publ. Co., Cleveland, Ohio).

2-8 The unit cell of Cs^+Cl^- can be drawn as a cube with Cl^- occupying the corners and Cs^+ the center of the cube. We call it a primitive cell and not a compound cell. Why?

2-9 The crystal of Na^+Cl^- can be built from a small cube with the eight corners alternately occupied by Na^+ and Cl^-. How many of these cubes must be stacked together to form a FCC cubic cell?

3 / GROWTH AND AGGREGATION OF CRYSTALS

In crystalline solids the unit cell was said to contain the code for the growth of the whole crystal. It is natural to expect that it should also serve as a nucleus for this growth. The conditions under which such a nucleation and growth occur in real crystals will be examined below.

3-1 External Form and Internal Structure of Solids. There are two reasons why the external form of solids seldom reveals the regularity of their internal structure. One is simply the way they were made; most of them originate from melts which, upon freezing, take the shape of molds. The other is more fundamental; with a few exceptions, industrial and natural solids consist not of a single crystal but of many crystals grown together in a coherent mass, i.e., they are *polycrystalline*.

To understand this reason and its ramifications, we must examine how crystals are nucleated and how they grow. The process seems to be essentially the same whether solids are produced by the freezing of liquids, precipitation from saturated solutions, by electrolysis, or by condensation of vapors. Freezing of liquids is by far the most frequent process and is particularly interesting from the industrial point of view.

3-2 Nucleation and Growth. The formation of a stable nucleus of a crystal amidst a liquid mass is hampered by the disordered thermal motion of atoms. The problem has a *statistical* nature and belongs to the subject of thermodynamics, a more advanced course. Here we shall merely accept the result as a fact of observation. During the process of solidification of a large mass of liquid, a great number of small crystals (nuclei) precipitate from the parent medium. The nuclei grow by getting hold of atoms wandering in the liquid and attaching them in identical layers regularly spaced one after the other. These layers, of course, are nothing but crystallographic planes of the family. Since the crystal grows in more than one direction, several families of crystallographic planes must participate in the process of growth. The crystal frequently has a tendency to preserve a face already formed, especially if this face is one of the densest crystallographic planes. In such cases, the growth is the slowest in the direction normal to this face. In other instances, the atoms are attached more easily to the densest plane by a special mechanism to be described later, Section 3-6, and growth can then proceed more readily

FIG. 3-1 Crystal growth in preferred directions—dendrite (schematic)

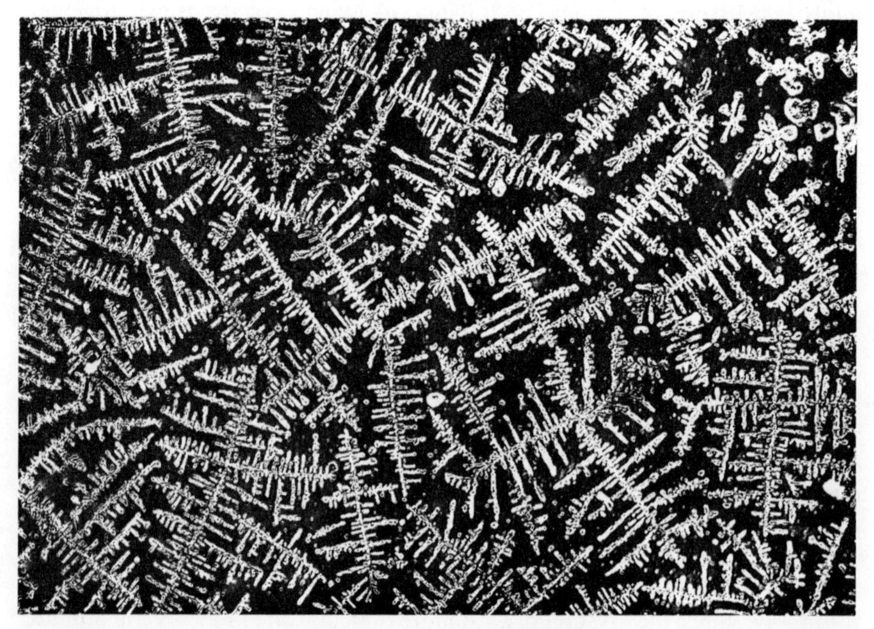

FIG. 3-2 Dendritic structure of an antimony-lead alloy. (Courtesy of A. Taub, The Technion, Haifa, Israel)

FIG. 3-3 Schematic interpretation of crystal growth. (From W. Rosenhain, *An Introduction to the Study of Physical Metallurgy*, Constable, London, 1935, by permission) ▶

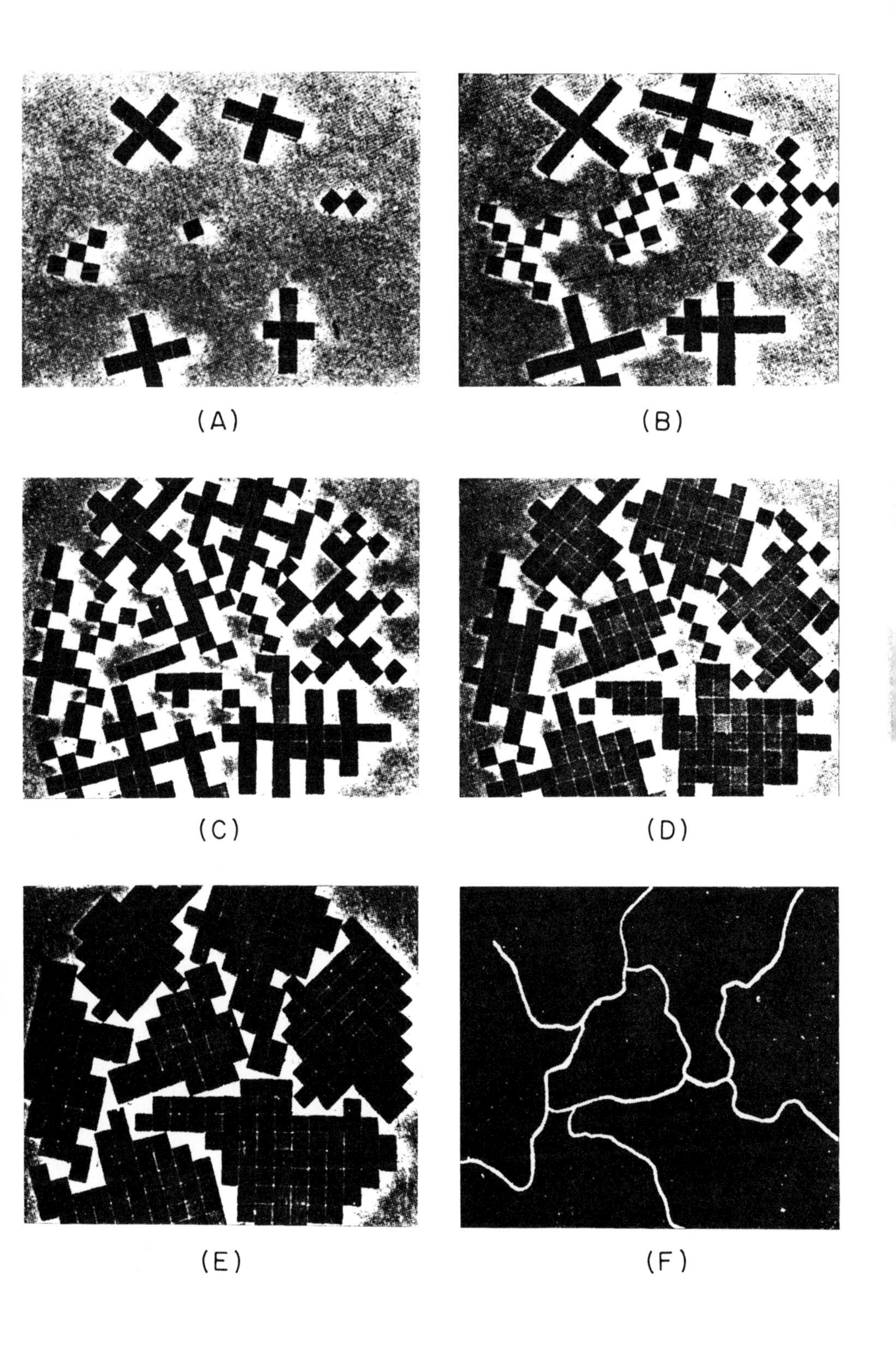

(A)
(B)
(C)
(D)
(E)
(F)

perpendicular to this plane. In either case, there is a direction along which the germinating crystal protrudes more deeply into the liquid. From this stem, other directions of *preferential* growth branch off. They become, in turn, seats of further branching, and so on. This configuration is depicted schematically in Fig. 3-1, and it can be readily recognized in an actual example of crystal formation, Fig. 3-2. The structure has a resemblance to a tree; hence its name *dendrite*, from Greek *dendron*, tree.

The growth stops wherever dendrites issuing from neighboring nuclei meet. The points of contact build *irregular* polygonal surfaces about the nuclei; these surfaces are, in effect, the boundaries of the crystals. The entire solid acquires a granular appearance; hence the names *grain* and *grain boundary* given to the crystal and its boundary in polycrystalline aggregates. Once the growth of the dendrites has been stopped, the liquid continues to freeze and bridges the interstices between the branches. The process of solidification ends when the last film of liquid—at the grain boundary—has been frozen. The successive steps of solidification and crystal growth are depicted schematically in Fig. 3-3.

If the temperature of the bath is fairly uniform, no direction is favored and the grains are equiaxed, as shown in Fig. 3-3f. Their size, however, depends on the number of other crystals they meet during their growth, more specifically on the interplay between their own rate of growth and the rate at which nuclei are formed (rate of nucleation). This interplay depends on the degree of undercooling, as will be shown below.

3-3 Role of Undercooling. At the temperature of melting, T_m, there is as much chance for a nucleus to be absorbed by the melt as to be precipitated from it. Hence at this temperature the rate of nucleation is nil. It increases to a maximum when the liquid is undercooled to a critical temperature, T_{cr}. Thereafter, if the material can be maintained in the liquid state, the rate of nucleation drops rather suddenly because of the decreased mobility of atoms. So does the rate of grain growth. The material can then remain in the state of a supercooled liquid, or in the *glassy state*, practically indefinitely. This is true of many minerals, particularly silicates. Metals cannot be undercooled below their critical temperature, T_{cr}. They crystallize spontaneously at this temperature without outside help, that is, without artificial seeding (see Section 3-4). Because of the apparent absence of foreign inclusions, the name *homogeneous crystallization* is used. It is of interest to note that in this type of crystallization the relative undercooling $(T_m - T_{cr})/T_m$ (in degrees Kelvin) is rather large, especially for metals (see Table 3-1).

The rate of grain growth follows more or less the pattern of grain nucleation. Even though the atoms are more mobile at the temperature of melting, it requires a certain degree of undercooling to maintain directionality of motion. So here, too, we find an optimum temperature of undercooling below which the rate of growth drops drastically.

3-4 Role of Impurities. Depending on the interplay between the rates of growth and nucleation, the size of the grain at the critical temperature, T_{cr}, can vary in large proportions. An important controlling factor is the amount and nature of the impurities which act as artificial centers of nucleation, commonly called *seeds*. The role of seeding is to stimulate crystallization above the critical temperature T_{cr} (*heterogeneous crystallization*) or, to say it differently, to decrease the degree of undercooling necessary to cause precipitation. Thus in artificial rain making, crystals of silver iodide serve as seeds

TABLE 3-1 REPRESENTATIVE MELTING POINTS AND CRITICAL TEMPERATURES OF UNDERCOOLING

Substance	t_m* (°C)	t_{cr} (°C)	$(T_m - T_{cr})/T_m$
Iron[2]	1535	1277	0.142
Lead[1]	327	—†	0.133
Nickel[1]	1455	—†	0.185
Platinum[1]	1773	—†	0.182
Tin[2]	232	—†	0.218
Germanium[1]	958	—†	0.178
Azobenzene[2]	68	36	0.093
Water[1]	0	—†	0.143
Mercury[1]	39	—†	0.197

* In round figures.
† Not reported.
[1] D. Turnbull, *Principles of Solidification*, Seminar on Thermodynamics in Physical Metallurgy ASM, 1950.
[2] D. S. Kamenetskaya, *The Effect of Impurities on the Production of Crystallization Nuclei in Supercooled Liquids*, Growth of Crystals, Reports at the first Conference on Crystal Growth 5–10 March 1956. In English: Consultants Bureau, Inc., New York, 1958.

for the formation of ice crystals from clouds. The precipitate may be large or small, depending on the way the seeds affect the rate of grain growth.

The importance of artificial seeding insofar as industrial metals are concerned lies in the possibility of grain refinement during casting. Small equiaxed grains are desirable in many applications. They impart to the metal almost equal properties in all directions (quasi-isotropy). They help effectively in producing smooth, regular surfaces during forming and shaping of complicated parts for cars and airplanes.

3-5 Temperature Gradient. Although the role of temperature gradient has not yet been considered, the existence of a temperature drop, ever so small, is indispensable if heat is to be extracted from the melt and the process of solidification is to continue. Furthermore, there are situations in which temperature distribution has a dominant influence on the form and size of the crystals. Two instances are of practical interest.

One of them occurs when metals are poured into long prismatic molds from which heat is extracted at a much faster rate through the walls than through the bottom. Take, for example, a long cylindrical mold, Fig. 3-4,

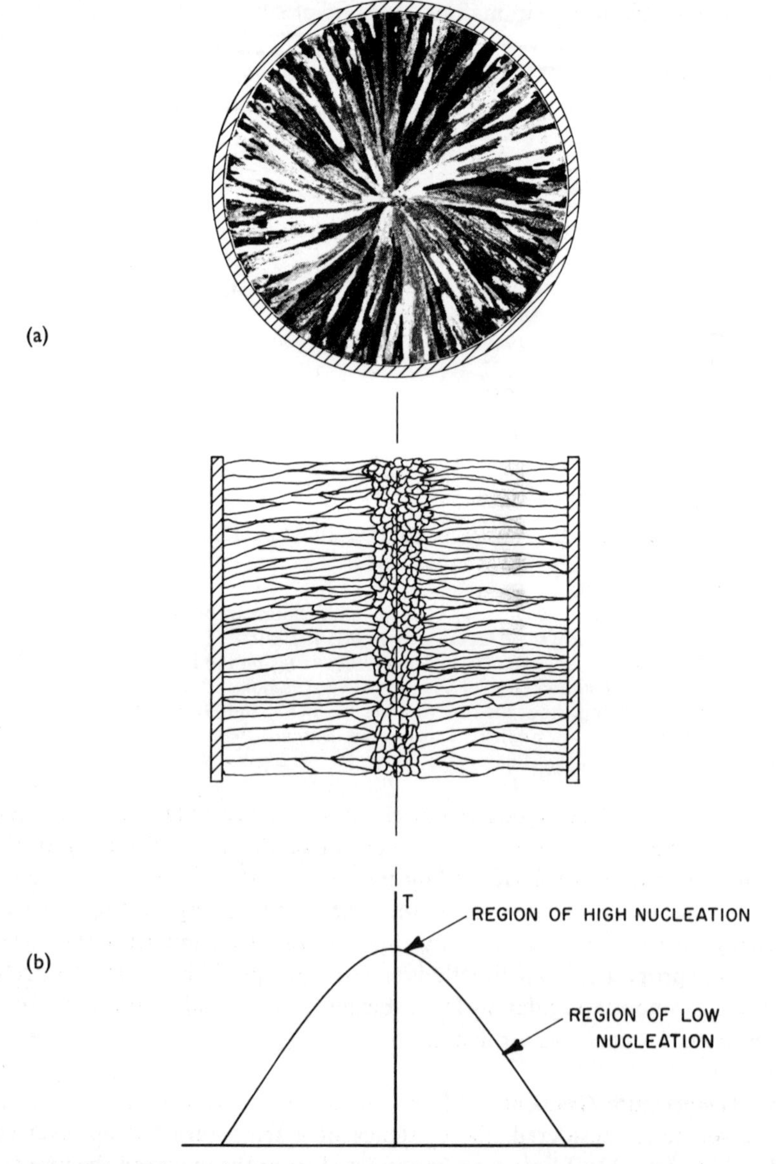

FIG. 3-4 Schematic diagram illustrating formation of columnar structure

in which the temperature drop occurs mostly in the radial direction, Fig. 3-4b. During cooling, the temperature of crystallization is reached first near the wall. This gives rise to a thin layer of small equiaxed crystals covering the wall (shaded portion in Fig. 3-4a). Thereupon, each of the small crystals grows inward at a rate which is much faster than the rate of nucleation of new crystals (the latter is slowed down considerably by the steep temperature rise). However, on reaching the center of the slab, the temperature gradient tapers off and so does the rate of growth. New centers of nucleation can now form, with the result that many new grains appear. The final structure, therefore, consists of *columnar* grains radiating from the wall inward and of more or less equiaxed grains in the center. This configuration is clearly seen in the photograph of an actual casting, Fig. 3-5. The columnar grains not only are elongated in the radial direction, they also have

FIG. 3-5 Columnar structure in chill cast nickel. (From J. L. Walker, "Structures of Ingots and Castings; Liquid Metals and Solidification," American Society for Metals, 1958, by permission)

a preferential crystallographic plane normal to this direction. For the body- and face-centered cubic crystals, this happens to be the plane of the cube. On account of the two factors, the columnar shape and the preferred crystallographic orientation, such a structure is often undesirable. One of the many purposes of metal working, particularly forging, subsequent to casting, is to convert the columnar structure into a more random one with small equiaxed grains (see Section 9-17).

The other case of practical interest is the production of *single* crystals. The single crystal technology has lately become quite important because of many engineering applications (supersonics, semiconductivity, dielectric polarization, etc.). Non-metallic crystals are taking the commercial lead, but single metal crystals are of especial interest in the study of the basic mechanical behavior of solids (see Section 9-6). There are also important industrial applications for these crystals—until recently single crystals of tungsten were used extensively as filaments in electric bulbs.

The growth of single crystals from the liquid is not unlike that of columnar grains during casting. In one of the current techniques, crystallization starts from a nucleus in the coolest portion of the container, Fig. 3-6, and it progresses through a temperature gradient. To insure continuous growth, the

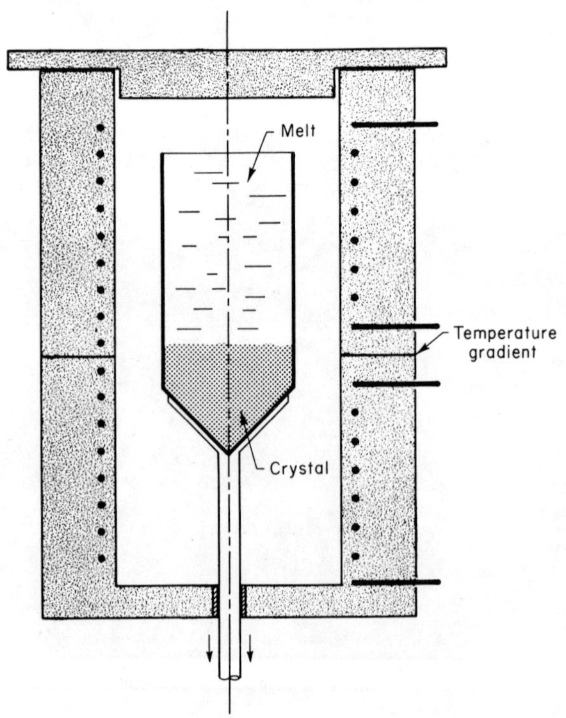

FIG. 3-6 Cross section of furnace for single crystal production. (From A. R. Von Hippel, *Molecular Science and Molecular Engineering*, Technology Press, M.I.T., Cambridge, Mass., and Wiley, New York, 1959, by permission)

container is lowered from the furnace at the rate of the crystal growth. For a temperature gradient of about 10°C/cm, the rate of growth varies between 1 and 100 cm/hr. The lowest figure refers to non-metals, the highest to metals endowed with good thermal conductivity (see Chapter 16). Crystals of several centimeters in diameter have been produced by this technique.

The nucleus at the coolest part of the container is either formed spontaneously or is seeded. The latter procedure is used when crystals of a certain orientation are desired.

3-6 Role of Dislocations. The detailed mechanism of crystal growth from melts is still a matter of considerable debate. However, in cases where growth proceeds in the direction normal to the densest plane, it is likely that the mechanism is the same as that predicted and observed in the process of crystal growth from vapors by condensation.[1] This mechanism involves a local defect of crystal structure called a *dislocation*.

To introduce the concept of dislocations, suppose first that during the process of condensation from vapor, a layer of atoms precipitates on top of an already built face of a perfect crystal, Fig. 3-7. For convenience a

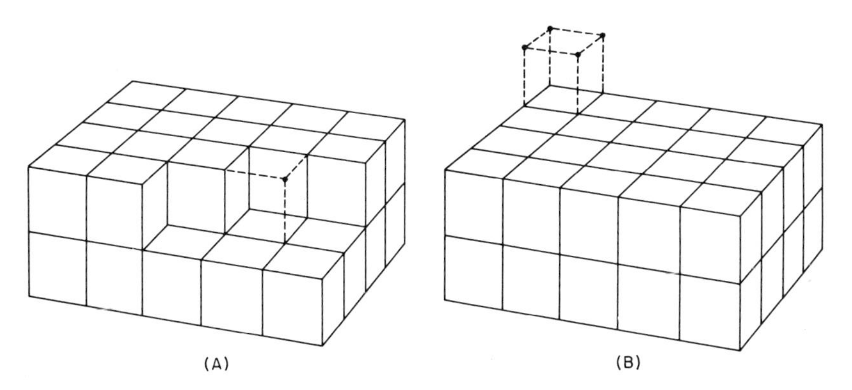

FIG. 3-7 Growth of a perfect crystal (schematic)

simple cubic unit cell is assumed. When the process is in the stage depicted by Fig. 3-7a, only one atom is needed to build the unit cell (see Section 2-4). We can say that at this particular stage growth proceeds with the least number of atoms per unit volume (least concentration). However, when the layer is finished and a new one is started on its top, the concentration of atoms is suddenly quadrupled (four atoms are now needed to build the corner cell, Fig. 3-7b). In other words, to keep the process going continuously, the concentration (and vapor pressure) must correspond to that of four atoms per unit cell instead of one. Yet nothing of the sort is actually observed. On the contrary, the vapor can be maintained at a much lower pressure without

[1] F. C. Frank, *Advances in Physics*, **1**, 91(1952).

hampering the growth. It is as though the same layer continued to climb (without a break) to the next level, and so on. The only way it can do it is by winding itself up in a sort of a ramp or a screw. An accident of growth similar to a partial mountain slide could initiate such a process. It is depicted in Fig. 3-8. A movement of shear, one atomic layer deep, has taken place

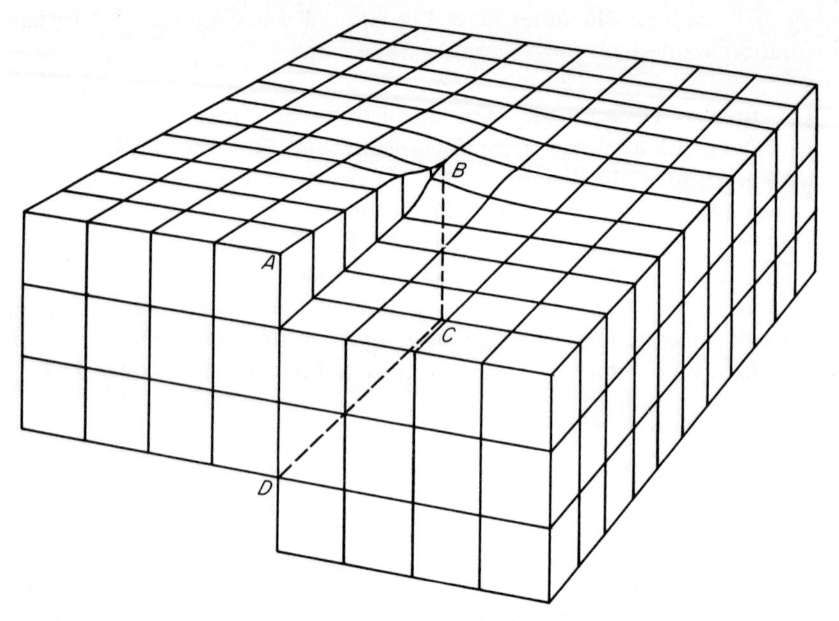

FIG. 3-8 Formation of a screw dislocation by a shearing movement. (From W. T. Read, Jr., *Dislocations in Crystals*, McGraw-Hill, New York, 1953, by permission)

in the frontal portion of the crystal on the plane *ABCD* without reaching the rear. The line *BC* separates the sheared portion of the plane from the unsheared one. At a certain distance from this line, the movement of shear has brought the upper layers of atoms in coincidence with the lower ones so that the unit cells are again matched and the regularity of crystal structure is preserved. Only at the close vicinity of the line *BC* are the atoms mismatched or dislocated. Hence the name of *dislocation* given to this local linear defect.[2] It is clear from the two sketches, Fig. 3-9, that the atoms can now attach themselves to the top surface in a never-ending succession of spirals. Such a growth has been actually observed, Fig. 3-10.

It is still too early to say whether these observations, which are of rather recent origin, can be generalized and applied to other cases of crystal growth. Accidents of growth must have been of common occurrence during the forma-

[2] More exactly, the term *screw dislocation* is used to differentiate it from another type of dislocation described in Chapter 9.

tion of the earth's crust. There exists today a reasonable amount of evidence that the so-called igneous rocks, which constitute the deeper strata of this crust, are products of solidification from melts. These rocks, as a rule, are aggregates of several polycrystalline minerals ranging from quartz to ferromagnesian minerals (olivine, augite, etc.) and ores.[3] They exhibit all known

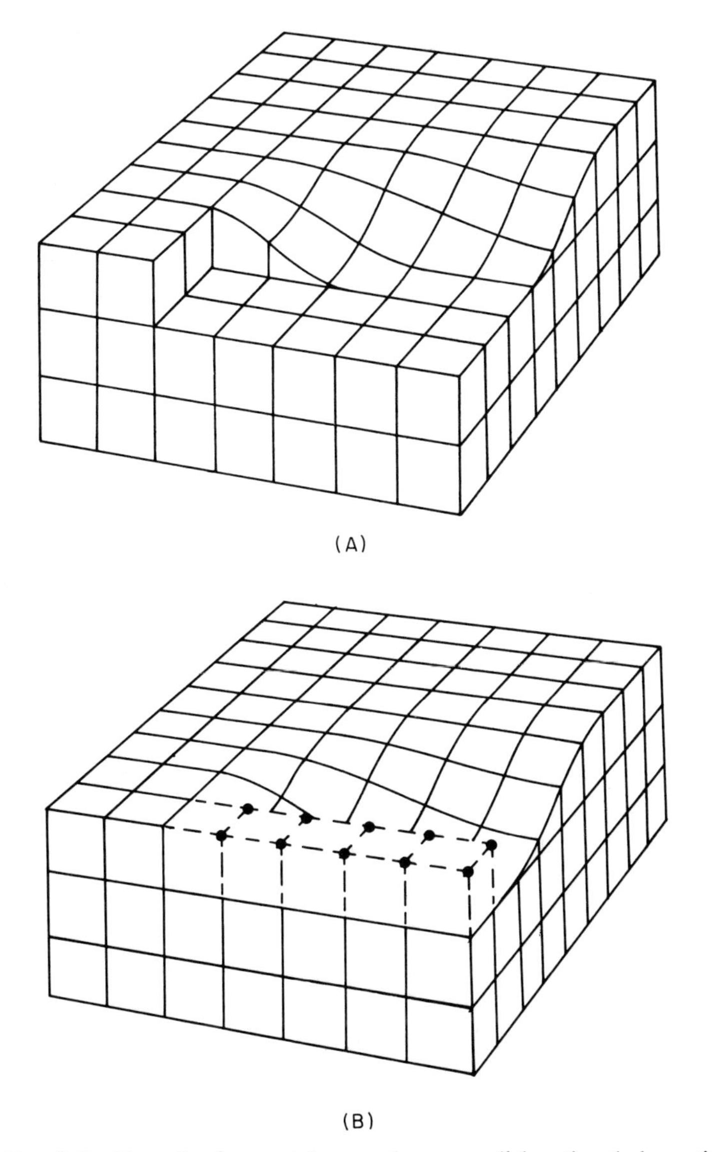

FIG. 3-9 Growth of a crystal around a screw dislocation (schematic)

[3] H. Jeffreys. *The Earth*, Cambridge U.P., New York, 1952.

characteristics of crystal growth obtainable in the laboratory including coarse and fine grain structure and preferred orientation.[4]

Similar observations have been made on the formation and structure of ice in glaciers, which cover about one-tenth of the land surface of the globe

FIG. 3-10 Electron micrograph of paraffin crystal showing spiral originating from a dislocation. (From Dawson and Vand, *Nature*, **167**, 476, 1951)

in a constantly regenerating layer several hundreds of feet deep.[5] Many factors that affected the formation and growth of crystals two billion years ago are still in operation today, whether in the laboratory or in nature itself.

3-7 Regularity of Structure and Local Imperfections. The analysis of nucleation and grain growth suggests that a certain amount of disorder or a defect of structure appears to be necessary to stimulate, if not actually originate, the process. In nucleation, the stimulus comes from the presence of foreign atoms acting as seeds. If these atoms remain in the solid after freezing, they either form isolated inclusions or are incorporated in the crystal structure. In both cases they create a local disorder merely because they are either larger or smaller than the atoms of the nucleated material (such as the magnesium used for nucleation of graphite in cast iron).

In grain growth, the source of disorder is the dislocation—a linear defect of crystal structure—which provides the necessary stimulus. Both defects seem to promote the process by their mere presence. They do not spread all over the crystal; they remain local. Thus the concentration of

[4] H. S. Washington and L. H. Adams, "The Chemical and Petrological Nature of the Earth's Crust," *Internal Constitution of the Earth*, Volume VII, Dover, New York, 1951.

[5] M. F. Perutz, "Glaciers," *Science News*, 6, Penguin Books, 1948.

foreign atoms acting as seeds seldom exceeds a small fraction of one percent. Likewise, the disorder about the dislocation line does not extend practically beyond 25 to 50 atomic distances. These are important points to bear in mind, for they show that the solid in bulk does preserve the features of regularity and stability that are characteristic of the ideal crystal structure. Only sporadically is there departure from orderliness.

In actual design, the engineer must rely on those properties that depend chiefly on the crystalline nature of the solid, because these properties also possess a high degree of stability. Yet he cannot ignore those properties that result from the presence of defects. In fact, it is these properties that he must learn to control if his design is to succeed. We shall come across both kinds of properties in Part II.

3-8 Summary. As a rule, industrial solids are made up of many crystals, that is, they are *polycrystalline*. This type of structure is caused by *nucleation* of numerous small crystals within the parent medium. The nucleated crystals grow in preferred crystallographic directions forming *dendrites*. The final result is the production of *irregular* polygonal grains (and grain boundaries).

The size of grains is governed by the interplay of the *rate of growth* and the *rate of nucleation*. Each rate reaches a maximum at some critical temperature, T_{cr}, not necessarily always the same, below the melting point, T_m.

Foreign atoms (seeds) favor and stimulate nucleation above T_{cr}. They may also cause grain refinement. *Screw dislocations*, local linear defects of crystal structure, act similarly in promoting growth.

Preferential growth occurs in the direction of maximum temperature gradient. This tendency is utilized in the production of *single* crystals.

References

ELEMENTARY

1. M. F. Perutz, "Glaciers," *Science News*, **6**, Penguin, Baltimore.
2. W. L. Bragg, *Concerning the Nature of Things*, Dover, New York, 1955.

ADVANCED

1. D. Turnbull, "Principles of Solidification," Seminar on Thermodynamics in Physical Metallurgy, American Society of Metals, 1950.
2. F. C. Frank, *Advances in Physics*, **1**, 91 (1952).
3. A. R. Verma, *Crystal Growth and Dislocations*, Wiley, New York, 1952.

Problems

3-1 Explain why artificial seeding produces a finer grain than spontaneous crystallization in castings.

3-2 A metal is cast in a square prismatic mold with relatively thick and good heat-conducting bottom and walls. Sketch the formation of columnar structure using Fig. 3-4 as a guide.

3-3 If a metal is cast in the form of a thin pancake instead of a long ingot, is it likely to get a more or a less pronounced columnar structure? Why?

3-4 Using the result of Problem 3-3, explain the reason for casting pure aluminum in a good conducting mold which, as the metal is poured, is progressively lowered into a tank with running water.

3-5 What effect has stirring on grain refinement?

3-6 Continue the build-up of unit cells in Fig. 3-9 to obtain an additional $\frac{1}{4}$ turn of the spiral.

3-7 In a FCC crystal there is one foreign atom in every 50th unit cell. What is the atomic percent of the impurity?

3-8 Consider that the disorder about a dislocation line involves 16 BCC unit cells so that the dislocation can be treated as a square tube, 4×4 atomic distances thick. How many atoms per 1 cm length of the dislocation line are affected by the disorder?

3-9 Let edge a of the unit cell in Problem 3-8 be 3.0 Å and let there be 10^8 dislocation lines per square centimeter. What percent of atoms is disordered in 1 cm^3?

4 / DETERMINATION OF STRUCTURE OF SOLIDS

It has been implied in previous chapters that the properties of common solids depend on their granular as well as their atomic, or crystal, structure. The study of both of these aspects of structure of solids is equally important. The methods used for the determination of grain and crystal structure, respectively, complement each other to some extent; one makes up for certain deficiencies of information found in the other, as will appear below.

4-1 Determination of Grain Structure. Most of the information related to the structure of grains has been obtained by visual examination of the surfaces of solids. Yet even in natural rocks the exposed faces seldom reveal the genuine features of their granular structure. Atmospheric and water erosion often produce patterns that are neither characteristic nor lasting. In metals, the exposed face generally bears the marks of previous treatments and/or is covered with a layer of oxide. Freshly cleaved surfaces are free of the above shortcomings. They have provided useful and, sometimes, essential information regarding the influence of structure on the brittle behavior of solids (see Chapter 8). By far the most frequent and reliable method of examination is the one making use of a preliminary preparation of surface. The preparation consists essentially of establishing a smooth face free of incidental markings and scratches. In the final stages it also involves polishing which often—and for metals invariably—produces a specular surface. Additional treatments are then necessary to reveal the grains (a mirror reflects everything but itself!).

With transparent minerals (quartz, felspars, etc.), the specimen is ground down to a thin slice (from 20 to 40 microns thick) so it can be examined by transmitted light. Most minerals occurring in nature are optically anisotropic. That is, they refract light differently in different crystallographic directions. This property enables identification of the grains to be made by use of polarized light because they exhibit different shadings and colorings, depending on their orientation with respect to the plane of polarization of the light.

The use of polarized light for the identification of minerals is not unlike the use of dyes for the identification of structural parts in the unit cell of living organisms. There, too, the observation is made on thin sections of tissues (a few microns thick) which are almost uniformly transparent. The dye is absorbed selectively by the most important part of the cell, the nucleus, which can thus be identified. Because of its ability to be colored, the substance of the nucleus is called chromatin (from Greek *chromos*, color).

Opaque minerals (such as olivine), ores, and metals must be viewed in reflected light. If the specimen contains minerals of various kinds—for example, a rock sample—single hard grains stand out in relief from the softer background. Polarized light also helps to determine the structure. If, however, the solid is homogeneous and optically isotropic—as most metals are—neither of these methods works, and etching must be resorted to.

Etching is done usually by subjecting the polished surface to the quick action of chemical reagents. The strength of the reagent and the duration of attack are adapted not only to the nature of the material but also to the method of inspection. Specimens viewed with the unaided eye usually require more prolonged etching and stronger reagents.

There are various etching mechanisms and several of them can occur with the same reagent:

1. The grains are attacked in specific crystallographic directions (as a rule, normal to the densest planes). This results in the formation of steps which have the same orientation in each grain, but are variously tilted from grain to grain, Fig. 4-1. Therefore, when viewed from a particular direction,

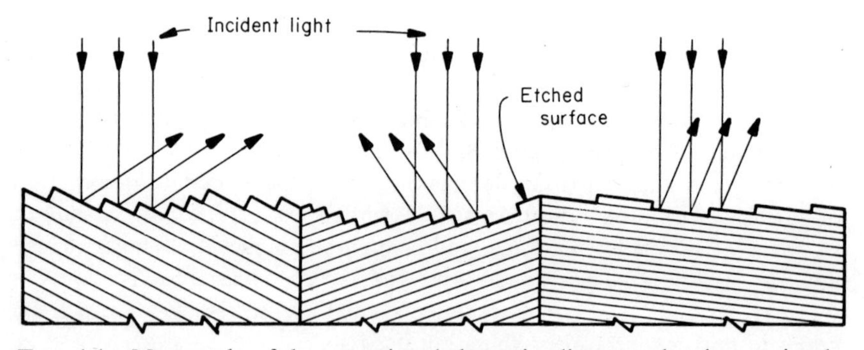

FIG. 4-1 Macroetch of large grains (schematic diagram showing variously oriented grains)

some of the grains will be seen reflecting the incident radiation more strongly than others, Fig. 4-2. The grains can then be readily differentiated by their degree of luster, which changes noticeably as the specimen is rotated.

2. The grains are attacked at a different rate, depending on the particular crystallographic plane uncovered by etching, Fig. 4-3. Those less deeply etched will appear in relief against their deeper-etched neighbors and will cast a shadow outlining their boundaries.

3. The reagent attacks preferentially (it grooves) the grain boundary that has a less orderly arrangement of atoms and is therefore more vulnerable to chemical action. The outline of the grains will then appear dark because

Fig. 4-2 Etched surface of an aluminum alloy

Fig. 4-3 Surface etched to different depths (aluminum oxide embedded in refractory oxides). (From Bierlein, Mastel, and Newkirk, *J. Amer. Ceramic Soc.*, **41**, 198, 1954)

light is more widely scattered from the groove than from the plane surface, Fig. 4-4.

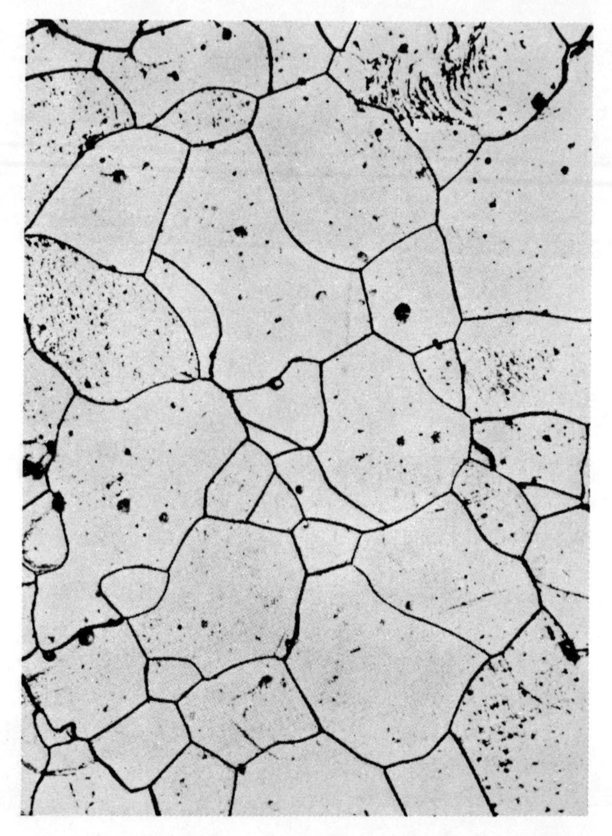

FIG. 4-4 Etched surface showing grain boundaries. (From Albert Sauveur, *The Metallography and Heat Treatment of Iron and Steel*, McGraw-Hill, New York, 1935, by permission)

4. It happens finally that grains are stained differently by the reagent. This usually occurs among neighboring grains belonging to various crystal structures, rather than among variously oriented grains of the same crystal structure, Fig. 4-5.

The overall depth of etch decreases from mechanism 1 to 4. The required depth and mechanism depend chiefly on the mode of inspection which, in turn, depends on the size of the grains.

Grains larger than 10^{-3} m can be viewed easily with the unaided eye, Fig. 4-2. If they are within the range of 10^{-4} to 10^{-3} m, a magnifying glass or studio camera is used. These provide a magnification of between $\times 2$ to $\times 10$. Both types of inspection are termed *macroscopic*.

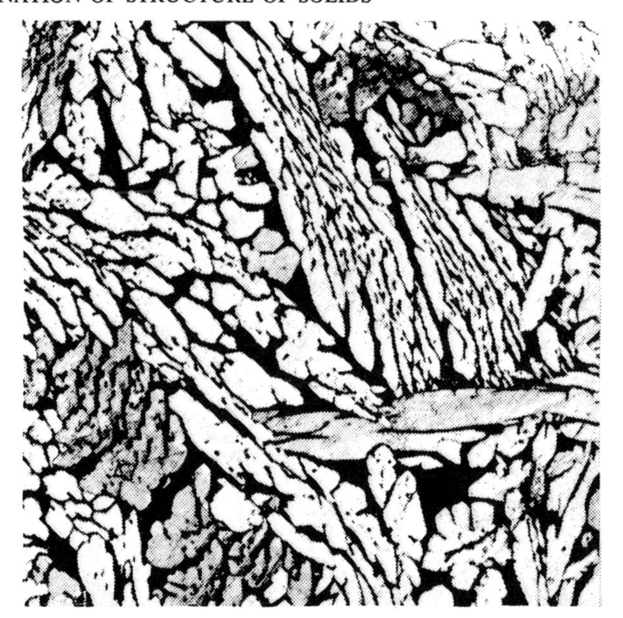

FIG. 4-5 Etched surface showing two-phase structure. (Courtesy American Brass Company)

4-2 Light and Electron Microscopy. The ordinary light microscope, with magnifications ranging from $\times 50$ to $\times 2000$, is the most common means of *microscopic* inspection. It is particularly suited to grains varying in size between 10^{-7} and 10^{-5} m. These sizes are commonly found in natural rocks and industrial metals.

Grains smaller than the wavelength of visible radiation (less than 5000 Å) cannot be resolved by light microscopy. They can, however, be examined with the aid of an electron microscope.

In an electron microscope, a stream of rapidly moving electrons is made to converge on the specimen. On passing through matter, electrons are absorbed and scattered like light waves. The electron waves, however, can be made a great deal shorter than light waves (as much as 100,000 times shorter) simply by increasing the velocity of electrons. The resolving power is correspondingly higher. Grains smaller than 100 Å in diameter have been examined by this technique, Fig. 4-6.

Standard equipment enables the examination only of thin, transparent sections about one micron thick. Opaque metallic surfaces can be explored indirectly by examining replicas made in plastic materials such as collodion, formvar, and polystyrene. Surface irregularities can be made more visible by exposing the replica to metallic vapors (e.g., a gold-palladium alloy, Fig. 4-7). The vapors condense along the ledges and cast a shadow on the image. Recently, additional details have been uncovered by using thin metallic films in transmission electron microscopy.

FIG. 4-6 Electronmicrograph of Kaolinite Particles. (Courtesy of Georgia Kaolin Company, Elizabeth, N.J.)

It is likely that as the technique and resolving power of electron microscopy continue to improve, not only more details of crystal structure but also the underlying pattern of atomic arrangement will be uncovered. At this point, electron microscopy will meet a powerful rival: the X-ray diffraction method, which today holds a position of leadership almost unchallenged in the determination of crystal structure.[1]

4-3 X-Ray Diffraction. X-ray diffraction produces interference patterns (*diffraction lines*) rather than images. In this respect it resembles the technique used to measure surface roughness of solids by means of optical flats (interference fringes). In both cases the radiation is used as a probe. The oncoming

[1] See, however, the role of electron microscopy in the study of imperfections of these structures: R. W. Honeycombe, "New Horizons in Metallography," *The Metallurgist*, **1**, Series 1, p. 34 (Jan. 1960).

FIG. 4-7 Electronmicrograph of a shadowed replica of an irradiated uranium specimen. (Courtesy of T. K. Bierlein and B. Mastel, Hanford Laboratories, General Electric Company)

waves impinge on the particles of matter and set them in vibration. In responding, the particles act like so many independent small emitters; they rebroadcast the oncoming waves. This behavior is characteristic of the manner in which all radiant energy interacts with matter, from radio waves 10^3 m long down to gamma rays with wavelengths shorter than 10^{-11} m. Huygens—a contemporary of Newton—was first to postulate such a behavior for light waves. Hence, the name "Huygens' principle," under which it is known in physics.

The re-emitted signals are too weak to be detected singly, but under proper conditions of regularity stipulated below, they can reinforce each other in particular directions. If these are known, the location of the re-emitters with respect to each other can also be determined. Therein lies the power of X-ray diffraction to reveal the structure of solids. For in the case of X-rays the re-emitters are atoms, and to obtain their relative positions is to determine the crystal structure of the solid.

We turn now to a more detailed analysis of the phenomenon of diffraction. We begin with the simple case of an equidistant row of atoms *ABCD*, Fig. 4-8. Suppose the incident radiation is a narrow beam of parallel monochromatic X-rays issued from a distant source. It is directed at right angle to the line *ABCD* so the waves arriving at the atoms are all in phase (for example, they are all at their peaks or troughs). This particular direction has been chosen for simplicity of computation, but the conclusions have general validity as will appear later.

Since X-ray radiation is of an electromagnetic nature—as are radio waves and visible light—it sets the negatively charged electrons in vibration (the positively charged nucleus is too heavy to be markedly affected). But a vibrating electrical charge behaves exactly as an electric oscillating circuit: it emits (or, more correctly, re-emits) radiation of the same frequency as the incident radiation. However, instead of following one direction, it is scattered in all directions.[2] More specifically, the atoms become new and independent sources of radiation that spreads in the form of spherical waves of ever-increasing radii, such as AK_0, AM_0, and AP_0, Fig. 4-8. These

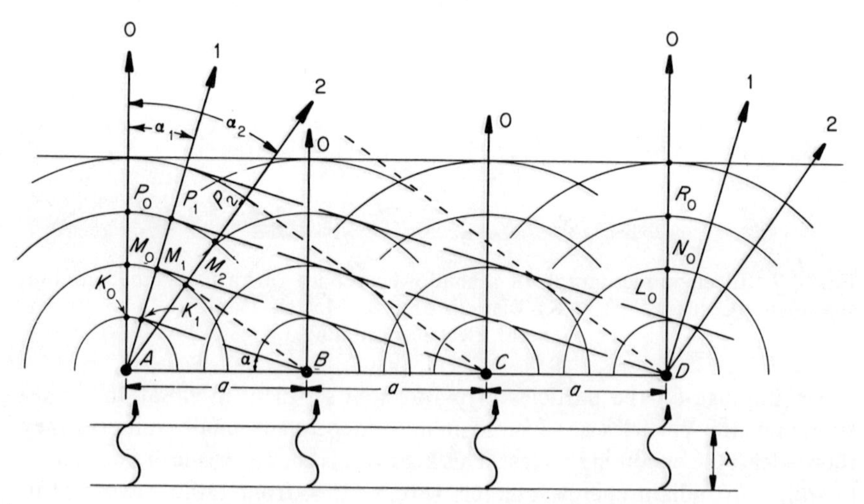

FIG. 4-8 X-ray diffraction by rows of atoms

waves will reinforce each other in those particular directions in which they form an advancing front (here, a plane) with all points in phase. One such a front obviously will follow the direction of the incident radiation forming what is called a zero-order diffraction (or no diffraction of radiation). It is represented successively by the planes K_0L_0, M_0N_0, and P_0R_0 perpendicular to the

[2] This is also called *coherent* scattering, in distinction to the much less intense incoherent one in which the frequency also is modified.

plane of the paper. Other advancing fronts, at an angle to the incident radiation, also will be formed. This will happen every time neighboring wavelets issued from $ABCD$ will again be in phase, but their paths will differ by an integral number of wavelengths. Thus along the wave fronts BK_1, CM_1, and DP_1 advancing in, and perpendicular to, the direction α_1, the neighboring wavelets differ by one wavelength. Consequently, a reinforcement or *first-order diffraction* (deviation from incident direction) will occur in the α_1 direction. Similarly, a *second-order diffraction* will occur in the α_2 direction, since the wavelets along the fronts BM_2, CP_2, etc., advancing in this direction differ by two wavelengths, and so on.

If a detector, such as a photographic film, is placed around the specimen, there will be pronounced blackening of the film in the directions of diffraction α_1, α_2, etc. (not counting, of course, the much more pronounced blackening in the direct path of the incident direction). From the location of the blackened regions on the film, the angles α_1, α_2, etc., can be determined. This information, in turn, will enable us to obtain the distance between the atoms if the value λ of the wavelength is known. Consider, for example, the triangle AK_1B. AK_1 is equal to λ, and BK_1 (a segment of the advancing wave front of the first-order diffraction) is perpendicular to AK_1. Hence,

$$AB = \frac{\lambda}{\sin \alpha_1} \tag{4-1}$$

Likewise, for the second-order diffraction (from triangle ABM_2),

$$AB = \frac{2\lambda}{\sin \alpha_2} \tag{4-2}$$

Equations (4-1), (4-2), etc., show that in order to produce diffraction—and thus compute the relative distance AB—we must use wavelengths λ that do not exceed this distance. However, if the waves are too short, say one hundredth of AB, the first-order diffraction is too close to the incident beam to be observable, and the higher orders of diffraction are too weak to be usable. Since most of the atomic distances are of the order of an angstrom (10^{-10} m), the X-rays used for the diffraction analysis must have wavelengths of the same order of magnitude.

Compared with the X-rays used in therapy or medical radiography, those used for diffraction analysis are at least 10 times longer. Their penetrating power is correspondingly much smaller. Yet they are still able to penetrate a layer of matter from 1000 to 10,000 atomic distances deep, depending on the density of the specimen. This circumstance complicates the above simple analysis made for one single row of atoms. It is easy to see that waves diffracted from many rows of atoms will interfere with each other. If they are even slightly out of phase, they will end up by cancelling each other.

This can be seen as follows: Suppose the waves emitted by successive rows are out of phase only 1/100 of a wavelength. Nevertheless, every pair of waves, 50 rows apart, will be out of phase half a wavelength; that is, the trough of one will coincide with the crest of the other and they will cancel each other.

It follows that the analysis of real three-dimensional crystals cannot be carried out by X-ray diffraction unless the matching of phases between the successive rows is very close indeed.

4-4 Bragg's Law. W. H. Bragg has shown that the above stringent condition can be easily satisfied if the atoms of successive rows are located on crystallographic planes in such a way that the incident and diffracted rays make equal angles with these planes. To put it differently, exact matching of phases will occur on a set of planes of the same crystallographic family if, in addition to requirement Eq. (4-1), the angle between the incident and diffracted beams is bisected by these planes.

To prove this point, suppose that in Fig. 4-9 the rows of atoms *ABC*,

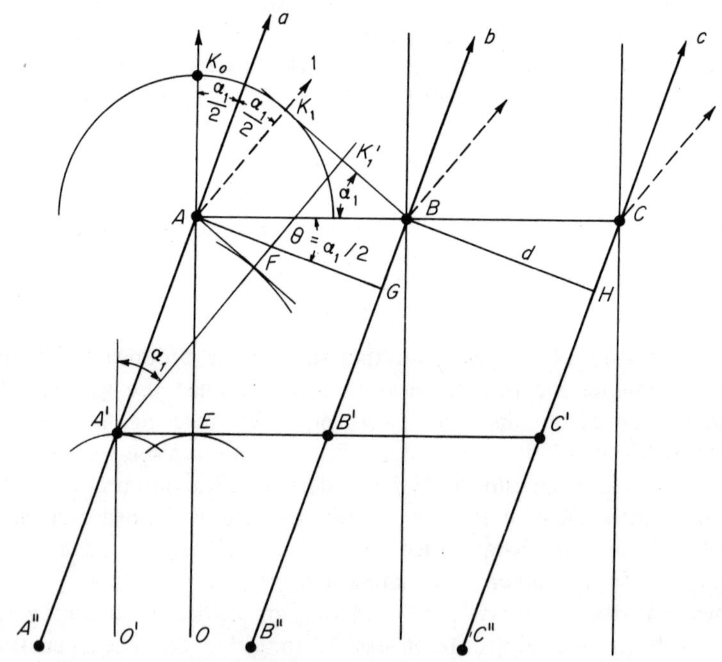

FIG. 4-9 Diffraction by groups of atoms in parallel planes

A'B'C', and *A''B''C''* are arranged alternatively on planes *a*, *b*, and *c* of the same family, bisecting the angle α_1 between the incident and diffracted beams AK_0 and AK_1. For convenience, this family of planes has been represented as being perpendicular to the plane of the paper. A wave front reaching atom *A'* will reach atom *A* after a time EA/c, where *c* is the velocity of wave propagation. During this time, the wave diffracted from *A'* in the direction α_1 will cover the distance $A'F$. But X-rays have practically the same velocity of propagation in solids as in air, that is, they are practically not *refracted* (note the difference with diffracted). Hence, $A'F = EA$. From the equality of triangles $A'AE$ and $AA'F$, it follows that $\measuredangle A'EA = \measuredangle A'FA = \pi/2$. That is, AF is a portion of an advancing wave front in the direction of diffraction α_1. Hence, the wave emitted in this direction from A' is in phase with that emitted from A and so is a wave emitted from any other point (atom) on the plane a. However, if this is true of plane a, it must be true also of planes b, c, and any other plane of the same crystallographic family.

In conclusion, all atoms belonging to the same family of crystallographic planes reinforce each other in the direction α_1, provided that the incident and diffracted beams make equal angles with these planes and that Eq. (4-1) is fulfilled. (Note that equality of angles is not achieved for the second-order diffraction in the direction α_2, Fig. 4-8. Hence, this diffraction will not occur.)

We shall now replace condition Eq. (4-1)—which is unnecessarily restrictive—by a more general one involving the characteristic interplanar distance d between neighboring planes of the family under consideration. We first observe that whether or not there is actually an atom A, belonging to plane a and located on the line ABC normal to the incident beam, is immaterial, since other atoms in this plane emit waves in phase with B and C in the direction of diffraction. Thus, AB is merely a construction line. Call $\theta = \alpha_1/2$ the angle which the incident beam makes with the family of planes abc. The diffracted beam makes the same angle with this family.

From triangle ABG we have

$$AG = AB\cos\theta \tag{4-3}$$

By combining Eq. (4-3) with Eq. (4-1) and putting $AG = d$ (interplanar distance) and $\alpha_1 = 2\theta$,

$$d = \frac{\lambda\cos\theta}{\sin 2\theta} = \frac{\lambda\cos\theta}{2\sin\theta\cos\theta}$$

or

$$\boxed{\lambda = 2d\sin\theta} \tag{4-4}$$

This is the famous *Bragg's law of diffraction*, which is at the heart of every method of the determination of crystal structure. An application of this law to the case of cubic crystals follows.

4-5 Identification of Planes. Miller Indices. There are several experimental methods for determining the angle of diffraction θ. A particularly simple one will be described later. If θ and λ are known, the value of d can be computed from Eq. (4-4). In the course of an experiment, several diffraction angles are recorded. To each of them there corresponds a different value of d, and, as a rule, a different family of crystallographic planes. One of the problems of X-ray analysis is to determine the type and dimensions of the unit cell from these data.

In the case of the cubic lattice, the determination is relatively easy. It requires, however, some knowledge of the elements of crystallography. Because of the growing use of crystal geometry in fields of engineering (such as transistor technology and magnetics), these elements will be briefly reviewed.

The interplanar distance d is an important but not a sufficient characteristic of a family of planes. To identify the orientation of the family in the crystal lattice, we must refer the planes to a system of coordinates. These are most conveniently chosen in the direction of the three edges of the unit cell. Any lattice point, of course, can be used as an origin. Consider, for example, the cubic cell $OABC$, Fig. 4-10a, and the three axes OA, OB, and OC, or x, y, and z.

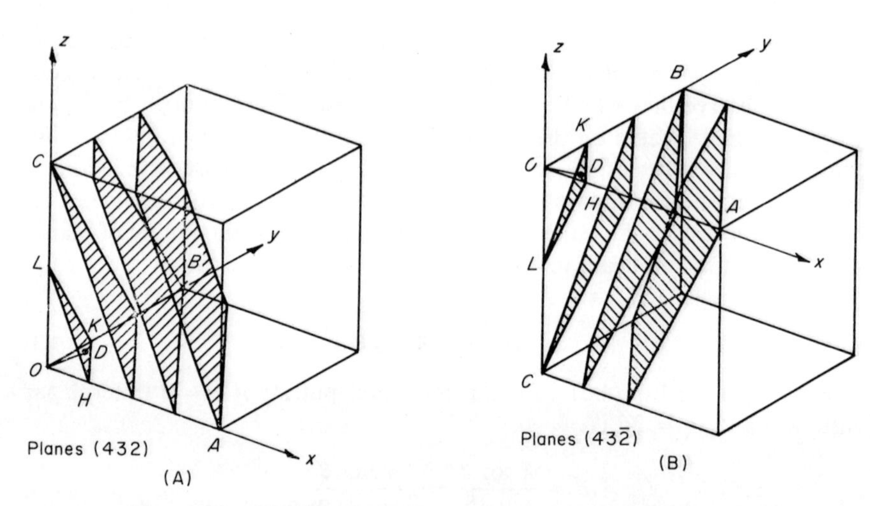

FIG. 4-10 Identification of crystal planes by Miller indices

Every family of crystallographic planes must contain planes which pass through the origin O and the three lattice points ABC. Since planes of the same family are equidistant, there will be an integral number of them between O and A, O and B, and O and C. Call hkl the number of planes between O and A, O and B, and O and C, respectively (excluding the origin). This is also the number of intercepts the planes will make with the three edges OA, OB, and OC. They are called the indices of the family of crystallographic planes and are enclosed in parentheses, e.g., (432) in Fig. 4-10a. It is clear that if the indices are given in an established order, for example, if they follow the order of axes OA, OB, and OC, each of the planes can be drawn in one and only one fashion. Note, however, that use must also be made of negative numbers. To avoid confusion, the minus sign is put above, and not in front of, the number, for example, $(43\bar{2})$. This is seen in Fig. 4-10b, in which the planes of family $(43\bar{2})$ have been drawn within the unit cell. The identification of one plane of the family identifies all of them. The plane closest to the origin is generally chosen: plane *HKL*, Fig. 4-10a.

Planes parallel to one of the axes have, of course, no intercepts with this axis, and the corresponding index is 0. Hence the faces of the cube are identified as (100), (010), and (001), respectively. Some of the important planes in the cubic lattice are shown in Fig. 4-11 with their indices.

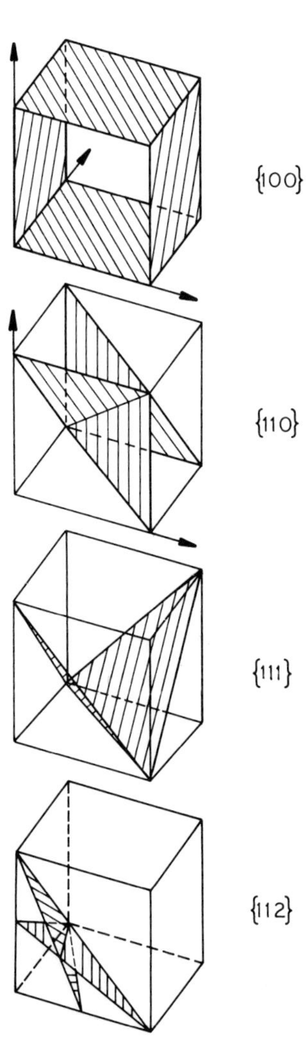

FIG. 4-11 Prominent planes in the cubic lattice

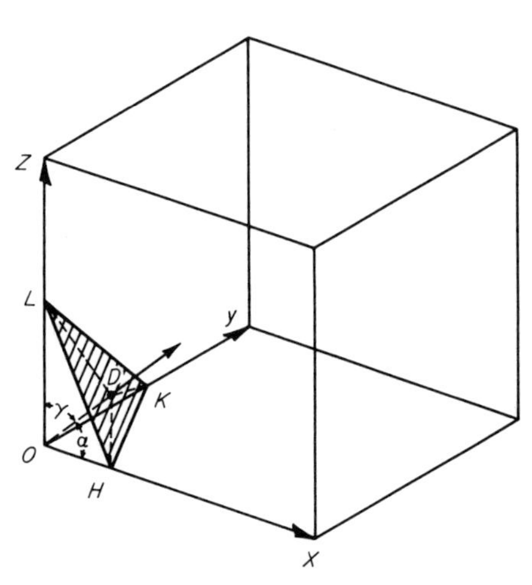

FIG. 4-12 The determination of the interplanar distance *d*

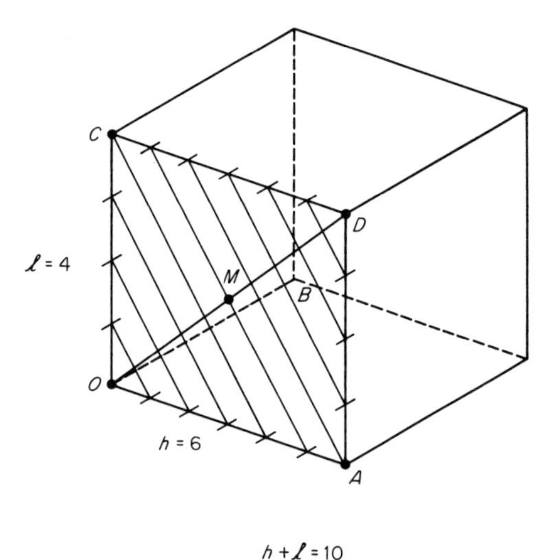

FIG. 4-13 The face-centered cubic cell

Looking at these planes, the student will realize that some of them are equivalent, that is, they differ merely because of the order in which the indices are written, but a suitable rotation of the axes will bring one in coincidence with the other. Families of this nature are said to be of the same form. We indicate all these families by enclosing their indices in braces $\{hkl\}$.

While on the subject of indices, we may mention that a crystallographic direction can be identified similarly. For example, by writing [121], we indicate that the particular direction is obtained by moving one unit translation a in the OA (or x) direction, two units in the OB (or y) direction, and one unit in direction OC (or z). To identify the direction, we enclose the indices in brackets, $[uvw]$. Negative indices—with a minus sign above the number—indicate translations in the opposite (negative) directions to those of $+x$, $+y$, $+z$. As with planes, equivalent directions are said to be of the same form and are enclosed in angle brackets, $\langle uvw \rangle$. For example, $\langle 111 \rangle$ indicates all cube diagonals, irrespective of their directions.

4-6 Computation of the Unit Cell. We are now able to rewrite Bragg's law in a form more suitable for the computation of the unit cell. We first express the interplanar distance d in terms of a (edge of the unit cell) and the indices (hkl) of the corresponding family of crystallographic planes. To this end we consider the plane HKL nearest to the origin, Fig. 4-12. There is a plane of the same family passing through the origin (but not shown). Therefore, if OD is normal to the plane HKL, it is also an interplanar distance d of the family. From the right triangles OHD, OKD, and ODL we have, by calling the angles HOD, KOD, and LOD α, β, and γ, respectively,

$$\cos\alpha = \frac{OD}{OH}$$

$$\cos\beta = \frac{OD}{OK} \tag{4-5}$$

$$\cos\gamma = \frac{OD}{OL}$$

From analytical geometry we know that

$$\cos^2\alpha + \cos^2\beta + \cos^2\gamma = 1 \tag{4-6}$$

Hence

$$\left(\frac{OD}{OH}\right)^2 + \left(\frac{OD}{OK}\right)^2 + \left(\frac{OD}{OL}\right)^2 = 1 \tag{4-7}$$

or

$$\frac{1}{OH^2} + \frac{1}{OK^2} + \frac{1}{OL^2} = \frac{1}{OD^2} \tag{4-8}$$

But

$$OH = a/h, \quad OK = a/k, \quad OL = a/l \tag{4-9}$$

and

$$OD = d$$

Substituting Eq. (4-9) in Eq. (4-8) we have, after simplification,

$$d = \frac{a}{\sqrt{h^2 + k^2 + l^2}} \tag{4-10}$$

Substitution of Eq. (4-10) in Bragg's law, Eq. (4-4), yields

$$\frac{2a \sin \theta}{\sqrt{h^2 + k^2 + l^2}} = \lambda \tag{4-11}$$

from which the edge of the unit cell can be computed if the indices (hkl) are known. The latter are selected according to the rules detailed below.

4-7 Indices of Simple, Face-Centered, and Body-Centered Cubic Lattices. Equation (4-11) shows that the smaller the diffraction angle θ, the lower is the sum of the squared indices hkl. Thus if all possible diffraction angles are recorded in succession and none is omitted, the results can be indexed by beginning with the three smallest integers. Three different cases must be distinguished:

1. The cell is a simple cube; that is, it contains only one lattice point. In this case all combinations of indices can occur. We begin with {100}, then {110}, then {111}, then {200}, and so on. Table 4-1, column 2, lists the first 10 indices and the sums of their squares (simple cubic).

2. The cell is a face-centered cube, that is, it contains four lattice points. In this case, the only permissible combinations of indices are hkl, all odd, or all even.

The proof is as follows: Consider one of the faces, such as that formed by OA and OC, Fig. 4-13. It is easy to see that if OA is divided by a family of planes in h parts and AD in l parts, the diagonal of the face is divided by this family in $h + l$ parts. However, one of the planes of the family must pass through the middle point M, since this is a point of the lattice. Hence $h + l$ must be even (divisible by two) and h and l are either both odd or both even. The same reasoning can be applied to the faces OA and OB, and OB and OC. Hence the indices hkl must be either all odd or all even. Table 4-1, column 3, lists the indices belonging to the FCC space lattice. The lowest possible indices are {111}, because zero is considered as even.

3. The cell is a body-centered cube, i.e., it contains two lattice points. Here the only permissible combinations are $h + k + l =$ even.

The proof is the same as above, except that instead of the face diagonal, the cube diagonal is considered. The latter is divided into $h + k + l$ parts

TABLE 4-1 EXAMPLE OF INDICES IN SIMPLE, FACE-CENTERED, AND BODY-CENTERED CUBIC LATTICES

hkl	$h^2 + k^2 + l^2$		
	Simple	Face-Centered	Body-Centered
100	1	—	—
110	2	—	2
111	3	3	—
200	4*	4	4
210	5	—	—
211	6	—	6
220	8*	8	8
{300, 221}	9	—	—
310	10	—	10
311	11	11	—

* Higher-order diffraction.

if the edges of the cube are divided into h, k, and l parts, respectively. Since the middle point on the cube diagonal is a lattice point, one of the $h + k + l$ planes must pass through it; hence $h + k + l$ must be even. The lowest possible indices therefore are {110}, as listed in Table 4-1, column 4.

Before proceeding, a brief description of one of the current and useful experimental methods might be helpful. It is the powder method, or Debye-Sherrer and Hull method (after the names of its inventors).

The sample is reduced, if possible, to a fine powder so that the grains can take any orientation in space. In this fashion some of the grains will be so orientated that a family of crystallographic planes that can possibly contribute to X-ray diffraction will find itself in a position to do so.

Short of a powder, a fine-grained polycrystalline specimen (grain size of the order of 0.1 to 0.01 mm) is also suitable.

A monochromatic beam of X-rays is made to pass through a narrow pinhole and fall on the specimen, Fig. 4-14. The X-rays diffracted from the incident direction at the various angles θ impress a strip of photographic film which is snugly wrapped about the wall of the cylindrical camera. The latter encloses the specimen and protects the film from light exposure. The film is provided with two holes: one for the pinhole and the other for an X-ray absorber (a fluorescent screen) in the direct path of the incident beam. This device is used to prevent excessive darkening of the film (solarization) in the neighborhood of the zero-order diffraction.

When the film is flattened out, after X-ray exposure and darkroom processing, it has the appearance shown in Fig. 4-15. The angular position of the diffraction lines can be readily determined from the fact that the distance

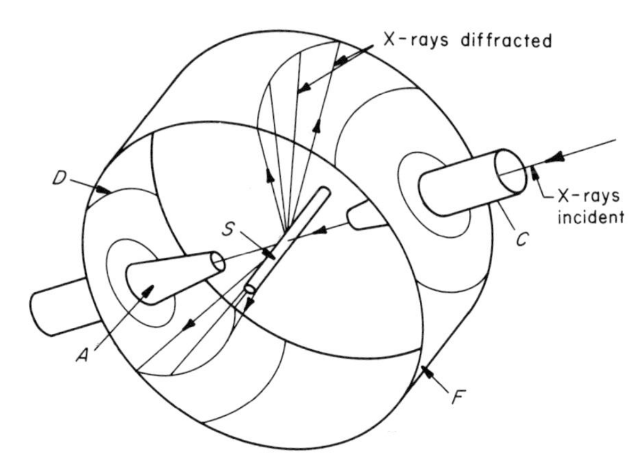

FIG. 4-14 Camera for X-ray diffraction of powders (schematic). C, Collimator; S, Specimen; F, Film; A, Absorber of transmitted radiation; D, Diffraction line

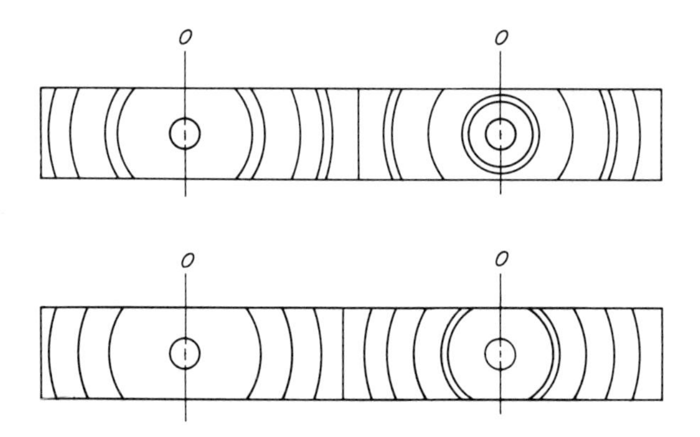

FIG. 4-15 X-ray diffraction patterns of powdered samples

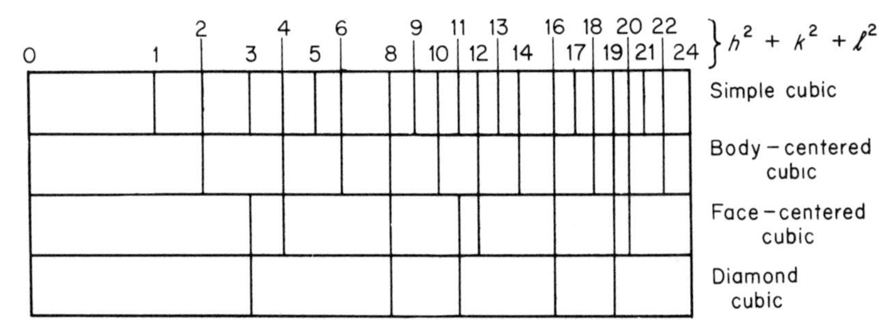

FIG. 4-16 Comparison of X-ray diffraction patterns. (From C. S. Barrett, *Structure of Metals*, McGraw-Hill, New York, 1952, by permission)

O–O separating the centers of the incident and absorption holes corresponds exactly to π.

The indices of the diffraction lines are determined by inspection and trial. The comparison of patterns obtained from FCC and BCC lattices shows that there is a marked difference in the sequence of diffraction lines in both cases. This can be readily understood by referring to Table 4-1, and even better by looking at Fig. 4-16, in which the values of columns 2, 3, and 4, Table 4-1, have been plotted to an arbitrary scale.

4-8 Example of Identification of Crystal Lattice from X-Ray Diffraction Data

Given $\lambda = 1.7853$ Å and diffraction angles 2θ, shown in column 1, Table 4-2, determine the type and size of the unit (cubic) cell of aluminum.

Solution. We compute θ, $\sin\theta$, and $\sin^2\theta$ as shown in columns 2, 3 and 4, Table 4-2. We observe that the ratio of the first two $\sin^2\theta$ is close to $\frac{3}{4}$. We conclude from Table 4-1 that the lattice is FCC. Thus the first set of indices is {111}, the second {200}, etc. Squaring Eq. (4-11) and solving for a^2, we get

$$a^2 = (\lambda/2)^2(h^2 + k^2 + l^2)/\sin^2\theta \tag{4-12}$$

from which the value of a^2 can be obtained from each diffraction angle. The average value of a can thus be computed ($a = 4.042$ Å, which is close to $a = 4.04153$ Å, reported for 99.5% aluminum).

TABLE 4-2 COMPUTATION OF TYPE AND SIZE OF UNIT CELL

2θ	θ	$\sin\theta$	$\sin^2\theta$	$h^2 + k^2 + l^2$	a^2(Å^2)
0	0	—	—	—	—
45	22.50	0.3825	0.1465	1 + 1 + 1	16.35
52.5	26.25	0.4420	0.1960	4 + 0 + 0	16.36
77.4	38.70	0.6250	0.3910	4 + 4 + 0	16.33
94.5	47.25	0.7345	0.5395	9 + 1 + 1	16.33

Average $a^2 = 16.343$ Å^2; hence, $a = 4.0420$ Å.*

* For a more exact determination of a, see standard textbooks on X-ray diffraction analysis.

4-9 Note on Image Formation Versus Diffraction. One might infer from previous considerations that there are two distinct modes of exploration of matter by means of radiation:

1. Image formation as in light and electron microscopy, or in visual inspection. In the latter case, the image is formed directly on the retina (in the back of the eye).
2. Diffraction as in optical flats and X-ray analysis.

However, closer examination of image formation shows, as the Danish physicist Abbe pointed out some hundred years ago, that the distinction between the two sorts of signals is less basic than it would seem at first sight.

Consider, for example, an object consisting of an opaque screen pierced with small circular holes A, B, and C, Fig. 4-17. The images of these holes

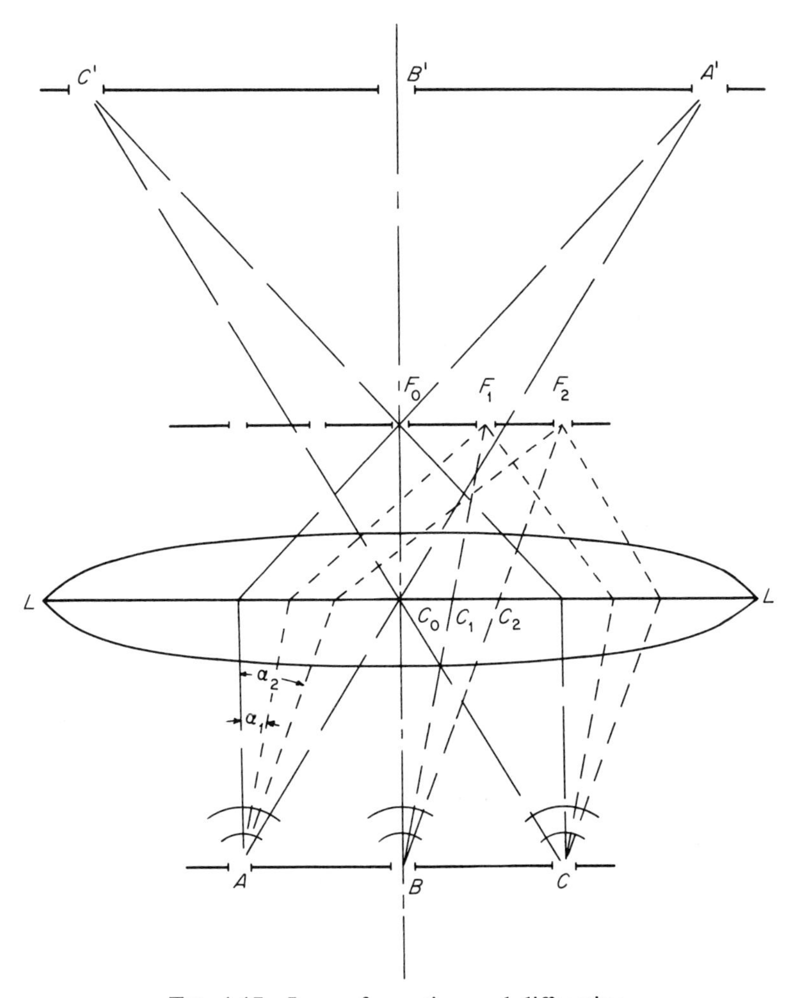

FIG. 4-17 Image formation and diffraction

through lens LL can be obtained as explained in high school physics by drawing two sorts of rays from each hole: one ray such as AC_0A' through lens center C_0 and the other parallel to the axis. The first ray will emerge from the lens practically without change of direction, and the second will be refracted toward the focal point F_0. The intersection of the two rays marks the position of the image A'. The location of images B' and C' is obtained similarly.

Now consider the image formation from the point of view of diffraction. We say that for the image to be truly representative of the object, all radiation emitted from the holes A, B, and C must converge to the image of holes A', B' and C', respectively. If the holes are sufficiently small, they can be considered as centers of emission of spherical waves. These will interact as explained previously (Fig. 4-8), by forming advancing plane wave fronts in the direction of the zero, first, second, etc., diffraction orders, respectively. An advancing plane wave front, however, can be considered as a bundle of parallel rays. The rays of zero-order diffraction are parallel to the axis, and, therefore, on passing through the lens, they will converge to the main focus F_0. Similarly, rays at an angle α_1, α_2, etc., to the axis will converge to secondary foci F_1, F_2, etc. The closer the convergence, the better is the quality of the lens.

Foci $F_0, F_1, F_2, \ldots$, however, as easily seen, are nothing more than locations of diffraction spectra after refraction through the lens. With perfect convergence, they, in turn, can be considered new centers of radiation emission. In fact, we could put a screen pierced with holes $F_0, F_1, F_2, \ldots$, in the paths of the rays without affecting in the least the image formation, since in the ideal case all radiation issuing from holes A, B, C, is concentrated at F_0, $F_1, F_2, \ldots$, and nowhere else. The spherical waves spreading from centers $F_0, F_1, F_2, \ldots$, again interfere between themselves. We know in advance, however, that the ultimate outcome of this interference will be reinforcements at the locations of the images A', B', and C' and cancellations elsewhere.

In conclusion, from the viewpoint of diffraction, image formation consists of three steps:

1. Formation of diffraction spectra of zero-order, first-order, second-order, and so on.

2. Convergence of these spectra at focal points $F_0, F_1, F_2, \ldots$, after refraction through lens LL.

3. Emission of spherical waves from points $F_0, F_1, F_2, \ldots$, and their mutual interference (reinforcements and cancellations).

In the case of X-ray diffraction, the image formation does not go beyond step 1, since X-rays cannot be refracted by lenses as light and electron waves can. However, as W. L. Bragg (cowinner of a Nobel prize with his father, W. H. Bragg) has shown, it is possible to complete the steps by transposing the diffraction patterns on a series of suitably oriented templates and by photographing them one after the other on the same photographic film. In this ingenious procedure, the templates replace the bundles of diffracted rays. The lens of the photographic camera focuses the light waves passing through the templates at points similar to $F_0, F_1, F_2, \ldots$, of Fig. 4-17 and brings them into interference (reinforcement) at images similar to A', B', and C'. Since bundles of diffracted X-rays are being issued from individual atoms, the images will be those of atoms. As G. Gamow pointed out,[3]

[3] *One Two Three... Infinity*, Mentor, New York, 1953.

the procedure is similar to that used in polychromy, where each color is printed with a separate plate. The superposition of these prints produces a picture of the object in its natural colors.

Figure 4-18 is a reproduction of one of the composite photographs of

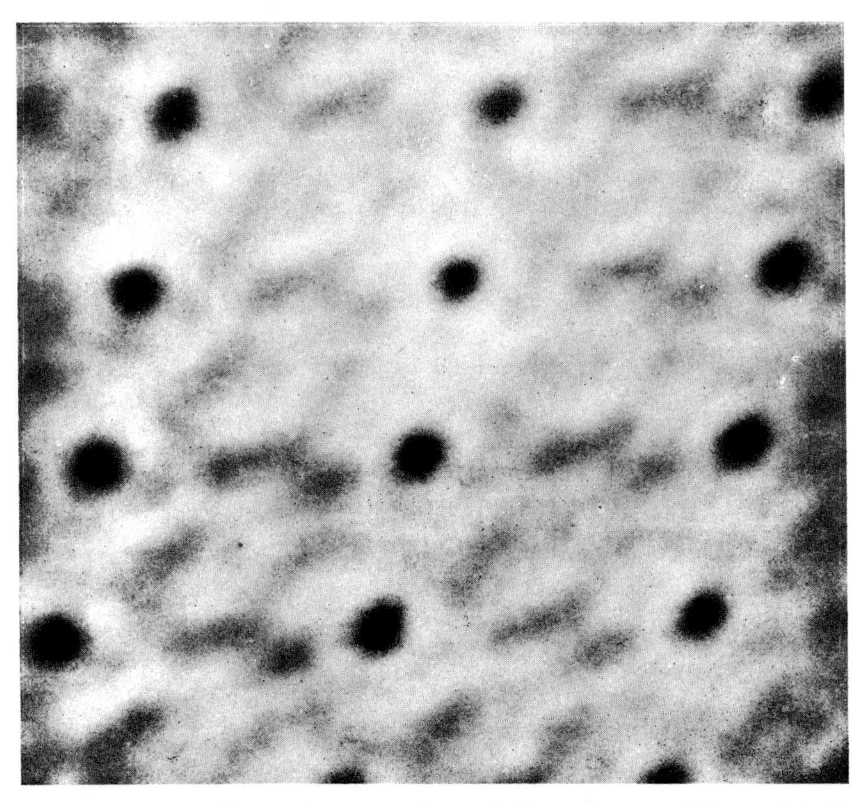

FIG. 4-18 Image of atoms in an actual crystal. (From Bragg and Bragg, *Zeit. F. Krist.*, **70**, 489, 1929)

crystal structure made by W. L. Bragg. The periodicity and regularity of the structure is at once apparent from the photograph. The images of individual atoms are markedly blurred. This defect is only in part due to the lack of optical resolution. It is also caused by the restlessness of the posing objects (atoms) at room temperature. As the temperature increases, the picture becomes more and more blurred until it loses all resolution at the melting point of the substance.

The improvement in electron microscopy is apt to do away with the rather tedious and delicate technique devised by Bragg. However, it is not likely to improve markedly on the resolution of the image itself. In addition to the blur caused by temperature vibration, there is the unavoidable lack of resolution caused by the interaction between waves and particles and deriving from the fundamental behavior of matter and energy (the indeterminacy principle).

4-10 Summary. Grains of polycrystalline aggregates can be identified in transmitted visible light if they are transparent, or by reflection if they are opaque. Polarized light is used when the material is optically anisotropic. Opaque isotropic materials (e.g., metals) require preliminary surface preparation (polishing and etching).

Details of structure smaller than the wavelength of visible radiation can be explored by means of electron microscopy. The exploration extends as far down as molecular structure. Precise determination of crystal structure, however, calls for the use of X-ray diffraction.

Information supplied by X-ray diffraction is not as direct as that provided by image formation. Its manipulation requires the use of Bragg's diffraction law and elements of crystallography. The determination of the type and size of the unit cell in a cubic lattice is a good example of application.

Diffraction and image formation are the intermediate and final stages of the process of interaction between matter and radiation on which our knowledge of the external world is ultimately based.

References

ELEMENTARY

1. W. L. Bragg, *Concerning the Nature of Things*, Dover, New York, 1954.
2. G. Gamow, *One, Two, Three...Infinity*, Mentor, New York, 1953.

ADVANCED

1. W. H. Bragg and W. L. Bragg, *The Crystalline State*, Bell & Sons, London, 1949.
2. C. S. Barrett, *Structure of Metals*, McGraw-Hill, New York, 1952.
3. R. W. K. Honeycombe, "New Horizons in Metallography," *Metallurgist*, **1**, Series 1, 34, 1960.
4. G. Thomas, *Transmission Electron Microscopy in Metals*, Wiley, New York, 1962.

Problems

4-1 Two adjacent grains of a polycrystalline cubic metal are oriented in such a way that in one of them the plane of the cube and in the other the dodecahedral plane (refer to Table 2-1) are parallel to the surface. If etching builds steps parallel to the octahedral plane, at what angles will a light beam normal to the surface be reflected from each of these grains?

4-2 A monochromatic X-ray beam with a wavelength of 2.2 Å falls on an octahedral plane of a crystal with $a = 3.5$ Å. At what angle must the octahedral plane be tilted with respect to the incident beam to produce diffraction? What is the angle the diffracted beam will then make with the incident beam?

4-3 A monochromatic X-ray beam with a wavelength of 1.78 Å is diffracted by a dodecahedral plane of a BCC crystal so that the diffracted beam makes an angle of 36° with the incident beam. Compute the size a of the unit cell.

4-4 Compute the interplanar distances of planes {112}, {122}, and {102} in a cubic crystal the size of whose unit cell is $a = 4.1$ Å.

4-5 In what ratio are the diffraction angles θ_1 and θ_2 corresponding to the first- and second-order diffraction from the same family of crystallographic planes? (Hint: For the second-order diffraction, the path difference is twice the wavelength.)

4-6 Given $\lambda = 1.5405$ Å and the size of a BCC crystal $a = 3.1648(W)$, compute the first four diffraction angles to be expected from a powdered sample.

4-7 In what ratio are the first two diffraction angles in a FCC crystal?

4-8 Given $\lambda = 1.7853$ Å and the sequence of diffraction angles 2θ of a cubic crystal lattice shown in Table 4-3 below, compute the average value of a and find what metallic element could give this particular diffraction pattern. (Note: Exclude simple cubic lattice.)

TABLE 4-3

Diffraction line	2θ *(in degrees)*
1	47.2
2	68.8
3	87.75
4	106.25
5	123.80
6	156.75

4-9 If an error of 0.1° is made in the measurement of the diffraction angle, what relative error will be made in the evaluation of the interplanar distance at diffraction angles of 30° and 70°? (Hint: The differentiation of Bragg's law for constant λ gives: $\Delta d \sin\theta + d\cos\theta\,\Delta\theta = 0$, whence $\Delta d/d = -\Delta\theta \text{ cotan } \theta$.)

4-10 Referring to the result of Problem 4-9, prove that the same errors are made in the evaluation of the size a of the unit cell. Make a decision regarding the advisability of using large diffraction angles for precision measurements of a.

II / GENERAL PROPERTIES OF MATERIALS

"On the one (view) there is nothing to be gained by looking into the structure of substances. . . . On the other view, the nature of things as we know them will depend on the properties of these atoms of which they are composed . . . . The latter view turns out to be far nearer the truth than the former; and for that all may be grateful who love to enquire into the ways of Nature." **Sir William Bragg**

5 / DEFINITION AND SUBDIVISION OF MATERIAL PROPERTIES

When designing a structure, device, or process, the engineer is generally more interested in the properties of the materials he will use than in their atomic or crystal structure. Yet he knows—or he ought to know—that the more intimate his knowledge of "the nature of things," the more quickly and more confidently he will be able to pick out the right kind of material. Why this is so will appear from the following chapters, in which some of the most general material properties are described and discussed. Before we go into more detail, however, it will prove instructive to examine what we mean by a material property. We shall briefly analyze when a property is or is not solely dependent on the atomic and crystal structure. We shall make a distinction between structure-sensitive and structure-insensitive properties and shall explain the meaning and role of a technological property.

5-1 What is a Material Property? Various materials respond differently to the same stimuli and constraints. For example, polished metal surfaces reflect almost all of the incident visible radiation, sometimes with selective coloring (and absorption), as in gold, copper, and their alloys, whereas polished surfaces of many minerals, like quartz and alkali halides, transmit almost all of this radiation unchanged. The former are opaque; the latter are transparent. Similarly, solids subjected to small deformations as a rule recover their original shape and dimensions after the applied loading is removed, whereas liquids and related substances, like putty, tar, and wax, do not. The former are elastic; the latter are viscous, as will be explained in more detail in Chapters 6 and 12.

We could easily multiply these examples. In all of them the quality of the response to imposed stimuli and constraints is determined by the nature of the material. We define this quality as a *material property*. Thus, opacity is a property of metals, transparency is a property of many minerals, elasticity is a property of solids, viscosity is a property of liquids, and so on.

In engineering applications it is not enough to know how a material responds to imposed stimuli and constraints; we must also learn *how much* it responds. Thus, under identical loading, an aluminum rod will be found to deform elastically three times as much as the same rod made of iron. The material property here enters as a quantitative factor in the relationship between load and deformation. We can therefore define a material property quite generally by saying that it is a factor which affects qualitatively or quantitatively the response of a given material to imposed stimuli and constraints.

The properties of matter encountered in chemistry are seen to be in accord with this definition. Thus, the mass of a given (imposed) volume of matter is determined (affected) by its density; the weight of a given number of atoms of an element is determined by its atomic weight; etc.

In engineering design, the stimuli and constraints commonly imposed on a system are forces, electric fields, temperature gradients, and so on. The responses they cause are deformations, electric charges, amounts of heat, etc. In all these interactions there appears a material property that affects the magnitude of the response: modulus of elasticity, dielectric constant, thermal conductivity, etc. The material property, as we shall see, is always defined in such a way as to be *independent of the shape and dimensions* of the particular component of system to which it refers, just as density or atomic weight are independent of the shape and dimensions of the sample used for their determination.

One may wonder what is to be gained by such a definition. The point is that by having a material property dependent only on the material itself, we can single out this factor from all other factors in design and manipulate it freely without fear of upsetting the already established framework into which it fits. Thus, suppose we wish to redesign a water tank and make it of aluminum instead of steel. Without touching any other variable in the existing design we can at once determine how much lighter the tank will be by comparing the densities of aluminum and steel; how much more it will deform under the same weight of water by comparing the moduli of elasticity; whether this deformation will still be elastic; and to a certain extent how much more the tank will cost. The same is true of other engineering systems, such as a heat exchanger in which one kind of a circulating fluid is to be replaced by another.

5-2 Material Property and Design. It should not be inferred from the foregoing that materials have no influence on design. Every engineering task, it has been said,[1] makes use of space (geometry), time, energy, and human as well as material resources. It often happens that there is sufficient leeway in the apportionment of space, as when designing the shape and dimensions of structural members, and that the time element is not unduly restrictive, e.g., the longevity of modern cars. Material resources are necessarily limited, however, as are energy and human resources. This circumstance confers, or ought to confer, top priority to the last three items in design. Yet in most of the conventional types of technology, such as bridge and building construction, the material factor does not appear as a rule until one has to design the shape and dimensions of individual members, that is, almost at the last stages of design. This is so because here one relies generally on the previously used

[1] M. Tribus, *Thermostatics and Thermodynamics*, Van Nostrand, Princeton, N.J., 1961.

type of material, a procedure which yields no new dividends but entails little risk. However, in an entirely new type of technology, such as nuclear or space technology, past experience is seldom a guide. Disregard for the material properties at the early stages of design is apt to lead to specifications no existing material can satisfy.

A timely consideration of material properties does not imply awareness of existing limitations alone; it also means appreciation of possible improvements. A constant interplay between the material and other design factors is particularly fruitful. Thus, the exceptionally high strength of fine glass filaments, discussed in Chapter 8, could be put to good use in rocket design, because a special spinning process has been devised for the construction of the casing of the combustion chamber.

Similarly, the appreciation of possible improvements does not come solely from an up-to-date stockpile of material properties. Rather it is brought about by a deeper insight into "the nature of things." We will show that such an insight is particularly rewarding if the material property can be directly related to the atomic and crystal structure of the material.

5-3 Material Property and Structure of Matter. According to our definition, the material property colors, so to speak, the response which a given component of an engineering system makes to imposed stimuli and constraints. On the present view, this coloring is produced in each material by a specific set of parameters that characterize the configuration, or position, and the motion of elementary particles: atoms and their components. On the same view, both the position and the motion of elementary particles have a statistical behavior. It follows that material properties, too, must behave statistically, and that in all rigor they should be handled by statistical methods.[2]

1. Properties Based on Structure. In many instances it is possible to forgo the statistical apparatus and to derive the needed relationships using available tools of algebra and calculus alone. What are these instances? Obviously they are those in which the position and the motion of the elementary particles themselves can be approximated by a nonstatistical model. Such a model is provided on the subatomic level by the Bohr atom. On the atomic level it is represented by states and modes of aggregation in which the position of the elementary particles can be considered as being practically fixed. Since motion of elementary particles is thus virtually excluded from any but the subatomic level, this model is describable for all practical purposes in terms of the position or configuration of atoms alone. Properties based on such a model are said, in short, to be *based on structure.* Elasticity of solids, mentioned earlier, obviously belongs to this category. Elasticity also implies *stability of structure*, i.e., a tendency of the substance to restore its original configuration when the stimulus or the constraint is removed. We shall find

[2] Tribus, *ibid.*

in Chapter 13 another property based on this tendency. It is called dielectric polarization.

All properties based on stability of structure are of considerable interest in design, particularly when the stimuli and constraints imposed on engineering systems produce only small displacements of elementary particles from their original stable configurations. It will be shown in Chapters 6 and 13 that in this case the material property becomes a characteristic constant dependent only on the atomic and crystal structure of the material. It then becomes possible to conceive and to compare rather straightforwardly designs based on the use of different materials and to adjust the design factors beforehand to obtain the most satisfactory solution. To put it differently, a timely insight into "the nature of things," far from being mere academic curiosity, is likely to save time and labor by disclosing a quicker and a surer path to the solution.

2. Properties Based on Motion of Elementary Particles. Although the foregoing refers specifically to properties based on structure, there are properties such as viscosity, and electrical and thermal conductivities, discussed in Chapters 12, 15, and 16, which are associated with motions of elementary particles that extend well beyond the subatomic level and cover several atomic distances. Motions of this kind as a rule cannot be approximated by a nonstatistical model. This is particularly true of random motions caused by thermal agitation. Recourse to statistical methods is then indispensable to determine the corresponding material property.

Actually, the distinction between properties based on structure and properties based on motion of elementary particles is more than a simple matter of methodology. It also implies a different set of guiding principles. The principle of structural stability was invoked to define properties such as elasticity that are based on the tendency of the substance to recover its original, stable configuration. A similar principle of *statistical stability* can be invoked to define properties such as viscosity, which are based on the motion of elementary particles. Statistical stability has to do with the tendency of a system to assume the most probable state, or alternatively, with our own tendency to describe the results of a random process in the most unbiased way.[3] The precise definition and the proper use of statistical stability, however, must be deferred to more advanced courses. Here we will merely borrow the final results, which as far as material properties are concerned, will consist of introducing a specific factor depending either on temperature, mean frequency, mean free path, or any other factor characteristic of random motion.

To base a material property on structure alone, or on motion of elementary particles alone, is an expediency which, in design, is dictated and justified only by the nature of the stimuli and constraints imposed on the system. Under static loads, elasticity can very satisfactorily be accounted for by a nonstatistical model, and it can be based on structure only. This no longer is

[3] M. Tribus, *ibid.*

possible when high-frequency vibrations are imposed on the system, for then nonelastic effects in the form of damping introduce a statistical factor. Likewise, viscosity of liquids near the melting point involves some temporary stability of structure which can be disregarded near the boiling point. Awareness of these facts does not detract, however, from the usefulness of considering the factor of structure apart from the factor of "motion." This is particularly advantageous in cases where their effects on the material property are practically independent of each other, as will appear in Chapters 13 and 14.

5-4 Structure-Insensitive and Structure-Sensitive Properties. In discussing properties based on structure, we have tacitly implied a perfect crystal structure. Considerations of Chapter 3 nevertheless make it quite clear that real crystals contain imperfections. What is the effect of crystal imperfections on material properties? The answer is twofold. So long as the imposed stimuli and constraints produce no significant changes in the number and configuration of imperfections, the response of the system is very nearly as though there were no imperfections. This is so because, as pointed out in Chapter 3, the bulk of the material preserves the features of an ideal crystal structure. It follows that the corresponding material property is little, if at all, affected by the presence of imperfections. We say it is *structure-insensitive.* Properties based on stability of structure are obviously structure-insensitive. On the other hand, when the number or configuration of imperfections undergo a change under the imposed stimuli and constraints, the change may be significant enough to affect the response of the system and, by implication, the corresponding material property. In this case the material property is said to be *structure-sensitive.* It is a characteristic feature of structure-sensitive properties that they are much more affected by the magnitude of the imposed stimuli and constraints and by factors such as composition or grain size than the structure-insensitive properties. Instances of such behavior will be found in Chapter 9, which deals with plasticity. By thus being more vulnerable to extraneous effects, structure-sensitive properties are understandably much less predictable than structure-insensitive properties. In this unwelcome distinction, they are probably second only to the creep properties discussed in Chapter 12. Creep properties, in addition to being structure sensitive, also depend on the motion of elementary particles, and the nature of this dependence makes them even less predictable than the properties that are simply structure-sensitive, as will appear in Chapter 12.

5-5 Technological Properties. The material property has been defined as being independent of the shape and dimensions of the component to which it refers. It appears logical to require that it should also be independent of the shape, dimensions, and nature of the tools used to produce the desired response. There are instances, however, in which either one or the other set of factors cannot be entirely eliminated from the quantitative expression of the material property. Rather than to discard the result—which, as we shall see below, would be quite unwise—it is preferable to retain it for what it is worth in current technology. Hence its name of *technological property*.

An outstanding example of a technological property is *hardness*. For metals, hardness is defined as the resistance offered by the metal to a tool which indents its surface. The deeper or wider the indentation under a given load, the less is the resistance and the softer is the metal. It turns out that the result is greatly affected by the shape, size, and nature of the tool. Harder and sharper tools will make the metal appear softer. The result thus also tells us something of the tool, whereas to qualify as a material property it should tell us nothing that does not concern the material itself. This shortcoming notwithstanding, hardness has been retained as a technological property because of its obvious usefulness and convenience. For one thing, hardness is a very sensitive gauge of the efficacy of heat treatments. For another, it involves only a small volume, and the indentation does relatively little damage to the piece. Hardness also correlates well with tensile strength—a plastic property described and defined in Chapter 9.

5-6 Summary. Material property is a factor which affects qualitatively or quantitatively the response of a given material to imposed stimuli and constraints. By definition, it depends *only* on the nature of the material itself. In principle, all properties have a *statistical behavior*. However, properties based on structure can be derived approximately from a nonstatistical model of atomic and crystal structure. Properties based on motion of elementary particles cannot as a rule be derived from such a model. Properties based on structure are particularly useful in design if in addition they are also based on the *stability* of structure. They are then as a rule independent of crystal imperfections. They are called *structure-insensitive*, as opposed to *structure-sensitive* properties, which do depend on crystal imperfections. Properties not fulfilling the condition of independence of shape and dimensions implied in the definition of the material property are called *technological* properties.

References

ELEMENTARY

1. J. P. Frankel, *Principles of the Properties of Materials*, McGraw-Hill, New York, 1957.

ADVANCED

1. M. Tribus, *Thermostatics and Thermodynamics, Part I*, Van Nostrand, Princeton, N.J., 1961.

Problems

5-1 The elastic deformations of bars of equal diameters and lengths made of aluminum, copper, and iron are in the ratio of 3:2:1. In what ratio will the deformations be if the size of the bars is doubled?

5-2 The elastic deflection of an iron beam is 0.1 in. What will be the deflection of the beam if iron is replaced by copper, other things being equal? (Use data of Problem 5-1.)

5-3 Would the prediction of Problem 5-2 still hold near the melting point of copper? Justify your answer.

5-4 Is elastic deformation influenced by crystal imperfections? Justify your answer.

5-5 Is the critical temperature of undercooling, discussed in Section 3-3, a structure-sensitive property or a structure-insensitive property? Why?

5-6 In the Brinell hardness test, named after the Swedish engineer who conceived it, a hard ball is pressed into a flat surface of a metal to be tested. Let D be the diameter of the ball, P the load with which it is pressed, and d the diameter of the indentation. Then the Brinell hardness number BHN is defined as follows:

$$\text{BHN} = P/A \tag{1}$$

where A is the spherical area of the indentation. From solid geometry we have

$$A = (\pi D/2)(D - \sqrt{D^2 - d^2}) \tag{2}$$

If BHN were a material property, what would be the relationship between d_1 and d_2 for two different loads P_1 and P_2 but the same ball diameter D? (Note: The actual relationship is not very far from the computed one.)

5-7 Same question as Problem 5-6 but for different ball diameters D_1 and D_2 and the same load P. (Note: The actual relationship between d_1 and d_2 is not very far from the computed one if d_1 and d_2 are small compared to D_1 and D_2.)

5-8 Suppose the ball were replaced by a hard, square pyramid with an apex angle of 90°. What would be the corresponding pyramid hardness number (PHN)?

5-9 What would be the side of the square indented by the pyramid of Problem 5-8 in terms of D and d of the Brinell hardness test, if PHN were equal to BHN? (Note: The actual value differs from the computed one.)

6 / MECHANICAL PROPERTIES: ELASTICITY

Elasticity is without doubt one of the most general properties of matter. It is found not only in solids but also in liquids and gases, in which it is associated with their compressibility. In this chapter, however, its manifestations in solids are given special attention because, as we shall see, elasticity in solids is closely related to the stability of the internal structure.

6-1 Definition and Manifestations. The property for which solids are probably most valued and utilized in engineering is their *cohesion*, the resistance they offer to forces tending to change their shape or dimensions. In the form of shelters, buildings, weapons, and tools, solids have been used since the dawn of civilization to sustain or apply forces. That this action was in reality a reaction on the part of the solid tending to resist deformation had passed largely unnoticed until the second half of the 17th century. Even Galileo seems to have been unaware of this fact, although he had a very clear picture of the ability of solids to resist loads by virtue of their cohesion.[1] Galileo can hardly be blamed for this oversight. The building materials most used in his time—stone and masonry—deformed so little before fracture that the existence of any deformation could easily have remained undetected by the instruments then available. We know today that this deformation largely disappears when the load is removed.

Experiment shows that in almost all solids deformation behaves that way if it is small enough. We say that deformations in solids are elastic when they are recoverable. The word "elastic" implies springing back—a behavior readily observable in springs and rubber bands. This is probably why it caught the attention of Robert Hooke (1635–1703), almost a contemporary of Galileo, for Robert Hooke was interested in watch springs, not in rigid beams.

Springs are used not so much to sustain loads as to store *elastic energy*, i.e., that form of energy which is associated with elastic deformation. Since the latter is recoverable, elastic energy is recoverable too, and it can be released either gradually, as in watchworks, or suddenly, as in trigger mechanisms.

Up to the discovery of black powder[2] and firearms in Europe (around 1300), elastic energy was widely utilized in battles to fight the enemy from a distance.

[1] Galileo Galilei, *Two New Sciences*, 1638. English translation, Macmillan, New York, 1933.

[2] Black powder was used in China long before its discovery in Europe, not as a means of destruction, but as an ingredient in fireworks.

We find its applications in medieval crossbows and Roman catapults—engines designed to throw stones and other heavy projectiles on enemy fortifications.

In what follows we shall study the manifestations of elasticity in its relation both to forces and to energy.

6-2 Elasticity and Interatomic Forces. Elasticity is not merely related to interatomic forces; it is directly derivable from them. We shall prove this point for the relatively simple case of ionic bonding. The results will then be extended by inference and analogy to other types of bonding and to the solid state in general.

We begin by an analysis of the forces acting between two ions, and we build up from there to the behavior of the entire ionic crystal.

Electrostatic Attraction. It is known from elementary chemistry and physics that an attraction exists between a positively charged cation and a negatively charged anion. If the distance r between their centers is large compared to the ionic radii, the force of attraction f can be computed fairly accurately from Coulomb's law:[3]

$$f = k\,\frac{e_A e_C}{r^2} \tag{6-1}$$

Here e_A and e_C are the electric charges of the anion and cation, respectively, and k is a coefficient whose value depends on two factors: (a) the surrounding medium, e.g., air or water, and (b) the choice of units. Insofar as the interior of crystals is concerned, the medium is of no influence. Regarding the units, we recall that in the MKSQ system f is measured in newtons, e_A and e_C in coulombs, and r in meters. As a result, the left-hand side of Eq. (6-1) has the dimensions of newtons ($=$ kgm/sec^2) and the expression $e_A e_C/r^2$ on the right-hand side has the dimensions $(\mathrm{Q/m})^2$. To make the dimensions consistent on both sides of Eq. (6-1) a conversion factor is needed—akin to the mechanical equivalent of heat in converting work into heat. The conversion factor is determined experimentally; its value k_0 is 9×10^9 kgm^3/(Q^2 sec^2).

On the other hand, no conversion factor is needed if recourse is made to the still widely used CGS units. For the sake of convenience we will drop the coefficient k from Eq. (6-1), thus, in effect, adopting the CGS system. In ionic crystals, the negative charge is equal to the positive charge and both are equal to the product ez of the charge of the electron e by the valency z. Thus, in CGS units, Eq. (6-1) can be written to read

$$f = \frac{e^2 z^2}{r^2} \tag{6-2}$$

[3] Charles Coulomb (1736–1806), French physicist noted for his contributions to friction and electricity.

In Fig. 6-1 the anion A_0 has been placed at the origin of a coordinate system and the cation C_0 at a distance r on the abscissa. If the force acting on C_0 is plotted on the ordinates, its variation with r is represented by the curve f. By virtue of Newton's law of action and reaction, an equal and opposite force is acting on A_0.

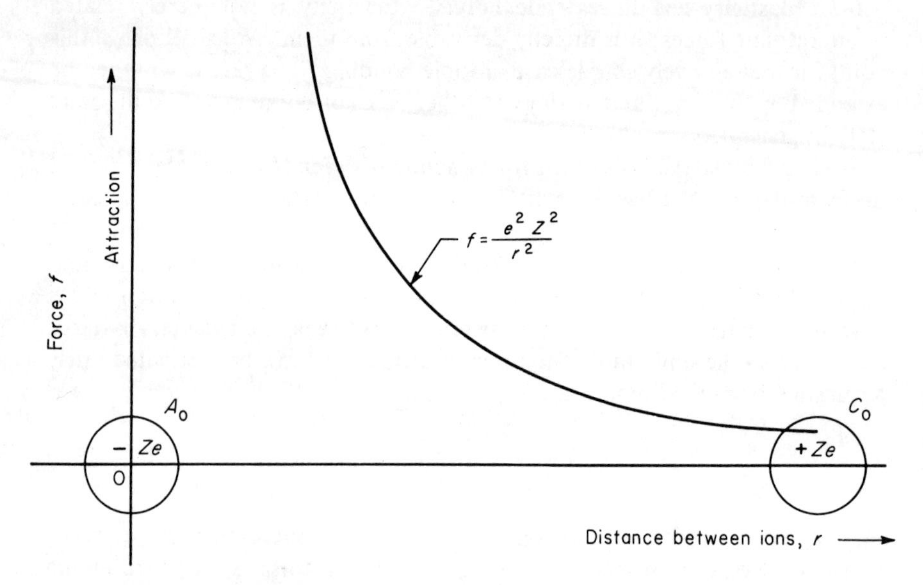

FIG. 6-1 Force of attraction between anion A_0 and cation C_0

We shall now add a long chain of cations and anions to A_0 at successive intervals $r = A_0C_0$ to the left of the origin, Fig. 6-2. Their action on C_0 will

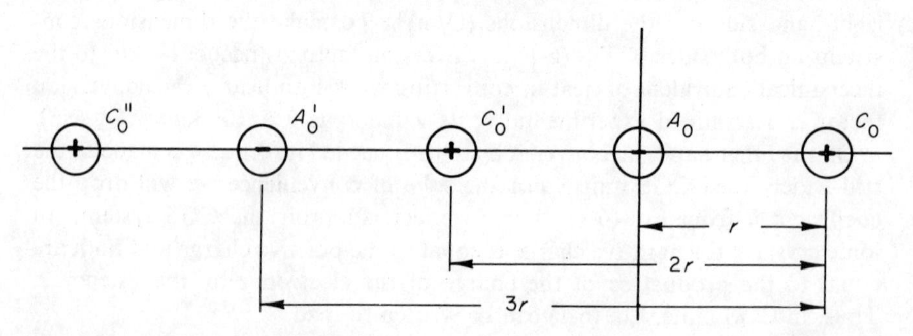

FIG. 6-2 Force of attraction between chain of ions A_0, C'_0, A'_0, C''_0, and cation C_0

consist alternately of repulsive and attractive forces superimposed on f. Each of them, however, will be weaker than the preceding one because of the progressively increasing distance from C_0. The total force acting on C_0 will now be the sum total f_1, such that

$$f_1 = \frac{e^2z^2}{r^2} - \frac{e^2z^2}{(2r)^2} + \frac{e^2z^2}{(3r)^2} - \cdots \tag{6-3}$$

This is a rapidly converging series. If we stop at the 10th and 11th terms, respectively, the following inequalities will be found:

$$0.82e^2z^2/r^2 > f_1 > 0.81e^2z^2/r^2 \tag{6-4}$$

Thus the whole chain, including A_0, attracts the cation C_0 with a smaller force than the isolated anion A_0.

The above computation can be extended to a layer of ions, Fig. 6-3a, and

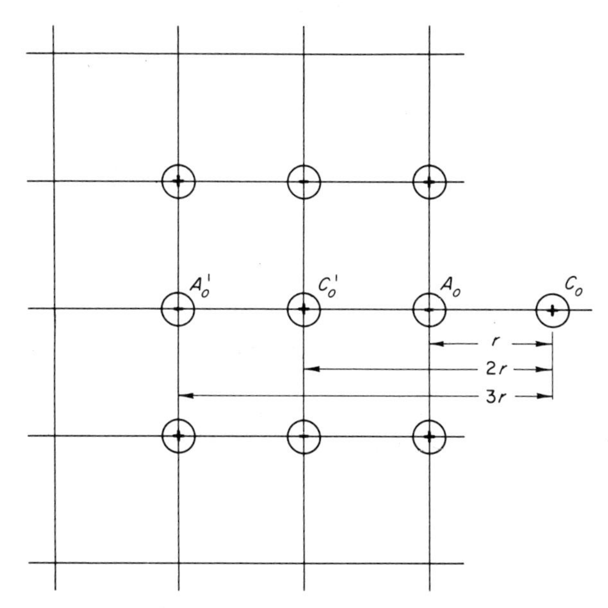

FIG. 6-3a Force of attraction between layer of ions and cation C_0

to a sequence of layers stacked in the manner shown in Fig. 6-3b. The latter is characteristic of the Na^+Cl^- type of structure, which many ionic crystals possess. The computation, however, is quite tedious and of no direct interest to us; the result alone is important. Let f_a represent the force of attraction exerted on C_0 in the direction C_0–A_0 by the array of ions, Fig. 6-3b, spaced in the crystal at intervals $r = A_0$–C_0; then the result of the computation is

$$f_a = 0.29e^2z^2/r^2 \tag{6-5}$$

That is, the force of attraction of this array is less than one-third of that exerted by a single anion.

Electrostatic Repulsion. The electrostatic attraction f_a between the array of ions and the cation C_0 is counteracted by the mutual repulsion of the electron shells of all ions. This action, negligible at large distances, becomes predominant when the distance r is so small that the electron shells begin

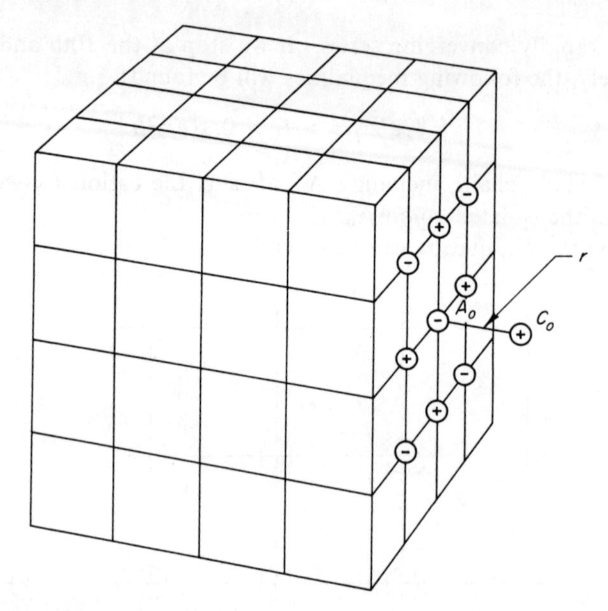

FIG. 6-3b Force of attraction between ionic crystal and cation C_0

impinging on each other. To account for such an action we must assume that the force of repulsion f_r varies a great deal more rapidly with r than the force of attraction f_a. This assumption is fulfilled by making the exponent of r in Eq. (6-5) greater than 2. We write

$$f_r = -B/r^n \tag{6-6}$$

where $n > 2$ and B is a coefficient to be determined. (The exact value to be assigned to n will be indicated below.)

The relative variation of f_a and f_r with r is represented schematically in Fig. 6-4, in which f_a is plotted with the plus sign, f_r with the minus sign. The combined effect of attraction and repulsion is plotted as curve f. From what has been said, it follows that there must be a distance $r = r_0$ where $f = 0$. This distance corresponds to the position of equilibrium of ions in actual crystals, and it can be determined from X-ray diffraction analysis.

We can use the above information to determine the value of B in Eq. (6-6). We write

$$f = f_a + f_r = 0.29e^2z^2/r^2 - B/r^n \tag{6-7}$$

For $r = r_0$, $f = 0$, or

$$0 = 0.29e^2z^2/r_0^2 - B/r_0^n$$

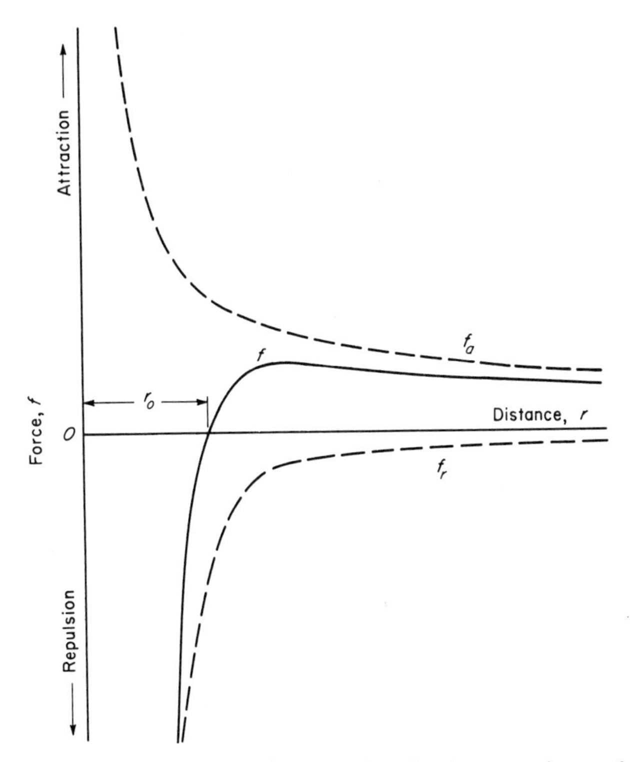

FIG. 6-4 Variation of electrostatic attraction f_a, electrostatic repulsion f_r, and $f = f_a + f_r$

whence

$$B = 0.29e^2z^2r_0^{n-2} \tag{6-8}$$

Substitution of Eq. (6-8) in Eq. (6-7) yields

$$f = 0.29\,\frac{e^2z^2}{r^2}\left[1 - \left(\frac{r_0}{r}\right)^m\right] \tag{6-9}$$

where for convenience we have put $m = n - 2$. Equation (6-9) represents a functional relation between the variables f and r. The quantities e, z, r_0, and m are fixed for a given crystal, but we must still assign a value to m. We noticed previously that the exponent $n(= m + 2)$ reflects the repulsion of closed-shell electrons. It is natural to expect that n should increase with the number of electrons, or what amounts to the same thing with the number of closed shells. On the basis of theoretical considerations, which we omit, the values of Table 6-1 can be assigned to m.[4]

Nature of Elasticity. According to Eq. (6-9), $f > 0$ if $r > r_0$. Attraction prevails, and to maintain the ion C_0 at the equilibrium distance r a tensile

[4] L. Pauling, *The Nature of the Chemical Bond*, p. 339, Cornell, Ithica, N.Y., 1948.

TABLE 6-1 VALUES OF EXPONENT m*

Type of Closed-shell Structure	*Representative Ions*	m
He	Li^+Be^{++}	4
Ne	$F^-Na^+Mg^{++}$	6
A	$Cl^-K^+Ca^{++}$	8
Kr	Br^-	9
Xe	I^-	11

* In case of different types of cations and anions, the corresponding values of m are averaged.

force must be applied. If the force is removed, $f = 0$ and the distance r_0 is restored. The same is true when $r < r_0$, except that this time the applied force must be compressive. Thus the equilibrium state corresponding to r_0 is a stable one.

We shall see in the next section that the above behavior is shared by all ions of the crystal and hence by the solid as a whole. We will prove that the resistance that ionic crystals offer to the change of dimensions and the recoverable nature of this deformation have their origin in the existence and stability of ionic bonding. The same can be shown to be true for the change of shape, but the derivation is much more complicated, so it will be omitted. The extension to other types of bonding requires a mastery of a rather formidable technique of modern physics. We shall therefore assume the validity of this extension by inference.

The content of this section can thus be summarized by saying that *the elasticity of solids has its origin in the existence and stability of interatomic bonding.*

6-3 Hooke's Law Derived. Before proceeding further we shall extend the validity of Eq. (6-9) to all ions in the crystal. We observe that if the ion C_0 belongs to a layer of ions parallel to the vertical layers of the crystal, to the left of the origin, Fig. 6-5, the other ions in this layer have no influence on the force f. This is so because their lines of action are normal to f. By the same argument, the forces acting on each of these ions in the direction C_0–A_0 are not influenced by the presence of the rest of them. Also in the middle portion of the layer, far from the boundaries of the crystal, every ion, whether cation or anion, is subjected to the same force f, as is clearly seen from Fig. 6-5. What goes for one layer goes for the other layers. Thus every ion in every layer is subjected to the same force f. For practical purposes we shall reword this statement. Imagine an external force f applied to each ion of the first layer containing C_0 and directed to the right. The sum total F of these external forces will displace the first layer with respect to the second one, and will thus activate restoring forces on the part of the latter of the same magnitude but in the opposite direction, Fig. 6-5. By virtue of Newton's law of action and reaction, the second layer in turn will be subjected to the force F, and the attending displacement in turn will cause restoring forces in the third layer,

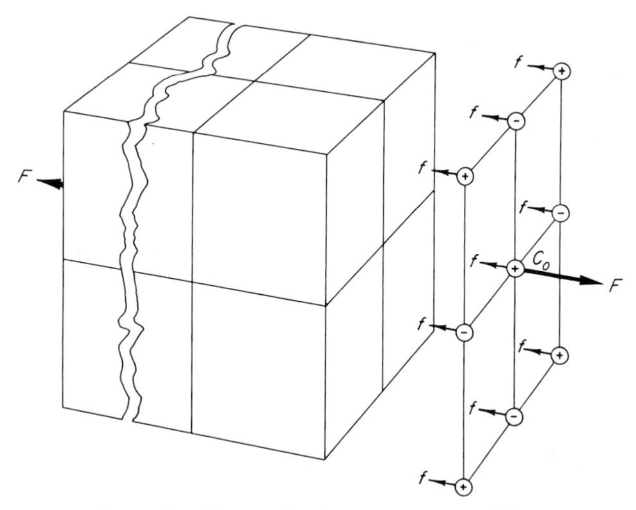

FIG. 6-5 Force F acting on a layer of ions

and so on. In this fashion, the action will reach the last layer to the left, where it will be counteracted by an external reaction, equal to F but in the opposite direction.

We can use the above argument to good advantage to modify Eq. (6-9) so that it will contain the externally applied, and hence measurable, force F rather than the atomic, and hence somewhat elusive, force f. Before doing so, we shall take additional advantage of the fact that most materials have only small elastic deformations.

Small Deformations. Put in Eq. (6-9)

$$r = r_0 + \Delta r \tag{6-10}$$

where $\Delta r/r_0 \ll 1$ (the symbol $\ll$, meaning very small compared to). Since f is a function of r, we can write, recalling the definition of the derivative,

$$\left|\frac{f(r_0 + \Delta r) - f(r_0)}{\Delta r}\right|_{\Delta r \to 0} = f'(r_0) \tag{6-11}$$

or, as a good approximation, since $\Delta r/r_0 \ll 1$

$$f(r_0 + \Delta r) - f(r_0) = f'(r_0)\,\Delta r \tag{6-12}$$

But $f(r_0) = 0$ and

$$f'(r) = 0.29e^2z^2\left[\frac{-2}{r^3} + (m + 2)\,\frac{r_0{}^m}{r^{m+3}}\right] \tag{6-13}$$

hence, by substituting $r = r_0$ in Eq. (6-13) and making use of Eqs. (6-10) and (6-12),

$$f(r) = f(r_0 + \Delta r) = \frac{0.29e^2z^2m}{r_0^3}\Delta r \tag{6-14}$$

Equation (6-14) establishes the relevant relationship for small deformations between two atomic quantities: the force on the single ion f and the change of distance Δr between two neighboring ionic layers.

To replace these atomic quantities by macroscopically measurable quantities, we observe that if F is the force acting on a large number N of ions in a layer, then

$$f = F/N \tag{6-15}$$

On the other hand, if S is the area occupied by these N ions, then, recalling that the area occupied by one ion is r_0^2, we have

$$N = S/r_0^2 \tag{6-16}$$

hence

$$f = Fr_0^2/S \tag{6-17}$$

In like manner, calling Δl the macroscopically measurable increase of distance l_0 over a large number of layers and observing that the distance between two neighboring layers is r_0,

$$\Delta r = \Delta l\, r_0/l_0 \tag{6-18}$$

Substitution of Eqs. (6-17) and (6-18) in Eq. (6-14) yields

$$\frac{Fr_0^2}{S} = \frac{0.29e^2z^2m}{r_0^2}\frac{\Delta l}{l_0}$$

whence

$$F = \left(\frac{S}{l_0}\frac{0.29e^2z^2m}{r_0^4}\right)\Delta l \tag{6-19}$$

Since all quantities enclosed in the parentheses are fixed, we can write

$$\frac{S}{l_0}\frac{0.29e^2z^2m}{r_0^4} = K, \text{ a constant} \tag{6-20}$$

and

$$F = K\Delta l \tag{6-21}$$

Equation (6-21) shows that the increase of length Δl caused by force F is *proportional* to F. This, in substance, is the law Robert Hooke announced in 1678 following his studies on springs. The constant K quite fittingly is called the spring constant.[5]

[5] Actually, Hooke proved the validity of the law by experimenting with long wires. He suspended them from the top of a staircase and determined their extension under various loads from the variation of the distance between their lower end and the ground floor. He worded the law in concise Latin, as was customary in his time, thus making it the shortest law in physics. Here it is: *Sic tensio ut vis* (Such is extension as is force). See also S. Timoshenko, *History of Strength of Materials* ("With a Brief Account of the History of Theory of Elasticity and Theory of Structures"), McGraw-Hill, New York, 1953.

6-4 Modulus of Elasticity. The constant K in Eq. (6-20) contains the cross-sectional area S and the length l_0, which may vary from sample to sample. We can make Hooke's law independent of these external factors by referring the force to unit area and the increase of length to unit length. Accordingly, using the Greek letter σ, we define it as

$$\sigma = F/S \tag{6-22}$$

and call the new quantity *stress*. Likewise, using the Greek letter ε, we define

$$\varepsilon = \Delta l/l_0 \tag{6-23}$$

and call the new quantity *strain*. With these notations, Eq. (6-19) reads

$$\sigma = \frac{0.29e^2z^2m}{r_0^4}\,\varepsilon \tag{6-24}$$

or, *strain is proportional to stress* (for small deformations).

The coefficient of proportionality contains only the four fundamental quantities e, z, m, and r_0, characteristic of the internal structure of the solid. This coefficient is called the *modulus of elasticity*.

The modulus of elasticity can also be determined experimentally. By using a technique similar to that devised by Hooke, we obtain a somewhat different modulus of elasticity, called Young's modulus[6] (the reason for this discrepancy is given below; see Poisson's ratio). It is generally designated by the letter E. By putting

$$K = ES/l_0 \tag{6-25}$$

in Eq. (6-21) and recalling Eqs. (6-22) and (6-23), there follows

$$\sigma = E\varepsilon \tag{6-26}$$

We notice that σ has the dimensions of force per unit area, whereas ε, being a ratio of two lengths, has no dimensions. Hence E also has the dimensions of force per unit area. Table 6-2 lists the conversion factors for σ and E from the English units—pounds and inches—to the CGS and MKSQ units.

Poisson's Ratio. When the experimental value of E is compared to the coefficient of proportionality in Eq. (6-24), it is found that the computed value is much larger; see example below. One of the reasons for the observed discrepancy is the omission of the influence of lateral contraction in the computation. This contraction can be shown to be a necessary corollary of

[6] After the name of T. Young (1773–1829)—philosopher, mathematician, physicist, physician, and Egyptologist—who apparently was the first to use it in his lectures (1807).

TABLE 6-2 CONVERSION FACTORS FOR STRESS AND MODULUS OF ELASTICITY

English	CGS	MKSQ
1 lb/in.^{2} (also psi)	6.89×10^4 dyn/cm^2	6.89×10^3 N/m^2
1.45×10^{-5} lb/in.^{2}	1 dyn/cm^2	0.1 N/m^2
1.45×10^{-4} lb/in.^{2}	10 dyn/cm^2	1 N/m^2

the extension under axial loading if the interatomic forces are to remain in equilibrium in the direction normal to the axis. Its omission from the computation has been made for the sake of simplicity. If this contraction is referred to a unit width or thickness it becomes—like its axial counterpart—a strain, the *transverse strain* ε_t. The two strains can be related to each other by the ratio

$$\mu = -\frac{\varepsilon_t}{\varepsilon} \tag{6-27}$$

called *Poisson's ratio* after S. D. Poisson (1781–1840), a French mathematician who was one of the first to compute its value.[7]

Illustrative Example.

Determine the Young's modulus E and the Poisson's ratio μ from the data listed in Table 6-3 and referring to the extension of a circular rod of sodium chloride crystal in the direction of the cube axis. Compare the experimental result with the computed value E_0.[8]

Solution. We plot, in Fig. 6-6, the load P as the ordinate and the extension Δl as the abscissa. From the slope of the straight line fitted through the experimental points and passing through the origin, the value of the spring constant K is found to be 3.05×10^5 lb/in. Hence, by Eq. (6-25) the experimental value of Young's modulus is

$$E = Kl_0/S = 8 \times 10^6 \text{ lb/in.}^2 = 5.35 \times 10^{11} \text{ dyn/cm}^2$$

In Fig. 6-7 the values of ΔD are plotted as a function of Δl. From the slope ($= 0.16 \times 10^{-1}$) of the straight line fitted through the experimental points and passing through the origin, the value of μ is obtained as follows:

$$\mu = 0.16 \times 10^{-1} \times 5/0.5 = 0.16$$

[7] The computed value of μ for *isotropic* and *quasi-isotropic* materials, e.g., polycrystalline metals, turns out to be 0.25, irrespective of the internal structure. The experimental values for metals vary between 0.3 and 0.4. The reason for this discrepancy remained quite obscure until modern physics succeeded in clarifying the role of free valence electrons in the phenomena of interatomic attraction.

[8] For the sake of comparison, experimental values have been extrapolated to the absolute zero after L. Hunter and S. Siegel, *Phys. Rev.*, **61**, 84(1942).

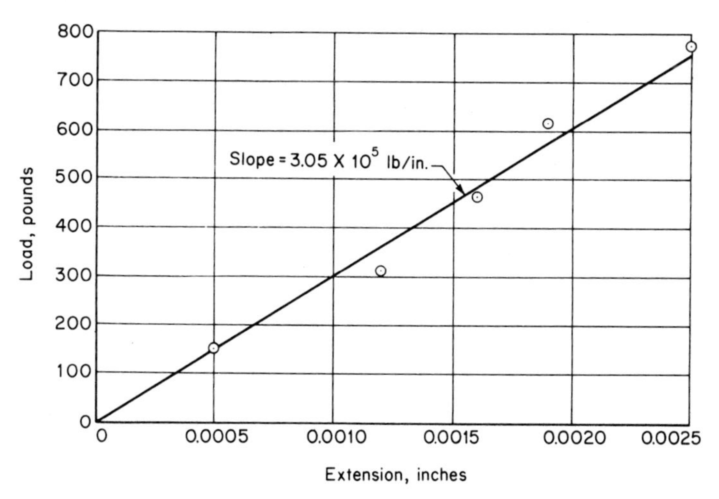

FIG. 6-6 Plot of load versus extension

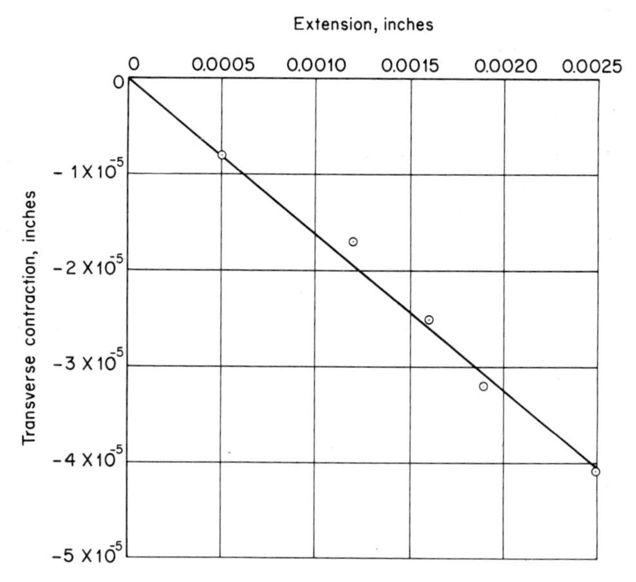

FIG. 6-7 Plot of transverse contraction versus extension

TABLE 6-3 DETERMINATION OF MODULUS OF ELASTICITY

Load, P (lb)	*Extension,* Δl (in.)	*Transverse Contraction,* ΔD (in.)
155	0.05×10^{-2}	0.08×10^{-4}
310	0.12×10^{-2}	0.17×10^{-4}
465	0.16×10^{-2}	0.25×10^{-4}
620	0.19×10^{-2}	0.32×10^{-4}
775	0.25×10^{-2}	0.41×10^{-4}

Note: Length of rod, $l_0 = 5$ in., diameter of rod, $D = \frac{1}{2}$ in., cross-sectional area, $\pi D^2/4 = 0.196$ in.^{2}

The theoretical value E_0 of the modulus of elasticity of Na^+Cl^- under the assumption of $\mu = 0$, is obtained from Eq. (6-24). It reads

$$E_0 = 0.29z^2me^2/r_0^4 \tag{6-28}$$

In this expression the electronic charge, $e = 4.774 \times 10^{-10}$ in CGS electrostatic units, $z = 1$, $m = 7$ (from Table 6-1) and $r_0 = 2.79$ Å (from X-ray analysis). Substitution in Eq. (6-28) yields

$$E_0 = 7.6 \times 10^{11} \text{ dyn/cm}^2$$

The correction for lateral contraction will reduce this value to 5.2×10^{11} dyn/cm^2, which is in reasonable agreement with the experimental value. (The correction factor is $1 - 2\mu$. It can be deduced from the relation between the Young's modulus and the bulk modulus of elasticity; see Eq. (6-42) below.)

Modulus of Elasticity in Compression. It is obvious from Eq. (6-24) that the modulus of elasticity in compression is the same as in tension. The lateral deformation becomes in this case a lateral *expansion*.

Shear Modulus of Elasticity, G. Restoring forces operate on the layers of ions, Fig. 6-5, not only when the latter are pulled away from each other, but also when they are displaced by Δs laterally, or *sheared*, with respect to each other, Fig. 6-8. By analogy with Eq. (6-21), we can write

$$F_1 = K_1 \Delta s \tag{6-29}$$

and, by proceeding as with extension,

$$F_1/S = \tau \tag{6-30}$$

and

$$\Delta s/l_0 = \gamma \tag{6-31}$$

The Greek letter τ stands for *shear stress*, and the Greek letter γ stands for

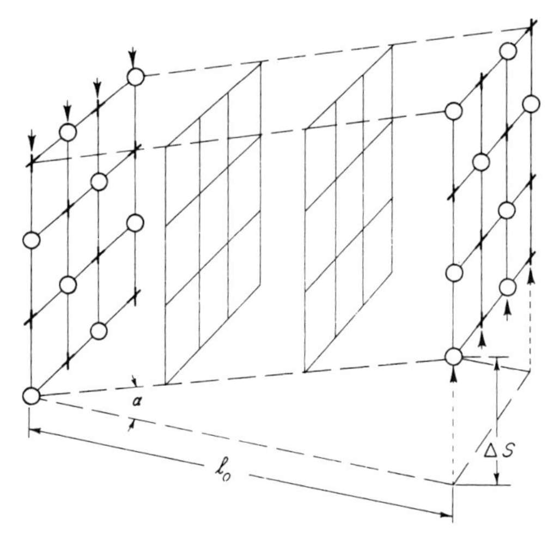

FIG. 6-8 Shear of layers of ions

shear strain. If we substitute for F_1 and Δs from Eq. (6-30) and Eq. (6-31) in Eq. (6-29), there follows

$$S\tau = K_1 l_0 \gamma$$

whence

$$\tau = G\gamma \tag{6-32}$$

with

$$G = K_1 l_0 / S$$

G is called *shear modulus of elasticity*. Equation (6-32) is thus seen to be an adaptation of Hooke's law to shear deformation.

Since Δs is small, the ratio $\Delta s/l_0$ ($= \tan \alpha$) is approximately α, Fig. 6-8. On the other hand, the change in volume is zero, since the distance r_0 between the layers remains constant. Thus the shear modulus of elasticity, G refers to a type of deformation in which only angular changes occur, i.e., changes of shape but no changes of *volume*. This is at variance with axial tension, because there the unit cell is transformed into an elongated prism, and the volume is increased. The changes during compression are in the opposite direction.

There exists a relation between G and E despite the different nature of deformation which they characterize. This relation is derived currently in textbooks and courses of strength of materials. It reads

$$G = \frac{E}{2(1 + \mu)} \tag{6-33}$$

Depending on the value of μ, G is from 2 to 2.8 times smaller than E.

Bulk Modulus of Elasticity. The modulus of elasticity E involves changes of shape as well as volume. We can, however, derive a counterpart to the shear modulus, i.e., a modulus of elasticity embodying only volume changes, by proceeding as follows:

1. We first express the volumetric change of a rectangular prism in terms of the changes of its linear dimensions. Let l, a, and b be its length, width, and thickness, respectively. Then the volume v is

$$v = lab$$

Assuming l, a, and b undergo only small increments Δl, Δa, and Δb, we can obtain the change Δv of volume v with sufficient accuracy by reducing the increments to differentials. With this approximation the rules of differentiation yield

$$\Delta v = \Delta(lab) = ab\,\Delta l + lb\,\Delta a + la\,\Delta b \tag{6-34}$$

or, dividing the left side of Eq. (6-34) by v and the right side by lab $(= v)$, respectively,

$$\Delta v/v = \Delta l/l + \Delta a/a + \Delta b/b \tag{6-35}$$

The terms on the right-hand side of Eq. (6-35) are strains. Call them ε_l, ε_a, and ε_b, respectively. By analogy, the relative change of volume $\Delta v/v$ can be called volumetric strain ε_v. With these notations, Eq. (6-35) reads

$$\varepsilon_v = \varepsilon_l + \varepsilon_a + \varepsilon_b \tag{6-36}$$

2. Next we derive the expression for ε_v under axial tension in terms of the longitudinal strain ε_l and Poisson's ratio μ. We observe in accordance with Eq. (6-27) that

$$\varepsilon_a = \varepsilon_b = -\mu\varepsilon_l \tag{6-37}$$

whence, by accenting ε_v to indicate it refers to axial tension,

$$\varepsilon'_v = \varepsilon_l - 2\mu\varepsilon_l$$

or

$$\varepsilon'_v = \varepsilon(1 - 2\mu) \tag{6-38}$$

where the subscript l has been dropped for convenience.

Using Eq. (6-38), we can rewrite Eq. (6-26) to read

$$\sigma = \frac{E}{1 - 2\mu}\,\varepsilon'_v \tag{6-39}$$

The same relation holds, of course, for compression.

3. Suppose now a cubic crystal is subjected to equal compression along the three edges of the cube. By analogy with the pressure exerted by liquids, which we know from elementary physics to be equal in all three directions, we call this type of loading *hydrostatic compression*. (Note that, in principle, hydrostatic tension is also possible.) We seek to express the hydrostatic pressure σ in terms of the volumetric strain, ε_v.

To this end we invoke the principle of superposition, which states that for small deformations the stress acting in each direction produces the same effect as if it acted alone. The change of volume produced by each stress is given by Eq. (6-39), but the volumetric change figuring in this equation is only one-third of the volumetric change actually occurring when the effects of all three stresses are superimposed. Putting, therefore,

$$\varepsilon'_v = \varepsilon_v/3 \tag{6-40}$$

we have for hydrostatic compression (and tension)

$$\sigma = \frac{E}{3(1 - 2\mu)}\,\varepsilon_v \tag{6-41}$$

We notice finally that the type of deformation defined by Eq. (6-41) involves only a change of volume. This can be shown easily with reference to Fig. 6-5. It is clear that under hydrostatic compression or tension the interionic distances r_0 will undergo equal changes in all three directions, thereby modifying the size of the unit cell but preserving the shape of the cube.

By analogy with Eq. (6-26), the coefficient of proportionality between σ and ε_v in Eq. (6-41) is called the *bulk modulus of elasticity*. Denoting it by the letter B, we have

$$B = \frac{E}{3(1 - 2\mu)} \tag{6-42}$$

an expression for the bulk modulus of elasticity in terms of the Young's modulus E and Poisson's ratio.[9]

The inverse of the bulk modulus of elasticity is called *compressibility*. It is expressed accordingly in in.^{2}/lb, cm^2/dyn or m^2/N, depending on the choice of units.

Note: Equation (6-42) breaks down for materials like rubber, for which μ is close to 0.5. As seen from Eq. (6-38), these materials deform under axial tension with little or no change of volume. The test in axial tension (or compression) provides, therefore, little or no information regarding the ability of these materials to withstand hydrostatic pressure, and it cannot be used to derive the value of B. The bulk modulus of elasticity, like that of liquids and gases, must be determined for such solids by direct experimentation.

[9] Looking in retrospect, we recognize that Eq. (6-9) was derived under the assumption of hydrostatic pressure and that Eq. (6-24) was derived from the above equation by limiting the change of r_0 to axial direction. It follows that ε in Eq. (6-24) is one-third of ε_v figuring in Eq. (6-41). By equating the stresses σ in both equations and putting $\varepsilon = \varepsilon_v/3$, we get

$$0.29e^2z^2m/r_0^4 = E/(1 - 2\mu)$$

or

$$E = 0.29e^2z^2m(1 - 2\mu)/r_0^4 \tag{6-43}$$

6-5 Modulus of Elasticity and Periodic Table. Even with the perfected tools of modern physics, very few elastic moduli have been computed so far from first principles because of inherent mathematical difficulties. These are the moduli of elasticity of elements of Group I (lithium, sodium, potassium, rubidium, and cesium) and a few selected elements from other groups (copper, magnesium, aluminum).[10] On purely dimensional grounds, the expression for the elastic moduli, in terms of the electron charge e and the closest approach r_0, is expected to be the same as that derived previously for ionic crystals, Eq. (6-28). By analogy with this equation, we can write for the bulk modulus of elasticity B, for which there is much experimental data available,

$$B = Ce^2/r_0^4 \tag{6-44}$$

in which C is a numerical coefficient yet to be determined.

Equation (6-44) can be rewritten in a form more convenient for analysis by taking the logarithms of both sides. There follows

$$\log B = \log Ce^2 - 4 \log r_0 \tag{6-45}$$

Subject to the condition that C is constant, Eq. (6-45) represents a linear variation of $\log B$ with $\log r_0$, with the slope of the straight line equal to 4.

In Fig. 6-9 several of such lines are shown. They have been fitted through the points plotted from the experimental values of B and r_0. It is seen that the fit is reasonably good for the elements of Groups I, II, III, and IV. For each of these groups a relation of the type Eq. (6-45) applies with a different coefficient C. The values of C are listed in Table 6-4. The perusal of Fig. 6-9 and Table 6-4 leads to several interesting conclusions:

TABLE 6-4 VALUES OF C FOR GROUPS I, II, III, AND IV OF THE PERIODIC TABLE

Group	*I*	*II*	*III*	*IV*
C	0.5	1.6	2.0	1.3

1. Within the same group of the periodic table the bulk modulus of elasticity varies as the inverse fourth power of the closest approach, r_0.

2. For the Groups I, II, III, and IV the coefficient C is little affected by the increase of the number of closed electron shells around the nucleus of the atom. For example, there are two closed shells in Na^+ and five in Cs^+; yet the coefficient C is practically the same in both cases. This is at variance with the numerical coefficient $0.29z^2m$ computed for the case of the ionic bonding Na^+Cl^-, Eq. (6-28), in which the numerical value of m does depend on the number of closed shells; see also Table 6-1.

[10] H. Brooks, "Accomplishments and Limitations of Solid-State Theory," *The Science of Engineering Materials*, J. E. Goldman, Ed., Wiley, New York, 1957.

3. There is less than a fourfold increase of C from the monovalent Group I ($z = 1$) to the bivalent Group II ($z = 2$). The increase is very slight from Group II to III, and it is replaced by a decrease (from 2 to 1.3) on passing to Group IV. By comparison with the "ionic" coefficient $0.29z^2m$, this trend can be interpreted as a transition of the type of bonding from the ionic to the

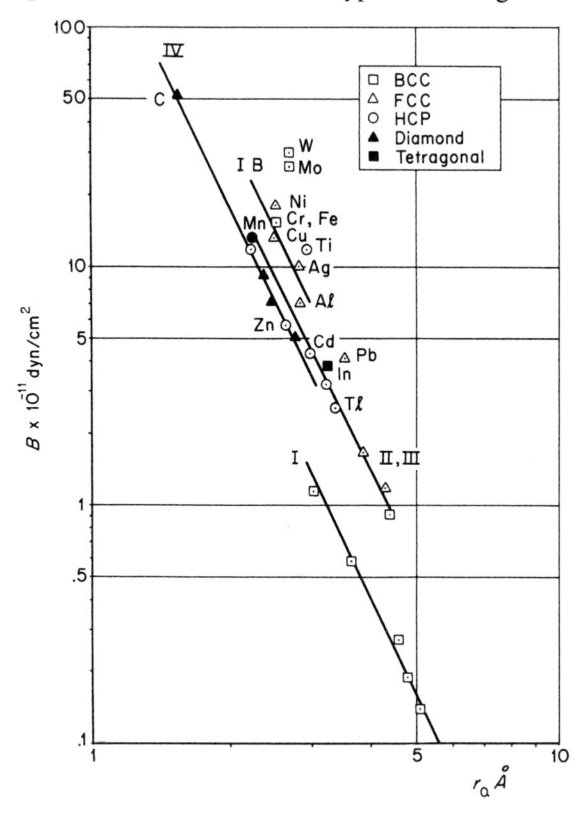

FIG. 6-9 Log B versus log r_0 for selected elements of the periodic table

metallic one and from the latter to the covalent bond of Group IV. The drop of the coefficient C on passing from Group III to IV is in line with the above interpretation; see also Section 1-7. So is the abnormally high value of the coefficient C (= 2.75) for Pb, an element of a clearly metallic character, even though belonging to Group IV.

4. There is less regularity in the behavior of the heavier elements, such as Cu, Ag, and Zn Significantly, the transition elements are characterized not only by high values of C—as high as 7.6 in the case of W—but also by relatively small values of r_0.[11] On both counts, their moduli of elasticity are understandably high. The exceptional behavior of Mn, noticed elsewhere[11] is likewise manifest here.

[11] L. Pauling, *loc. cit.*

Remark. From the close relationship that exists between the elastic moduli B, E, and G, the above conclusions are expected to apply also to E and G. The trend of the experimental data, however, is less regular, presumably because it is affected by the directional properties of these moduli, at variance with the bulk modulus, which by definition is a scalar property, independent of direction.

Note. Relationships of the type represented by Eq. (6-44) are particularly useful in anticipating properties of new synthetic materials. The previously mentioned synthetic modification of the natural boron nitride, BN, is a case in point (see footnote to Section 1-4). Its "diamond" crystal structure, together with the value of $r_0 = 1.58$ Å, anticipated from the covalent radii of B and N, would lead us to predict that the value of the bulk modulus of the new material—when it is determined—should be very nearly the same as that of diamond.

Molecular Bonding. There are far less data available on the bulk moduli—or compressibility—of molecular solids, i.e., solids held by secondary bonds, than of solids held by primary bonds. In the ideal case, the molecular bonding arises from the separation of the centers of positive and negative charges in an otherwise neutral molecule. This has been explained in Section 1-8 for inert elements. However, the same situation exists in every molecule in which the centers of positive and negative charges fail to coincide. It can be brought about by interaction with an adjacent molecule—as in inert elements—or by the structure of the molecule itself—as in water (see Section 13-8). In the first instance we speak of an *induced electric dipole*, in the second of a *permanent electric dipole*. As shown in Section 6-8, Illustrative Problem 2, the action of the dipole involves the product of one of the charges ez (+ or −) by the distance of separation d. This product, ezd, is called a *dipole moment*. Dipole moments figure prominently in the theory of dielectrics, a point which will be further considered in Chapter 13. In the theory of intermolecular attraction they play the same role as isolated charges in interatomic attraction. The force of attraction between two isolated dipole moments is computed in Illustrative Problem 2. If r, the distance separating the centroids MM, Fig. 6-10, is large compared to d, the force of attraction f_d is

$$f_d = 6e^2z^2d^2/r^4 \tag{6-46}$$

Equation (6-46) differs from Eq. (6-2) by the presence of the factor $(d/r)^2$, introduced to account for the dipole moment ed. Following a line of reasoning similar to that developed for interatomic attraction, we can express the bulk modulus of elasticity of molecular solids by a formula analogous to Eq. (6-44). We write, as previously,

$$B = Ce^2/r_0{}^4 \tag{6-47}$$

However, C now contains the factor $(d/r_0)^2$ in addition to the factors considered in the case of ionic crystals.

In Table 6-5 are listed values of the bulk modulus B and the distance of closest approach r_0 for some molecular solids as well as liquids. The values of

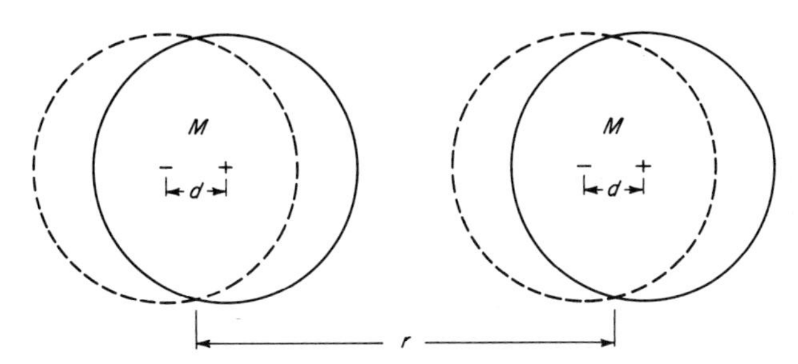

FIG. 6-10 Interaction between dipole moments

C are computed from Eq. (6-47). It is seen that there is not much difference in the compressibility between liquids and solid inert elements. The corresponding bulk moduli, however, are one order of magnitude lower than for most solids held by primary bonds.[12] The same is true of the coefficient C. There is nonetheless an overlap with the weaker metals of Group I, Fig. 6-9, and polystyrene appears even more rigid than potassium. This is true only for the glassy state below 80°C, in which polystyrene is not only rigid but also brittle. Around 120°C it behaves more like rubber, and its modulus of elasticity drops below 10^7 dyn/cm^2, i.e., by as much as three orders of magnitude. Other plastics act similarly.

TABLE 6-5 BULK MODULI, DISTANCES OF CLOSEST APPROACH AND COEFFICIENT C FOR SOME MOLECULAR SOLIDS AND LIQUIDS

Substance	r_0 (Å)	B (dyn/cm^2 10^{11}	C	*State*
Neon	3.21	0.10	0.046	Solid
Argon	3.84	0.16	0.152	
Nitrogen	3.00*	0.19	0.065	
Polystyrene	4.00*	0.38	0.42	
Water	2.76	0.20	0.05	Liquid
Benzene	3.90*	0.10	0.10	

* Based on molecular radii given by L. Pauling, *The Nature of the Chemical Bond*, p. 189, Cornell, Ithaca, N.Y., 1948.
Source: A. V. Tobolsky, *Properties and Structure of Polymers*, Wiley, New York, 1960.

[12] This appears to be due to the factor d/r_0, which, for water, for example, is less than 0.1.

6-6 Elastic Energy. Mention was made at the beginning of this chapter of the ability of elastically deformed bodies to store energy. This energy accordingly is called the *elastic energy*. It can be accumulated in deformed solids either statically, through the work of external forces, or dynamically, through the absorption of kinetic energy in impact. It is of interest to compare the amount of energy which can be stored elastically to the amount of energy which can be stored under other forms of energy, such as electricity.

We begin by expressing elastic energy in terms of the work done by external forces. More specifically, let l_0 be the length and S the cross-sectional area of a bar subjected to an axial force F, such as a load suspended from one end while the other end is kept fixed. An increment dF in the force F will cause its point of application to move downward by an amount dx corresponding to the increase of length of the bar, Fig. 6-11. The applied force will thus do

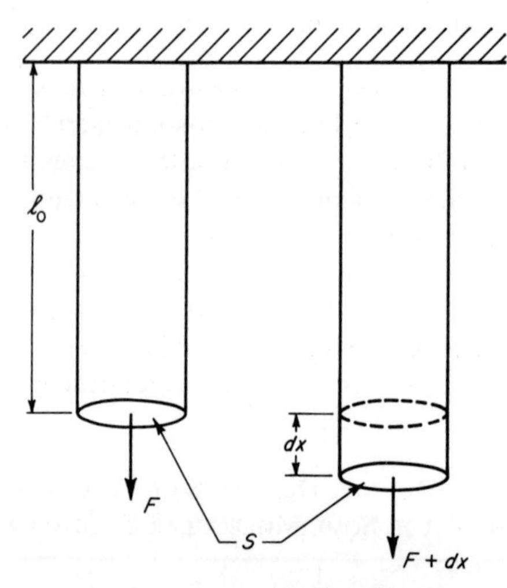

FIG. 6-11 Work of deformation

work, and if the deformation is elastic, the work will serve to increase the elastic energy by an increment dW. We can write, accordingly,

$$dW = (F + dF)\,dx = F\,dx \tag{6-48}$$

if the higher-order differential $dF\,dx$ is neglected.

However, prior to the application of dF, the bar already had undergone an extension x due to force F. By virtue of Hooke's law, x is proportional to F, or, using Eq. (6-21),

$$F = Kx \tag{6-49}$$

where K is the spring constant. Substitution of Eq. (6-49) in Eq. (6-48) yields

$$dW = Kx\,dx \tag{6-50}$$

If the bar has been extended progressively from $x = 0$ to $x = \Delta l$, the total elastic energy W stored in this process can be obtained by summing up the elementary contributions given by Eq. (6-50). This amounts to an integration of the left side of Eq. (6-50) from $x = 0$ to $x = \Delta l$, i.e.,

$$W = \int_0^{\Delta l} Kx \, dx = K \frac{(\Delta l)^2}{2} \tag{6-51}$$

We shall replace K by E in the right side of Eq. (6-51) using Eq. (6-25):

$$K = ES/l_0$$

whence

$$W = ES(\Delta l)^2/2l_0$$

or, by putting

$$S = v/l_0$$

where v is the volume of the bar, and noticing that $\Delta l/l_0 = \varepsilon$,

$$W = \frac{1}{2} E\left(\frac{\Delta l}{l}\right)^2 v = \frac{1}{2} E\varepsilon^2 v \tag{6-52}$$

Equation (6-52) gives the amount of elastic energy stored in volume v of a solid which has been subjected to strain ε under axial tension. Obviously, the same expression is valid for axial compression.

For the purpose of comparison with other forms of energy, it is more convenient to refer the elastic energy to a unit mass. If ρ is the density of the material and M its total mass,

$$v = M/\rho$$

and the elastic energy u per unit mass becomes

$$u = W/M = E\varepsilon^2/2\rho \tag{6-53}$$

Alternatively we can express u in terms of σ instead of ε by substituting for ε from Eq. (6-26)

$$\varepsilon = \sigma/E$$

There follows

$$u = \sigma^2/(2E\rho) \tag{6-54}$$

Equation (6-54) shows that the higher the stress the larger is the amount of elastic energy stored per unit mass of a given material. We shall see in the next chapter that the maximum stress attainable in currently available materials does not exceed $0.01E$. Hence,

$$u_{\max} = (0.01E)^2/(2E\rho) = 5 \times 10^{-5}E/\rho \tag{6-55}$$

To establish an upper limit we will substitute for E and ρ the values pertaining to diamond, probably the strongest solid known. If E is expressed in newtons per square meter and ρ in kilograms per cubic meter, the value of $u_{\max}$ will be given in joules per kilogram. There follows, with $E = 8.5 \times 10^{11}$ N/m² and $\rho = 3.5 \times 10^3$ kg/m³,

$$u_{\max} < \frac{5 \times 10^{-5} \times 8.5 \times 10^{11}}{3.51 \times 10^3} = 12.1 \times 10^3 \text{ J/kg}$$

By comparison, the amount of electric energy stored, for example, in a 120-amp-hr, 6-V car battery with a useful weight (plates and acid) of 15 kg is

$$u = \frac{120 \times 6 \times 3600}{15} = 175 \times 10^3 \text{ J/kg}$$

or almost 15 times more.

This example indicates that elastic energy cannot compete with other forms of energy as a prime mover and even less as a source of destructive power. Its usefulness is confined to the various mechanical applications mentioned previously, such as watchworks, trigger mechanisms, and springs.

6-7 Summary. Elasticity of solids has its origin in the existence and stability of interatomic and intermolecular bondings. The displacements caused by small elastic changes of shape and volume are proportional to the applied forces, in accordance with Hooke's law. This law can also be formulated in terms of *stresses* and *strains*, in which case the coefficient of proportionality is called the *modulus of elasticity*. The dimensions of the modulus of elasticity are force per unit area.

Depending on the mode of deformation, the modulus of elasticity varies: we use E, the Young's modulus, in axial tension and compression, G, the shear modulus, when only changes of shape occur; and B, the bulk modulus, when the deformation is reduced to volumetric changes. For isotropic and quasi-isotropic solids, the three moduli are simply interrelated by means of *Poisson's ratio*, the ratio of transverse to longitudinal strain under axial load.

The moduli of elasticity of solid elements reveal regularities characteristic of the periodicity of their atomic structures. The inverse fourth power dependence of B on the closest approach r_0 has been derived for ionic crystals and has been found to apply reasonably well to Groups I, II, III, and IV of the periodic table.

For the molecular type of bonding, the values of moduli of elasticity are one order of magnitude smaller than for most solids held by primary bonds. In plastics, however, the transition from glassy to rubbery state can lower these values by as much as three orders of magnitude.

The recoverable nature of elastic deformation makes it possible to store elastic energy in solids and to release it under controlled conditions. However, the amount of energy thus stored per unit mass is too small to serve as a prime mover or as a source of destructive power in competition with chemical, let alone nuclear, fuels.

6-8 Illustrative Problems

1. Compute the bulk and Young's moduli of elasticity for magnesium, using data of Table 6-4 and Table 2-1, and assuming the Poisson's ratio $\mu = 0.30$.

Solution. Magnesium belongs to the elements of Group II; hence, from Table 6-4, $C = 1.6$, and, from Table 2-1, $r_0 = 3.196$ Å. Recalling that the electric charge e of one electron is 4.774×10^{-10} CGS electrostatic units, we have, from Eq. (6-44),

$$B = \frac{1.6 \times 4.774^2 \times 10^{-20}}{3.196^4 \times 10^{-32}} = 3.55 \times 10^{11} \text{ dyn/cm}^2$$

The measured value is 3.4×10^{11} dyn/cm². We also have, from Eq. (6-42), with $\mu = 0.3$,

$$E = 3 \times 3.55 \times 10^{11}(1 - 0.60) = 4.26 \times 10^{11} \text{ dyn/cm}^2$$

as against the measured value of 4.3×10^{11} dyn/cm².

This value of E refers to a polycrystalline specimen with randomly oriented grains. Single crystals of magnesium exhibit values of E ranging from 5.1×10^{11} to 4.2×10^{11}, depending on which crystallographic direction is subjected to axial tension. The dependence of Young's modulus on crystallographic direction, i.e., its crystal anisotropy, is a characteristic of single crystals. Thus, in the BCC iron, the Young's modulus varies from 28.3×10^{11} dyn/cm² in the cube diagonal direction to 13.2×10^{11} dyn/cm² in the cube direction. The corresponding values for copper are 19.2×10^{11} dyn/cm² and 6.7×10^{11} dyn/cm². For aluminum they are 7.6×10^{11} dyn/cm² and 6.3×10^{11} dyn/cm². However, the modulus of elasticity of tungsten is 39×10^{11} dyn/cm² in all crystallographic directions. There is no satisfactory explanation of this exceptional behavior.

2. Derive the expression for the force of attraction f_d between two isolated dipole moments given by Eq. (6-46).

Solution. We apply Coulomb's law to each pair of charges depicted in Fig. 6-10. There follows

$$f_d = e^2z^2\left[\frac{1}{(r + d)^2} - \frac{1}{r^2} - \frac{1}{r^2} + \frac{1}{(r - d)^2}\right] \tag{6-56}$$

Rearranging the terms, we have

$$f_d = e^2z^2\left[\frac{1}{(r + d)^2} - \frac{1}{r^2}\right] - e^2z^2\left[\frac{1}{r^2} - \frac{1}{(r - d)^2}\right] \tag{6-57}$$

If d is small compared to r, we can write approximately in accordance with Eq. (6-12) by putting $\Delta r = d$, $f(r_0 + \Delta r) = 1/(r + d)^2$, and $f(r_0) = 1/r^2$

$$\frac{1}{(r + d)^2} = \frac{1}{r^2} - \frac{2d}{r^3} \tag{6-58}$$

In the same manner, by putting $f(r_0 + \Delta r) = 1/r^2$ and $f(r_0) = 1/(r - d)^2$, we have

$$\frac{1}{r^2} = \frac{1}{(r-d)^2} - \frac{2d}{(r-d)^3} \tag{6-59}$$

Substituting for $1/(r + d)^2$ the value from Eq. (6-58) in the first parentheses, Eq. (6-57), and for $1/r^2$ the value from Eq. (6-59) in the second parentheses, Eq. (6-57), we obtain, after simplification,

$$f_d = -2e^2z^2d\left[\frac{1}{r^3} - \left(\frac{1}{r-d}\right)^3\right] \tag{6-60}$$

Applying once more the operation indicated by Eq. (6-12) to the expression in the parentheses, Eq. (6-60), that is, putting $\Delta r = d$, $f(r_0 + \Delta r) = 1/r^3$, and $f(r_0) = 1/(r - d)^3$, we have

$$f_d = \frac{6e^2z^2d^2}{r^4} \qquad \text{q.e.d.}$$

References

ELEMENTARY

1. Galileo Galilei, *Two New Sciences*, Macmillan, New York, 1933.
2. J. P. Frankel, *Principles of the Properties of Materials*, McGraw-Hill, New York, 1957.

ADVANCED

1. W. H. Bragg and W. L. Bragg, *The Crystalline State*, Bell and Sons, London, 1949.
2. L. Pauling, *General Chemistry*, Freeman, San Francisco, 1948.
3. C. Kittel, *Introduction to Solid State Physics*, McGraw-Hill, New York, 1956.
4. H. Brooks, "Accomplishments and Limitations of Solid State Theory," in monograph, *The Science of Engineering Materials*, J. E. Goldman, Ed., Wiley, New York, 1957.

Problems

6-1 Compute the Young's moduli of steel, copper, and aluminum from the following data:

Metal	*Diameter* (in.)	*Length* (in.)	
		No Load	*Under* 1000-*Pound Load*
Steel	0.20	1000	1001.06
Copper	0.25	2000	2002.04
Aluminum	0.35	3000	3003.06

6-2 Compute the theoretical value of the modulus of elasticity E_0 of K^+Cl^-, if $r_0 = 3.14$ Å.

6-3 On the basis of Eq. (6-44) and Table 6-4, determine the ratio of the moduli of elasticity of Li and Cs.

6-4 On the basis of Eq. (6-44) and Table 6-4, determine the ratio of the moduli of elasticity of Li and Cd assuming equality of r_0.

6-5 Compute the modulus of elasticity of Be using Table 6-4 and $r_0 = 2.22$ Å.

6-6 Compute the elastic energy stored in a steel bar 3 in. in diameter and 10 in. long subjected to a load of 150,000 lb.

6-7 Compute the relative amounts of energy stored in the same volume of Fe and Al for a strain of 0.1%.

6-8 If the linear thermal expansion is 10^{-5}/°C, compute the change of the modulus of elasticity due to a temperature variation of 500°C.

7 / PROPERTIES RELATED TO ELASTICITY: 1 SPECIFIC SURFACE ENERGY

Surface energy is a phenomenon closely related to, but less apparent than, elasticity, as we shall see. Its manifestations are confined to the surfaces of solids and liquids. In both cases they are the result of interatomic or intermolecular forces displayed at the surface. In this chapter we shall derive the pertinent relationships and describe some of the engineering applications of surface energy.

7-1 Manifestations. Unlike elasticity, surface energy does not come directly within the reach of our senses. There are, however, many indirect manifestations of which we are aware: the rise of water in capillaries, the spread of oil films over the surface of water, the wetting action of liquids, and the water-repellent action of organic coatings. The manifestations in solids are less apparent. One of the most noticeable is the tendency of crystals to cleave along preferred crystallographic planes. Before trying to relate these phenomena to surface energy, it is necessary to introduce the concept of surface energy itself. This can be done best by analyzing the action of interatomic forces at the surfaces of ionic crystals.

7-2 Surface Energy and Interatomic Forces. Consider an ionic crystal of the Na^+Cl^- type, Fig. 7-1. We inquire under what conditions this crystal can be split in two—a process obviously leading to the formation of two new surfaces. Let the split occur between atomic layers a and b. This means the two layers have been pulled away from each other a distance r_1 sufficiently large to overcome their mutual attraction.

Since there is no way layers a and b can be pulled alone, we must imagine that the whole crystal has been pulled up to the breaking point and that the break has occurred between a and b more or less accidentally.[1] We will show that if the deformation is purely elastic, a minute crack between a and b is sufficient to cause the crystal to split in two, with the two parts contracting separately and pulling the layers a and b away from each other. In this process all the elastic energy accumulated in the crystal can be recovered—although as a rule it is dissipated in sound and vibrations. The only exception

[1] In practice, the break is localized by making a deep cut, or notch, and forcing a wedge into the notched area. This procedure makes use of the phenomenon of brittle fracture treated in Chapter 8.

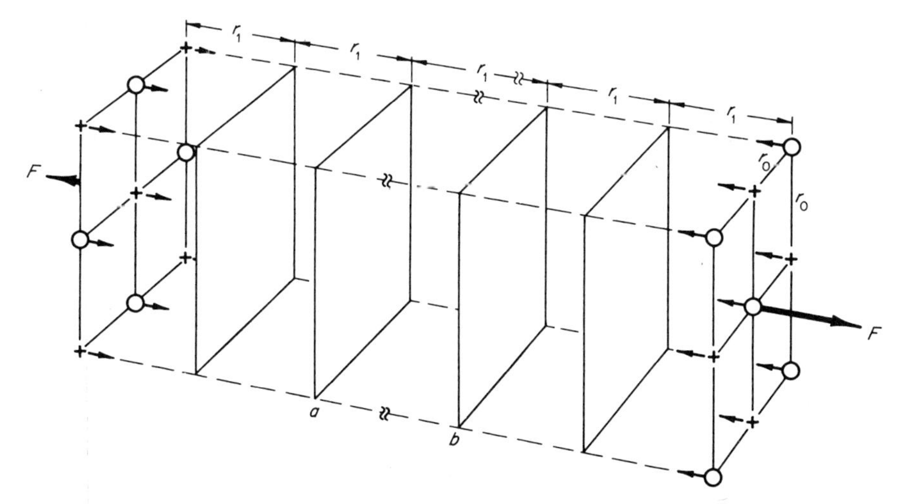

FIG. 7-1 Ionic crystal pulled up to the breaking point

is the elastic energy which has accumulated in the volume between the layers *a* and *b*. This energy has not been recovered. We visualize that it has been transferred in equal amounts to thin layers of crystal underlying the two new surfaces *a* and *b* in both crystal fragments. We shall find that this condition also applies to liquids. The various surface phenomena mentioned previously can thus be viewed as being indirectly related to the existence of this new form of energy, which accordingly is called *surface energy.*

Guided by the above preliminary remarks, we shall now proceed to cover the successive steps leading to the evaluation of surface energy. We shall then use the results to interpret its most significant manifestations in solids and liquids, including the phenomenon of surface tension.

Cohesive Force. We begin by computing the force necessary to overcome the attraction between the layers *a* and *b*, Fig. 7-1. This is the same as computing the force of attraction acting on each ion of the layer and summing up the contributions from all of them. In doing so, it is generally assumed that the process of splitting the crystal in two is accompanied by no lateral displacements. Under these circumstances the force acting on one ion of the Na^+Cl^- type crystal can be approximated by Eq. (6-9), namely,

$$f = [0.29z^2e^2/r^2][1 - (r_0/r)^m] \tag{7-1}$$

where r is measured in the axial direction only.[2] The fixed quantities e, z, r_0, and m have been defined previously.

In Fig. 7-2 the variation of f with r has been reproduced from Fig. 6-4 on a larger scale. It is seen that the value of f increases from zero to a maximum

[2] The approximation consists of extending the principle of superposition invoked in the derivation of B, Eq. (6-42), to strains as large as 25%; see Table 7-1.

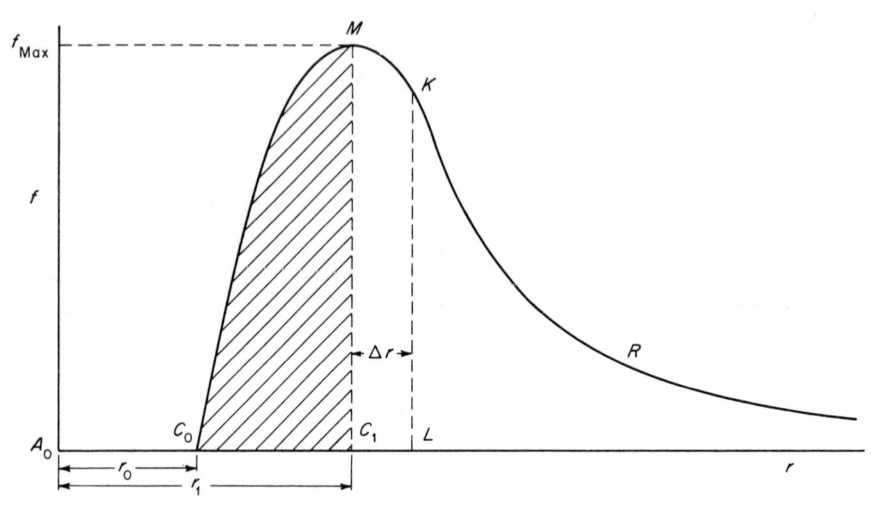

FIG. 7-2 Variation of the force of attraction f acting on the ion as a function of the distance r between layers

f_{max} as r increases from r_0 to the value r_1 and then gradually decreases to zero as r tends to infinity. It follows that the force necessary to overcome the force of attraction must at least be equal to f_{max}.

To find the maximum value of f, we form the derivative of the expression on the right-hand side of Eq. (7-1) with respect to r and make it equal to zero for $r = r_1$. There follows

$$\frac{df}{dr} = 0.29z^2e^2\left[\frac{-2}{r^3} + \frac{(m+2)r_0{}^m}{r^{m+3}}\right] \tag{7-2}$$

and

$$\frac{-2}{r_1{}^3} + \frac{(m+2)r_0{}^m}{r_1{}^{m+3}} = 0 \tag{7-3}$$

from which

$$\frac{r_1}{r_0} = k = \left(\frac{m+2}{2}\right)^{1/m} \tag{7-4}$$

Substitution of (7-4) in (7-1) yields

$$f_{max} = \frac{0.29z^2e^2}{r_1{}^2}\left(1 - \frac{2}{m+2}\right) = \frac{0.29z^2m}{k^2(m+2)}\frac{e^2}{r_0{}^2} \tag{7-5}$$

f_{max} is called the cohesive force of the ion.

Surface Energy. According to the preliminary remarks made previously, the surface energy is equal to half of the elastic energy accumulated in the volume between the layers a and b, Fig. 7-1, under the cohesive force f_{max}. Without loss of generality, we can limit the computation to the volume occupied by one ion and then multiply the result by the number of ions in the layer. Since the *deformations are no longer small*, the expression of the elastic energy given by Eq. (6-52), Section 6-6, cannot be used. However, the trend of reasoning leading to this expression subsists. We imagine a force f applied to the ion and its point of application displaced by dr when its value is increased by df. The applied force will thus do work, and since the deformation is elastic, the work will serve to increase the elastic energy, in the volume occupied by the ion, by an increment dw. Accordingly,

$$dw = f\,dr \tag{7-6}$$

The total amount of energy stored in this volume on moving the ion from its initial position r_0 to r_1 is

$$w = \int_{r_0}^{r_1} f\,dr \tag{7-7}$$

Substituting for f its expression from Eq. (7-1) and performing the integration we get

$$\begin{aligned} w &= \left| 0.29z^2e^2\left(-\frac{1}{r} + \frac{r_0{}^m}{(m+1)r^{m+1}}\right)\right|_{r=r_0}^{r=r_1} \\ &= -\frac{0.29z^2e^2}{r_1}\left[1 - \frac{1}{m+1}\left(\frac{r_0}{r_1}\right)^m\right] + \frac{0.29z^2e^2}{r_0}\left[1 - \frac{1}{m+1}\right] \end{aligned} \tag{7-8}$$

The last expression in Eq. (7-8) can be simplified by making use of Eq. (7-4). There follows

$$w = \frac{0.29z^2e^2}{r_0}\left[1 - \frac{1}{m+1}\right] - \frac{0.29z^2e^2}{kr_0}\left[1 - \frac{2}{(m+1)(m+2)}\right] \tag{7-9}$$

an expression which is further rearranged for future use to read

$$w = \frac{0.29z^2m}{m+1}\frac{e^2}{r_0}p \tag{7-10}$$

with

$$p = 1 - \frac{m+3}{k(m+2)} \tag{7-11}$$

Before proceeding, we will observe that when the whole crystal has been pulled up to the breaking point, the force applied to each ion has nearly the maximum value given by Eq. (7-5) and represented by MC_1 in Fig. 7-2. A crack Δr formed between layers a and b, Fig. 7-1, will increase their distance of separation to $r_1 + \Delta r$ with the attending decrease of the attractive force to the value KL, Fig. 7-2. This will cause an unbalance of forces on the remaining layers, to counteract which the two parts of the crystal will contract, thus reducing the value of r below r_1 in these layers. The contraction will lead to an increase of Δr with further reduction of force, and so on, until the original distance r_0 has been recovered between all layers except between a and b.

Here the distance Δr, far from being reduced, keeps growing at the expense of the contraction occurring in the two parts of the crystal. (To see this more clearly, imagine the two end layers of the crystal rigidly held during contraction.) In the end, this distance becomes many orders of magnitude larger than r_0, even for a very small crystal. For example, in a crystal only 0.1 cm long, the distance of separation for $r_1/r_0 = 1.20$ (see Table 7-1) will be 0.02 cm, or about 10^6 atomic distances. Any vestige of attraction will have disappeared at such a distance. The crystal will be definitely split in two with the formation of two new surfaces, *a* and *b*.

7-3 Specific Surface Energy. Equation (7-10) is an expression of the elastic energy converted into surface energy and referred to one ion. According to Eq. (6-16) of the previous chapter, there are $1/r_0^2$ ions per unit area of the layer. Hence the elastic energy per unit area is w/r_0^2. The surface energy per unit area is half of this value, being equally assigned to the two new surfaces. We write, accordingly, using the Greek letter ω to designate *surface energy per unit area*,

$$\omega = \frac{0.145z^2m}{(m+1)}\frac{e^2}{r_0^3}p \tag{7-12}$$

The name currently given to ω is *specific surface energy*. In CGS units ω is expressed in erg/cm². Since all quantities figuring on the right-hand side of Eq. (7-12) are given, the value of ω can be computed.[3]

Example. Compute the value of the specific surface energy of Na^+Cl^-.

Solution. From the example, Section 6-4, we take the values of $e = 4.774 \times 10^{-10}$ electrostatic units, $z = 1$, $m = 7$, and $r_0 = 2.79 \times 10^{-8}$ cm. Substituting m in Eq. (7-4) and Eq. (7-11), we obtain $k = 1.25$ and $p = 0.11$. Consequently, Eq. (7-12) gives

$$\omega = \frac{0.145 \times 7 \times (4.774 \times 10^{-10})^2 \times 0.11}{8 \times (2.79 \times 10^{-8})^3} = 146 \text{ erg/cm}^2$$

In like manner, Eq. (7-12) can be used for the computation of the specific surface energy of other ionic solids of the Na^+Cl^- type. The pertaining data for computation and the computed values of the specific surface energy ω_c of some of these solids are listed in columns 2 to 6, Table 7-1.

The same method of derivation is applicable to other types of ionic solids, and in principle it could be extended to other types of bonding. However, the mathematical difficulties of computation here are at least as great as those attending the determination of bulk moduli of elasticity, Section 6-5. On

[3] It is of interest to note that ω depends on the same fundamental quantities z, m, e, and r_0 as the theoretical modulus of elasticity E_0 in Eq. (6-28), Chapter 6. By eliminating the common factor $0.29z^2me^2/r_0^4$ from Eq. (7-12) and Eq. (6-28) we obtain

$$\omega = 0.5pE_0r_0/(m+1).$$

TABLE 7-1 SPECIFIC SURFACE ENERGY OF Na^+Cl^- TYPE IONIC CRYSTALS

1	2	3	4	5	6	7	8
Crystal	r_0 (Å)	$r_1/r_0 = k$	m	p	ω_c (erg/cm²)	ω_f (erg/cm²)	T_f (°K)
LiF	2.01	1.29	5	0.11	395	250	1143
LiCl	2.52	1.26	6	0.11	190	140	883
NaF	2.3	1.26	6	0.11	260	202	1263
NaCl	2.79	1.25	7	0.11	146	114	1073
NaBr	2.98	1.24	7.5	0.10	118	107	1043
NaI	3.23	1.22	8.5	0.11	93	88	933
KF	2.66	1.25	7	0.11	170	142	1163
KCl	3.14	1.23	8	0.10	100	96	1073
KBr	3.29	1.22	8.5	0.11	88	89	1003
RbF	2.81	1.24	7.5	0.10	140	128	1073
RbCl	3.27	1.22	8.5	0.11	90	98	993
RbBr	3.42	1.21	9	0.10	80	88	1003
RbI	3.66	1.20	10	0.09	65	80	943
MgO	2.10	1.26	6	0.11	1320	—	—

purely dimensional grounds, an expression similar to Eq. (7-12) can be written for any type of primary bonds as follows:

$$\omega = C_1 e^2/r_0{}^3 \tag{7-13}$$

where C_1 is a numerical coefficient of the same nature as C in Eq. (6-44). However, judging from a few available data, this coefficient does not exhibit the same regularity as C with regard to the periodic table. There are also serious difficulties associated with the experimental determination of ω because the magnitude of surface energy is greatly affected by the degree of contamination of surfaces of solids and liquids by foreign atoms. Specific surface energy is particularly hard to measure in solids, because solids do not exhibit the concomitant phenomenon of surface tension so readily observable in liquids.

7-4 Surface Tension. Surface tension is a property of liquid surfaces closely associated with the specific surface energy. It is manifest in liquids rather than solids because in liquids it can produce changes of shape that are largely unopposed by restoring forces, whereas in solids these changes are strongly resisted by the restoring shear forces.

The concept of surface tension can be best understood by analyzing more closely the nature of surface energy. In liquids as in solids, surface energy is due to the existence of interatomic and intermolecular forces. The presence of such forces in liquids is evidenced in every hanging drop of water. The mechanism by means of which the drop breaks away from the sustaining surface is in every respect similar to the mechanism of splitting a crystal in two. In fact, this is one of the current methods of the determination of the specific surface energy, as we shall see in Section 7-5. Moreover, the experimental results for fused alkali halides are not too different from the values computed for solid crystals as shown in columns 6 and 7, Table 7-1.[4] We are therefore justified in extending to liquids the use of the diagram Fig. 7-2 and the related equations.

We recall that Eq. (7-6) expresses the increase of elastic energy dw in terms of the work $f\,dr$ done on the ion. In Fig. 7-2 the product $f\,dr$ represents the increase of area under the curve C_0MKR. Likewise the integral in Eq. (7-7) can be viewed as a difference of two areas: (1) the area under the portion C_0MKR and (2) the area under the portion C_1MKR of the curve. In both cases, the point R corresponds to very large values of r ($r \to \infty$).

For ionic crystals of the Na^+Cl^- type, the magnitudes of these areas are given by the first and the second term, respectively, on the right-hand side of Eq. (7-9). They both represent amounts of work. More specifically, the larger area, under C_0MKR, corresponds to the amount of work necessary to remove an ion—and more generally an atom or a molecule—from the position of equilibrium r_0 to infinity.[5] The area under C_1MKR corresponds obviously to a lesser amount of work. We say that the position r_1, to which this lesser amount of work refers, is less stable than the position r_0. (In fact, it is unstable in so far as the elastic behavior is concerned.) This criterion of stability is the same as that developed in Chapter 1 for various aggregations of atoms.

When the crystal or the liquid is split in two, the difference in the amounts of work corresponding to positions r_0 and r_1 of one atom or molecule is divided between at least two atoms or molecules, and presumably more are involved, since conceivably several layers beneath the two surfaces could be affected by the split. Their configuration is therefore more stable than that corresponding to r_1; yet it is less stable than when they occupy the position of equilibrium r_0. Since the molecules inside the liquid *are* in such a position, the "surface" molecules seek to gain more stability by crowding inside. The word molecule rather than ion is used henceforth, because the liquids of practical interest are mostly molecular. The conclusions, however, apply to any kind of liquid—atomic and ionic, as well as molecular. The result is a greater compacting of the liquid in the interior and the concomitant appearance of surface tension.

To prove this point we recall a phenomenon familiar from elementary physics. A drop of liquid floating in air or in another liquid—with which it

[4] The computed values can be made to agree closer with the experimental ones if they are corrected for the practically linear variation of ω between room temperature and the temperature of fusion T_f at which the measurements were made.

[5] It is of interest to note that, according to Eqs. (7-9) and (7-10) and the values of p shown in column 5, Table 7-1, the amount of elastic energy converted to surface energy is an almost constant fraction of this work for alkali halide crystals.

does not mix—is known to assume the shape of a sphere, Fig. 7-3a. A particularly striking example is provided by the formation in water of large spherical drops of an organic liquid called ortho-toluidine.[6]

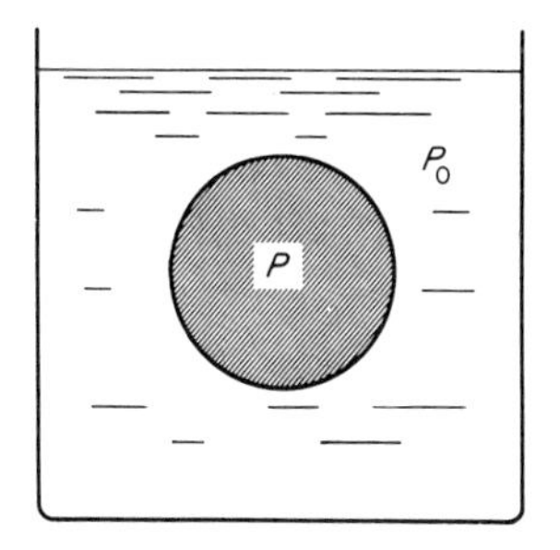

FIG. 7-3a A drop of an immiscible liquid (ortho-toluidine) in water

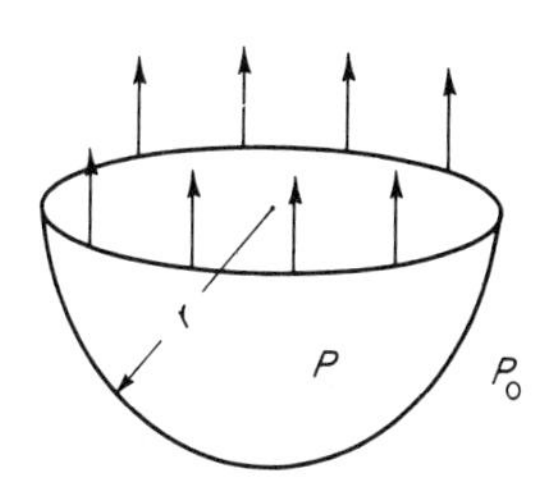

FIG. 7-3b Surface layer of a spherical drop under pressure difference $p - p_0$

The spherical shape is consistent with the tendency of molecules to move from the surface to the interior of the drop. By doing so, they obviously make the surface smaller. The smallest surface they can thus impart to a fixed volume is that of a sphere.

We shall now improve on this elementary picture in two ways. If the surface of the drop shrinks, its surface energy will decrease. At the same time, the pressure inside the drop will increase due to the transfer of molecules from the surface to the interior of the drop. We can also visualize that the surface layers, by shrinking, compress the drop from without. By virtue of action and reaction, an equal pressure is exerted on the surface layer from within. Let Δp be this pressure. In effect, Δp is the difference $p - p_0$ between the pressure p inside the drop and the pressure p_0 in the surrounding medium, Fig. 7-3a.

The surface layers behave under pressure Δp as a thin-walled spherical container; they develop circumferential tensile forces resisting the action of the pressure, Fig. 7-3b. Let r be the radius of the drop. If the thickness of the surface layers is neglected, the equilibrium of forces acting on the diametral section yields

$$\pi r^2 \Delta p = \pi r^2 (p - p_0) = F \qquad (7\text{-}14)$$

where F is the sum total of the tensile forces applied to the circumference $2\pi r$.

We next determine the difference $p - p_0$ in terms of the specific surface energy ω. If the surface shrinks by a differential dS, the radius of the drop contracts by dr. The shrinking of the surface liberates an amount of surface energy

$$d\Omega = \omega \, dS \qquad (7\text{-}15)$$

[6] Sir William Bragg, *Concerning the Nature of Things*, Dover, New York, 1954.

which is converted into the work of deformation produced by the pressure difference $p - p_0$ acting on the surface S of the sphere, Fig. 7-4. Since each point of the surface moves by dr during contraction, the work of the sum

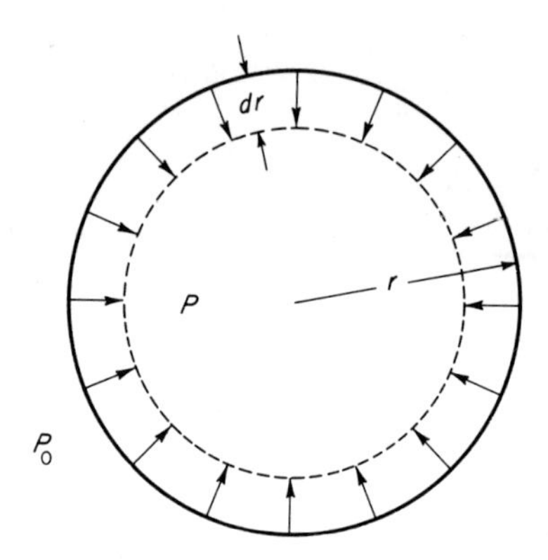

FIG. 7-4 Work done by the surface layer when the radius of the drop contracts by dr

total of forces applied to the surface of the sphere is $(p - p_0)S\,dr$ (if higher-order differentials are neglected; cf. Eq. (6-48), Chapter 6). Equating this expression to $d\Omega$ in Eq. (7-15), we get

$$\omega\,dS = (p - p_0)S\,dr \tag{7-16}$$

But

$$S = 4\pi r^2$$

and

$$dS = 8\pi r\,dr$$

Hence,

$$\omega 8\pi r\,dr = (p - p_0)4\pi r^2\,dr$$

and, on simplifying further,

$$p - p_0 = 2\omega/r \tag{7-17}$$

Substitution of $(p - p_0)$ from Eq. (7-17) in Eq. (7-14) yields

$$2\pi r\omega = F \tag{7-18}$$

As expected, the sum total of forces F acting on the circumference is proportional to its length. If we let γ be the tension per unit length,

$$F = 2\pi r\gamma \tag{7-19}$$

By equating F in both Eqs. (7-18) and (7-19), we get, finally,

$$\gamma = \omega \tag{7-20}$$

That is, the tension per unit length of the circumference is a property numerically equal to the specific surface energy ω. Like the latter, γ is a property of the liquid; it is called *surface tension.*

In the CGS system, the units of γ according to Eq. (7-19) are dyn/cm. The units of ω, we recall, are erg/cm^2. Since erg = dyn $\times$ cm, Eq. (7-20) is dimensionally consistent.

The numerical equality of γ and ω is frequently a source of confusion. Of the two, the specific surface energy is a more fundamental and a more general concept. It applies to solids and liquids alike. Surface tension, we saw, derives its origin essentially from the tendency of liquid surfaces to contract. In that sense, it is a more restricted concept.

7-5 Adsorption. Wettability. Crowding inside the drop is not the only way "surface" molecules can gain greater stability. They can also become more stable by making bonds with foreign molecules. Since their need for additional stability cannot be very great—the intermolecular distances at the surface being probably much closer to r_0 than r_1 (Fig. 7-2)—the type of bonds they form must be a great deal weaker than any of the bonds considered in Chapter 1. We distinguish between adsorption and wettability depending on whether the surface molecules attach foreign molecules to their own surface or attach themselves to foreign surfaces. Adsorption is common to liquids and solids; wettability clearly is a characteristic of liquids alone.

Adsorption. By imparting more stability to the surface molecules, adsorption lowers the specific surface energy. Gaseous adsorption being no exception, the atmosphere above the surface plays an important role in the determination of the specific surface energy. This is particularly true of chemically active liquids like fused metals. As a rule, the specific surface energy of such liquids is determined in neutral atmospheres (nitrogen or hydrogen).

Adsorption of moisture plays an equally important role in the determination of the specific surface energy of glass. The loss of strength discussed in Chapter 8 is largely attributed to the adsorption of moisture on the surface of glass.

Wettability. One of the common manifestations of wettability is the distortion of a liquid drop deposited on solid surfaces, Fig. 7-5. Consider a molecule in such a drop at the intersection M of three interfaces: liquid-solid, liquid-gas, and solid-gas. It is subjected to three forces: attraction to its own kind of molecules, $\overline{ML}$; attraction to the molecules of solid, $\overline{MS}$; and surface tension, $\overline{MG}$, along the tangent to the liquid-gas interface at M. The equilibrium of forces in the ML direction yields

$$ML - MS + MG\cos\theta = 0 \tag{7-21}$$

whence

$$\cos\theta = \frac{MS - ML}{MG} \tag{7-22}$$

The angle θ is called the *contact angle* between the liquid and solid. If $MS > ML$, $\cos\theta$ is positive and θ is smaller than 90°; if $MS < ML$, $\cos\theta$ is negative and θ is larger than 90°. In the first instance the drop is drawn out, Fig. 7-5a. In the second it is balled up, Fig. 7-5b. We say that the drop wets the surface if $\theta < 90°$ and that it does not wet the surface if $\theta > 90°$.

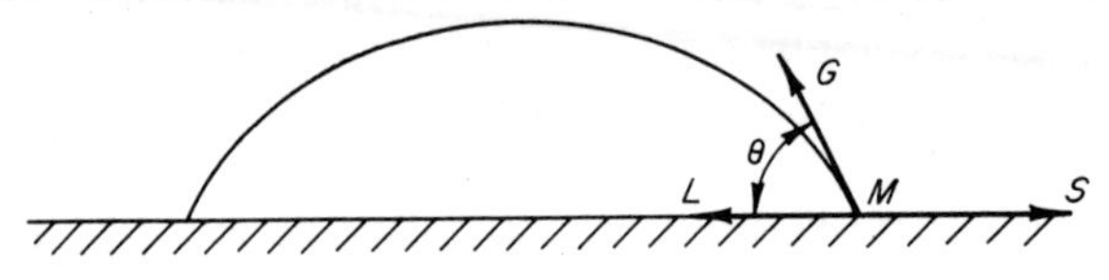

FIG. 7-5a Manifestation of wettability

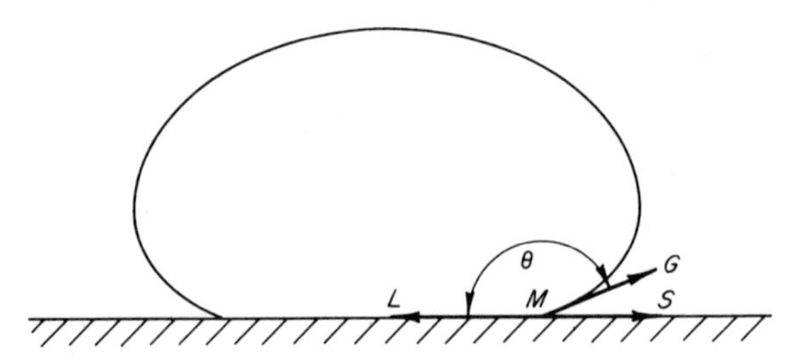

FIG. 7-5b Manifestation of non-wettability

When $MG < MS - ML$, Eq. (7-22) breaks down. There is no equilibrium, and the drop continues to spread by covering the surface with a film that gets thinner and thinner until the build-up of intermolecular attraction in the liquid stops the process. The same phenomenon occurs when the underlying surface is that of another liquid, the spreading of oil on water being a classic example.

Oil spreads on water, but water does not spread on oiled surfaces. (Water is heavier than oil; hence, oiled solid surfaces must be used.) The reason is the difference of surface tensions; oil has a surface tension of less than 25 dyn/cm. The corresponding value of MG is smaller than $MS - ML$; hence, oil builds a thin film on water. On the other hand, the surface tension of water is almost three times as large; 73 dyn/cm. The corresponding value of MG is larger than $MS - ML$, and there is no film formation.

The values of 25 dyn/cm and 73 dyn/cm refer to liquid-air interfaces. At the water-oil interface the surface tension of water is smaller than 73 dyn/cm, there being a certain amount of bonding between the oil and water molecules.[7]

[7] The bonding is due to the existence of the active group COOC at the end of the long chain molecule of oil. Because of its attraction to the water molecule, this end is called *hydrophylic*.

However, the actual value of the interfacial tension between two liquids *A* and *B* depends also on other factors, chiefly on the degree of solubility of *A* in *B* and *B* in *A*. As a rough approximation, the interfacial tension *A* – *B* can be taken to be the difference between the surface tensions of *A* and *B* in air. Table 7-2 gives some idea of the degree of approximation afforded by this rule.

TABLE 7-2 INTERFACIAL SURFACE TENSION BETWEEN TWO LIQUIDS AT 18°–20°C*

Liquids	*Interfacial Tension A–B* (dyn/cm)	*Surface Tension in Air*	
		A (dyn/cm)	*B* (dyn/cm)
Water-benzene	35	73.05	28.85
Water-carbon tetrachloride	45	73.05	26.95
Water-*n*-hexan	51.1	73.05	18·43

* Source: *Handbook of Chemistry and Physics*, 37th Ed., Chemical Rubber Publishing Co., Cleveland.

The relatively large value of about 50 dyn/cm of the interfacial water-oil tension is responsible for the known phenomenon of objects heavier than water—some insects, for example—being able to rest on its surface if they are oiled. In Fig. 7-6, *d* is the diameter of an oiled needle floating on water. By

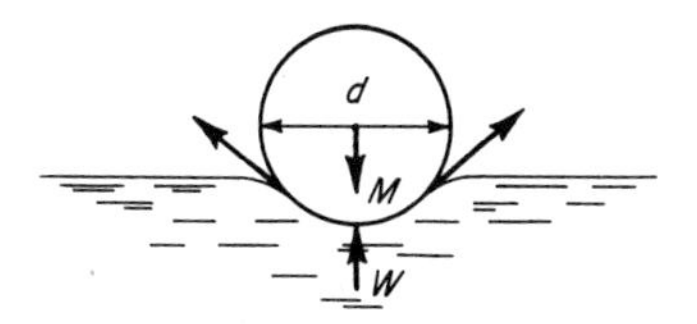

FIG. 7-6 Oiled needle floating on water

making a small depression in the surface layers, the needle is able to balance its own weight against the combined action of the vertical component of interfacial tension and the hydrostatic drive of the displaced water volume. Obviously there is a limit to the carrying capacity of the surface layers; see Problem 7-6.

The same phenomenon in reverse can be produced by holding a small quantity of water at the bottom of a well-oiled sieve, Fig. 7-7. The overhanging layers will support the pressure *p* of the water, provided the opening $2r$ of the mesh is small enough. The condition of equilibrium is similar to that given by Eq. (7-17). The waterproofing of raincoats and the stabilization of soils by water-repellent aggregates are based essentially on the same principle.

Although in the above applications we seek to *maintain* the interfacial water-oil tension, there are equally important industrial applications in which it is necessary to *remove* or, at least, to reduce this tension. The desired result is achieved through the use of appropriate solvents in water. Depending on the nature of the end product—see below—they are called *detergents* or *emulsifiers*. The best known detergent is soap.

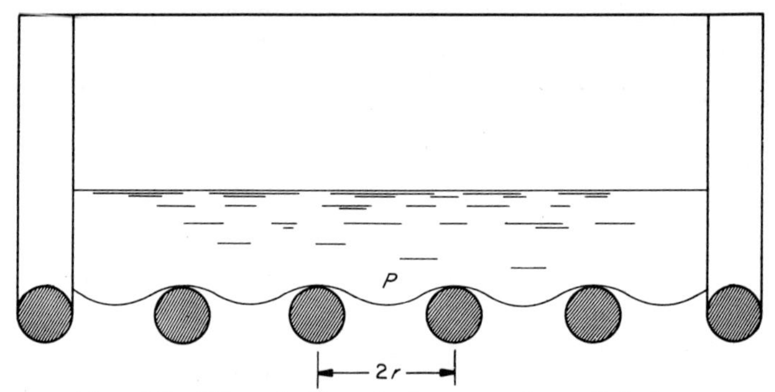

FIG. 7-7 Water held at the bottom of an oiled sieve

Like oil, soap is a derivative of hydrocarbons. It has a long chain molecule, with one end having more affinity for the water molecule (hydrophylic) and the other end having more affinity for the oil molecule (lipophylic). Because of this divided loyalty, the molecules of soap reach the surface of water with the lipophylic end standing up. They are thus able to form a film which has a surface tension almost identical to that of oil. As a result oil or any other greasy substance can form very tiny droplets when in contact with such a film, even under a very moderate pressure—e.g., by shaking or churning. The reason is apparent from Eq. (7-17). It is seen that to maintain a finite value of $p - p_0$ the radius r of the drop must be small if ω is small.

Once in the liquid, these droplets stay in suspension, thanks to a protective coating of soap molecules that shield them from the repulsive action of water molecules. This in essence is what happens when soiled linen or fabrics are washed in soap solution. Other detergents have a similar action.

If the oily and greasy substances are not merely to be removed from stained surfaces but evenly distributed in the solution, in the form of an emulsion, the solvents are called emulsifiers. Their field of action covers an impressive range of applications: cutting oils, paints, mayonnaise, homogenized milk, ice cream, to say nothing of cosmetics and lotions.

7-6 Determination of Surface Tension. Capillarity. According to Eq. (7-22), when a liquid wets a surface, the attraction of surface molecules to foreign molecules outweighs the attraction to their own kind of molecules. As a rule, it is also stronger than the effect of surface tension. Thus when a drop of liquid gathers at the end of a thin-walled tube to which it adheres, the break occurs in the surface layers, Fig. 7-8, and not at the wall. Let q be the weight of the drop at the moment of break and r the radius of the tube. Then

$$2\pi r\gamma = q \tag{7-23}$$

a relation from which γ can be determined.

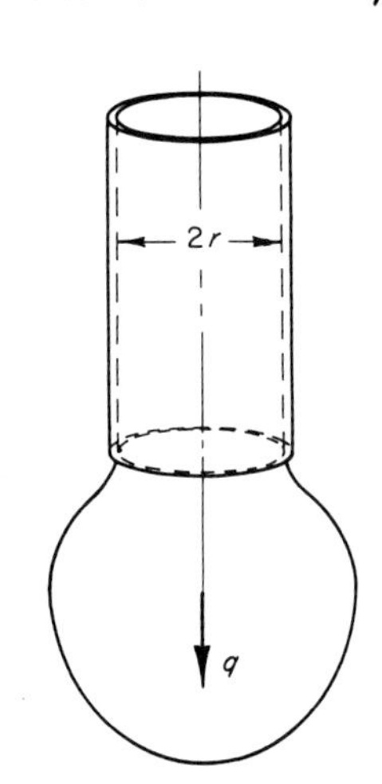

FIG. 7-8 Determination of surface tension by the break of a liquid drop

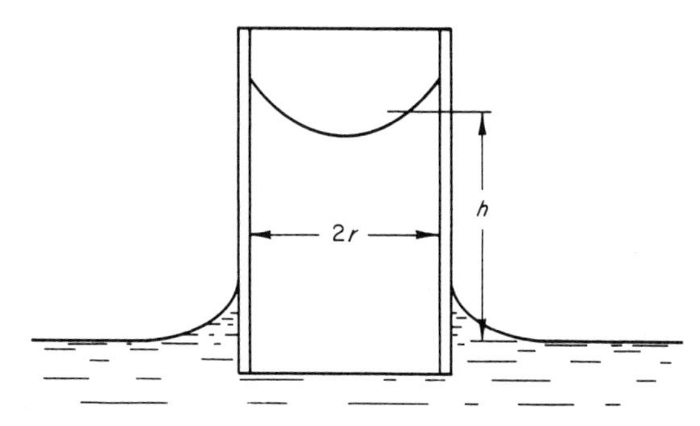

FIG. 7-9 Rising of water in a capillary tube (concave meniscus)

This method, although less accurate than the current methods of determination of surface tension which we omit, is quite instructive when it comes to explaining the related phenomenon of capillarity. The rising of water in very thin (capillary) tubes, Fig. 7-9, is familiar from elementary physics. It is due to the surface layers pulling behind them a column of water while moving up the walls of the tube. The motion stops when the weight of the column balances the forces which keep the surface layers attached to the tube. The situation is similar to that of a flexible clothesline stretching and sagging under the weight of washing. If we isolate the surface layers and the hanging column from the tube and the molecules of liquid adhering to its walls, Fig. 7-10, we can write the following equation of equilibrium in the vertical direction:

$$2\pi r\gamma \cos \theta = \pi r^2 h\delta g \tag{7-24}$$

Here r is the radius of the tube, h is the height of the column, g is the acceleration of gravity, and δ is the density of the liquid.

Equation (7-24) can be simplified to read

$$h = 2\gamma \cos \theta/(r\,\delta g) \tag{7-25}$$

Equation (7-25) shows that if r is small enough, the liquid can reach considerable height. Capillary action of wood vessels contributes to pulling sap to the top of trees as tall as the sequoia (300 feet and more).

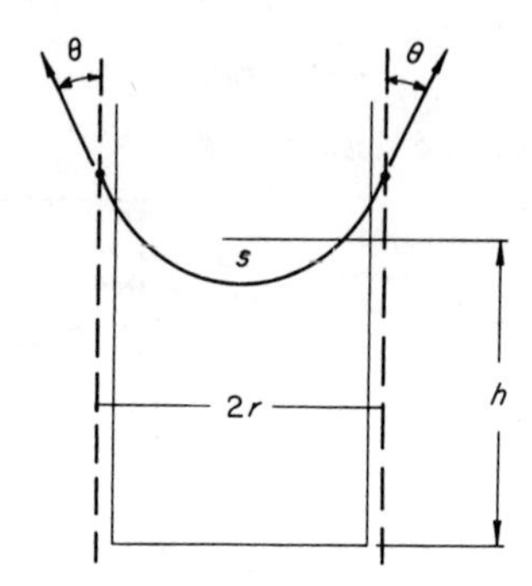

FIG. 7-10 Column of water hanging on the surface layer s in a capillary tube

If attraction to its own kind of molecules outweighs the adhesion of surface molecules to the molecules of the tube, the liquid is depressed below the level from which the tube protrudes, Fig. 7-11. As in the case of wetting, Fig. 7-5a and 7-5b, the surface of the liquid is stretched when the liquid is lifted, Fig. 7-9, and it is balled up when the liquid is depressed. We say that the liquid builds a concave meniscus in the first instance and a convex meniscus in the second one.

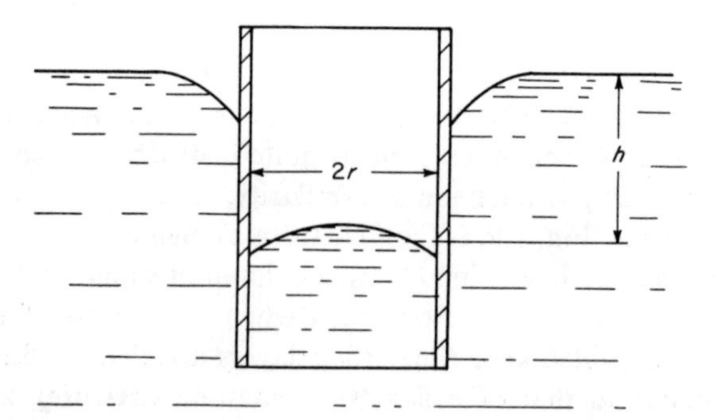

FIG. 7-11 Depression of the level of a non-wetting liquid in a capillary (convex meniscus)

7-7 Summary. Surface energy like elasticity is due to interatomic and intermolecular attractions in solids and liquids. It gives rise to the specific surface energy ω, a property which for ionic crystals depends on the same fundamental characteristics of atomic and crystal structure as modulus of elasticity.

In liquids, a property of surface layers concomitant with the specific energy is the surface tension γ. It has the same numerical value as ω but different dimensions. Specific surface energy is measured in units of energy per unit area, whereas surface tension is measured in units of force per unit length.

Adsorption and wettability are phenomena related to surface tension, particularly wettability, which gives rise to interfacial tension between two liquids. The interplay between wettability and surface tension is also manifested in the action of detergents and emulsifiers, as well as in capillarity.

References

ELEMENTARY

1. W. L. Bragg, *Concerning the Nature of Things*, Dover, New York, 1954.
2. J. P. Frankel, *Principles of the Properties of Materials*, McGraw-Hill, New York, 1957.

ADVANCED

1. M. Born and O. Stern, *Preuss. Akad. Wiss. Ber.* **48**, 901–913, 1919.
2. K. L. Wolf, *Physik und Chemie der Grenzflächen*, Springer Verlag, Berlin, 1957.
3. *Structure and Properties of Solid Surfaces*, monograph, R. Gomer and C. S. Smith, Eds., U. of Chicago, 1953.

Problems

7-1 Check the computed value of the specific surface energy for RbCl. Show steps of computation.

7-2 Solve Problem 7-1 for MgO.

7-3 Using values of Table 7-2 and assuming the interfacial tension to be equal to *ML* in Eq. (7-22), determine which of the two liquids will spread and which will not spread on the surface of the other.

7-4 The surface tension of mercury is about 480 dyn/cm and the interfacial water-mercury surface tension is 375. Compute the contact angle of a water droplet deposited on the surface of mercury.

7-5 What is the weight of a water droplet, breaking away from a thin-walled glass tube 0.5 cm in diameter?

7-6 What is the maximum diameter of an oiled steel needle capable of floating on water? (Hint: The needle must be half immersed in water.)

7-7 Establish the relevant relationship between interfacial oil-water surface tension, specific gravities of steel and water, and the diameter of a steel needle immersed in water only one quarter of its diameter.

7-8 What size of capillaries is needed to raise a column of water 10 meters above the surface? (Assume contact angle is 0°.)

7-9 How much will a column of mercury be depressed below the surface in a capillary 0.01 cm in diameter? (Assume $\gamma = 400$ dyn/cm and a contact angle of 180°.)

7-10 Two soap bubbles of two different diameters are joined as shown in the sketch below. Which of the two will disappear? Why?

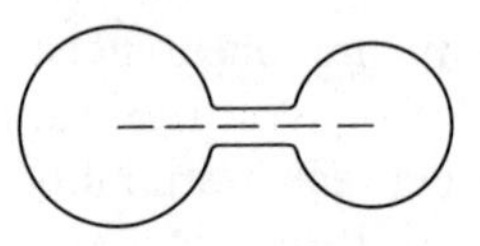

7-11 Explain the repellent action of a rainproof fabric. How close must it be woven? Give a qualitative estimate of the size of the mesh.

7-12 Does ice cream contain an emulsifier? Why?

8 / PROPERTIES RELATED TO ELASTICITY: 2 BRITTLENESS

Surface energy plays an important role in the phenomenon of brittle fracture, considered in this chapter. The direct cause of brittleness, however, is ascribed to the presence of minute cracks in solids, as will be explained. We shall also consider the limitations that brittleness imposes on materials in practical applications.

8-1 Manifestations. In Section 6-1 we mentioned that Galileo was apparently unaware of the existence of small deformations preceding fracture in materials such as stone and masonry. Yet he understood perfectly well that to produce fracture the forces that "bind the parts of the solid together" must be overcome. How large are these forces?

To answer this question we must distinguish between two types of fracture: *brittle* fracture, which under normal atmospheric conditions[1] is encountered mostly among minerals, ceramics, and polymeric materials (plastics), and *ductile* fracture, characteristic of most metals. In the first instance, there is little or no apparent deformation; in the second, there is considerable deformation before fracture. Both phenomena are rather complicated, and to get some understanding of their nature we must resort to simplifications. The elastic behavior of solids provides a sufficient approximation to the brittle behavior with which we are concerned here. On the other hand, ductile fracture cannot be dissociated from the plastic behavior of solids treated in Chapter 9 and accordingly it *must be* excluded from present considerations.

8-2 The Cohesive Strength. We shall first inquire how much stress a solid can theoretically sustain before it splits in two. For ionic crystals the answer can be readily obtained using the computations of the previous chapter, and in order of magnitude this answer also applies to solids held together by other primary bonds.

We use Eq. (7-5), which gives the expression of the force f_{max} necessary to overcome the attraction exerted by an ionic crystal of the Na^+Cl^- type on each ion of a layer such as *a* or *b*, Fig. 7-1. If r_0 is the distance separating

[1] The conditions under wnich minerals cease to be brittle are discussed in Chapter 9.

two close ions in the layer, their number per unit area is $1/r_0^2$, and the force per unit area, or stress, is

$$\sigma_{max} = \frac{f_{max}}{r_0^2} \tag{8-1}$$

σ_{max} is called the cohesive strength of the crystal. Substituting for f_{max} from Eq. (7-5) we obtain

$$\sigma_{max} = \frac{0.29z^2m}{k^2(m+2)}\frac{e^2}{r_0^4} \tag{8-2}$$

where e is the charge of the electron, z is the valency, m is the repulsive exponent (Table 6-1), and k is a coefficient defined by Eq. (7-4).

We shall simplify Eq. (8-2) by substituting for $0.29z^2m(e^2/r_0^4)$ the theoretical value E_0 of the modulus of elasticity, Eq. (6-28), Chapter 6. This yields

$$\sigma_{max} = \frac{E_0}{k^2(m+2)} \tag{8-3}$$

Taking alkali halides as an example, we can use the data of Tables 7-1 and 6-1, for k and m, respectively. The value of σ_{max} is then comprised between two limits, namely,

$$0.09E_0 \geq \sigma_{max} \geq 0.06E_0 \tag{8-4}$$

Since, according to the example of Section 6-4, E_0 is about 13% larger than the Young's modulus E, we can write for an order of magnitude approximation

$$\sigma_{max} = 0.1E \tag{8-5}$$

In words, the cohesive strengths of ionic crystals—and, by inference, of solids in general—is about one tenth of their Young's moduli. Since E is of the order of 10^{12} dyn/cm^2, or 10^7 lb/in.^{2}, for the majority of strong solids, including ceramic materials, the corresponding cohesive strength is of the order of 10^{11} dyn/cm^2, or 10^6 lb/in.^{2}—quite a substantial figure, considering that the hydrostatic pressure at the deepest point in the ocean does not exceed 20% of this value.

8-3 Brittle Fracture Strength. Griffith's Law. Experiment shows that the actual fracture strength of real solids falls short of the computed value of the cohesive strength by as much as three orders of magnitude, varying between 2000 and 40,000 lb/in.^{2} for most ceramic materials. Such a large discrepancy cannot be explained by chance variation. Griffith[2] postulated that it must have a deep-seated cause in some inherent defects of structure, or structure imperfections. In looking for their nature, he was naturally aware of the role a crack can play in weakening the strength of a brittle material.

[2] A. A. Griffith, "The Phenomena of Rupture and Flow in Solids," *Philosophical Trans. Roy. Soc.* (*London*), **A221,** 163(1920).

It is a matter of current experience that if a porcelain cup develops a crack, it does not take very much to shatter it completely. Even a scratch suffices to weaken considerably the strength of a brittle solid—a property utilized extensively in cutting window panes and glass tubes to predetermined sizes. Another characteristic manifestation of brittleness is that once a crack begins to grow, less and less force is required to spread it further. Griffith has shown that if a piece of brittle material is subjected to a constant tensile stress σ, cracks above a certain length c will propagate spontaneously *whatever the size of the piece.*

To see what this implies, consider a thin plate of glass, Fig. 8-1, subjected to a constant stress, $\sigma = P/bt$. If an artificial crack is produced in the middle portion of the plate—far from the edges—the cracked plate will be able to sustain the load as long as the crack does not exceed a critical length c. A crack that is longer than c will begin to spread spontaneously, and the plate will be split in two whatever its width b. If the stress σ is increased, the critical length of the crack will be smaller.

By means of carefully devised tests—since artificial cracks of predetermined lengths are not easy to cut in glass—Griffith was able to correlate the critical length of the crack c to the applied tensile stress. If c_1 and c_2 are two cracks of different lengths, the stresses σ_1 and σ_2 necessary to make these cracks propagate are in the inverse ratio of the square roots of c_1 and c_2. That is,

$$\frac{\sigma_1}{\sigma_2} = \frac{\sqrt{c_2}}{\sqrt{c_1}} \tag{8-6}$$

Hence,

$$\sigma_1\sqrt{c_1} = \sigma_2\sqrt{c_2} = \text{constant} \tag{8-7}$$

By a theoretical analysis (see Section 8-6), Griffith was also able to determine the nature of the constant. He showed that it had a characteristic value for each material, depending on its Young's modulus of elasticity E and its specific surface energy ω. The exact formulation of Griffith's law is

$$\sigma\sqrt{c} = \sqrt{4E\omega/\pi} \tag{8-8}$$

For ordinary glass, ω is about 200 erg/cm^2 and $E = 6 \times 10^{11}$ dyn/cm^2 (from G. W. Morey[3]). Hence approximately

$$\sigma\sqrt{c} = 1.23 \times 10^7 \text{ dyn/cm}^{3/2} \tag{8-9}$$

If Eq. (8-9) is represented by a plot of σ versus c, Fig. 8-2, the curve is of a hyperbolic type. The stress increases steeply for very small cracks. The point P on the curve corresponds to the tensile strength, of about 10^9 dyn/cm^2 (15,000 lb/in.^{2}), of an ordinary polished piece of glass without visible cracks. Since this stress was so far below the theoretical cohesive strength of 6×10^{10}

[3] *The Properties of Glass,* Reinhold, New York, 1954.

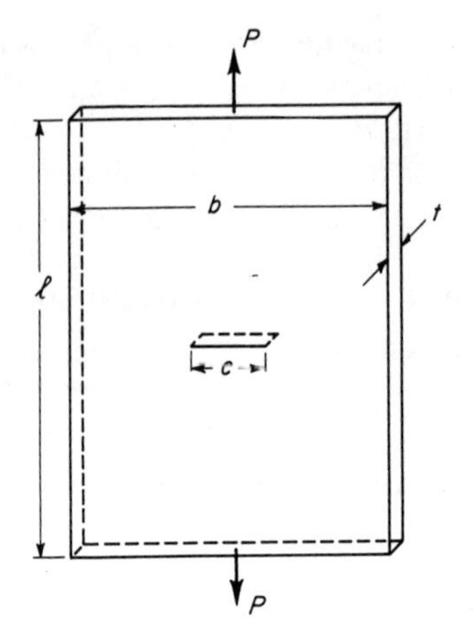

FIG. 8-1 Plate of glass with crack c subjected to axial tension

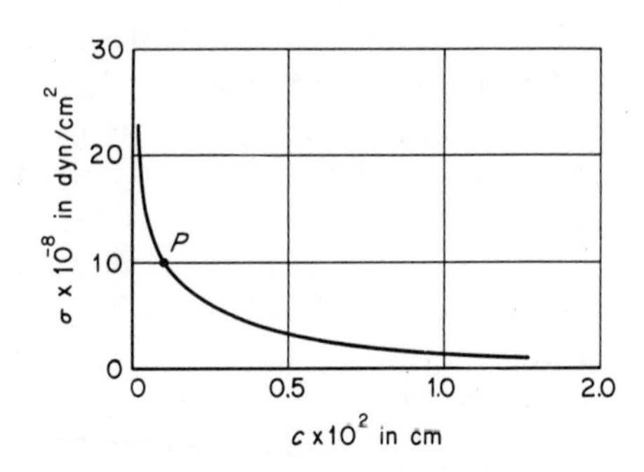

FIG. 8-2 Relation between length of crack c and brittle fracture strength of ordinary polished glass

dyn/cm^2, Eq. (8-5), Griffith made the bold assumption that invisible cracks, presumably formed during solidification, exist in the interior of the piece. According to Eq. (8-9), the length of these cracks should be of the order of 10^{-4} cm, or 10,000 Å, well within the range of resolution by ordinary light; see Section 4-2. However, the width of the crack presumably is less than 100 Å. Hence, recourse to electron microscopy seems mandatory. So far this technique has not proved successful in revealing Griffith cracks.[4] The theory is nonetheless of considerable interest to the engineer: if the size of the cracks could be reduced, the strength of currently available brittle materials would improve in accordance with Eq. (8-8).

The following observation supports this prediction. Freshly drawn filaments of glass and quartz exhibit fracture stresses which approach the theoretical cohesive strength; the smaller the diameter, the closer is the approach. Filaments (also called "whiskers") of other minerals as well as metals exhibit similar behavior. Obviously, the smaller the diameter of a filament, the smaller is the crack it can harbor.

The size of the crack, however, is not the only factor to contend with: the surface tension is equally important. If freshly drawn filaments are exposed to air, they lose strength rapidly, because moisture and oxygen of the air are adsorbed to the surface cracks and reduce their specific surface energy ω; see Section 7-5. Since the phenomenon of adsorption as a rule is accompanied by progressive corrosion, a glass rod subjected to a fraction of its virgin fracture strength will end up by breaking in two if exposed to air for a sufficient length of time. This phenomenon of delayed fracture has also been observed in rocks. It is enhanced by a rise of temperature, but it can be greatly reduced—and even suppressed—in an inert atmosphere. A protective

[4] F. M. Ernsberger, *Proceedings of the Royal Society* (London), **A257**, 213(1960).

coating would seem to be no less effective. This possibility deserves full attention in view of the growing use of mineral bodies, or ceramics, in high-temperature technology. At present, it is still a subject of intense exploration.

8-4 Compressive Versus Tensile Strength. It is an established fact that materials which fail by brittle fracture are stronger in compression than in tension: as a rule about ten times stronger. The greater strength in compression can be justified theoretically: it, too, depends on the critical length of a spontaneously propagating crack. True, cracks normal to the compressive stress cannot be pried open and will not propagate under any circumstances, but in solids, cracks are oriented at random. If the crack is at an angle to the applied compressive force, it is subjected to shear in addition to compression, as a simple analysis of forces will show. There exists a critical length for spontaneous crack propagation in shear as there is in tension. If the shear stress associated with this length is computed in terms of the applied compressive stress, the latter turns out to be eight times larger than the stress computed from Eq. (8-8).[5] Ratios greater than eight—sometimes as high as 50—have been reported for glass. They can perhaps be explained if it is assumed that surface cracks—the most potent sources of fracture—are apt to grow faster normal to the surface, in tension, than at an angle to the surface, in compression, under the influence of atmospheric corrosion.

Whatever the reason, the greater resistance to compressive stresses can be put to good use by increasing the overall load-carrying capacity of a structural element made of a brittle material. This is achieved by prestressing the element during fabrication in such a way that the vulnerable surface is subjected to initial compression. The latter subtracts from the tension imposed by the external loading. The structural element is thus able to sustain greater loads than without the prestress. Current applications of this preventive measure are tempered or safety glass and prestressed concrete. Future applications can be anticipated in ceramic materials for high temperature technology.

8-5 Size Effect. In all circumstances it is the largest crack that constitutes the *weakest link* in brittle fracture. The crack concentration per unit volume is rather immaterial. Statistically, there is greater probability of finding large cracks in a large body than in a small one. Therefore, as a rule, large samples of brittle material fracture at a lower stress (not lower load!) than small ones, just as large communities are more prone to epidemics than small ones. This statistical phenomenon is known as *size effect*. It is an important consideration in design, especially if the design is based on data from scaled-down models.

[5] A. A. Griffith, "The Theory of Rupture," *Proc.* (*First*) *Intern. Congr. Appl. Mech.*, 55(1924).

8-6 Derivation of Griffith's Law. The derivation of Griffith's Law is similar to the derivation made in Section 7-2 in relating surface energy to interatomic forces. It, too, is based on the interplay between the elastic energy accumulated in the body under the applied tensile stress σ and the surface energy of the spreading crack.

To derive the pertinent relationship, consider first that the plate, Fig. 8-3a,

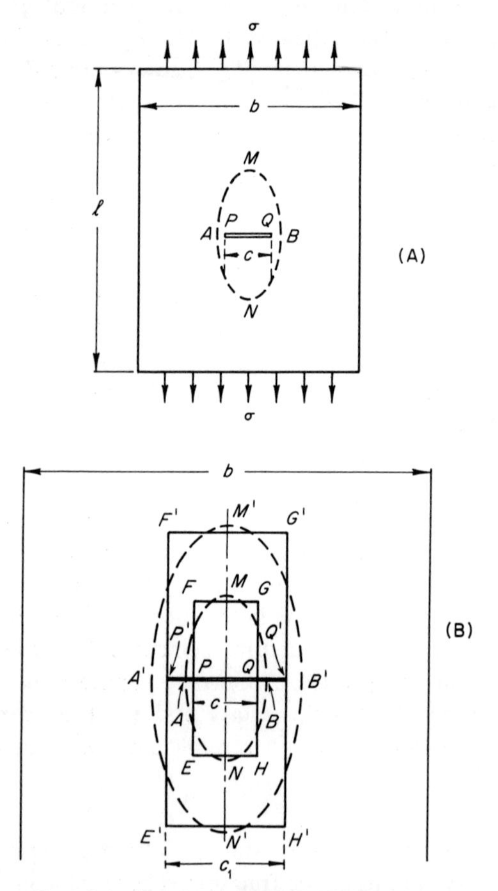

FIG. 8-3 Derivation of Griffith's law

contains no crack. Then the elastic energy W stored under applied stress σ is in accordance with the equation given in Section 6-6:

$$W = \frac{E\varepsilon^2 v}{2} \tag{6-52}$$

where v is the volume of the plate and ε the strain produced by σ. Since

$$\varepsilon = \frac{\sigma}{E}$$

we can substitute σ for ε in Eq. (6-52). This yields

$$W = \frac{\sigma^2 v}{2E} \tag{8-10}$$

However, if the plate does contain a crack, the amount of elastic energy stored under the same conditions is smaller. This can be seen as follows.

Suppose the crack is small compared to l and b and that it cuts all the way across the thickness t. Obviously, the two faces of the crack are free of normal stress. The latter, however, builds up from zero to σ as we proceed inwards and away from the crack. If the line $AMBN$, Fig. 8-3a, represents the boundary beyond which the stress has recovered its full value σ, then the elastic energy U_1 contained in the volume $AMBN$ is

$$U_1 < \frac{\sigma^2}{2E} S_{AMBN} t \tag{8-11}$$

where S_{AMBN} is the area bounded by $AMBN$. We can therefore write that this elastic energy is

$$U_1 = \frac{\alpha\sigma^2}{2E} S_{AMBN} t \tag{8-12}$$

where α is a fraction yet to be determined. The loss U of elastic energy due to the presence of the crack then is

$$U = \frac{(1 - \alpha)\sigma^2}{2E} S_{AMBN} t \tag{8-13}$$

The loss is the greater the larger the crack. More specifically, the loss increases as c^2. This follows from the observation that as long as the crack is small compared to l and b, the shape of the boundary $AMBN$ remains the same whatever c.

To adduce a further proof, consider $AMBN$ and $A'M'B'N'$ corresponding to two different crack lengths c and c_1, Fig. 8-3b. Let $EFGH$ and $E'F'G'H'$ be two rectangles built on c and c_1, respectively, such that

$$S_{AMBN} = EFxc = 2PFxc \tag{8-14}$$

and

$$S_{A'M'B'N'} = E'F'xc' = 2P'F'xc_1 \tag{8-15}$$

Then, by virtue of the fact that $AMBN$ is similar to $A'M'B'N'$, the two rectangles are also similar to each other, or,

$$PF/P'F' = c/c_1 \tag{8-16}$$

Hence, on dividing Eq. (8-14) by Eq. (8-15) and using Eq. (8-16),

$$S_{AMBN}/S_{A'M'B'N'} = c^2/{c_1}^2 \tag{8-17}$$

or, rearranging the terms,

$$S_{AMBN}/c^2 = S_{A'M'B'N'}/{c_1}^2 = \text{constant} \tag{8-18}$$

Finally,

$$S_{AMBN} = \beta c^2 \tag{8-19}$$

where β is the value of the constant in Eq. (8-18), yet to be determined.

Substituting for S_{AMBN} from Eq. (8-19) in Eq. (8-13) we find that the loss of elastic energy due to the presence of the crack c is

$$U = \frac{\beta(1 - \alpha)\sigma^2 c^2 t}{2E} \tag{8-20}$$

It follows that an increase Δc of the crack will bring about a corresponding loss ΔU of the elastic energy. However, it will *also* bring about *an increase* $\Delta \Omega$ of surface energy on the two faces of the crack. According to Eq. (7-15), this increase is proportional to the increase of the area $2t\,\Delta c$ of the two faces; that is,

$$\Delta \Omega = 2\omega t\,\Delta c \tag{8-21}$$

where ω is the specific surface energy.

If the crack is to spread spontaneously—without being helped by the external load—the loss of elastic energy ΔU must be sufficient to provide for the needed increase of surface energy $\Delta \Omega$, i.e.,

$$\Delta U = 2\omega t\,\Delta c \tag{8-22}$$

or

$$\Delta U/\Delta c = 2\omega t \tag{8-23}$$

At the limit,

$$dU/dc = 2\omega t \tag{8-24}$$

or, on differentiating Eq. (8-20) with respect to c,

$$\beta(1 - \alpha)\sigma^2 ct/E = 2\omega t \tag{8-25}$$

Finally, after reduction and rearrangement of terms,

$$\sigma^2 c = \frac{2E\omega}{\beta(1 - \alpha)}$$

or

$$\sigma\sqrt{c} = \sqrt{\frac{2E\omega}{\beta(1 - \alpha)}} \tag{8-26}$$

The expression on the right-hand side contains E and ω, which are constant for a given material. The coefficient $2/\beta(1 - \alpha)$ can be either determined experimentally or computed using a more involved derivation. Its value is $4/\pi$. Equation (8-26) then becomes

$$\sigma\sqrt{c} = \sqrt{4E\omega/\pi}$$

which is Eq. (8-8), written previously.

8-7 Summary. Solids exhibit brittle behavior when they deform elastically almost up to the breaking point. The amount of deformation is small, and the stress at fracture is several orders of magnitude lower than the computed cohesive strength.

The loss of strength is ascribed to a characteristic defect in solids: the presence of minute cracks, presumably formed during solidification. The tensile stress under which the largest of these cracks begins to propagate spontaneously—thus causing failure—is then shown to be of the right order of magnitude compared to the theoretical cohesive strength.

Compressive stress can also induce spontaneous crack propagation at an angle to the applied force through its shear component. The magnitude of the stress, however, is about 10 times larger than in tension. The greater resistance to compression is utilized to increase the load-carrying capacity of a structural element by precompressing it or a part of it during fabrication.

Considerable improvement of resistance occurs when the size of the crack is reduced, as in filaments, or whiskers. An important weakening agent in this case, as in other cases, becomes then the reduction of specific surface energy by atmospheric contamination. Future applications of ceramic materials in high-temperature technology are predicated on the ability to cope with this twofold problem: internal cracks and surface damage.

References

ELEMENTARY

1. J. P. Frankel, *Principles of the Properties of Materials*, McGraw-Hill, New York, 1957.

ADVANCED

1. A. A. Griffith, "The Phenomena of Rupture and Flow in Solids," *Phil. Trans. Roy. Soc.* **A221**, 163, 1920.
2. "Fracture," *Proc., Intern. Conf.*, Technology, M.I.T., Cambridge, Mass., and Wiley, New York, 1959.
3. C. Gurney, "The Effect of Surface Conditions on the Strength of Brittle Materials," Monograph 13, *Properties of Metal Surfaces*, Institute of Metals, London, 1953.
4. *Structure and Properties of Solid Surfaces*, monograph, R. Gomer and C. S. Smith, Eds., U. of Chicago, 1953.

Problems

8-1 Compute the brittle fracture strength of NaCl on the assumption that the incipient cracks are about 10,000 Å long.

8-2 If the delayed fracture of glass is ascribed to the growth of a surface crack, what is the rate of growth necessary to bring about a delayed fracture, after 10 days, under a stress of 5000 lb/in.^{2}, if freshly annealed glass breaks at 20,000 lb/in.^{2}? (Note: Use Eq. (8-8) and assume a constant specific energy.)

8-3 Glass does not manifest delayed fracture in a vacuum. Why?

8-4 An external metallic thin-walled cylinder is shrouded on a ceramic thin-walled cylinder so as to subject the latter to the maximum compressive strength. How much can the internal pressure be increased in comparison to the maximum pressure the ceramic container can sustain without the external backing?

9 / MECHANICAL PROPERTIES: PLASTICITY

Growth of incipient cracks was shown in Chapter 8 to be responsible for the brittle behavior of solids. In this chapter another type of structural defect—already encountered in Chapter 3 and called dislocation—is held responsible for their plastic behavior. We shall describe the characteristic manifestations of the attending plastic deformation, discuss the basic assumptions regarding its origin, and show how these assumptions account for the observable plastic properties of crystalline solids.

9-1 Manifestations. Slip and Slip Lines. We pointed out in Chapter 6 that small deformations follow Hooke's law and are recoverable. Experiments show that, except for the deformations characterizing the rubbery behavior of polymers, only small deformations are recoverable. Most solids either fracture in a brittle manner or exhibit a drastic change in the *mode* of deformation when the strain exceeds the order of 0.1%. In the latter case, the strain ceases to be proportional to stress, and the deformation does not disappear when the load is removed. The body undergoes a permanent change of shape. It can thus be reshaped to suit a particular purpose, especially when its form can be substantially altered without causing fracture. This is essentially a characteristic of the so-called plastic bodies, like baker's dough, wax, clay, etc. These bodies will be shown in Chapter 12 to be either not truly solid or not truly crystalline. However, the same general type of deformation is encountered in truly crystalline solids like metals. Hence the name *plastic deformation* is given to both manifestations. We shall find that the underlying process is also the same in both cases. It consists of a *slip*, or glide, of one part of the body over the other. However, the similarity is more formal than basic. In crystalline solids the slip mechanism is largely determined by the nature and stability of the crystal structure.

Experiments show that with the onset of plastic deformation a single metal crystal, such as a crystal of aluminum, subjected to axial pull, splits in several parts gliding over each other in the manner depicted schematically in Fig. 9-1, a and b. The axial tension also produces a change in the interatomic distances. This change is so small compared to slip, however, that it can be overlooked when describing the mechanism of plastic deformation.

As a rule, metals having close-packed structures slip on the densest crystallographic planes, which are the basal planes in HCP crystals and the octahedral planes in FCC crystals. Similarly, the direction in which slip occurs is

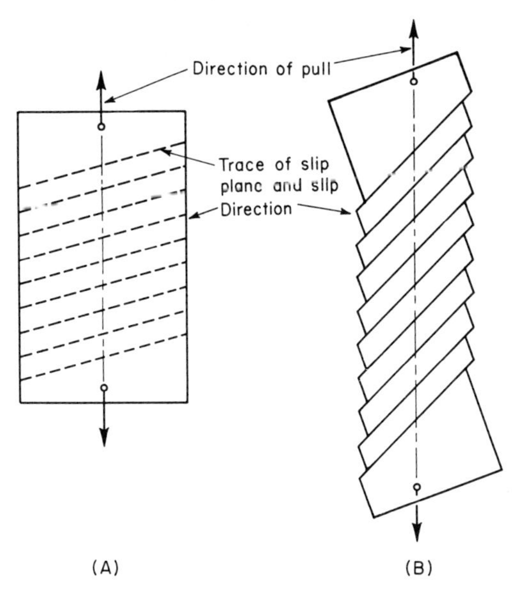

FIG. 9-1 Slip in single metal crystal subjected to axial tension (schematic): (a) specimen and slip planes before slip; (b) specimen and slip planes after slip

the densest crystallographic direction in the slip plane. In HCP crystals it is one of the base diagonals; in FCC crystals it is one of the face diagonals. Metals possessing BCC structure also slip in the densest direction, along the body diagonal, but the plane containing this direction is not necessarily the densest crystallographic plane.

The onset of plastic deformation in a polycrystalline aggregate is manifested by the appearance of a grating of parallel lines called *slip lines* covering the polished face of a grain. The slip lines stop at the grain boundary, Fig. 9-2, suggesting that the grating is the trace of slip planes cutting the polished surface of the specimen. Observations by means of electron microscope indicate that what appears under an ordinary microscope as a line is in reality a slip band made up of several slip planes, a few hundred atomic distances apart and displaced thousands of atomic distances with respect to each other, as shown schematically in Fig. 9-3. The slip bands themselves are separated by crystal blocks containing about 10,000 crystallographic planes on which no slip has taken place. To say it differently, at the start of plastic deformation only about 0.1% of the crystallographic planes of the same family are involved in slip. This is quite at variance with elastic deformation, in which all crystallographic planes participate from the very beginning, as explained in Section 6-3. Like nucleation and grain growth, Chapter 3, the onset of plastic deformation appears to be a local event. The presumption is that here, too, a defect of crystal structure provides the necessary stimulus. This presumption is strongly supported by the analysis of slip in a perfect crystal.

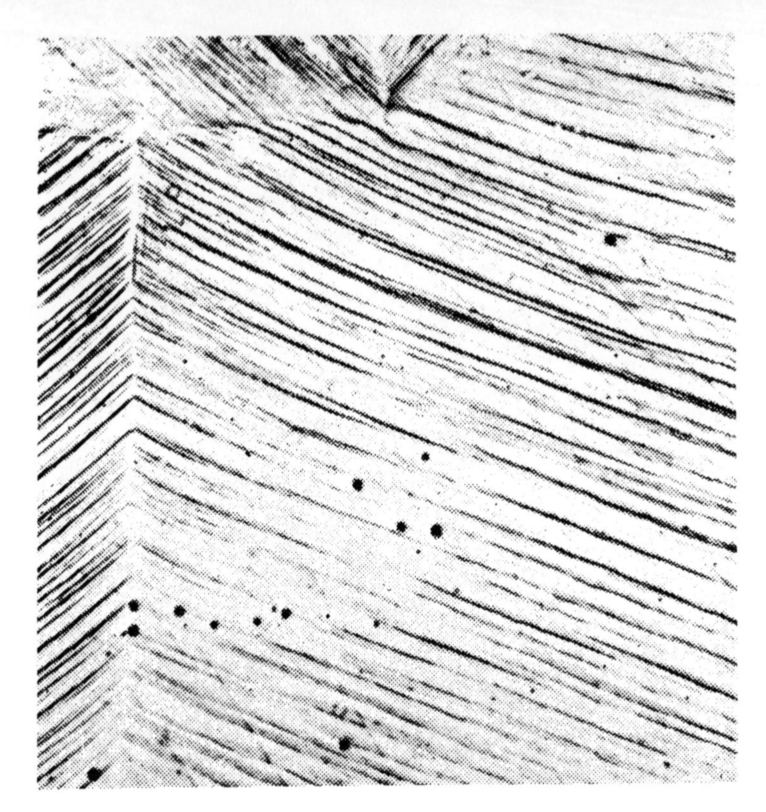

FIG. 9-2 Slip lines in grains of an actual polycrystalline specimen. (From R. S. Williams and V. O. Homerberg, *Principles of Metallography*, McGraw-Hill, New York, 1939. Used by permission)

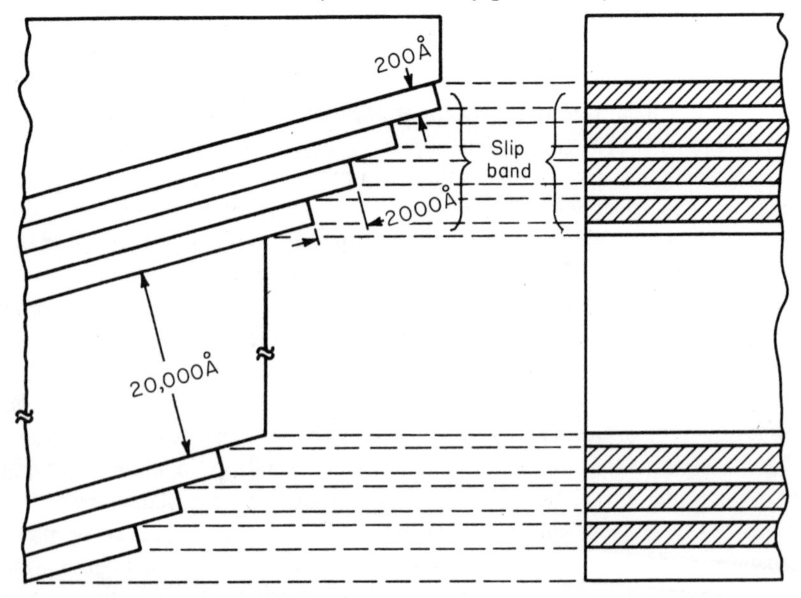

FIG. 9-3 Slip bands as viewed under an electron microscope (schematic). The atomic distance is taken here as 2 Å

9-2 Slip in a Perfect Crystal. Consider first one layer of atoms in a close-packed crystal structure, Fig. 9-4a. Suppose the atoms behave like hard, frictionless spheres. (As will appear below, this assumption makes our

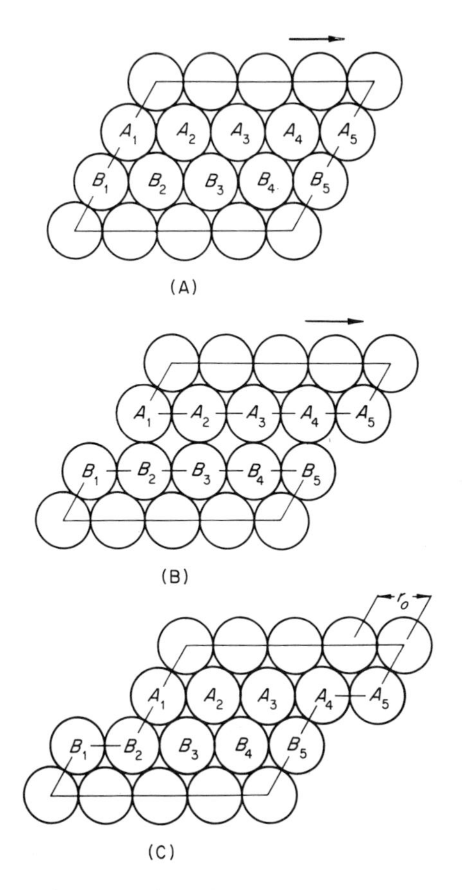

FIG. 9-4 Slip in a perfect two-dimensional close-packed crystal: (a) before slip; (b) during slip; (c) after slip

estimates more conservative.) To have one portion of this layer slip past the other, the last row of atoms of the upper portion—atoms *A*—must be lifted atop the underlying row of atoms *B*, as shown in Fig. 9-4b. Once in this position, atoms *A* will slide down spontaneously into their new troughs between atoms *B*, Fig. 9-4c. The upper portion would thus have slipped exactly one atomic distance in the densest direction. This is the distance of the closest approach, r_0.

In the process of lifting, a force applied in the direction of slip must overcome the attraction *N* exerted on each atom *A*. It must thus do work in half of the atomic distance, $r_0/2$, Fig. 9-5. Let *T* be the force applied to atom *A* and let y be the corresponding displacement. Then the work w done in $r_0/2$ is

$$w = \int_0^{(1/2)r_0} T\,dy \tag{9-1}$$

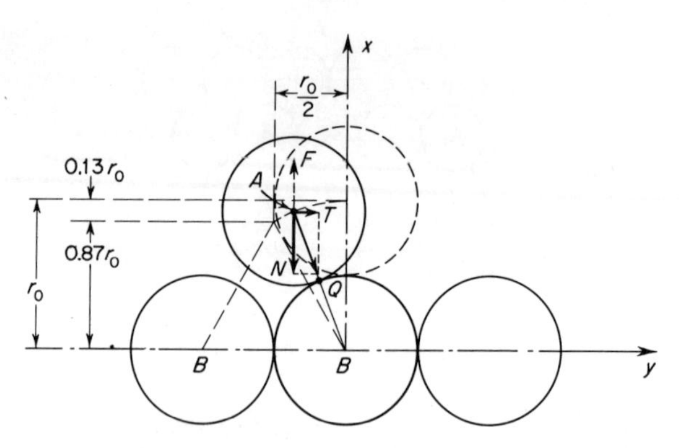

FIG. 9-5 Forces acting on an atom during slip (schematic)

This work is exactly the same as the work a force F, opposing the attraction N, would have done by pulling atom A up to level r_0 from level $0.87r_0$. (This follows from the fact that the resultant of T and N does no work, since it passes through the point of contact Q between the atoms A and B and is perpendicular to the path taken by A. Hence the sum of works done by its components T and N is also nil.) Let x be the displacement in the direction of F. Then

$$w = \int_0^{0.13r_0} F\,dx \tag{9-2}$$

Comparison of Eq. (9-1) and Eq. (9-2) yields

$$\int_0^{(1/2)r_0} T\,dy = \int_0^{0.13r_0} F\,dx \tag{9-3}$$

In what follows we will be interested only in the average value T_{av} of T. We can therefore rewrite Eq. (9-3) to read

$$\tfrac{1}{2}r_0 T_{av} = \int_0^{0.13r_0} F\,dx \tag{9-4}$$

If the force of attraction obeyed Hooke's law, we also could write (see Eq. (6-49), Chapter 6)

$$F = Kx$$

and by Eqs. (6-25) and (6-51),

$$\tfrac{1}{2}r_0 T_{av} = \frac{ES(\Delta l)^2}{2l_0} \tag{9-5}$$

Here, E is the Young's modulus in the x direction, S is the area over which F

acts, $\Delta l = 0.13r_0$, and $l_0 = 0.87r_0$. Since T_{av} acts over the same area S, we can define

$$\tau_{av} = \frac{T_{av}}{S} \tag{9-6}$$

as the average stress necessary to shear the close-packed aggregate, Fig. 9-4a, in the densest crystallographic direction. We would thus get, after substituting for T_{av} in Eq. (9-5) the quantities from Eq. (9-6), expressing Δl and l_0 in terms of r_0 and reducing the terms,

$$\tau_{av} = \frac{(0.13)^2}{0.87} E$$

or, in round figures,

$$\tau_{av} = 0.02E \tag{9-7}$$

However, the validity of Hooke's law for displacements as large as $0.13r_0$ is seriously in doubt. According to Fig. 7-2, the forces of attraction increase less than proportionally to these displacements, and the corresponding work is smaller than the expression, Eq. (9-5). Thus the value of $0.02E$ must be considered as an upper bound for τ_{av}.

Note. We can also estimate the lower bound by observing that the greatest deviation from proportionality occurs at the attainment of the cohesive force f_{max}, at point M of Fig. 7-2. For an ionic bonding, f_{max} is given by Eq. (7-5). Assuming f_{max} has been reached when atom A was lifted from equilibrium level $0.87r_0$ to level r_0, we can evaluate the corresponding repulsion exponent m by substituting $k = r_0/0.87r_0 = 1.15$ in Eq. (7-4). This yields $m = 15$. The work against the forces of attraction is now given by Eq. (7-10). On substituting for $0.29z^2me^2$ the expression including E_0 from Eq. (6-28), and recalling that the equilibrium distance of separation in the x direction is $0.87r_0$ rather than r_0 we get

$$w = 0.0043E_0r_0^3 \tag{9-8}$$

Since this is less than the actual work done by T_{av} we can write, using Eq. (9-4),

$$\tfrac{1}{2}r_0T_{av} > 0.0043E_0r_0^3 \tag{9-9}$$

Substituting for T_{av} from Eq. (9-6) and recalling that the area S assigned to atom A in close-packed crystal structures is $0.87r_0^2$, we finally obtain

$$\tau_{av} > 0.01E_0$$

also, since $E_0 > E$,

$$\tau_{av} > 0.01E \tag{9-10}$$

Admittedly, this computation was made for a hypothetical ionic crystal. However, the method has nothing to do with the nature of bonding. It is merely a mathematical device to fit a curve of the type represented by Eq. (6-9) to specified values of f and its derivative df/dr. To the extent that these values sufficiently characterize the behavior of the hypothetical crystal, the right-hand expression in inequality (9-10) represents a lower bound of τ_{av}.

We conclude that, for an order of magnitude estimate, the average shear stress necessary to initiate slip in a perfect close-packed crystal can be taken as 1.5% of E. The same order of magnitude can be reasonably expected in three-dimensional perfect crystals.

9-3 Slip in an Imperfect Crystal. Dislocations. Experiments show that slip in actual single crystals of metals begins under a shear stress that is at least two orders of magnitude lower than the value of 1.5%E computed for a perfect crystal. This fact, coupled with the local onset of plastic deformation mentioned in Section 9-1, makes it plausible that slip should be due to local imperfections of crystal structure. To study the nature of these imperfections we resort to a plane model of hard balls. A layer of such balls is drawn in Fig. 9-6a. The configuration is almost, but not quite, close-packed. Looking at the rows of balls A and B, we notice that ball A_1 fits exactly in the hollow between B_1 and B_2. So would any ball preceding A_1, if the sketch were extended to the left. In like manner, ball A_7 fits exactly in the hollow between B_8 and B_9, and so would any ball following A_7, if the sketch were continued to the right. At the approach to the center, however, there is a growing misfit, because row B has one ball more than row A between pairs A_1B_1 and A_7B_8. This fact is also emphasized by the extra row of balls such as $B_5C_5D_5\ldots$, aligned with one or the other densest direction that is not a direction of slip. The misfit is greatest at the end of the extra row, where ball A_4 is atop ball B_5. This kind of misfit is generally called a dislocation. As shown later, the screw dislocation described in Chapter 3 is but one of the many possible configurations such a misfit can assume in real crystals. They all share one common characteristic: they can be viewed as a defect of crystal structure resulting from a *partial* shear movement. This has been shown to be true of the screw dislocation, and it applies equally well to our present model.

The occurrence of a partial shear movement is clearly indicated in Fig. 9-6a. Assuming the upper part of the aggregate slips in the direction of the arrow, it is seen that ball A_7 has already slipped past ball B_8 and has taken up a new position of equilibrium to the right. So have balls A_8 and A_9. On the other hand, ball A_1 is still in its original site prior to slip, to the left of B_2, and the same would apply to all balls preceding A_1 if the sketch were extended in that direction. Thus, the dislocation separates the sheared portion of the row of balls A from the unsheared portion.

To explain next how such a structural defect can induce slip to occur at a much lower shear stress than the theoretical value of 1.5%E, we observe that if all balls A were atop balls B, as in Fig. 9-4b, no stress would be necessary to achieve slip. The slip would start spontaneously and involve the entire row of balls A at the same time. Thereafter, however, the balls would simultaneously reach new positions of stable equilibrium, and to resume slip, a shear stress of the theoretical magnitude would be necessary.

The situation is quite different in the presence of a dislocation. In Fig. 9-6a

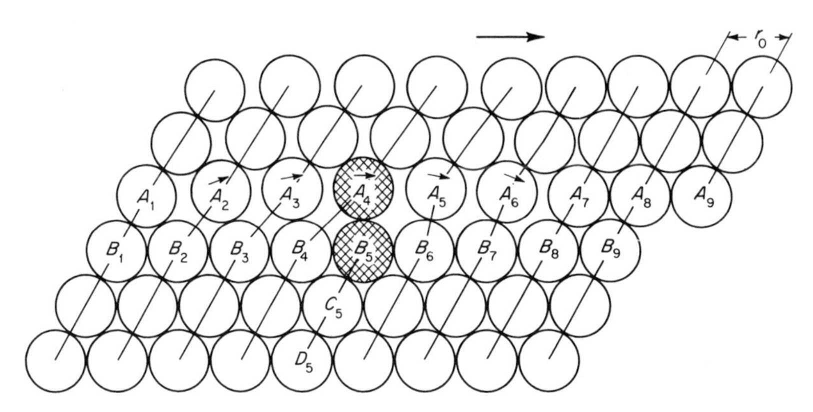

FIG. 9-6a Slip in a plane model containing a dislocation. Position of the dislocation before slip

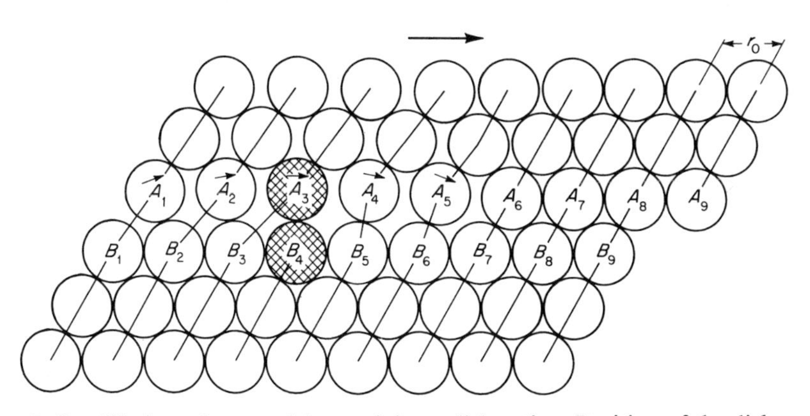

FIG. 9-6b Slip in a plane model containing a dislocation. Position of the dislocation after slip of one atomic movement

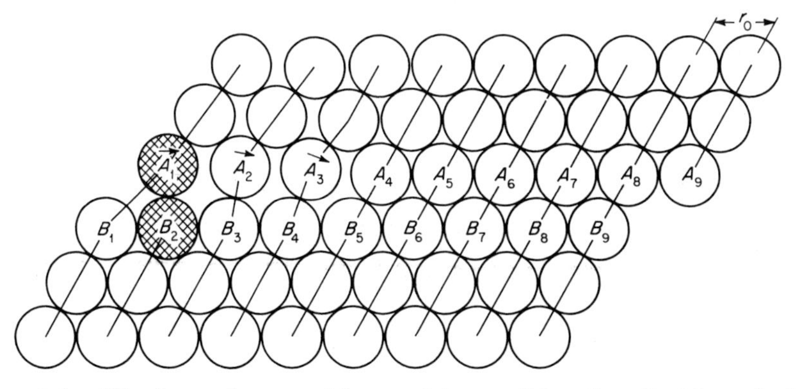

FIG. 9-6c Slip in a plane model containing a dislocation. Position of the dislocation before leaving the crystal

only one ball—A_4—is atop another ball. Balls A_5 and A_6 are already on their way down, and balls A_2 and A_3 are still on their way up. The process of slip is now progressive and local instead of going on simultaneously everywhere. In the example of Fig. 9-6a it is confined to five balls in the row. Moreover, every ball moves in steps of $r_0/6$ instead of $r_0/2$, as is true for a perfect close-packed aggregate. At each step the dislocation moves one atomic distance to the left, involving the next pair of balls, A_3 and B_4 in Fig. 9-6b. It thus reaches the last pair to the left, A_1 and B_2 in Fig. 9-6c, whereupon it moves completely out of the aggregate. Every ball A has now slipped past the underlying ball B and has slid down into a new position of stable equilibrium. Row A has undergone a complete shear movement, and the upper portion of the aggregate has been displaced exactly one atomic distance r_0 to the right. The final configuration is now the same as for the perfect aggregate, Fig. 6-4c. The shear stress needed for this process, however, is much smaller. At worst, if each ball had to be lifted individually without assistance from its neighbors, the force would be one-third of that computed for the perfect aggregate.[1] At best, if the balls were linked and rolled without friction, no force would be required, since the momentum of the balls rolling downward would suffice to lift the balls moving upward over the hump and keep the process going.

Neither of these extremes applies to real atoms. In the model of Fig. 9-6a, some of the balls in the upper rows are seen to be loose and held apart from each other. In real atoms, forces of attraction would intervene to close the gaps. By doing so they would squeeze the close-packed lower rows of atoms, giving rise to antagonistic repulsive forces. The deformation would be the greatest near the dislocation, as depicted schematically in Fig. 9-7.

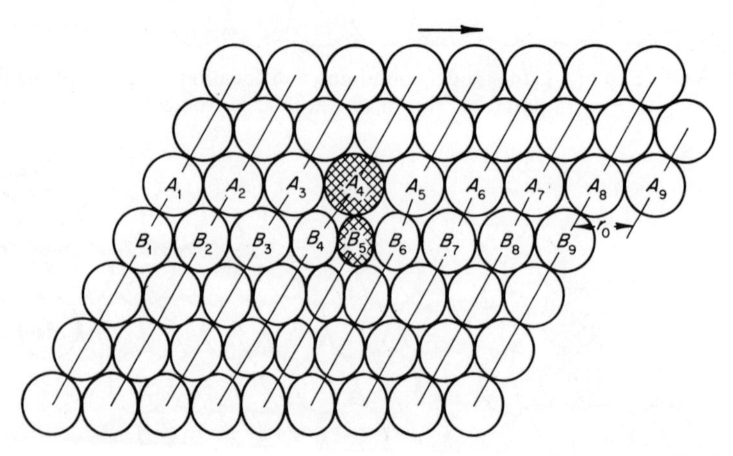

FIG. 9-7 Extension and compression around a dislocation, due to attractive and repulsive forces

[1] In Eq. (9-5) both r_0 and Δl are to be divided by 3. However, Δl is squared, so the value of T_{av} must also be divided by 3.

A model approximating this behavior rather closely has been made using a soap bubble raft.[2] The soap bubbles adhere to each other by virtue of surface tension, discussed in Chapter 7. Moreover, they are relatively soft and deformable. The deformation attending a dislocation produced in such a raft can be recognized by careful inspection of the photograph, Fig. 9-8.

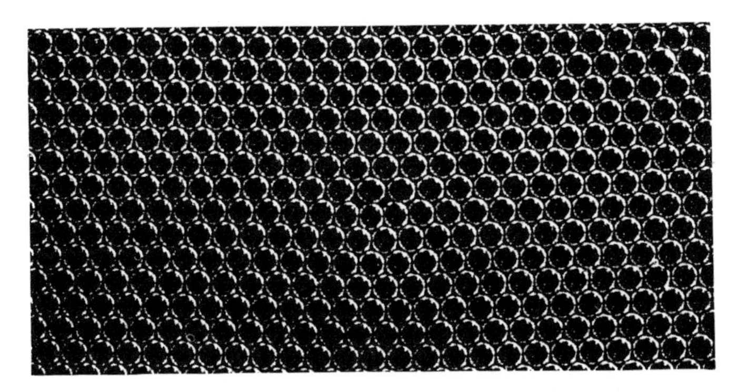

FIG. 9-8 Photograph of a bubble raft containing a dislocation in the center. (Sir Lawrence Bragg and J. F. Nye, *Proc. Roy. Soc.*, **A**, 190)

A rather involved computation, which we must omit, shows that the interplay between the attractive and repulsive forces caused by the deformation locks the dislocation in its position every time one of the atoms is exactly atop the other. A finite shear stress is then necessary to keep the dislocation moving. Under simplifying assumptions the magnitude of this stress has been found to be of the order of magnitude given by the results, Section 9-6.[3]

The validity of the dislocation model for plastic deformation does not rest solely on the above argument. It is based primarily on direct observation of the motion of dislocations, particularly by electron microscopy in thin metal foils. To provide the necessary background for these observations, we turn from the plane model, Fig. 9-6, to real three-dimensional crystals.

In a three-dimensional structure, the pair of sliding rows of atoms A and B is replaced by a pair of slip planes, and the sheared portion of each plane is separated from the unsheared portion by a line—the *dislocation line*. In Fig. 9-9a we have sketched the lower of the two slip planes in a close-packed crystal structure. It is generally one of the densest planes. For clarity, the upper slip plane is identified only by dots representing the positions of the centers of atoms. In the equilibrium position these dots match the centers of hollows formed by three contiguous underlying atoms, for example, point A_7 in Fig. 9-9a. We see that between the matched pairs of upper and lower rows of atoms a_1b_1 and a_7b_8 there is one row of atoms more in the lower slip plane

[2] W. L. Bragg and J. F. Nye, *Proc. Roy. Soc.* (*London*), **A190**, 474(1947).

[3] See, for example, A. H. Cottrell, *Dislocations and Plastic Flow in Crystals*, Clarendon (Oxford U.P.), New York, 1953.

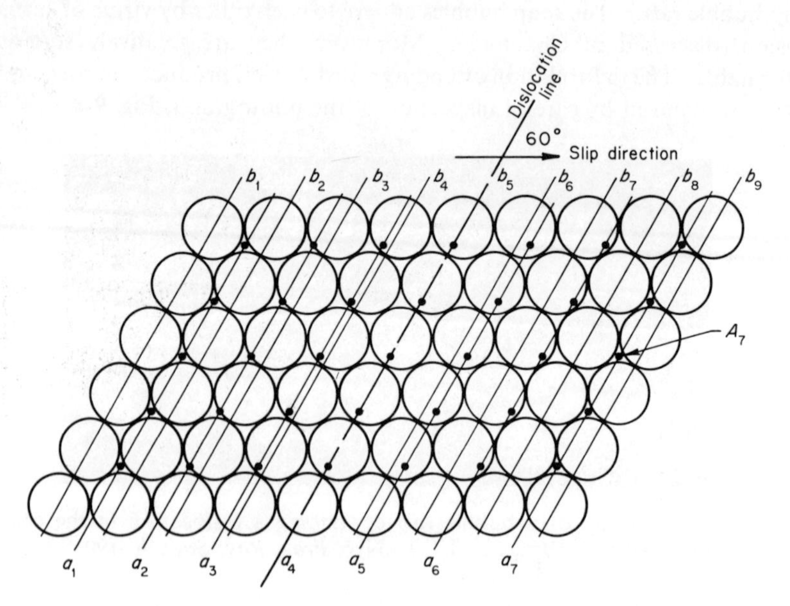

FIG. 9-9a Dislocation line in a three-dimensional close-packed structure. Dislocation line at 60° to the slip direction

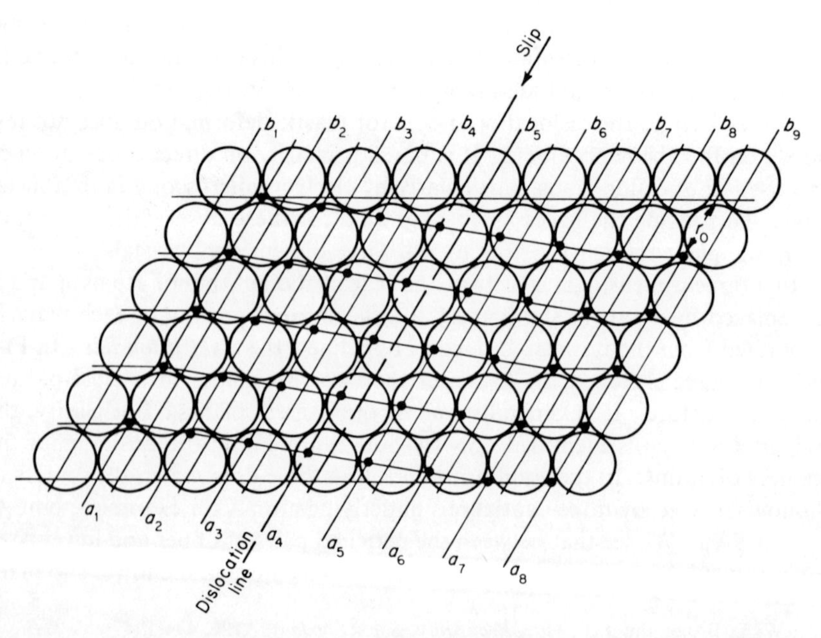

FIG. 9-9b Dislocation line in a three-dimensional close-packed structure. Dislocation line parallel to the slip direction (screw dislocation)

than in the upper slip plane. This causes a mismatch of the upper and lower rows of atoms that are between a_1b_1 and b_8a_7. The greatest mismatch occurs in the center, where the upper row a_4 rides on top of the lower row b_5. Again, as with the model in Fig. 9-6, we can view the mismatch between rows a_4 and b_5 as a defect of crystal structure—*a dislocation line*—resulting from a partial shear movement. In particular, with the direction of slip indicated by the arrow, row a_7 and all rows to the right are seen to have already slipped past the underlying rows of atoms and settled down into their new positions of equilibrium, while row a_1 and all rows to the left are still in their original positions, prior to slip.[4] The width between a_1 and a_7 is called the *width* of the dislocation line. According to current observations, this width is of the order of 10 atomic distances, r_0, for most metals.

In Fig. 9-9a the dislocation line coincides with one of the densest directions and makes an angle of 60° with the direction of slip. There is nothing unique in either this orientation or this angle. In Fig. 9-9b the direction of slip is aligned with the dislocation in the same densest direction of slip. The distances between the rows in the upper and lower slip plane are now unchanged, but the atoms of rows a_2b_2 to a_6b_6 between a_1b_1 and a_7b_7 are mismatched. The greatest mismatch occurs again between the atoms of rows a_4 and b_5. The partial shear movement which produces this mismatch is identical to that described in Chapter 3. It, too, results in a screw. We conclude that a screw dislocation is by definition aligned with the direction of slip. A dislocation line perpendicular to the direction of slip is called an *edge dislocation*. These particular configurations are convenient for mathematical analysis, but in real crystals they are neither typical nor frequent. The dislocation line can have any shape and orientation in the slip plane. Its only defining characteristic is that it separates the sheared portion from the unsheared portion of the slip plane. Several such dislocations are shown in Fig. 9-10.

9-4 Twinning. One of the most noteworthy features of the slip mechanism is that it leaves the configuration of atoms unchanged, even though the atoms in the slip planes have changed partners. At variance with this mechanism, there exists in nature another type of plastic deformation, which modifies the configuration of atoms by transforming the sheared portion of the crystal into a mirror image of the unsheared portion, as shown in Fig. 9-11. Such a deformation is called *twinning*. Twinning is infrequent in cubic metal crystals, particularly in FCC, but is rather common in other metal crystals and in minerals. We utilize the FCC as an example because here the mechanism of twinning is relatively simple.

As in the case of Fig. 9-9, we sketch one of the densest planes, Fig. 9-11a, and mark the superimposed plane by means of dots. The sketch is tilted with

[4] The argument remains the same, if the direction of slip is reversed, or if we consider the motion of the lower slip plane with respect to the upper one, rather than vice versa.

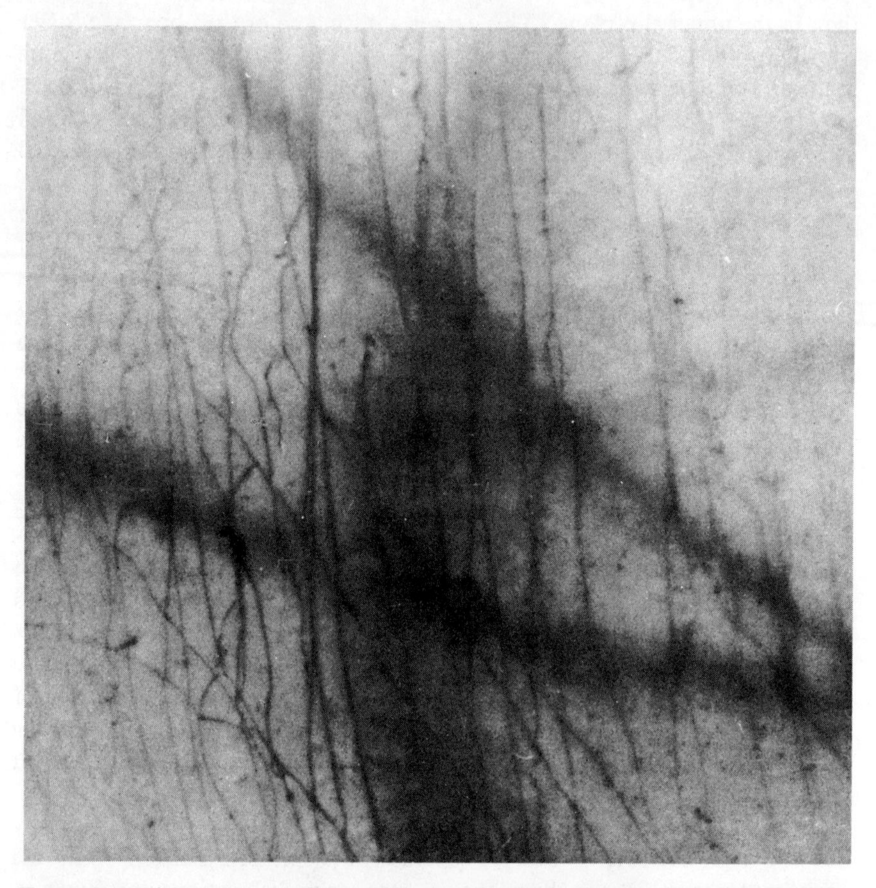

FIG. 9-10 Dislocations in bent beryllium specimen. (Courtesy S. Gelles, Nuclear Metals, Inc., Massachusetts; and F. Wilhelm, The Franklin Institute Laboratories, Contract No. AF 33 (616)–7065)

respect to Fig. 9-9 so that the line bisecting the angle between two densest directions is horizontal. The visualization of the twin mechanism is thereby made more easy in the vertical projection, Fig. 9-11b.

In the process of slip, the atoms move in the slip direction by one atomic distance, *MN*, as symbolized by the dots. However, the point *N* can also be reached from *M* in two steps, *MP* and *PN*, instead of one. If the atoms are pictured as rigid spheres, they will be climbing over barriers in the *MP* and *PN* directions that are lower than in the *MN* direction. There is reason to believe that this is the way they actually move. For, if the application of the force is very brief, as in explosive loading, the atoms get stuck half way in positions such as *P*, symbolized by open circles. The process, however, does not end there. The explosive wave passing through all upper layers will shear each of them in succession, with respect to the one below, by exactly the same

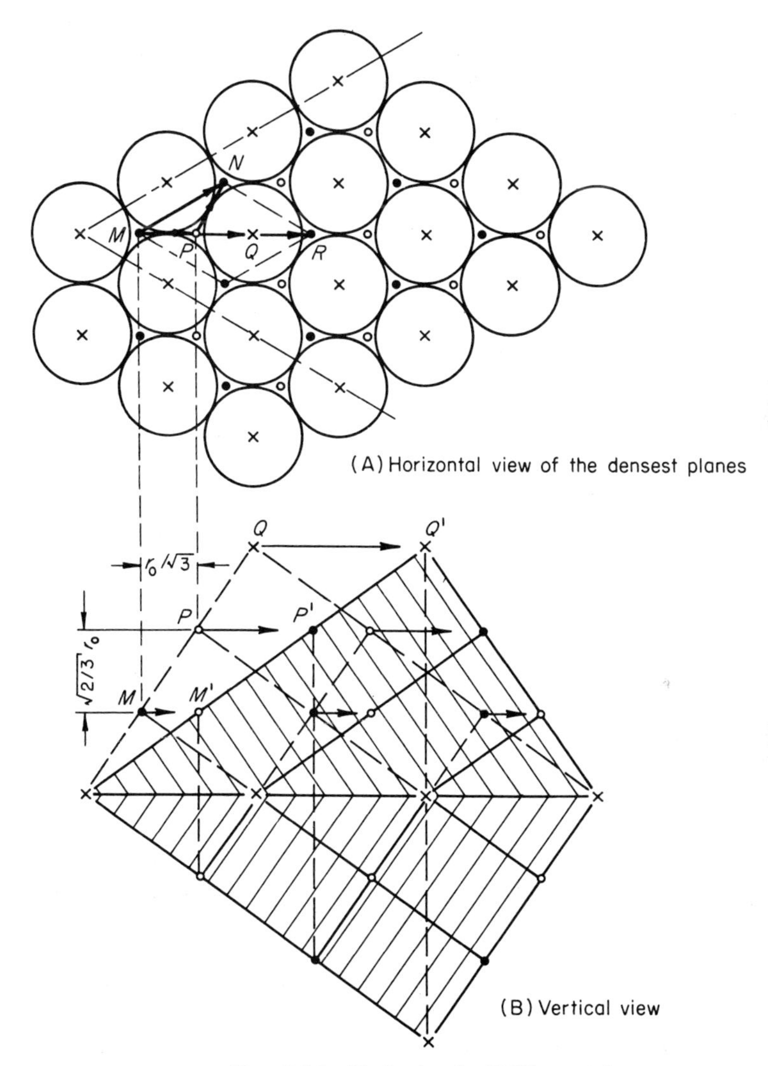

FIG. 9-11 Twinning in FCC crystal

amount and in the same direction. This is indicated by the arrows issued from points M, P, and Q, Fig. 9-11, a and b. Since each of the layers is carried in addition on the back of the one below, the final position of atoms symbolized by points M, P, and Q is indicated by M', P', and Q', Fig. 9-11b. We see that in its final position each of the atoms mirrors its opposite number in the unsheared portion of the crystal. The same, of course, is true of other atoms and all crystallographic directions and planes. The whole sheared portion becomes a mirror image, or a *twin*, of the unsheared portion. The cross-hatching in Fig. 9-11b serves to emphasize this particular aspect of twinning.

Because of difference in orientation, a twinned segment of a crystal reflects light at a different angle than the untwinned background. It can thus be easily identified under the microscope as a distinct band in a grain of a suitably etched specimen, Fig. 9-12.

FIG. 9-12 Twin bands in a gold-silver alloy subjected to explosive loading. (By permission from *Trans. AIME*, **221**, Feb. 1961, and courtesy A. S. Appleton, G. E. Dieter, and M. B. Bever)

Twinning of a perfect crystal would require a theoretical shear stress of the same order of magnitude as slip. The presumption is that here, too, dislocations are instrumental in initiating plastic deformation at the low stress levels observable experimentally. This presumption is no less valid than in the case of slip. However, the mechanism of twinning has been studied far less extensively than slip in relation to macroscopically measurable quantities in engineering applications. For that reason the following sections deal only with the slip mechanism, even though most of the conclusions apply qualitatively to twinning.

9-5 Distinctive Properties of Plastic Deformation. Regardless of its nature and its own direction of motion, any dislocation which has completely moved out of the crystal produces a shear displacement of one part of the crystal over the other in the direction of slip of exactly one atomic distance. This, in the case of the densest crystallographic direction, is the distance of the closest approach r_0. To account for the observed slip of about 1000 atomic distances, Fig. 9-3, at least that many dislocations must have moved out of the same slip plane. (The origin of so many dislocations is taken up briefly in Section 9-10.) This circumstance, coupled with the mechanism described in Section 9-3, accounts for three distinctive properties of the plastic deformation as opposed to the elastic deformation: its *magnitude*, its *permanence*, and its *absence of volume changes*.

1. The magnitude of plastic deformation is still considerable, even if only one out of 10,000 atomic planes is involved in the slip (as suggested in Fig. 9-3). The strain easily reaches 10% and more, instead of the 0.1% attainable by the elastic strain.

2. With the passage of each dislocation, the atoms which were in a condition of stable equilibrium prior to slip find themselves again in a condition of stable equilibrium in their new sites after slip. There is no tendency to recovery, and the deformation is permanent.

3. Finally, the new sites have the same configuration with the same atomic distances as the old sites. Hence there is no change of volume. To be more specific, the volume remains constant at the onset of plastic deformation only in single crystals where the motion of dislocations is largely unhampered. In later stages of plastic deformations and in polycrystalline aggregates, deviations from the simple mechanism of slip account for small changes of volume. (Some of the deviations are discussed in Section 9-13.) They are, however, less than 0.1%, and they can be practically overlooked in most if not all current applications.

9-6 Tension of Single Metal Crystals. Most of the basic information regarding plastic deformation in crystals has been secured by subjecting rods of single metal crystals to axial tension. The results of the tests also provide a basis for the prediction of plastic behavior of the currently utilized polycrystalline aggregates. An important feature of these tests is the *rotation* which the sliding portions of the crystal undergo under the application of an axial force.

Let a and b, Fig. 9-13a, be two adjacent blocks into which the specimen, Fig. 9-1a, has split at the onset of plastic deformation. Let F and F' be the tensile forces applied at both ends of the specimen and transferred to the centroids A_0 and B_0 of the blocks. After the blocks have slipped a small amount s, Fig. 9-13b, the two forces are no longer aligned. They form a force couple which causes the blocks to *rotate* as they slip a small angle around one of the centroids, say B_0. The rotation brings the forces F and F' back into alignment, but the distance B_0A_1 between centroids is now larger than B_0A_0, Fig. 9-13c. Since the same is true of every pair of blocks, the whole specimen has become larger in the axial direction. The axial elongation and the rotation are functions of the amount of slip s.

The pertinent relationships are most simple when the direction of pull O_0x

lies in the plane formed by the slip direction O_0T and the normal O_0N to the slip plane, Fig. 9-13a.

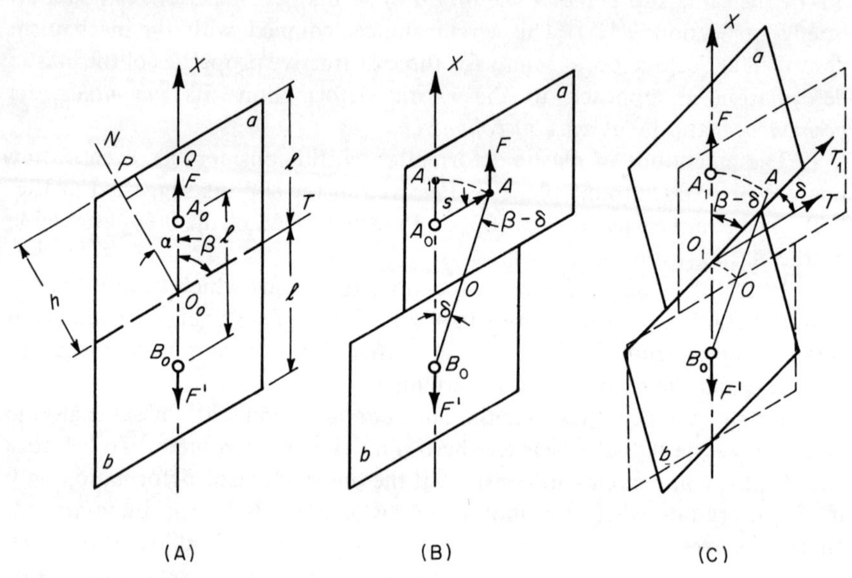

FIG. 9-13 Rotation during axial tension of single crystals: (a) before slip; (b) slip, no rotation; (c) slip and rotation

Assuming all three lie in the plane of the paper, we have from triangle B_0A_0A, with the notations given in Fig. 9-13, a and b,

$$\frac{\sin \delta}{\sin (\beta - \delta)} = \frac{A_0A}{B_0A_0} = \frac{s}{l} \tag{9-11}$$

Since δ is a small angle,

$$\sin \delta \approx \delta, \tag{9-12}$$

$$\sin (\beta - \delta) \approx \sin \beta \tag{9-13}$$

and, consequently, to a second-order approximation,

$$\boxed{\delta = \frac{s}{l} \sin \beta} \tag{9-14}$$

In like manner we can write, from the same triangle B_0A_0A,

$$\frac{B_0A}{B_0A_0} = \frac{\sin (180 - \beta)}{\sin (\beta - \delta)} = \frac{\sin \beta}{\sin (\beta - \delta)} \tag{9-15}$$

But

$$B_0A = B_0A_1 \tag{9-16}$$

and

$$B_0A_1 - B_0A_0 = \Delta l \tag{9-17}$$

where Δl is the increase of length in the axial direction. Using Eqs. (9-16) and (9-17) in Eq. (9-15), we have

$$\frac{\Delta l + l}{l} = \frac{\sin \beta}{\sin (\beta - \delta)} \tag{9-18}$$

Hence,

$$\frac{\Delta l}{l} + 1 = \frac{\sin \beta}{\sin (\beta - \delta)}$$

and

$$\frac{\Delta l}{l} = \frac{\sin \beta - \sin (\beta - \delta)}{\sin (\beta - \delta)} = \frac{2 \sin (\delta/2) \cos (\beta - \delta/2)}{\sin (\beta - \delta)}$$

Using again the small angle approximation for δ and putting $\Delta l/l = \varepsilon$ we obtain

$$\varepsilon = \frac{\delta \cos \beta}{\sin \beta} \tag{9-19}$$

or, in view of Eq. (9-14),

$$\varepsilon = \frac{s}{l} \cos \beta \tag{9-20}$$

Instead of l, it is more convenient to use the distance h separating the planes of slip, since then, by definition,

$$\frac{s}{h} = \gamma \tag{9-21}$$

where γ is the shear strain in the slip direction. We have, from triangle O_0PQ, Fig. 9-13a,

$$h = l \cos \alpha, \tag{9-22}$$

and, using Eqs. (9-21) and (9-22) in Eqs. (9-14) and (9-20),

$$\boxed{\delta = \gamma \sin \beta \cos \alpha} \tag{9-23}$$

and

$$\boxed{\varepsilon = \gamma \cos \beta \cos \alpha} \tag{9-24}$$

Since $\alpha + \beta = 90°$, we can also write

$$\delta = \gamma \sin^2 \beta, \tag{9-25}$$

$$\varepsilon = \gamma \sin \beta \cos \beta \tag{9-26}$$

We will mention in passing that Eqs. (9-23) and (9-24) remain valid in the more general case when the normal O_0N is out of the plane of the paper, i.e., out of the plane formed by the direction of pull O_0x and the slip direction O_0T. However, we shall dispense here with the necessary proof.

From Fig. 9-13c it is apparent that after the rotation of the blocks the angle between the slip direction O_1T_1 and the direction of pull O_1x is $\beta - \delta$ instead of β. That is, the rotation *tends to align* the slip direction with the direction of pull. This tendency is preserved even when the crystal forms a part of a polycrystalline aggregate, and it has a bearing on the directionality of properties caused by plastic deformation (plastic anisotropy), as we shall see in Section 9-13.

9-7 The Critical Shear Stress Law. An equally important result of tests on single metal crystals is the confirmation of the existence of a critical shear stress necessary to initiate plastic deformation. That a finite shear stress would be required to set a dislocation in motion was pointed out in Section 9-3. This stress was shown to be needed to overcome the locking effect caused by the interplay of the attractive and repulsive forces of atoms around the dislocation. Its magnitude is therefore expected to be a characteristic property of the underlying atomic configuration. We shall call it the *critical shear stress*, τ_{cr}.

To obtain the pertinent relationship between τ_{cr} and the axial tensile stress σ in single metal crystals, consider the equilibrium of forces on one of the potential slip planes a at the onset of plastic deformation, Fig. 9-14. F and F' represent the axial forces acting at both ends of the bar. They have been transferred to the centroid O of the slip plane. For simplicity we shall again restrict our analysis to experiments in which the direction of pull lies in the same plane as the slip direction and the normal to the slip plane. Under this restriction, the force F can be replaced by its components, T in the slip direction and N normal to the slip plane. We have, in particular,

$$T = F\cos\beta \tag{9-27}$$

At the onset of plastic deformation, T can be expressed in terms of the critical shear stress τ_{cr} and the area of the slip plane, as follows:

$$T = \tau_{cr} \times CD \times t \tag{9-28}$$

Likewise we can write, if σ is the axial stress,

$$F = \sigma \times AB \times t \tag{9-29}$$

Hence, on using Eqs. (9-28) and (9-29) in Eq. (9-27),

$$\tau_{cr} \times CD = \sigma\cos\beta \times AB \tag{9-30}$$

But $CD = EB$, and from triangle ABE,

$$AB = EB\cos\alpha = CD\cos\alpha \tag{9-31}$$

Combining Eq. (9-31) with Eq. (9-30), we obtain

$$\boxed{\tau_{cr} = \sigma\cos\beta\cos\alpha} \tag{9-32}$$

Note the difference between Eq. (9-32) and Eq. (9-24). The stresses are in the inverse ratio to the corresponding strains.

According to Eq. (9-32), the existence of a characteristic (and constant) critical shear stress τ_{cr} implies that the axial stress initiating plastic deformation is *not* constant but depends on the orientation of the slip plane and slip direction with respect to the axis of pull. If all lie in the same plane, $\cos \alpha = \sin \beta$, and we can rewrite Eq. (9-32) to read,

$$\sigma = \frac{\tau_{cr}}{\sin \beta \cos \beta} = \frac{2\tau_{cr}}{\sin 2\beta} \tag{9-33}$$

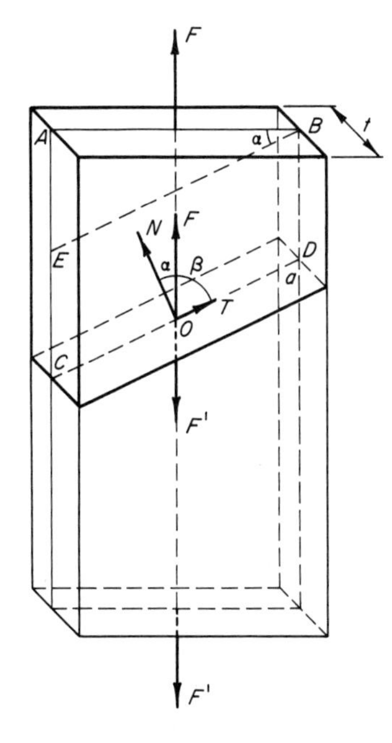

FIG. 9-14 Relation between axial stress and the critical shear stress in a single crystal subjected to tension

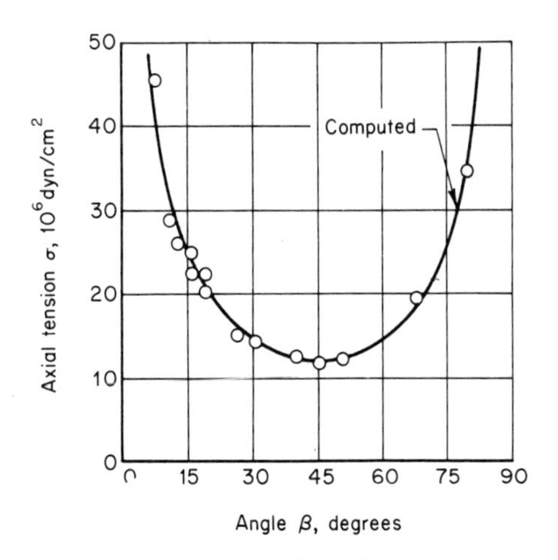

FIG. 9-15 Measured and computed values of axial stress in tensile tests of cadmium single crystals. Computed stress $\sigma = 2\tau_{cr}/\sin 2\beta$ (After Andrade and Roscoe)

The larger the angle 2β, the smaller is the axial stress initiating plastic deformation. The smallest value occurs for $\sin 2\beta = 1$ or $\beta = 45°$. For this angle,

$$\sigma_{min} = 2\tau_{cr} \tag{9-34}$$

The validity of the law embodied in Eq. (9-32) or Eq. (9-33) is demonstrated in the example, Fig. 9-15. The critical shear stress derived from these data is 5.8×10^6 dyn/cm^2 (see Problem 9-6), and it is of the predicted order of magnitude. Similar results were obtained on other metal single crystals.

Note. Although the above results do not prove that the locking mechanism, built into the dislocation and described in Section 9-3, is a necessary corollary of the critical shear stress law, they add greatly to the plausibility of the assumed model. This becomes particularly evident when considering the influence of the force N normal to the slip plane, Fig. 9-14. According to the model, Fig. 9-7, such a force would have to be a sizeable fraction of the cohesive atomic forces in order to markedly disturb the configuration of atoms about the dislocation. To say it differently, a stress normal to the slip plane is not expected to affect significantly the magnitude of the critical shear stress, τ_{cr}, unless it becomes commensurate with the cohesive strength of the crystal.

This expectation is well borne out by the experimental findings. The critical shear stress has been found to be unaffected by superimposed *hydrostatic pressures*[5] up to 40 atm (4.05×10^7 dyn/cm^2). Within these limits the critical shear stress is the same in tension as in compression. However, there are very definite indications that at pressures approaching one-half of the cohesive strength the critical shear stress might be at least doubled.[6] This is as though by decreasing the distance of the closest approach the hydrostatic pressure had called to life larger attractive and repulsive forces about the dislocation.

The influence of *temperature* is in the opposite direction. A rise in temperature lowers the magnitude of the critical shear stress. Thus, the resolved shear stress of zinc has been found to go down from about 9×10^6 to 4.5×10^6 dyn/cm^2 as the temperature went up from 200°K to 600°K. The volumetric strain ε_v—of about 2.7×10^{-2}—accompanying this rise in temperature appears to be of the same order of magnitude as the volumetric contraction corresponding to a two-fold increase of the critical shear stress under hydrostatic pressure.[6] It is as though thermal expansion has loosened the grip of the locking mechanism on the dislocation, by increasing the distance of the closest approach. However, these considerations are much too simple to account properly for the temperature influence which, by its very nature, must be treated on a statistical basis. This seems to be a rather difficult problem.[7] At any rate, below room temperature the influence of temperature is about the same as that of hydrostatic pressure, i.e., rather small for most single crystals.

At variance with hydrostatic pressure, *foreign atoms* in crystal structure greatly affect the magnitude of the critical shear stress. Thus, the critical shear stress of pure gold is almost doubled if only 5% of its atoms are replaced by silver atoms. Yet the critical shear stress of pure silver is even lower than that of pure gold. The presumption is that foreign atoms interact directly

[5] In standard courses dealing with the mechanical behavior of elementary structures, the so-called *strength of materials*, it is shown that hydrostatic pressure modifies the normal stress, but makes no contribution to the shear stress.

[6] P. W. Bridgman, *Studies in Large Plastic Flow and Fracture*, p. 289, McGraw-Hill, New York, 1952.

[7] E. Orowan, Chapter 3 of monograph, "Dislocations in Metals," M. Cohen, Ed., *A.I.M.M.E.*, New York, 1954.

with dislocations. It is conceivable that the silver ion, which is 8% smaller than the gold ion, is naturally pushed into row *B*, Fig. 9-7, to relieve the most compressed gold ion in the dislocation. This would decrease the mismatch and make the dislocation less prone to move at the particular spot. However, the quantitative treatment of interactions between point imperfections (foreign atoms, or vacancies), and dislocations is far from completely solved. It is currently an object of intensive investigations.

9-8 Slip in Polycrystalline Aggregates. The simple slip mechanism discussed in Section 9-5 comes to naught when two or more crystals or grains form a coherent aggregate—a state of affairs quite common in the majority of industrial metals. We shall show that in such aggregates the cohesion along the grain boundaries forces the individual grain to slip in several directions. In other words, plastic deformation in polycrystalline aggregates involves a *multiple* rather than a single slip mechanism.

To adduce the necessary proof we resort to a model. Let 1 and 2, Fig. 9-16a, be two adjacent grains having a common boundary *AB* aligned with the

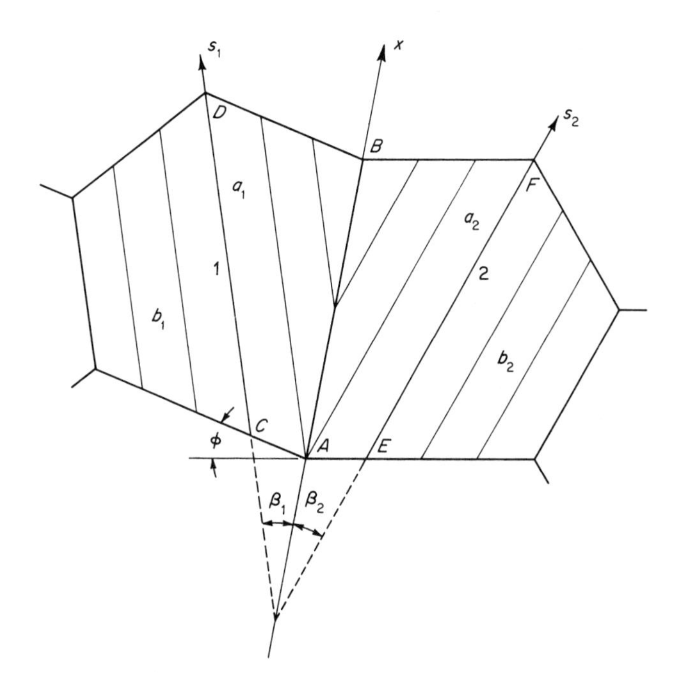

FIG. 9-16a Configuration of two adjacent grains (schematic). Slip planes and directions

direction of pull. Let *CD* and *EF* be the traces of the planes, normal to the plane of the figure, and s_1 and s_2 the directions along which the grains would slip if they were isolated crystals. In the absence of a coherent boundary *AB*,

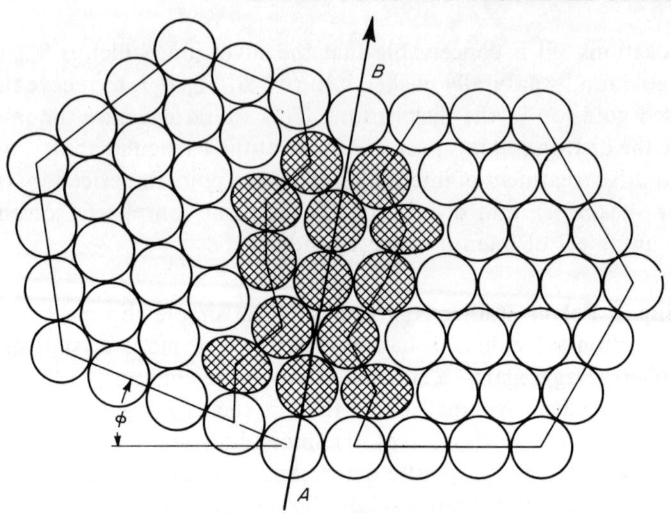

FIG. 9-16b Configuration of two adjacent grains (schematic). Boundary atoms in a close-packed aggregate

the two crystals would part ways after slip, as shown in Fig. 9-17a. They would rotate through an angle $\delta_1 + \delta_2$ with respect to each other because of the tendency of s_1 and s_2 to align themselves with the direction of pull. Assuming the crystals split in blocks 10,000 atomic planes thick, a plastic deformation of only 1% would be sufficient to pull the edges A_1 and A_2 more than one hundred atomic distances apart (see Problem 9-7). However, with a coherent boundary such a course of action is impossible.

To see why this is impossible, suppose the grains of the aggregate, Fig. 9-16a, build a close-packed crystal structure. A boundary exists between two adjacent grains because their crystallographic planes in the process of growth have assumed an arbitrary angle ϕ with respect to each other, Fig. 9-16b. As a result, the atoms are mismatched at the points of intersection in the manner indicated schematically by the shaded circles, Fig. 9-16b. However, the important point to retain is that the mismatch involves only a few atoms on each side of the boundary. This is also apparent in the soap bubble model, Fig. 9-18. Moreover, the mismatched atoms are still close enough to develop cohesive forces that are sufficiently strong to exclude any but small changes of interatomic distances under commonly applied loads. It follows that, in plastic deformation, polycrystalline aggregates must safeguard the fit of grains along their boundaries. The only way this can be accomplished is by allowing the grains to slip in more than one direction.

A graphical proof for the two-dimensional model, Fig. 9-16a, is offered in Fig. 9-17b. Each grain has now slipped in two directions and in such a way that the angular change caused by one slip is offset by the other. The grains match again along the boundary AB. The aggregate has been extended in the direction of pull and contracted perpendicularly to it.

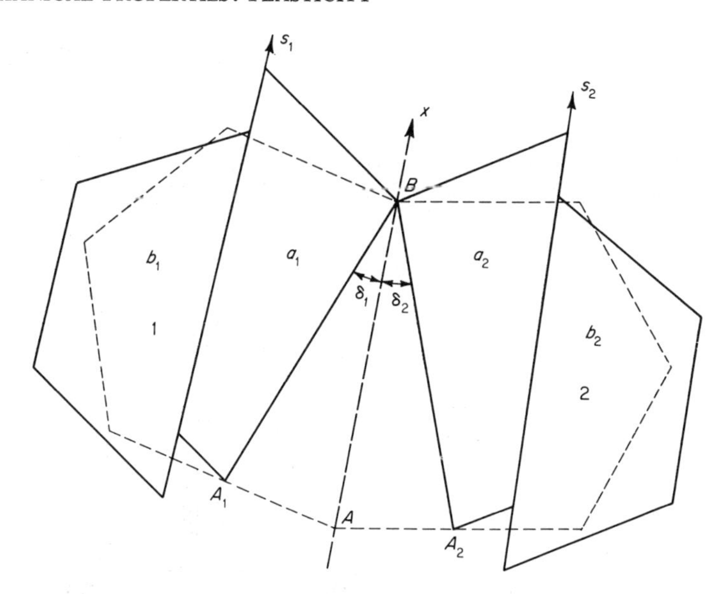

FIG. 9-17a Slip in a plane model of two adjacent grains. Single slip with no boundary coherence

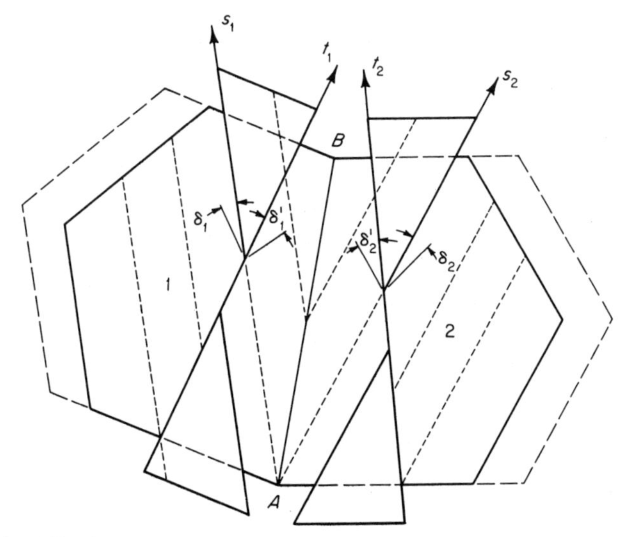

FIG. 9-17b Slip in a plane model of two adjacent grains. Double slip with boundary coherence

The extension of this argument to three-dimensional crystal aggregates shows that each grain must now slip in at least five directions to maintain the fit with its neighbors. We shall dispense with the necessary proof, since it requires knowledge of strain analysis currently not available at this level of presentation. Besides, the results based on a five-slip mechanism are not fully confirmed by observation. The actual mechanism of plastic deformation in polycrystalline materials appears to be a great deal more complicated.

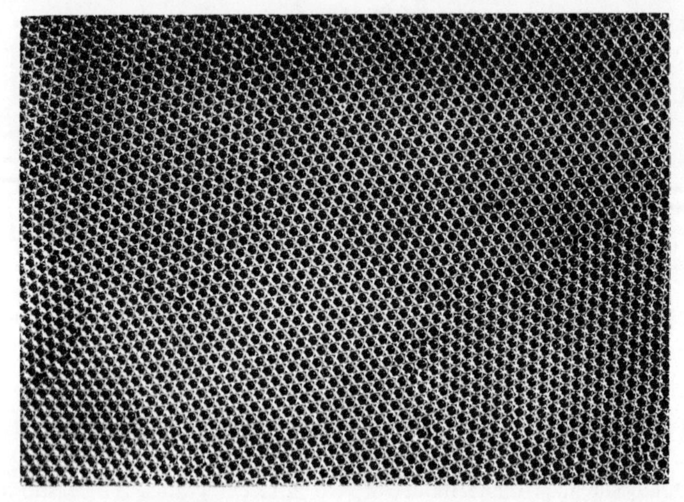

FIG. 9-18 Grain boundary in a soap bubble raft. (Sir Lawrence Bragg and J. F. Nye, *Proc. Roy. Soc.*, **A**, 190)

9-9 Onset of Plastic Deformation in Polycrystalline Materials. According to Eq. (9-33), single slip in a *loose* aggregate of crystals subjected to increasing axial tension would first begin in those crystals whose slip directions make the closest angles to 45° with the direction of pull. In a *coherent* aggregate each crystal slips in several directions. Some of them are closer to 45° than the others. Assuming the critical shear stress is the same in all of them, the slip will begin on the average at a higher axial stress than in a single crystal. A detailed computation has been made for FCC aggregates.[8] It is of little interest here except that it sets an upper limit of $3.06\tau_{cr}$ for the axial stress in a randomly oriented aggregate. The onset of plastic deformation in actual aggregates occurs at stresses which are often one order of magnitude higher than this limit. As a rule, the *smaller the grain size*, the higher the stress at which plastic deformation begins. The presumption is that grain boundaries offer additional resistance to the motion of dislocations. Several theories have been propounded to account for this influence, but they are too involved to be considered here.[9]

9-10 Generation of Dislocations. Strain Hardening. The complications surrounding the onset of plastic deformation are typical of properties which,

[8] In FCC crystals, the assumption of equal critical shear stress in all slip directions is justified on the ground that there are available for slip 12 equivalent face diagonals and four octahedral slip planes.

[9] See, for example, A. H. Cottrell, *op. cit.*

like the plastic deformation, depend on the defects of crystal structure rather than the crystal structure itself—the *structure-sensitive* properties. This becomes even more apparent when we examine the situation *after* the plastic deformation has set in. The model of Fig. 9-7 provides little clue to future events. It tells us that at the attainment of the critical shear stress any dislocation lying in the slip plane will be swept out of the crystal, causing thereby a shear displacement of one atomic distance. This should lead to a gradual exhaustion of dislocations as plastic deformation goes on. However, all direct and indirect evidence points to the contrary. The number of dislocations contained in the crystal *increases*, not decreases, with plastic deformation. It is as though each dislocation that moves out of the crystal produces two or more in its wake. Several ingenious devices have been conceived to account for such a feedback. They all defy description in terms of the knowledge available at this level of presentation. They also imply another aspect of plastic deformation, equally hard to explain: the dislocations *interact* with each other and with other structural defects in the crystal. They would eventually be stopped in their motions, unless the applied stress is continuously increased to overcome the rising tide of interactions. That is, each additional amount of plastic deformation requires an additional increment of stress. This behavior is called *strain hardening*.

The ability of metals to strain harden is one of their most important plastic properties. Unfortunately, like the onset of plastic deformation, it depends on many factors. The most conspicuous of them is the *already present* amount of plastic deformation. Each new volley of dislocations moving out of the crystal alters the existing pattern and configuration of dislocations left behind. As a rule, therefore, a different increment of stress will be required each time for the same additional amount of plastic deformation. Therein lies the main difference between elastic and plastic properties. Small departures from stable equilibrium cause only insignificant changes in the configuration and pattern of crystal structure during an elastic deformation. As a result, the modulus of elasticity is for all practical purposes a constant property of the material. Contrariwise, the ability of a material to strain harden is a variable property, because the underlying configurations of dislocations lack the stability of the bulk crystal structure. No wonder properties based on structural defects are so much less predictable than properties based on the crystal structure itself (as pointed out in Chapter 5)!

Note. The ability of metals to strain harden is influenced to a considerable extent by their purity and by the slip mechanism. Single crystals of aluminum of 99.999% purity can be deformed with little or no strain hardening during the first few percent of plastic strain, if they are so oriented that they slip by a single slip mechanism.[10] This is not possible in a polycrystalline aggregate,

[10] It is possible to produce a double slip in single crystals by so orienting them that the critical shear stress is reached simultaneously in two equivalent slip directions.

where the multislip mechanism causes dislocations to move on intersecting slip planes and interact with each other right from the start. Therefore, polycrystalline aggregates strain harden at the very onset of plastic deformation. (This appears to apply only to the grains in the bulk and not to the surface grains.[10a])

9-11 Stress–Strain Diagram. In the absence of an established quantitative relationship between measurable plastic properties and basic elements of the dislocations' structure and pattern, we turn to experimental findings. The pertinent information is currently described in terms of stresses and strains determined in axial tension of long cylindrical specimens.[11] It is convenient to consider separately the onset of plastic deformation within the range of small strains and the progress of plastic deformation beyond the range of small strains.

Yield Stress. A plot of stress versus strain, Fig. 9-19, reveals first a proportionality, specific to elastic deformation, by following the line OA. Departure

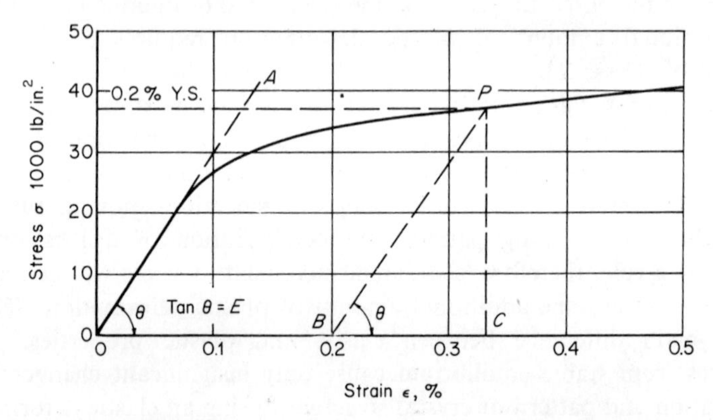

FIG. 9-19 Stress–strain diagram at small plastic strains

from proportionality denotes the onset of plastic strain which increases much faster than the stress. It is rather difficult to locate this point on the diagram, however, since it depends critically on the precision of the measuring instruments. To avoid ambiguity, the advent of plastic deformation has been characterized by a stress corresponding to a small, but easily measurable, amount of permanent, plastic strain. This stress is called the *Yield Stress* (Y.S.). The currently accepted value is the stress producing a permanent strain of 0.2%, or, briefly, the 0.2% Y.S. Strictly speaking, the permanent

[10a] D. Rosenthal and W. D. Groupen, *Second Order Effects in Elasticity, Plasticity and Fluid Mechanics*, Ed. M. Reiner and D. Abir, Pergamon Press, N.Y., 391–415, 1964.

[11] As will appear in Section 12-14, the rate of straining and temperature also must be specified.

strain can be determined only after the load has been removed. As long as the load is kept on it produces an elastic strain also. In Fig. 9-19 this strain can be subtracted from the total strain OC under stress PC by observing that on unloading it must obey Hooke's law, i.e., it must follow a line PB parallel to OA. A point B is thus reached at zero stress with OB representing the permanent strain. Conversely, if at point B, corresponding to 0.2% strain, a line is drawn parallel to OA, its intersection P with the stress–strain diagram determines the 0.2% Y.S. (see Problem 9-8).

Increase of Y.S. *by Strain Hardening.* After being unloaded from point P, Fig. 9-19, the specimen is actually longer by 0.2%. When reloaded, it will not begin to deform plastically, because of strain hardening, until after the stress PC is exceeded. Therefore, up to point P it will deform only elastically by following the line BP in reverse.[12] If nothing were known of the history of the specimen, a new 0.2% Y.S. could be determined by proceeding as previously. This Y.S. will be higher than CP because of strain hardening. In other words, as the plastic deformation keeps increasing, higher and higher yield stresses can be defined after each unloading and reloading. The term 0.2% Y.S. refers, however, to a material which has not been previously strain hardened, although admittedly an adequate proof of its virgin state would not be easy to produce.

Conventional and True Stress. When plastic deformation exceeds the range of small strains, say 1%, the change of dimensions must be taken into account in computing the stress. By definition (see Eq. (6-22), Chapter 6),

$$\sigma = F/S \tag{9-35}$$

where F is the applied load and S the *actual* cross-sectional area of the specimen. When the specimen extends, the cross-sectional area contracts by virtue of constancy of volume, Section 9-5. This contraction notwithstanding, the experimental data are plotted for the sake of convenience in terms of a *conventional* stress σ_0 rather than the true stress σ. The conventional stress is defined as the load F divided by the *original* area S_0 rather than the actual area S. Thus,

$$\sigma_0 = F/S_0 \tag{9-36}$$

A plot of conventional stress versus strain ε has the general aspect indicated by curve σ_0 in Fig. 9-20. The conventional stress can be viewed as the applied load scaled down by a constant factor S_0. The strain plotted on the abscissae

[12] Strictly speaking, the loading and unloading will not follow the same line and will not be purely elastic because of small changes in the pattern and configuration of dislocations. However, these departures from proportionality are so small that they can be neglected in most, if not all, engineering applications.

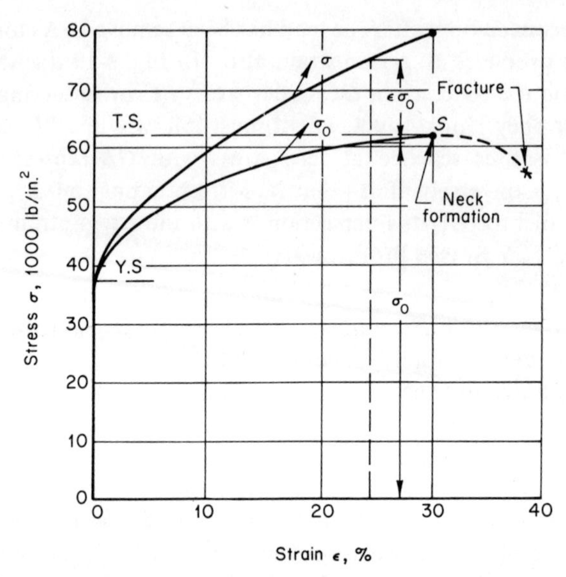

FIG. 9-20 Stress–strain diagram at large plastic strains

always includes the elastic component σ/E (not σ_0/E!), but for large strains, beyond 1%, this component is so small that it can be neglected (see Problem 9-13).

It is easy to convert the diagram of σ_0 versus ε into a diagram of σ versus ε, i.e., into a true stress–strain diagram. On dividing Eq. (9-35) by Eq. (9-36) we have

$$\sigma/\sigma_0 = S_0/S \tag{9-37}$$

By virtue of constancy of volume, the cross-sectional area decreases in the same ratio as the length increases. Thus, if l_0 and l represent the original and actual lengths of the specimen,

$$S_0/S = l/l_0 \tag{9-38}$$

Since by definition

$$(l - l_0)/l_0 = \varepsilon \tag{9-39}$$

we also have

$$\sigma/\sigma_0 = S_0/S_0 = l/l_0 = 1 + \varepsilon \tag{9-40}$$

whereupon

$$\sigma = \sigma_0(1 + \varepsilon) \tag{9-41}$$

Equation (9-41) shows that, in order to convert the conventional stress–strain diagram into a true stress–strain diagram, it suffices to increase each ordinate σ_0 by a fractional amount $\varepsilon\sigma_0$ corresponding to strain ε. A curve marked σ in Fig. 9-20 is thus obtained.

Tensile or Ultimate Strength. The curve σ, Fig. 9-20, shows that the increase $\Delta\sigma$ of the true stress needed to produce an additional increment $\Delta\varepsilon$ of plastic strain becomes smaller as ε gets bigger. This trend, which is clearly indicated by the slope $d\sigma/d\varepsilon$ of the tangent to the curve σ, appears to be a characteristic feature of strain hardening in all crystalline materials. According to Eq. (9-41), the corresponding slope $d\sigma_0/d\varepsilon$ of the conventional stress curve σ_0 is always smaller than $d\sigma/d\varepsilon$. There exists, therefore, a load F for which $d\sigma_0/d\varepsilon$ becomes zero long before $d\sigma/d\varepsilon$ vanishes. Since σ_0 is proportional to F, we can also write that, for this load,

$$dF/d\varepsilon = 0 \tag{9-42}$$

That is, the load reaches a maximum value, and further plastic deformation can proceed now without increase of load. The conditions of testing become unstable. They are characterized by the formation of a local contraction or a neck, Fig. 9-21, and are followed by fracture of the specimen in the necked-down section. These last stages of the test are quite hard to analyze and will not be considered further.

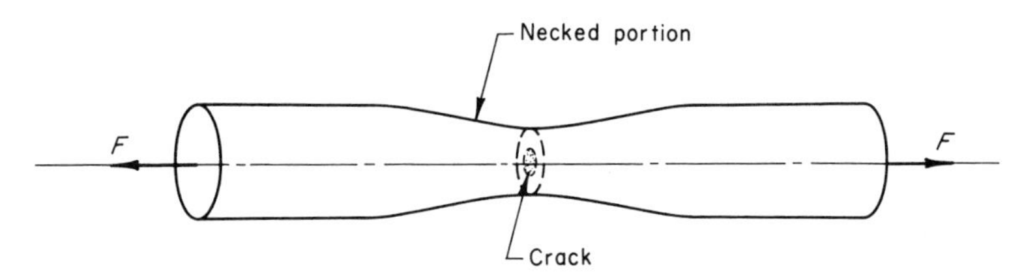

FIG. 9-21 Formation of a neck and crack in a tensile specimen

The conventional stress σ_0 corresponding to the maximum value of F is called the *Ultimate, or Tensile, Strength*, T.S., Fig. 9-20. The term refers to the *specimen*, not to the material. At the attainment of the maximum load, the material is still capable of further strain hardening, since $d\sigma/d\varepsilon$ is greater than zero. However, the specimen is not able to support a higher load, because its cross-sectional area decreases more rapidly than the material strain hardens.[13]

9-12 Plastic Deformation of Ceramic Materials. The stress–strain relationships described in Section 9-11 apply not only to metals but also to ionic and covalent crystalline materials, like ceramics. Admittedly, these materials behave in a brittle manner when tested under the same experimental conditions as metals. Yet, observations made on mountains and structure of

[13] This follows from Eq. (9-35), which, after differentiation, can be rewritten as follows:

$$dF/F = d\sigma/\sigma + dS/S \tag{9-43}$$

Since the cross-sectional area decreases, dS/S is negative. As long as $d\sigma/\sigma$ is larger than dS/S, $dF > 0$. When $d\sigma/\sigma$ becomes smaller than dS/S, $dF < 0$, and F goes through a maximum.

rock layers prove that under special conditions minerals, too, are capable of deforming plastically. What are these conditions? We observe first that ionic and covalent crystals contain dislocations—in addition to incipient cracks—no less than metals do. Dislocations exist even in diamond. However, in minerals, dislocations are probably much harder to move than in metals. It is likely that they interact more strongly and culminate in a critical crack before any number of them can leave the crystal.[14] It follows that if the formation or propagation of critical cracks could be delayed or prevented, minerals too should exhibit plastic deformation.[15]

The observed large-scale plastic deformation of rocks—in the form of folds—is in fact ascribed to a preventive action of high hydrostatic pressures in the interior of the earth. Hydrostatic pressures of equal magnitude have been applied in the laboratory to specimens of rock salt, quartz, marble, etc., subjected to tension and compression. They all yielded plastically with strains running well into 20% and more.[16]

It has also been known for some time that by preventing the growth of surface cracks (for example, by keeping the crystal in water) rock salt specimens could be deformed plastically to some extent. Recently the same observation was made on freshly cleaved single crystals of the refractory oxide MgO tested in air.[14] The implications of these investigations for high temperature refractory technology are self-evident.

In all circumstances the mechanism of slip has been found to be the same as in metals. The slip planes and slip directions may vary, but they always represent well-defined elements of crystal structure. On the other hand, glassy materials cannot be deformed by this type of slip mechanism under any circumstances: they lack the regularity and periodicity of crystal structure required for the formation of slip planes and slip directions.

9-13 Cold Working and Preferred Orientation. Recovery and Recrystallization. Strain hardening has been shown to be an inescapable by-product of plastic deformation of any significant amount. It is also a cumulative process. If a piece of metal is bent back and forth several times, the yield stress is increased after each bending and unbending. At the end the piece may be brought back to its original shape, yet it would have undergone considerable strain hardening at the location of former bends. We say it has been *cold-worked.*

Cold work is particularly severe in forming operations like rolling, wire

[14] E. R. Parker, "Fracture of Ceramic Materials," in monograph *Fracture*, The Technology Press, M.I.T., Cambridge, Mass., and Wiley, New York, 1959.

[15] Conversely, brittleness could be induced in an otherwise ductile material if dislocations were hampered in their motion to such an extent that they, too, would culminate in a crack before being able to leave the crystal. This appears to be the case with the BCC iron and other BCC metals like molybdenum and tantalum, which exhibit brittleness at low temperatures. For more detail see N. J. Petch, "The Ductile-Cleavage Transition in Alpha Iron," in the monograph *Fracture, ibid.*

[16] P. W. Bridgman, *op. cit.*

drawing, and swaging, where the application of lateral pressure eliminates or delays the advent of instability occurring in axial tension. Plastic deformations of considerable amount can thus be achieved, and yield stresses and tensile strengths can be reached that are of the order of 0.1 of the cohesive strength of the material, e.g., in wires of suspension bridge cables. These gains are not obtained without sacrifices. The material is now much less ductile. Presumably the entanglement and pile-up of dislocations causing strain-hardening have become so great that they promote formation and growth of cracks rather than further slip. In addition, cold work destroys the randomness of grain orientations, thereby depriving the polycrystalline material of a statistical equality of properties in all directions—the so-called *quasi-isotropy*. The grains exhibit now a *preferred orientation*, and the material properties are quite different in various directions.

The preferred orientation results from the tendency of several slip directions in each grain to align themselves with some common direction of deformation. For example, during wire drawing of aluminum the three face diagonals meeting at a corner of a cube are in a competition to align themselves with the direction of drawing similar to the tendency described in Section 9-8. They compromise by allowing the cube diagonal with which they make equal and small angles to take this direction instead. Since the same tug-of-war goes on in each grain, all end up by having their cube diagonals aligned more or less with the direction of drawing.

Preferred orientation is of considerable interest in some engineering applications—for example, magnetization in silicone steels, Section 14-16—but it is quite undesirable in others. So is, of course, the loss of ductility. This is particularly true of semifinished products, like sheet metals and wires, which must undergo still further forming operations, as in automotive, canning, or electric industries.

It is possible to restore to the cold-worked material much of its lost ductility by heating it to a temperature high enough to increase substantially the thermal agitation of atoms. The presumption is that local readjustments of structural defects can thus be made with the ensuing elimination of the excess of dislocations. The basic mechanism is still a matter of current debate, but the outcome is not. After cooling, the material recovers most, if not all, of its original ductility and softness. Hence the name *recovery* is given to this treatment. Recovery also eliminates voids or vacancies which are created by the interaction of dislocations and which account for a small increase of volume, not exceeding 1%.

To remove the preferred orientation as well, the temperature must be raised to a point at which a process of *recrystallization* can take place. This is a process of nucleation and grain growth of new crystals amidst the existing crystalline mass, similar to the formation of crystals amidst a liquid mass—or crystallization—described in Chapter 3. Like the phenomenon of crystallization, recrystallization has a statistical character, and its treatment must be postponed to a more advanced course. The statistics seem to be less random for recrystallization, because thereafter a certain amount of preferred orientation results.

The temperatures of both recovery and recrystallization are structure-sensitive properties, as are all properties based on structural defects. They depend on many factors: the degree of strain hardening, time of heating, amount of impurities, grain size, etc., in addition to the chemical nature of the material. The greater the degree of strain hardening, the lower are these temperatures. However, there appears to be practically a critical amount of strain hardening below which recrystallization will not occur. As a rough estimate, the recrystallization begins at $0.4T_f$, where T_f is the melting point measured on the absolute scale, that is, in degrees Kelvin.

9-14 Work of Deformation. Any force producing deformation in a body does work regardless of whether the deformation is elastic or plastic. However, the work due to the elastic component is stored in the form of elastic energy which is recoverable, whereas the major part of work due to the plastic component is dissipated in heat. (About 10% of this work goes into storing energy associated with strain hardening.) It is of interest to compare the amounts of work expended both ways during axial extension.

As in the case of a purely elastic deformation (Fig. 6-11, Chapter 6) a force F applied to the end of a bar subjected to tension does an amount of work

$$dW = F\,dx \tag{9-44}$$

if the end of the bar is displaced by the amount dx.

We can express F in terms of the conventional stress σ_0, Eq. (9-36). On the other hand, the displacement x being identical with the increase $l_0\varepsilon$ of the original length l_0 we also have

$$dx = l_0\,d\varepsilon \tag{9-45}$$

Using Eqs. (9-36) and (9-45) in Eq. (9-44), we obtain

$$dW = S_0 l_0 \sigma_0\,d\varepsilon \tag{9-46}$$

The product $S_0 l_0$ is the volume v of the specimen. Since this volume remains practically constant even for very large strain ε, it follows that

$$W = \int_0^{\varepsilon} S_0 l_0 \sigma_0\,d\varepsilon = v\int_0^{\varepsilon} \sigma_0\,d\varepsilon \tag{9-47}$$

The integral in Eq. (9-47) is the area under the curve σ_0, Fig. 9-20. We shall designate the ratio

$$W' = W/v \tag{9-48}$$

as the work of deformation per unit volume. There follows

$$W' = \int_0^{\varepsilon} \sigma_0\,d\varepsilon \tag{9-49}$$

Only a small fraction of this work, less than 10%, is converted into the recoverable, elastic energy. This can be shown as follows:

If σ is the true stress, the elastic component of strain, even for σ as high as $0.01E$, is still rather closely given by the ratio σ/E. Hence, by virtue of Eq. (6-52), the recoverable elastic energy per unit volume is

$$W'_e = \tfrac{1}{2}\sigma^2/E \tag{9-50}$$

We can also estimate the lower limit of the total work of deformation W' per unit volume from Fig. 9-20. We can set

$$W' > \tfrac{1}{2}(\text{Y.S.} + \text{T.S.})\varepsilon_{\text{max}} \tag{9-51}$$

where Y.S. and T.S. are the yield stress and tensile strength, respectively, and ε_{max} is the strain corresponding to T.S. Hence,

$$\frac{W'_e}{W'} < \frac{\sigma^2}{(\text{Y.S.} + \text{T.S.})\varepsilon_{\text{max}}E} \tag{9-52}$$

For convenience, we shall put

$$\text{Y.S.} = \alpha\text{T.S.} \tag{9-53}$$

where α is a fraction. We also have, by virtue of Eq. (9-41),

$$\sigma = \text{T.S.}(1 + \varepsilon_{\text{max}}) \tag{9-54}$$

Using Eqs. (9-53) and (9-54) in the inequality (9-52), we obtain

$$\frac{W'_e}{W'} < \frac{1 + \varepsilon_{\text{max}}}{(1 + \alpha)\varepsilon_{\text{max}}}\frac{\sigma}{E} \tag{9-55}$$

Putting σ/E as high as 0.01 and ε_{max} as low as 0.1, we arrive even with α as small as 0.1 at a value

$$\frac{W'_e}{W'} < 10\% \tag{9-56}$$

Therefore the balance of work, according to Eq. (9-51), and taking into account Eqs. (9-53) and (9-54), is

$$\boxed{W' - W'_e > 0.45\,\frac{\varepsilon_{\text{max}}}{1 + \varepsilon_{\text{max}}}\cdot\sigma} \tag{9-57}$$

With σ close to $0.01E$, ε_{max} of the order of 0.1, and E of the order of 10^{11} N/m^2, this balance amounts to 10^8 J/m^3. That part dissipated in heat is sufficient to produce a perceptible rise of temperature in the specimen (see Problem 9-14.)

9-15 Summary. Plastic deformation results from a *slip* or a glide of one part of a body over the other. In crystalline materials the slip planes and directions are *crystallographic planes and directions*. Metal crystals slip in the densest crystallographic direction. The slip plane containing this direction is the densest crystallographic plane in FCC and HCP crystals, but not necessarily in BCC crystals. The onset of plastic deformation in polycrystalline aggregates is manifested by the appearance of *slip lines* on the surface of a polished specimen. Under higher magnification they resolve into slip bands separated by about 10,000 atomic distances of undisturbed crystalline material.

The onset of plastic deformation occurs under stresses that are several orders of magnitude *lower* than the theoretical stress necessary to cause slip in a perfect crystal. A defect of crystal structure called *dislocation* is blamed for this shortcoming. Dislocation is a line defect which produces a progressive rather than simultaneous slip across the slip plane. It is a boundary that *separates* the sheared from the unsheared portion of the slip plane.

After slip, the configuration of atoms is the same as before. However, the configuration is modified in another type of plastic deformation called *twinning*, which transforms the sheared portion of the crystal into a mirror image of the unsheared portion. Twinning is infrequent in cubic metal crystals, but common in other metal crystals and minerals.

The mechanism of slip—also twinning—accounts for the *magnitude* and *permanence* of plastic deformation as well as for the *absence* of volumetric changes.

Axial tension of *single* metal crystals produces *rotation* of the sliding blocks as they slip. The rotation tends to *align* the slip direction with the direction of pull. The stress necessary to initiate slip follows the *critical shear stress law*, thereby confirming the existence of a critical shear stress for the onset of plastic deformation.

Axial tension of *polycrystalline* aggregates involves *more* than one slip direction in each grain. All slip directions, however, tend to align themselves with the direction of pull, causing a *preferred* orientation of the aggregate. The onset of plastic deformation does not follow the simple law for single crystals. Among various additional factors, the smaller the grain size, the higher is the stress for the initiation of plastic deformation in the aggregate.

The progress of plastic deformation in single crystals and in polycrystals is marked by *strain-hardening*. That is, each additional increase of plastic deformation requires an additional increment of stress.

Plastic properties are currently defined in terms of the stress–strain diagram obtained in axial tension. The advent of plastic deformation is marked by a stress producing a fixed amount of permanent strain, or the yield stress (Y.S.) —for example, the 0.2% Y.S. if the permanent strain is 0.2%. However, the ensuing strain-hardening continuously raises the value of the Y.S.

In dealing with large strains we must distinguish between *conventional* stress σ_0, defined as the axial load divided by the original cross-sectional area, and *true* stress σ, where the load is divided by actual cross-sectional area. If ε is the corresponding strain, $\sigma = \sigma_0(1 + \varepsilon)$. Experiment shows that $d\sigma_0/d\varepsilon$

reaches zero before $d\sigma/d\varepsilon$ does. The same, of course, applies to the axial load. Thus, the axial load reaches a maximum before the material ceases to strain-harden. Thereafter the conditions of testing become unstable. The value of the conventional stress corresponding to the maximum is defined as *ultimate strength*, or *tensile strength*. The term refers to the *specimen*, not to the material.

Under special conditions (e.g., under hydrostatic pressure), large plastic deformations can be produced in materials behaving currently in a brittle manner—ceramic materials, for example. In all circumstances, the mechanism of slip involves definite crystallographic planes and directions, as in metals.

Strain-hardening is a cumulative process. It increases even if plastic deformation is reversed (e.g., in alternate bending). A strain-hardened material is also said to be *cold-worked*. Severe cold-working of metals in forming operations (rolling, wire drawing) accounts for high yield and tensile strengths, as well as sharp drop in ductility and pronounced preferred orientation. Strain-hardening can be removed and the virgin characteristics essentially restored by heating the material to a temperature in the neighborhood of $0.4T_f$, where T_f is the melting point in absolute degrees. This causes *recovery* and *recrystallization*.

All plastic properties beginning with the critical stress and ending with the temperature of recrystallization are *structure sensitive*, i.e., they depend greatly on factors which only slightly affect the crystal structure and, by implication, the elastic properties of the material. Nor is the work of plastic deformation converted into a recoverable form of energy, like the elastic energy. Most of this work is dissipated in heat.

References

ELEMENTARY

1. J. P. Frankel, *Principles of the Properties of Materials*, McGraw-Hill, New York, 1957.

ADVANCED

1. W. Boas, *Physics of Metals and Alloys*, Wiley, New York, 1947.
2. C. S. Barrett, *Structure of Metals*, McGraw-Hill, New York, 1952.
3. A. H. Cottrell, *Dislocations and Plastic Flow in Crystals*, Clarendon Press, Oxford, New York, 1953.
4. *Dislocation in Metals*, monograph, American Institute of Metallurgical Engineers, New York, 1954.
5. W. T. Read, Jr., *Dislocations in Crystals*, McGraw-Hill, New York, 1953.

Problems

9-1 Two adjacent grains of a polycrystalline FCC cubic crystal are so oriented that in one of them the plane of the cube and in the other the dodecahedral plane (refer to Table 2-1, page 28) are parallel to the surface. Show possible orientation of slip lines in both of them.

9-2 In Fig. 9-6a an extra row of balls is indicated as $B_5 . C_5 . D_5$ in one of the densest directions that is not a direction of slip. Show that another extra row of balls can be shown if the alignment of balls is traced in the other densest direction.

9-3 Show the position of the centers of atoms *a*, Fig. 9-9a, if the dislocation is an edge dislocation, that is, if the dislocation line is perpendicular to the slip direction.

9-4 Show that the unit displacement *MP* in twinning, Fig. 9-11a, is $(1/\sqrt{3})r_0$ and that every third layer above the twin plane brings the atoms into a position such as Q', which also belongs to the untwinned crystal lattice.

9-5 A single crystal has been deformed 6% by sliding on a plane, making an angle of 30° with the direction of pull. The slip direction is in the plane formed by the direction of pull and normal to the slip plane. Compute how much the sliding blocks of the crystal will rotate during deformation.

9-6 Using data of Fig. 9-15, show the procedure for determining the value of the critical shear stress indicated in Section 9-7.

9-7 Assuming $\beta_1 = \beta_2 = 30°$ in Fig. 9-16a, compute the opening $A_1A + AA_2$ in Fig. 9-17a on the assumption that $AB = 20{,}000$ Å and the plastic strain $\varepsilon = 1\%$. (Hint: Use Formulae (9-23) and (9-24), Section 9-6.)

9-8 Prove that a line drawn through 0.2% on the abscissae parallel to *OA* will intersect the stress–strain diagram, Fig. 9-19 at point *P*, which by definition is 0.2% Y.S.

9-9 Obtain a point on the stress–strain diagram, Fig. 9-19, corresponding to 0.4 Y.S. Show that it can also be viewed as 0.2% Y.S. of a specimen that previously has been strained permanently 0.2%.

9-10 Obtain the true stress–strain diagram from the conventional stress–strain diagram, Fig. 9-20, if the scale of strains is doubled, that is, 20% instead of 10%, 40% instead of 20%, etc.

9-11 Draw a stress–strain diagram on the assumption that the strain-hardening obeys the relation

$$\Delta\sigma = 100{,}000\varepsilon^{1/2}\ \text{lb/in.}^2$$

Start with the yield stress = 10,000 lb/in.^{2} and end up with $\varepsilon = 100\%$. This being the true stress–strain diagram, convert it to conventional stress–strain diagram. What happens past $\varepsilon = 80\%$?

9-12 Show that there results a preferred orientation in which a cube direction is aligned with the direction of wire drawing, if four instead of three face diagonals meeting at a corner of a cube are in competition to align themselves with the direction of drawing. (Note: This explains, for example, why in gold 50% of grains have the [111] and 50% the [100] preferred orientation.)

9-13 Compute the amount of elastic strain at the total strain $\varepsilon = 30\%$, Fig. 9-20, by assuming the material is an iron alloy with $E = 30 \times 10^6$ lb/in.^{2} What percent of the total strain is this?

9-14 Using the diagram, Fig. 9-20, and assuming the whole work of deformation is converted into heat, compute the rise of temperature in an aluminum bar using the value of specific heat = 0.20 cal/g. (Hint: Convert specific heat into calories per cubic centimeter, since the work of deformation is per unit volume. Put $\alpha = 0.67$.)

10 / MECHANICAL PROPERTIES RELATED TO PLASTICITY: 1 FATIGUE STRENGTH

According to the findings of Chapter 9, a rod-like element of a structure or a machine subjected to increasing axial tension ends up by becoming unstable at the attainment of the tensile strength. When the load, instead of steadily growing, keeps oscillating back and forth, the life and usefulness of the element may be endangered by another phenomenon, called *fatigue*. Once a hotly debated and highly controversial subject, fatigue lost much of its mystery and ambiguity when it was found that it owed its origin to the same slip mechanism as plastic deformation. The subsequent description and analysis of fatigue are largely based on this finding.

10-1 Manifestations. That an element of structure or machine could prove less resistant to a load, when this load was reapplied many times than when it was kept on permanently—this was indeed something that was both puzzling and unacceptable to the early students of fatigue, around 1825. There would have been no problem had the load been sufficient to produce plastic deformation. It turned out, however, that the corresponding stress was well below the Y.S., and no visible marks of permanent deformation could be detected. At the end, the specimen would break in two in a seemingly unexpected and sudden manner, as though the material had become brittle. When retested in axial tension, however, the broken parts revealed no loss of ductility.

For all their strangeness and gravity, the early manifestations of fatigue did little to attract wider attention and even less to influence the design of structural and machine elements. They were all too infrequent, and whatever fatigue failures occurred were cured by "beefing up" the dimensions. Not until 1925 had an attempt really been made to give due recognition to the factor of "oscillating loads" in the design of structural and machine elements. The awareness came, as it always does, when the incidence of fatigue fractures had begun to multiply alarmingly with the wider use of high-speed machinery, particularly internal combustion engines.

Instances of oscillating loads are numerous in mechanical engineering. A rotating shaft bends under service loads in such a way that each fiber on the periphery is alternately extended and compressed. Parts of steering

FIG. 10-1 Smooth and jagged regions of a freshly broken section of an automobile spindle

mechanisms are subjected to reversed torques, turbine blades are bent back and forth. Structures can be similarly affected. Wind blowing intermittently on a bridge or chimney or gusts of wind impinging on an airplane wing may set parts of the structure in vibration and cause local oscillations of stress. Electrical and magnetic devices are also subject to fatigue. The problem of fatigue failures is important to the entire engineering profession.

10-2 Characteristics of Fatigue Failure. Progressive Fracture and Slip. Despite outward appearances, fatigue failure is neither sudden nor hidden. It is progressive and visible. Careful inspection reveals that, as a rule,

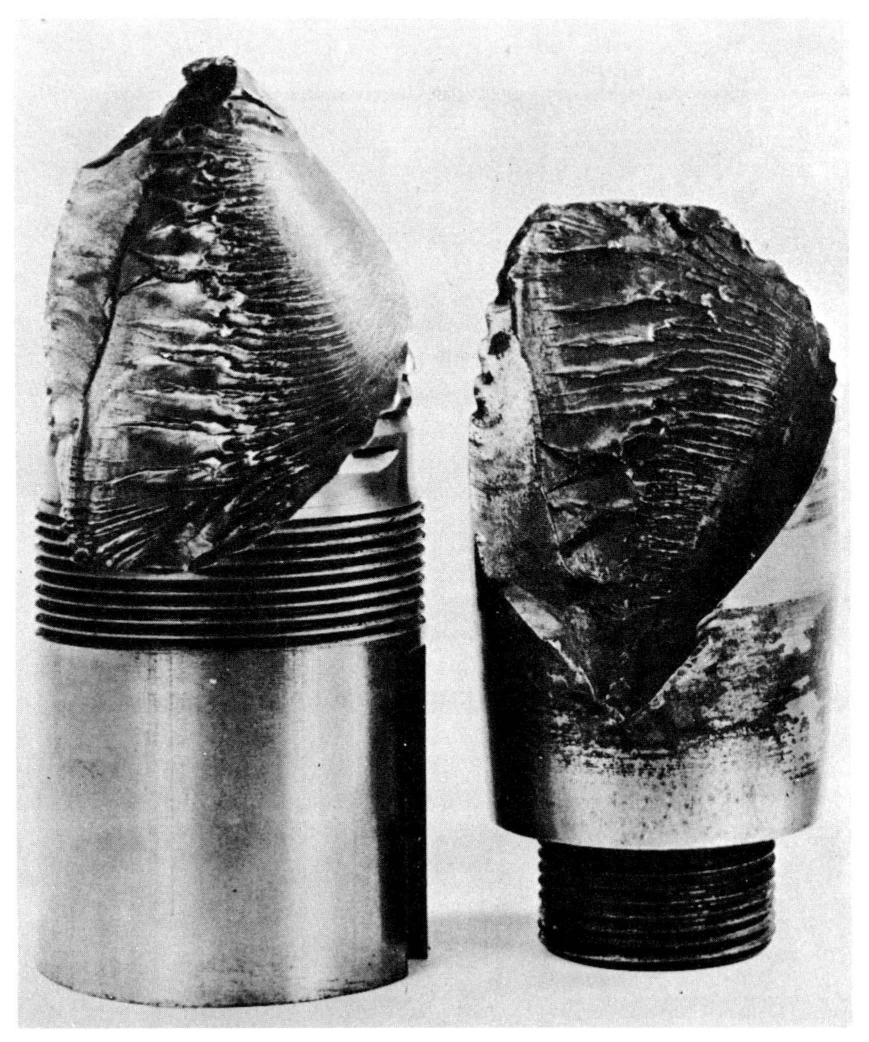

FIG. 10-2 Ripples on freshly fractured section of a shaft. (By permission from *Metal Fatigue*, G. Sines and J. L. Waisman, Eds., McGraw-Hill, New York, 1959, and courtesy T. J. Dolan, Univ. of Illinois)

fatigue fracture originates in a crack or a series of cracks which form on the surface of the specimen in the course of cyclic loading. The fracture spreads inward in ever-widening rings over the cross-sectional area. Ultimately, the unaffected portion of the section is reduced to a small core no longer capable of sustaining the applied load, and the specimen suddenly breaks in two. The regions corresponding to the progressive and sudden fractures can be easily identified in freshly broken sections, Fig. 10-1. One region is smooth and polished; the other is jagged and rough. The reason is not hard to find.

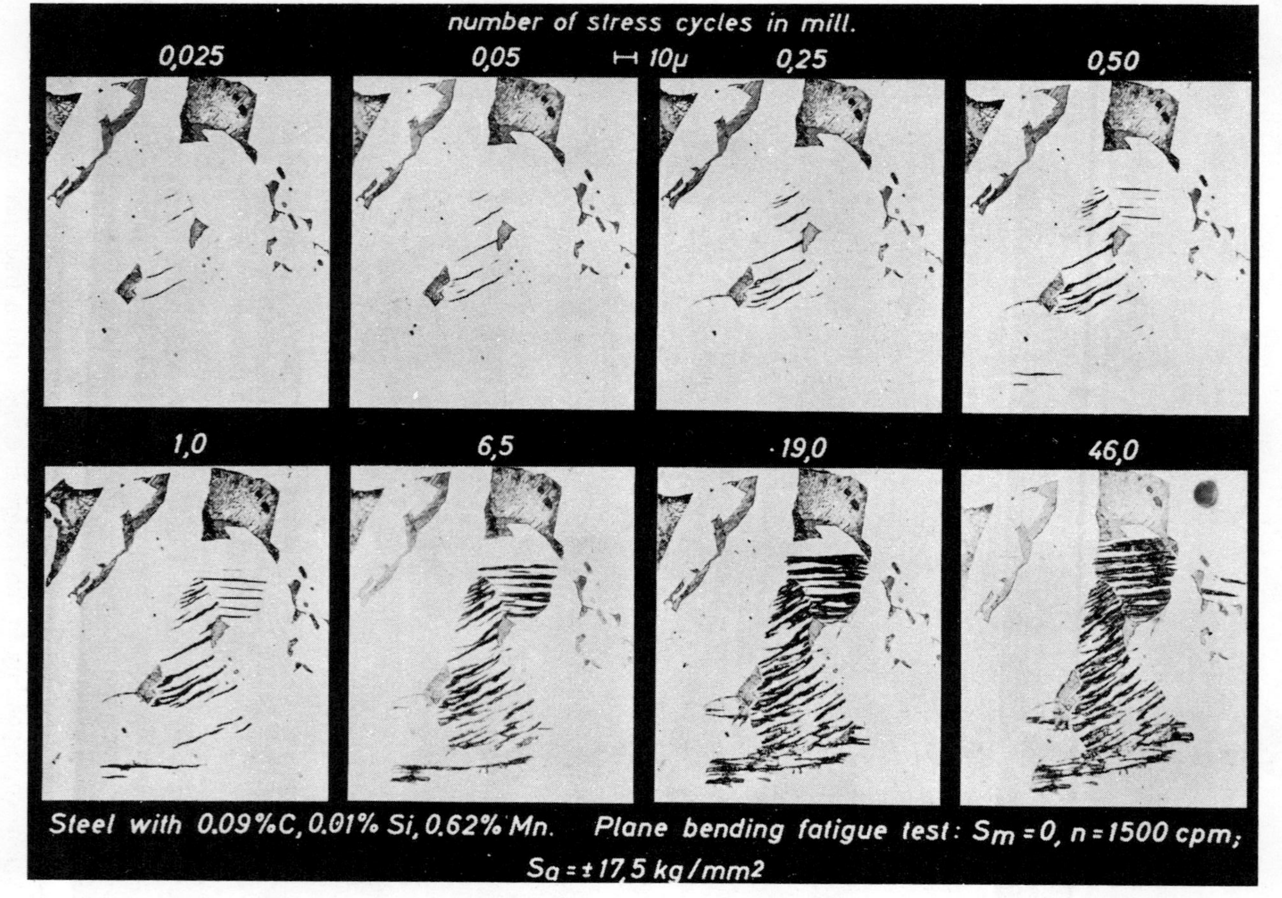

FIG. 10-3 Concentration of slip bands in isolated grains. (By permission from *Fracture*, B. L. Averbach et al., Eds., *Technology*, M.I.T., Cambridge, Mass., and Wiley, New York, 1959, and courtesy M. R. Hempel, Max Planck Inst., Dusseldorf)

While the fracture is progressing, the severed portions of the section rub and hammer against each other every time the alternation of loading closes the crack. This treatment ends up by smoothing out any roughness produced by the crack propagation. However, the roughness does not disappear in the

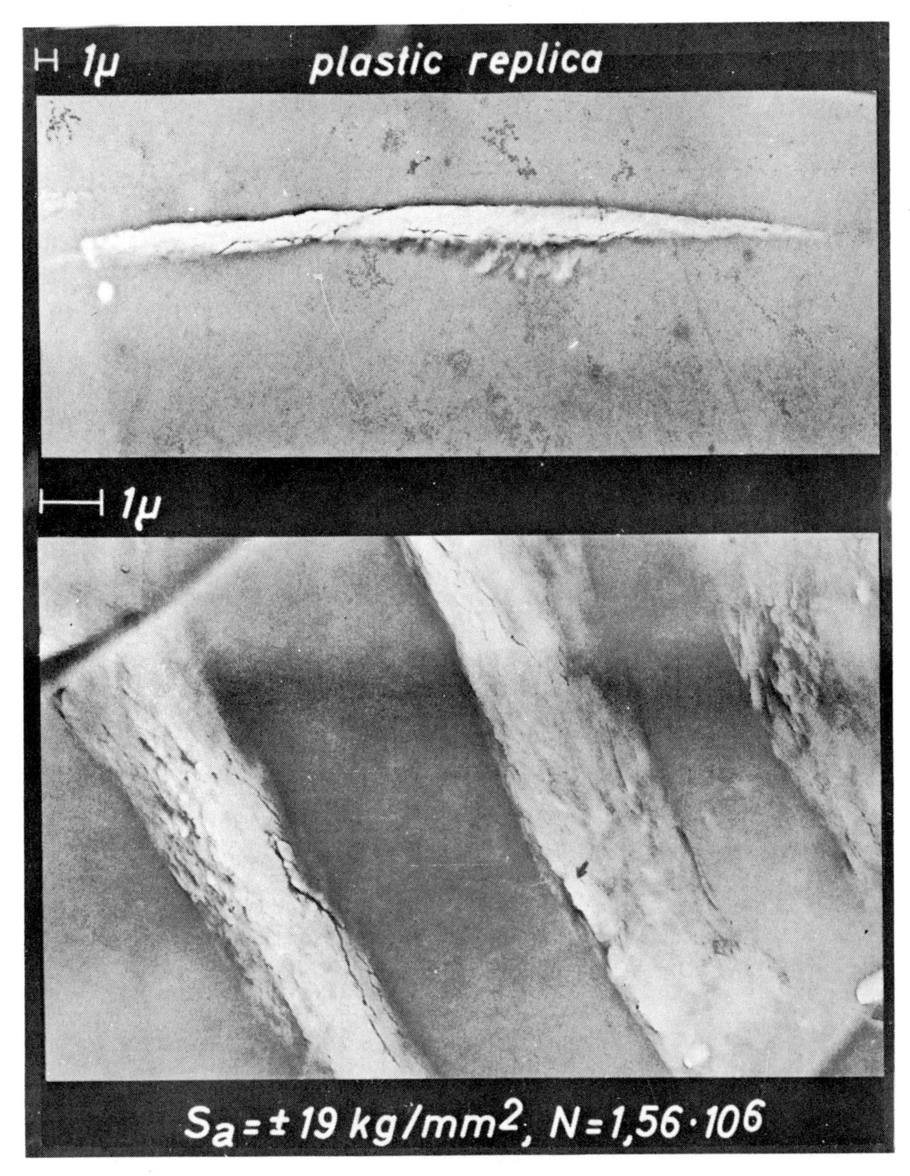

FIG. 10-4 Cracks on the surface of slip bands. (By permission from *Fracture*, B. L. Averbach et al., Eds., *Technology*, M.I.T., Cambridge, Mass., and Wiley, New York, 1959, and courtesy M. R. Hempel, Max Planck Inst., Dusseldorf)

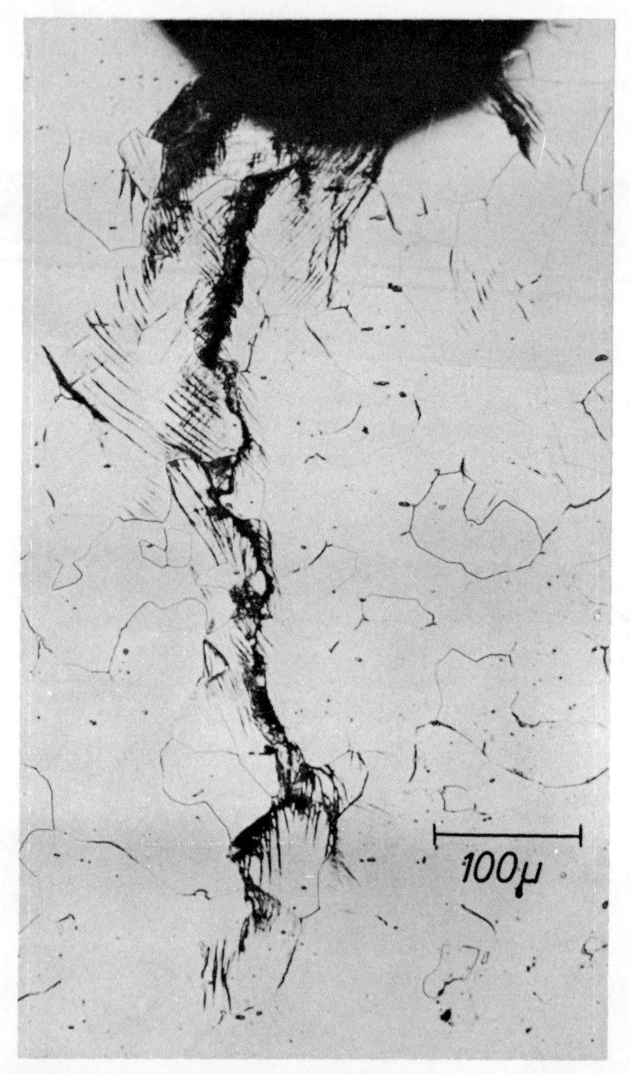

FIG. 10-5 Major crack leading to ultimate failure. (By permission from *Fracture*, B. L. Averbach et al., Eds., *Technology*, M.I.T., Cambridge, Mass., and Wiley, New York, 1959, and courtesy M. R. Hempel, Max Planck Inst., Dusseldorf)

core, because here the break occurs under a single load application in the last cycle.

Note. In many instances the smooth portion of the fractured section is covered with ripples lending a shell-like appearance to the surface, Fig. 10-2. The ripples seem to spread from a focal point at or near the surface. This focal point is often located in a surface irregularity (a notch, a keyhole) or in a structural defect (a foreign inclusion, a gas pocket). Both disturbances must be viewed as potential causes of fatigue failures—a point taken up more fully in Section 10-8. As for the ripples, they are believed to be caused by temporary halts and resumptions of the fracturing process. They are, in effect, boundary lines separating at each step the cracked from the sound portion of the section

In all circumstances the initiation of a crack is preceded by the appearance of slip lines that multiply as the load continues to cycle. However, instead of covering all grains with a uniform grid of parallel markings, the slip lines often concentrate on a few grains, and within these grains they are confined to isolated areas, or slip bands, Fig. 10-3. If the cyclic stress is above a certain level, some of the slip bands open up into very fine cracks, Fig. 10-4. In turn, some of the cracks continue growing on further cycling and merge into a major crack leading to ultimate fracture, Fig. 10-5.

This sequence of events makes it clear that fatigue is a result of a cumulative process involving slip. It is caused by alternation of the direction of slip, and, under certain critical conditions, the strength of the material is exceeded, giving rise to cracking and fracture. What is this cumulative process and what are these critical conditions? No completely satisfactory answer has yet been given to either question. As with plastic deformation, most of the pertinent information regarding fatigue strength must still be secured by direct experimentation.

10-3 Some Current Views on Fatigue Mechanisms. One way of approaching the problem of fatigue is to assume the existence of weak spots within the grain. The cycling stress can then cause these spots to deform plastically part way during the forward and backward phases of the cycle. On the other hand, the bulk of the material behaves wholly elastically during the entire cycle. As the cycling goes on, the material strain-hardens within the weak spots due to the cumulative action of plastic strain increments in both forward and backward directions. The spots now sustain a higher stress and a correspondingly higher elastic strain. They may end up by behaving wholly elastically before any fracture ensues. In that case the fatigued member can endure the applied cycling stress indefinitely.[1] Or the accumulation of plastic strain increments may strain-harden the weak spots to such a degree that they start developing cracks before the last vestige of plastic strain has disappeared. In that case continuation of cycling will cause fracture.[2]

Although the above approach emphasizes the role of strain-hardening at higher stress levels, a more recent approach pays closer attention to the behavior of surface grains in fatigue at low stress levels.[3] To explain this behavior we resort to a model. Let Fig. 10-6a represent a portion of a grain

[1] The existence of an endurance or fatigue limit is further considered in Section 10-5.

[2] E. Orowan, *Proc. Roy. Soc. (London)*, **A171**, 79(1939).

[3] M. A. Wood, "Some Basic Studies of Fatigue in Metals," in monograph *Fracture*, The Technology Press, M.I.T., Cambridge, Mass., and Wiley, New York, 1959.

adjacent to a free surface and subjected to pull and push in the horizontal direction. For simplicity, the grain is pictured as occupying the entire thickness of the specimen, in the direction perpendicular to the plane of the paper. The model has two types of slip planes in the slip band: planes t, which favor slip when the grain is extended, and planes c, which favor slip when the grain is compressed.

To see this more clearly, imagine that the dislocations have an easier escape by moving toward the free surface than by cutting their way inward through the maze of underlying grains. Depending on whether the compressed layer of atoms B, Fig. 9-7, is above or below the slip plane, the escape through the surface will occur on the t planes during tension and on the c planes during compression. A closer analysis of the dislocation movements will prove this point without difficulty.

The sequence of slips in slip band A after the first and the second cycle is depicted in Fig. 10-6, b_1c_1 and b_2c_2, respectively. It is seen that each cycle intensifies the gulf between the two faces of the slip bands A, turning it into

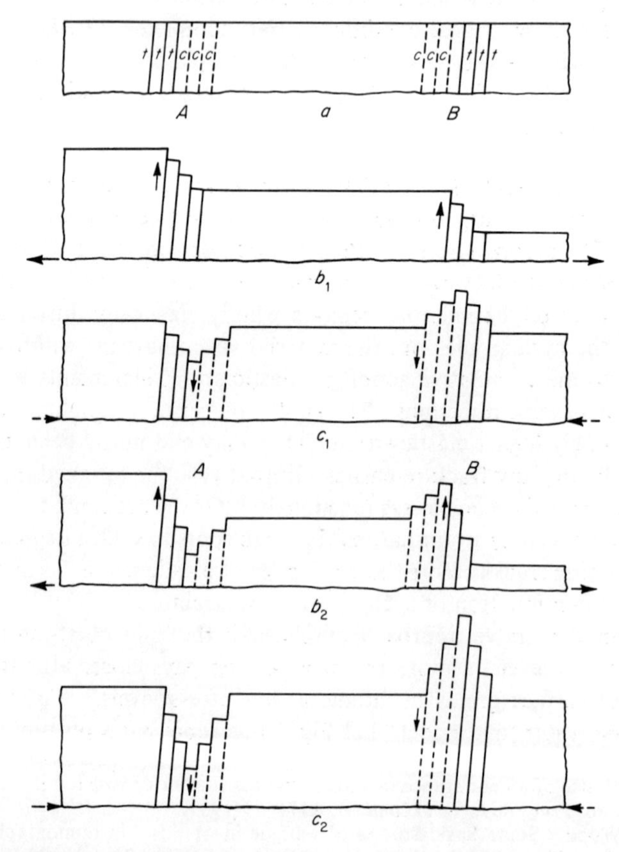

FIG. 10-6 Model showing formation of an intrusion and an extrusion in fatigue

a notch or "intrusion." A converse sequence of the t and c planes converts the gulf into a protuberance, or "extrusion," slip band B, Fig. 10-6. Several intrusions and one extrusion are visible in Fig. 10-7, a and b. It is of interest

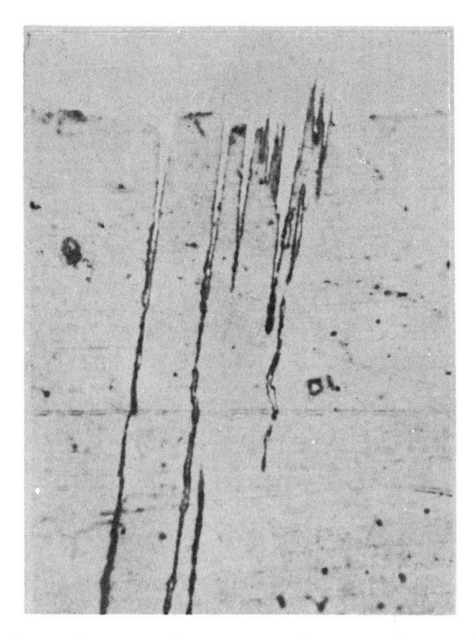

FIG. 10-7 Several intrusions and an extrusion on the surface of a fatigued specimen. (By permission from *Fracture*, B. L. Averbach et al., Eds., *Technology*, M.I.T., Cambridge, Mass., Wiley, New York, 1959, and courtesy W. A. Wood, University of Melbourne)

to note that some of the slip bands have opened up into fissures. As the cycling continues, the agglomeration of fissures at some depth below the surface leads to a crack formation, Fig. 10-8. Significantly, the crack appears to jump from one fissure to another rather than to follow the direction of a slip plane.

Neither the "strain-hardening" approach nor the "surface grain" approach are free from shortcomings when examined in detail. Moreover, no approach is yet able to predict measurable fatigue results from the behavior and configuration of dislocations at various stress levels. It appears likely that each is but an isolated aspect of a more complex fatigue mechanism which defies description in terms of structural changes alone. This presumption is strongly supported by the statistical nature of fatigue described below.

10-4 Statistical Nature of Fatigue. One of the most characteristic features of fatigue is the statistical behavior of the cumulative process leading to fracture. A population of apparently identical specimens subjected to the same cyclic load will fracture at widely different numbers of cycles. The difference may easily cover one or more orders of magnitude. Thus, out of

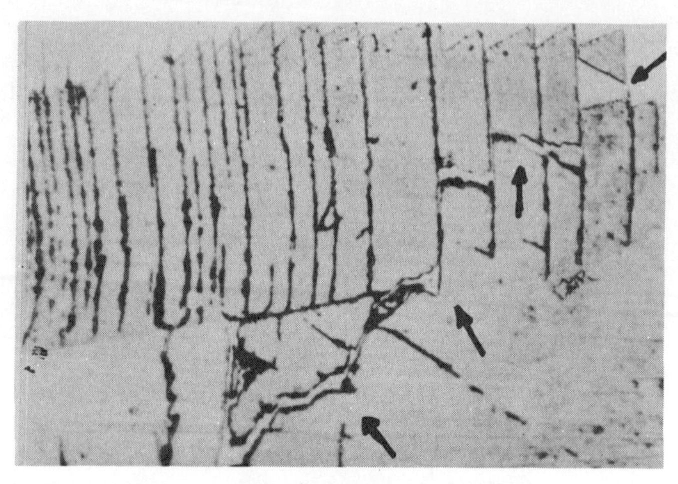

FIG. 10-8 Crack below the surface jumping from one fissure to another. (By permission from *Fracture*, B. L. Averbach et al., Eds., *Technology*, M.I.T., Cambridge, Mass., and Wiley, New York, 1959, and courtesy W. A. Wood, Univ. of Melbourne)

a population of 100 specimens, the first may break at 2×10^5 cycles and the next to the last may not fail before 5×10^6 cycles. (We must exclude the last specimen because it would correspond to 100% failures, which statistically means a certainty—a state of mind conceivable in matters of faith but not in matters of science.) How are we to deal with these data? We interpret them statistically. We say there is some risk of fracture at 2×10^5 cycles, but the chances, or probability, of survival are much greater than at 5×10^6 cycles. To be able to say more, we must know something about the distribution of the remaining 97 specimens. If the distribution curve were approximately normal, that is, if it were represented by the Gaussian error function, we could assign to the specimens fracturing at 2×10^5 cycles a probability of failure approaching 0.01, or, using its opposite, the probability of survival approaching 0.99. By the same token, the probability of survival at 5×10^6 cycles will be about 0.01. It turns out, however, that the number of cycles is not normally distributed. The peak of the distribution is shifted toward the lower limit, as shown schematically in Fig. 10-9a. Under these circumstances it is more convenient to work with the logarithms of the numbers of cycles, since the logarithmic scale extends the distance between the peak and the lower limit and thus makes the distribution more nearly normal, Fig. 10-9b. On that basis we would expect that the peak of the distribution curve would correspond to a number of cycles N such that $\log N = \frac{1}{2}(\log 2 \times 10^5 + \log 5 \times 10^6) = 6$, or $N = 10^6$, rather than to $N = \frac{1}{2}(2 \times 10^5 + 5 \times 10^6) = 2.6 \times 10^6$. It is clear that this peak represents the most frequently occurring or the most likely probability of survival which is equal to 0.5.

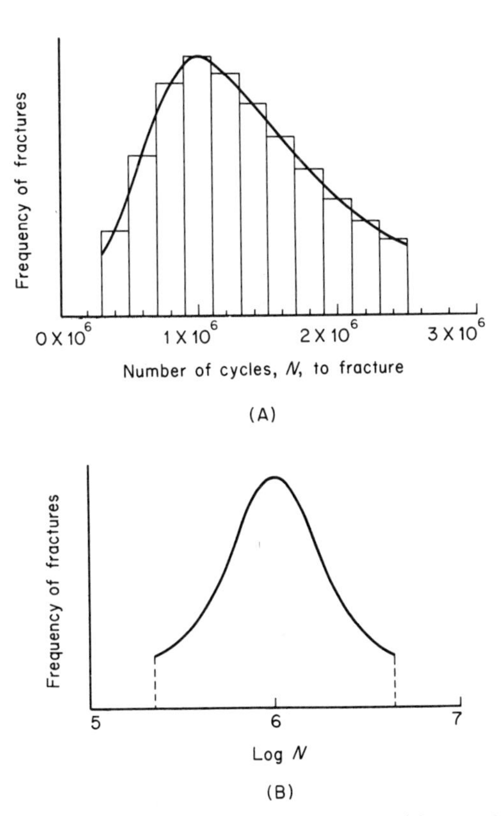

FIG. 10-9 Distribution of number of cycles to failure (a) on a linear scale and (b) on a logarithmic scale

In practice, we are interested in probabilities of survival much greater than 0.5, certainly no less than 0.99. However, if we aim at a high probability of survival, we must also submit a large population of specimens to the same cycling load. This procedure is unavoidable when it comes to the actual design, but it is prohibitive when studying the functional relationships between fatigue and various governing factors, because, as we will see, these factors are numerous. The current practice is to limit the population to one or two specimens and to assign to them the most likely probability of survival of 0.5.

10-5 The *S–N* Diagram. Fatigue Limit and Fatigue Strength. In possession of this preliminary information, we turn now to the main problem of fatigue. We wish to determine the stress level at which a given material can withstand a predetermined number of cycles N. In the laboratory tests this would normally imply, as we saw, a probability of survival of about 0.5.

To define the stress level more precisely we must consider the actual service conditions. In practice, however, no two pieces of machinery, no two elements of structure, undergo exactly the same type of fatigue loading during their lifetime. To achieve some degree of understanding of the underlying factors we must first reduce the general problem to a few simple cases. We begin by considering the case in which the applied stress oscillates between equal tension and compression of *constant* amplitude S, Fig. 10-10a. This type of loading will be called *reversed.* The span between $-S$ and $+S$ is called the *range.*

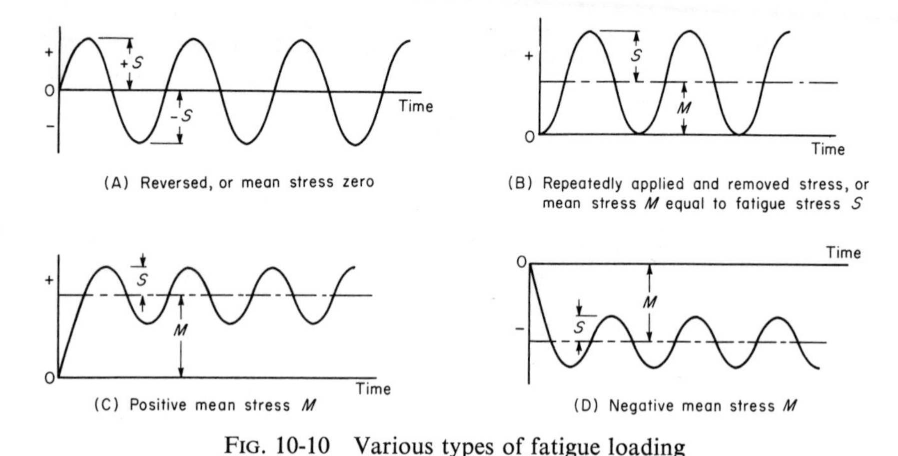

FIG. 10-10 Various types of fatigue loading

The smaller the amplitude S, the longer it will take to break the specimen. Experiment shows, however, that the relevant quantity here is not the time, but the number of cycles. A specimen will break sooner or later, depending on whether the frequency is high or low, at least up to 10,000 cycles per minute, but the number of cycles will be about the same in both cases. The results therefore are given in terms of the total number of cycles for fracture, N. In plotting the data, use is generally made of log S versus log N, rather than S versus N. This is done both to compress the scales and for design purposes, so the curves corresponding to various probabilities of survival are spaced more evenly, Fig. 10-11. It will be noticed that there is a steady increase of N as S decreases up to about 10^6 cycles. Thereafter a small decrease of S causes an appreciable increase of N.

For some materials, particularly for iron and iron alloys, the plot of log S versus log N shows a practically linear trend up to about 10^6 cycles and an almost horizontal trend thereafter, Fig. 10-12. Thus there seems to be a stress below which the fracture is unlikely to occur, no matter how large the number of cycles. We call this stress the *fatigue limit*, or *endurance limit.* For other materials, particularly for aluminum and aluminum alloys, there does not appear to exist a horizontal cutoff, Fig. 10-11. For these materials it is necessary to define a stress S that will not produce fracture before the

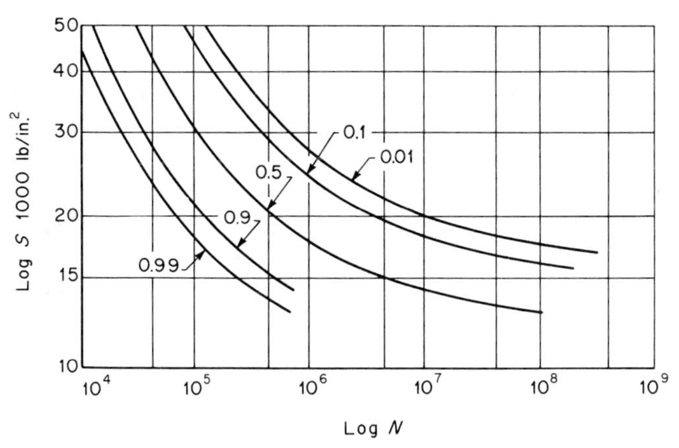

FIG. 10-11 *S* versus *N* curves with various probabilities of survival (logarithmic scale)

attainment of a number of cycles compatible with the general usefulness of the fatigued member in practice. Such a stress is called the *fatigue strength*. Like the yield stress, the fatigue strength is a conventional rather than an absolute limit. For many structural elements a fatigue strength at 2×10^6 cycles is sufficiently conservative, because it may take a long time to reach this number of cycles in practice. On the other hand, for a piece of a high-speed rotating machinery, a fatigue strength even at 50×10^6 cycles might not be enough, for this number of cycles could conceivably be reached during the useful life span of the piece. In most cases, however, a fatigue strength of 10^7 cycles would appear to be sufficient, especially if it is computed

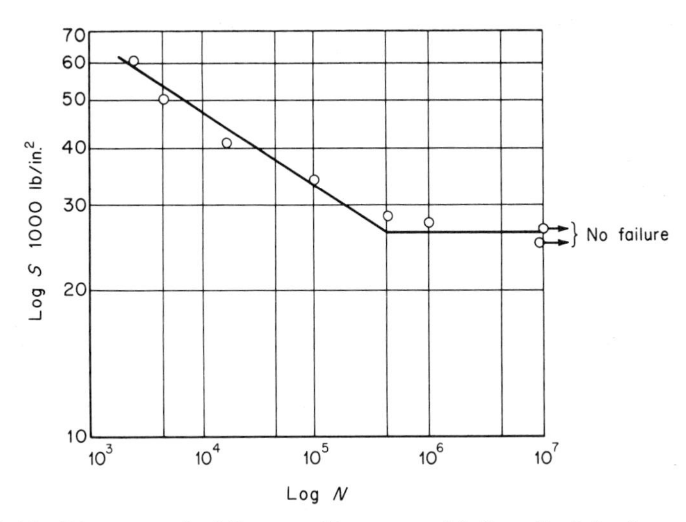

FIG. 10-12 Linear trend of *S* versus *N* curves and fatigue limit for iron and iron alloys (logarithmic scale)

for a probability of survival of 0.99 and for the most unfavorable combination of circumstances.

Unless otherwise stated, the term "fatigue strength" will be used henceforth to designate both fatigue strength and fatigue limit.

10-6 Correlation of Fatigue Strength with Plastic Properties. The existence of a common slip mechanism would lead us to expect that fatigue strength should correlate with certain plastic properties. Yet no satisfactory correlation has been derived, at least not with the critical shear stress in single crystals. On the other hand, there is little doubt that fatigue strength does depend on some basic shear criterion, for various types of fatigue loading could be successfully correlated between themselves using precisely this type of a criterion.[4]

There exists an empirical relationship between the reverse fatigue strength and the tensile strength, which so far has not been satisfactorily explained. It is found that in many instances the fatigue strength increases in direct proportion to the tensile strength. For iron and several iron alloys there is an approximate relationship which reads

$$\text{REVERSE FATIGUE LIMIT} = \tfrac{1}{2}\,\text{TENSILE STRENGTH}$$

For other materials, particularly aluminum and aluminum alloys, no such simple relationship exists.

10-7 Influence of Mean Static Stress on the Fatigue Strength. In the reverse type of loading, the stress oscillates about a mean stress equal to zero, Fig. 10-10a. However, it often happens that the mean stress is not zero. For example, when the load is repeatedly applied and removed, Fig. 10-10b, the cyclic stress may be described as a reverse stress of amplitude S oscillating about a mean static stress M equal to S. In general, however, M is not equal to S. It may be larger or smaller. It may be positive or negative, Fig. 10-10, c and d, where S, being an amplitude, has no sign.

The question that can be legitimately raised is this: How is the fatigue strength S influenced by M? The answer is provided in Fig. 10-13. The fatigue strength S is seen to decrease when the mean stress is tension and to increase when the mean stress is compression. The trend is practically linear up to the value of the mean stress equal to the yield stress. Thereafter, the situation is difficult to analyze because of the increasing amount of plastic deformation. The increase of the fatigue strength S caused by a mean compressive stress M is particularly noteworthy in view of the remedial measures discussed in Section 10-8.

[4] G. Sines, "Behavior of Metals under Complex Static and Alternating Stresses," in monograph, *Metal Fatigue*, G. Sines and J. L. Waisman, Eds., McGraw-Hill, New York, 1959.

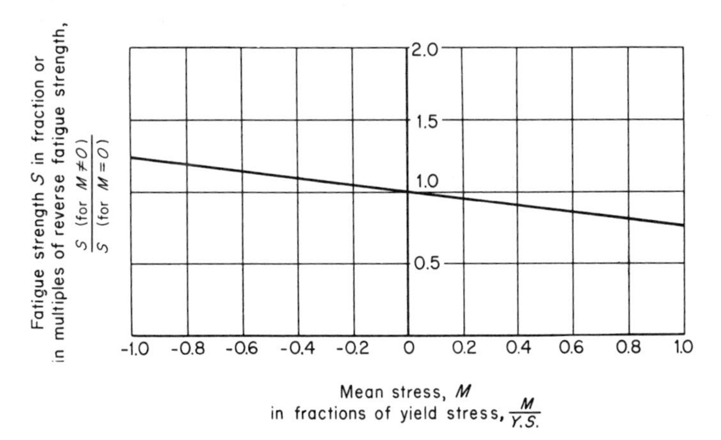

FIG. 10-13 Variation of fatigue strength with mean stress

10-8 Factors Affecting Fatigue Strength. Remedial Treatments. It should come as no surprise that fatigue strength—whether reverse or not—is a structure-sensitive property. Like yield strength, it is affected by many factors: chemical composition, grain size, amount of cold working—to name a few. The variation with temperature is similar to that of yield strength. Fatigue strength increases when the temperature is lowered, particularly below the ambient temperature. In addition, fatigue strength is critically influenced by *surface conditions*. This, too, is not surprising, considering the role played by surface grains in the generation of cracks.

Surface conditions can affect fatigue strength in three ways:

(a) through the geometry of the surface,
(b) through the physical nature of the surface layers, and
(c) through chemical environment.

Roughness, porosity, and foreign inclusions (slag, oxides) are characteristic geometrical and physical defects of metallic surfaces. Their presence can lower the value of fatigue strength by as much as 20%, depending on the material and the seriousness of the defect. Nothing, however, exceeds in destructiveness the action of a corrosive medium. By attacking the surface of a metal, chemical agents can reduce its fatigue strength to almost nothing. Obviously, fatigue strength cannot be considered as a property of the material alone unless all surface defects have been eliminated.

To combat the adverse action of these defects several remedial treatments are employed. If surface roughness cannot be avoided, its deleterious effect can be offset by subjecting the surface layers of a metal to a mechanical treatment called *peening*. In this treatment steel or sand shots impinge on the surface with a predetermined velocity and cold-work the surface layers by producing tiny indentations. Moreover, by being pushed out of the indentations, the surface layers become slightly overextended with respect to the untreated underlying layers. These layers react by trying to push the overextended surface layers back. They thus subject them to compression. During cycling, the compression acts as a static mean stress, which, by the findings of Section 10-7, helps further to increase the fatigue strength of the surface layers.

Another way of improving the fatigue strength is by heat treatment. Many iron alloys can be hardened by being heated to a high temperature and quenched in water. This treatment, when applied locally to the surface layers, substantially increases their fatigue strength. Further increase of strength can be achieved by combining heat treatment with chemical action of elements like carbon and nitrogen, which diffuse into the surface layers of iron at high temperatures—the so-called case hardening and nitriding. Finally, effective immunity against chemical corrosion can be secured by plating the surface of metals with *protective coatings.*

10-9 Fatigue of Ceramic Materials. While the foregoing referred mostly to metals, ceramic materials and minerals exhibiting perceptible amounts of plastic deformation are expected to fail likewise in fatigue under cycling loading. This has been found to be true of silver chloride, which is ductile at room temperature. However, the majority of ceramic materials are brittle under ambient conditions. We saw in Chapter 8 that brittle materials exhibit delayed fractures under moderate loads. These fractures will occur whether the load is cycled or not, and as a rule they do not involve the mechanism of slip. On that basis, the name "static fatigue," sometimes given to the phenomenon of delayed fracture, is likely to be misleading.

10-10 Design for Fatigue. In the discussion of factors affecting fatigue, Section 10-8, we deliberately left out the factors that depend on the size or shape of the fatigued member and the nature of the applied loading. These factors are often more decisive in design than all the others combined. The increasing incidence of fatigue failures could be rightly blamed on the disregard for the teachings of stress analysis in the first quarter of this century. Today the practicing engineer has learned to pay close attention to stress conditions created by the presence of notches, holes, reentrant angles, or surface irregularities of any sort. It can be said without exaggeration that the incidence of fatigue fractures decreases in direct proportion to the care with which the designer analyzes the stress situation in structural and machine elements.

The knowledge of the stress situation, no matter how consummate, does not solve all design problems in fatigue. One of the most important tasks is to assess correctly the effect of actual loading. Instances in which this loading is of constant amplitude and periodicity are exceptions rather than the rule. In general, the loading is neither constant nor steady. The situation is particularly complex for aircraft, which fly in all kinds of weather and are affected by the vibrations—mechanical and sonic—of their own power plants no less than by atmospheric conditions. Structures and machines are often subjected to brief overloads followed by longer periods of a more moderately fluctuating load. What is the cumulative effect on fatigue of these two types of loading—or any other types for that matter? No fully satisfactory answer has been found. Much of the current work on fatigue is devoted to the solution of this very important problem.

10-11 Summary. Fatigue is a manifestation of a cumulative process leading to *progressive fracture* under cyclic loading. All indications are that fatigue cracks *start at the surface* and spread inwards. The basic mechanism in fatigue is *slip*, the same as in plastic deformation. Slip lines, however, are generally confined to a fraction of the grains, and they are concentrated in *isolated* slip bands within the grain.

Fatigue has a *statistical* behavior. A population of apparently identical specimens breaks under the same cyclic loads at widely different numbers of cycles, N. The distribution is approximately *normal* when plotted against $\log N$. Smaller values of $\log N$ thus correspond to larger *probabilities of survival.*

In *reverse* axial loading the stress varies periodically from tension to compression of equal and constant amplitude S. The plot of $\log S$ versus $\log N$ reveals an almost horizontal cutoff for some materials. The corresponding stress is called the *fatigue limit*, or *endurance limit*. It is often well below the yield strength. In the absence of a cutoff, a stress causing fracture at a predetermined number of cycles, generally around 10^7, and with probability of survival generally about 0.99, is called the *fatigue strength. Reverse fatigue strength* correlates with the tensile strength for many metallic materials.

In reverse axial loading the *mean* static stress M is zero. When M varies within the limits of the yield strength from compression to tension, the fatigue strength S varies linearly from *higher* to *lower* values.

Fatigue strength is a structure-sensitive property. However, at variance with plastic properties it is also *critically* dependent on surface conditions: surface roughness, porosity, inclusions and, most of all, corrosive environment. Remedial treatments are peening, surface hardening, and protective coatings.

Ductile ceramics are prone to fatigue, as are metals. Brittle ceramics generally exhibit delayed fracture whether the load is cycled or not.

In many instances successful design for fatigue depends more on a judicious stress analysis of the structure than on improved fatigue properties of the material. Future progress however hinges mainly on our ability to cope with randomly varying loads.

References

ADVANCED

1. "Fracture," *Proc. Intern. Conference*, Technology, M.I.T., Cambridge, Mass., and Wiley, New York, 1959.
2. *Metal Fatigue*, G. Sines and J. L. Waisman, Eds., McGraw-Hill, New York, 1959.
3. WADC—University of Minnesota Conference on Acoustical Fatigue, W. Add, Project No. 7360, March 1961.

Problems

10-1 By examining the fracture of two seemingly identical specimens, it was found that the rough core in one of them was larger than in the other. Which one failed under a higher load and why?

10-2 At 40,000 lb/in.^{2} the probability of survival equal to 0.99 was found to occur at 80,000 cycles and the probability of survival equal to 0.01 at 500,000 cycles. Assuming a normal distribution with respect to $\log N$, compute N corresponding to the probability of survival = 0.5.

10-3 Draw a $\log S - \log N$ diagram using the data below for reverse fatigue strength.

Stress (10^4 lb/in.^{2})	*Number of Cycles to Failure*
25	20,000
20	70,000
17	200,000
15	1,000,000
12	20,000,000

Determine the fatigue strength for 5 million cycles and for 10 million cycles.

10-4 The reverse fatigue strengths obtained in Problem 10-3 is decreased 15% when the load is repeated (i.e., when mean stress M = fatigue stress S). What is the total maximum stress? What would be the change if the mean stress M were a compression of the same magnitude?

10-5 A tubular flagpole was found to break in fatigue at the base. Indicate the probable cause of fatigue and causes of failure. Suggest a remedy without "beefing up" the dimensions.

11 / MECHANICAL PROPERTIES RELATED TO PLASTICITY: 2 FRICTION COEFFICIENT

Plastic deformation has been shown to play a significant role in fatigue. Equally significant appears to be its role in the well-known phenomenon of friction, at least where metallic surfaces are involved. In this chapter we shall present the available evidence and show how it is related to the experimental laws of friction and to the friction coefficient.

11-1 Manifestation. The phenomenon of friction manifests itself whenever two solid surfaces rub against each other or slide over each other. The manifestation is twofold: (a) *thermal*—there is considerable amount of heat liberated in the process—and (b) *mechanical*—the surfaces in contact markedly resist the gliding motion.

As a *source of heat*, friction is one of the oldest phenomena put to use by mankind: the kindling of fire by rubbing two twigs against each other has been known since the dawn of civilization. It represents one of man's greatest discoveries. It is an art still practiced among primitive peoples (such as the Solomon Islands aborigines). Striking a match derives from the same phenomenon of friction.

The *resistance to glide* offered by friction probably has been known as long as its capacity to produce heat, for example, a knot tied in a rope to moor a boat, or the rope wrapped around the axle of a windlass to lift a load. Friction was one of the earliest mechanical phenomena given the status of law. The two basic laws of friction are named after the French engineer Amonton, who announced them in a note to the Academie Royale des Sciences in 1699, but the discovery rightly belongs to Leonardo da Vinci (1452–1519), who mentions them in his papers. The name of Coulomb, who described numerous experimental verifications in 1781, is also associated with these laws.

11-2 Amonton's Laws. The two basic laws of friction can be stated as follows.

Let P in Fig. 11-1 be a compressive force normal to two flat solid surfaces in contact, and let F be a force acting parallel to these surfaces. If F is of sufficient magnitude to overcome the resistance to glide, then the ratio $F/P = f$, called *coefficient of friction*, is

1. independent of the magnitude of P and
2. independent of contact area A.

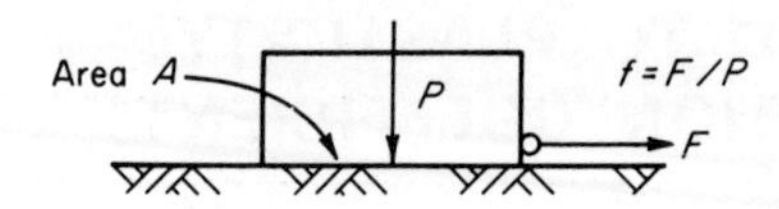

FIG. 11-1 Definition of friction coefficient

The experimental verification of the first law is straightforward. If F and P are measured independently at the *initiation* of glide, the ratio $F/P = f$ is found to be constant over a large range of loads. In the example of Fig. 11-2, the range of loads covers six orders of magnitude, from 10 mg to 10 kg.

The verification of the second law depends very much on what is meant by the area of contact. With care it is possible to prepare clean, flat surfaces in which the height of asperities is of the order of 10^{-5} cm. Even so, when brought in contact, these surfaces will touch each other only at a few high spots. From indirect measurements (from electrical resistance, for example), it has been concluded that the real area of contact can be as little as a fraction

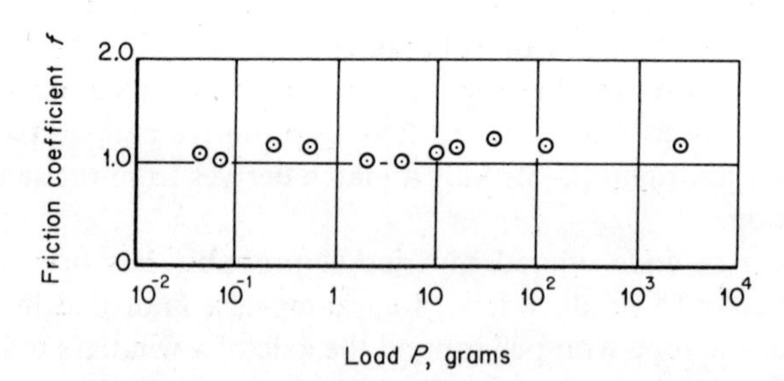

FIG. 11-2 Amonton's law. Steel block sliding on electrolytically polished aluminum surface (after Bowden and Tabor)

of 1% of the apparent area.[1] It is clear that under these circumstances the apparent area has little in common with the phenomenon of friction. Not so the real area, which will be shown to play an important role in the phenomenon of friction if plastic deformation is drawn in as a contributing factor.

11-3 Friction and Plastic Deformation. Evidence of plastic deformation, in the form of slip lines, has been produced by causing friction to occur on

[1] F. B. Bowden and D. Tabor, *The Friction and Lubrication of Solids*, Clarendon (Oxford), New York, 1954.

aluminum surfaces under loads as small as 200 dyn.[1] To initiate plastic deformation, a pressure of at least 10^8 dyn/cm^2 must have been developed, as explained in Section 9-9. It follows that the real contact area could not have been greater than 2×10^{-6} cm^2. Actually, if the asperities are not shallower than 10^{-5} cm, it is likely that the contact area is much smaller than 2×10^{-6} cm^2, at least at the beginning of loading, when the surfaces are barely touching each other at a few spots. Thereupon, however, the high spots begin deforming plastically under the applied load and flatten out. Less protruding spots come in contact and flatten out in turn. The deformation continues until the contact area has widened enough to support a pressure commensurate with the particular plastic properties of the metallic surfaces. If we assume that this pressure has a characteristic value p independent of the magnitude of the applied load, then the *real* contact area is proportional to the load, regardless of the size of the *apparent* contact area. However, there seems to be more to the phenomenon of friction than merely the flattening of high spots. Some sort of a bond also must have been created across these spots. When two different metallic surfaces are used, the tangential force F, in overcoming the resistance to glide, invariably shears the weaker of the two metals at the connecting spots. This would explain the dependence of friction on plastic deformation.

Amonton's two laws are a direct consequence of the above model. Thus, let τ be the value of the shear stress acting across the spots which bond the two metallic surfaces. Like the pressure p, τ can be assumed to have a characteristic value dependent only on the nature of surfaces. If A is the *real* contact area, then, by definition, the applied load P is

$$P = Ap \tag{11-1}$$

and the tangential force F is

$$F = A\tau \tag{11-2}$$

Dividing Eq. (11-2) by Eq. (11-1) yields

$$F/P = \tau/p = f \tag{11-3}$$

Since τ and p are assumed to be characteristic constants of the metallic surfaces, the same must apply to their ratio f. This conclusion is borne out by Amonton's first law, which makes f independent of P.

Amonton's second law follows directly from Eq. (11-3). Neither the true nor the apparent contact area enters this equation, thus making f independent of both areas. More specifically, when the load P is applied to a smaller apparent area, there are proportionally fewer high spots, but each of them is deformed proportionally more, so as to sustain the same constant pressure p. Thus, while the apparent contact area has changed, the true contact area has remained the same. So has the tangential force F. Consequently, the ratio $F/P = f$ has not been affected by the change of the apparent contact area.

11-4 Factors Affecting the Coefficient of Friction. Lubrication and Wear. The coefficient of friction of clean, unlubricated metallic surfaces is found generally to lie between 1.5 and 0.5. The upper limit is indicative of friction of pure metals on themselves. If bonding across the real area of contact were tantamount to true cohesion, a finite force F would be necessary to shear the metal, no matter how small P, and the coefficient of friction would be very high indeed. This is the case of spectroscopically pure metals outgassed in vacuum, in which complete seizure can take place. However, on admission of oxygen or air, the coefficient of friction falls back to the lower values given above. Friction of metals under ordinary conditions of cleanliness appears to be caused by the fact that the layer of oxide, which is formed on the surface, is broken at spots under the application of load. Temporary bonding occurs at these spots; but the oxide layer is reformed after the load P has been removed, and so seizure is prevented. The matching of mechanical properties of the oxide layer and underlying metal seems to have a significant influence on the coefficient of friction. Thus, under small loads, layers of copper oxide deform elastically about the same amount as the metallic copper underneath. Hence the layer of oxide remains largely unbroken, and the coefficient of friction is accordingly low, about 0.4. On the other hand aluminum oxide is much stiffer and more brittle than the softer aluminum substratum. It breaks under any load, and the coefficient of friction is correspondingly high, about 1.2.

This difference in behavior also helps one to understand the *role of lubricants.* If the lubricants form an adherent layer, the coefficient of friction is reduced to about 0.1. Adsorbed gaseous surface films may also be the reason for the low friction coefficients of such hard minerals as sapphire and diamond, for which f is of the order of 0.2. If surface films are removed by heating in vacuum, the friction coefficient of diamond on itself rises to very high values.

Chemical composition and type of structure, rather than surface conditions, seem to govern the frictional properties of polymers and plastics. The coefficient of friction may approach the value of unlubricated metals, and it may be even lower, as low as 0.04. The figure 0.04 refers to the fluorocarbon type of plastic known as *Teflon.* Rollers clad with Teflon find wide application for sliding doors. The friction coefficient remains low even at temperatures approaching 200°C.

Despite the relatively low values of friction coefficients, lubricated metals, minerals, and plastics finally wear out in service. The process of *wear* can manifest itself in a variety of ways: abrasion, corrosion, cracking, tearing, chipping, etc. High friction coefficients are indicative of rapid wear. To what extent bonding and shear contribute to wear damage is not entirely settled. Plastic deformation is not the only phenomenon involved. In addition, the asperities undergo repeated elastic compression in the course of sliding—a condition very much reminiscent of the fatigue phenomenon discussed in Chapter 10.[2]

11-5 Summary. The force necessary to overcome friction between two solids sliding over each other is proportional to the force with which these solids are pressed against each other. The coefficient of proportionality, called *coefficient of friction*, is independent of the apparent area of contact. Spectroscopically pure metals, outgassed in vacuum, seize upon each other and, if gliding is to occur, must be sheared exactly as in plastic deformation. The presence of oxide films and adsorbed gaseous layers on clean, unlubricated metal surfaces prevents seizure, but temporary bonding, presumably caused by plastic deformation at isolated real areas of contact, accounts for coefficients of friction between 0.5 and 1.5. An adherent layer of lubricant lowers these values to about 0.1. Values as low as 0.04 are found among inert plastics such as Teflon.

References

ADVANCED

1. F. B. Bowden and D. Tabor, *The Friction and Lubrication of Solids*, Clarendon Press, Oxford, New York, 1954.
2. "International Conference on the Nature of Solid Friction," *J. Appl. Phys.*, **32**, 1407–1454, August 1961.

Problems

11-1 It has been suggested (J. F. Archard, *Proc. Roy. Soc.*, **A243**, 190) that in wear, the peaks of asperities are deformed elastically by the process of rubbing. Could chipping and production of loose debris be accounted for in these cases by fatigue? What type of fatigue?

11-2 It has been found that at speeds of sliding reaching several feet per second, the coefficient of friction of low melting point metals like lead and tin is much lower than at the initiation of glide, when the speed is practically nil. The decrease is attributed to local melting. What has contributed to the melting?

11-3 In Section 1-8, the lubricating action of graphite was attributed to its flat layer structure and weak molecular bonding. Recent work shows that this is not the only contributing factor and that gases like oxygen and water vapor also intervene to lower the friction coefficient. What experiment would you suggest to prove this point?

11-4 Will problems of friction be more or will they be less troublesome in space than in terrestrial technology?

[2] L. Rozeanu and O. Preotesco, "Some Fundamental Aspects of the Wear Phenomena," *Rumanian Academy of Sciences*, IX, 169–185(1958). See also J. F. Archard, *J. Appl. Phys.*, **32**, 1420 (August 1961).

12 / MECHANICAL PROPERTIES: VISCOSITY AND CREEP PROPERTIES

So far, the mechanical properties of materials have been studied with no particular regard to time. Time becomes an important factor when the overall deformation of the material is caused not only by the change of configuration but also by the motion of elementary particles. The flow of liquids is particularly revealing in this respect. We begin by studying the viscous behavior associated with liquid flow[1] and extend our study to a similar behavior found in solids, where it is called *creep*.

12-1 Viscosity—Manifestation and Derivation. The viscosity of liquids is manifest in the simple operation of pouring. Water, oil, and syrup equally well adhere to (i.e., wet) the walls of the vessel, yet water flows easily whereas syrup flows very sluggishly, with oil showing an intermediate behavior. In all three instances the flow consists of a relative motion of layers of liquid sliding past each other, beginning with the layer next to the one that adheres to the wall of the vessel. We conclude that water, oil, and syrup offer different resistances to such a sliding or shearing motion, the resistance of syrup being the greatest. Similar differences in resistance are encountered in general whenever the flow of liquid is *laminar*, i.e., whenever it resembles the sliding motion of a stack of lamellae, as in the flow of water in deep rivers. The situation is a great deal more complicated when the flow becomes *turbulent*, as when coffee is vigorously stirred with a spoon in a cup. Fortunately, in the study of viscosity we need not concern ourselves with turbulent flow.

To better analyze the type of resistance offered by liquids to a laminar flow, we consider (Fig. 12-1) a prismatic portion of a liquid of thickness l contained between two plates: one stationary, the other animated with a uniform velocity v in the horizontal, or x, direction. By virtue of laminar flow, a continuous velocity gradient exists between the horizontal layers of the liquid. The velocity changes from zero, in the layer adherent to the bottom plate, to v, in the layer adherent to the top plate. The change will be

[1] Viscosity is also a characteristic property of gaseous flow, or of fluid flow in general, if no distinction is made between liquids and gases. However, gaseous viscosity is a direct consequence of the random motion of elementary particles. On that account its proper place appears to be in more advanced courses, such as thermodynamics, concerned with this type of motion.

proportionately smaller between closer layers. Let Δv be its value for two adjacent molecular layers a and b, Fig. 12-1.

Since liquids as a rule are amorphous and unstable, the resistance to flow cannot very well depend on either the regularity or stability of the molec-

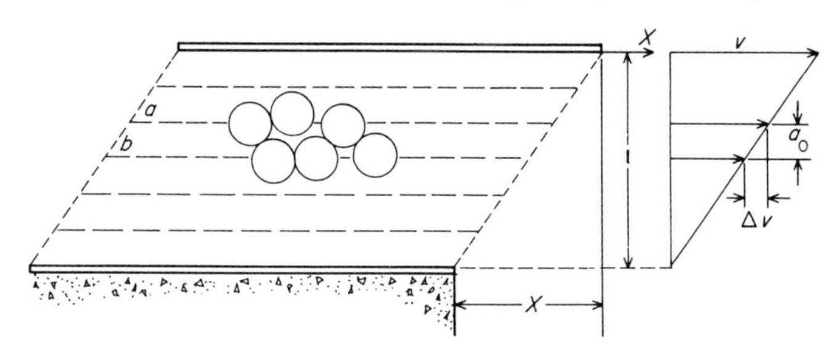

FIG. 12-1 Laminar flow of a liquid between two plates

ular arrangement which characterizes the solid state. However, it can—and it does—depend (as we shall see) on the existence of intermolecular forces. These forces, we recall from Chapter 7, are of the same order of magnitude as in solids. Near the melting point they maintain the molecules in close contact, so that the interchange of partners, a characteristic feature of liquid instability, can take place only between nearest neighbors. In passing from one layer to another, the molecule is thus subjected periodically to restoring forces of attraction toward its temporary position of equilibrium. Following Andrade,[2] we will assume that this period coincides with the natural period of thermal vibration δ of the molecule in the solid. We shall also assume for simplicity that the interchange of molecules in layers a and b is entirely confined to these two layers. However, the validity of the argument given below does not rest on this restriction.

If the laminar flow represented by Fig. 12-1 is to continue undisturbed, a molecule of mass m must lose momentum $m\,\Delta v$ when passing from layer a to layer b. Conversely, a molecule passing from layer b to layer a must gain momentum $m\,\Delta v$. In both cases the molecule must be given an impulse: against the direction of motion in the first case, in the direction of motion in the second case. The duration of impulse, according to Andrade, is not the whole period of vibration δ but only $\delta/4$, since this is the time during which the molecule, covering a distance equal to one amplitude of vibration, approaches the adjacent layer most closely in the downward or upward motion. Consequently, if f is the force needed to increase the momentum of the molecule when passing from layer b to layer a, the equality of impulse and momentum requires that

$$f\,\delta/4 = m\,\Delta v \tag{12-1}$$

Instead of δ we shall use its reciprocal ν, the number of vibrations per

[2] E. N. da C. Andrade, *Viscosity and Plasticity*, Chemical Publishing Co., New York, 1951.

unit time, or the frequency. Putting $1/\nu$ for δ and solving Eq. (12-1) for f, we get

$$f = 4\nu m\,\Delta v \tag{12-2}$$

The force f acts in the direction of increasing values of v, i.e., in the plus x direction. A force of the same magnitude but in the opposite, minus x, direction acts on a molecule passing from layer a to layer b.

Since both ν and m are constant for a given liquid and at a given temperature, we conclude from Eq. (12-2) that to maintain a velocity difference between adjacent layers, a force proportional to this velocity difference must be applied to each molecule.

As was true for elasticity, it is more convenient to express the law embodied in Eq. (12-2) in terms of macroscopically measurable quantities. To this end we assign an average cubical volume a_0^3 to each molecule. If M is the mass of the liquid per mole, ρ its density, and N_A Avogadro's number, we have, by putting $n = 1$ (one molecule per cubical volume) in Eq. (2-4), Chapter 2,

$$a_0 = \sqrt[3]{M/(N_A\rho)} \tag{12-3}$$

Furthermore, the area occupied by the molecule in each layer is a_0^2. Hence, the number of molecules per unit area is $1/a_0^2$. If all molecules had changed layers by changing partners, the force per unit area would be f/a_0^2. However, on the average only $\frac{1}{3}$ of the molecules change layers; the remaining $\frac{2}{3}$ exchange partners in the same layer with no loss or gain of momentum. Hence, the force per unit area, or stress, needed to maintain the velocity difference Δv is $f/3a_0^2$. This is a shear stress, since it acts in the plane of the layer. We have, therefore, by calling the shear stress τ,

$$\tau = f/3a_0^2 \tag{12-4}$$

Substitution of Eq. (12-4) into Eq. (12-2) and rearrangement of terms yields

$$\tau = \frac{4\nu m}{3a_0^2}\Delta v \tag{12-5}$$

In like manner we can replace the velocity difference Δv between adjacent layers by a velocity gradient v/l. Obviously,

$$\Delta v/a_0 = v/l \tag{12-6}$$

But

$$v = dx/dt$$

and, since l is a constant,

$$v/l = \frac{dx}{l\,dt} = \frac{d(x/l)}{dt} \tag{12-7}$$

The ratio x/l is the relative shear displacement, or shear strain, of the upper layer of the liquid with respect to the lower one. Putting

$$\gamma = x/l \tag{12-8}$$

we finally have

$$v/l = \frac{d(x/l)}{dt} = \frac{d\gamma}{dt} = \dot{\gamma} \tag{12-9}$$

where the dot over the symbol denotes differentiation with respect to time; $\dot{\gamma}$ is called *shear strain rate.*

Substituting Eq. (12-9) into Eq. (12-6) and replacing Δv in Eq. (12-5) by its expression from Eq. (12-6), we obtain the following expression of the viscosity law, derived by E. N. da C. Andrade in 1930:

$$\tau = \frac{4\nu m}{3a_0}\dot{\gamma} \tag{12-10}$$

12-2 Coefficient of Viscosity. According to Eq. (12-10), the shear stress τ is proportional to the shear strain rate $\dot{\gamma}$. The coefficient of proportionality is called the *coefficient of viscosity* or, frequently, merely the viscosity. It is generally denoted by the Greek letter η. Thus

$$\eta = \frac{4\nu m}{3a_0} \tag{12-11}$$

Hence, Eq. (12-10) can also be written to read

$$\tau = \eta\dot{\gamma} \tag{12-12}$$

Both τ and $\dot{\gamma}$ can be measured in special testing machines called viscosimeters. Thus η can be determined experimentally. According to Eq. (12-12), the units of η in the CGS system, generally utilized for liquids, are dynes seconds per square centimeter, or dyn sec/cm^2. The unit 1 dyn sec/cm^2 is called a *poise* (abbreviated P)—a word made up of the first five letters of the name of the French physician Poiseuille (1797–1869), who carried out the first exact measurements of viscous flow of water in pipes. The one hundredth part of a poise is called a *centipoise* (abbreviated cP). Viscosity of water at room temperature is almost exactly equal to 1 cP.

Newton's Law. There is a formal analogy between the law of viscosity embodied in Eq. (12-12) and the Hooke's law of elasticity expressed by Eq. (6-32). Both establish a proportionality: the former between stress and strain rate, the latter between stress and strain. The law of viscosity was discovered by Newton, a contemporary of Hooke, in 1685. However, its wording, even in Latin, lacked somewhat the conciseness of Hooke's language. Here it is in translation.

> "Hypothesis: that the resistance which arises from lack of slipperiness of the parts of liquid, other things being equal, is proportional to the velocity with which the parts of the liquid are separated from one another."

There is another more deeply seated difference between the two laws.

The modulus of elasticity, which is the proportionality factor in Hooke's law, depends only on the configuration of elementary particles, whereas the coefficient of viscosity in Newton's law depends also on their frequency of vibration, i.e., on the motion of these particles. Therein seems to lie one of the main reasons for the wider range of variation and greater sensitivity to temperature changes displayed by the coefficient of viscosity as compared to the modulus of elasticity.

Range of Variation of η. Influence of Temperature. The formula derived by Andrade implies cubical symmetry in the configuration of molecules and lack of coupling between them, so that each molecule vibrates independently of its neighbors. These assumptions apply fairly well to molten metals and alkali halides, but they are not valid for multiatomic and long chain molecules. As a rule, the more complex the molecule, the larger is the coefficient of viscosity of the liquid. The values cover a wide range varying from a fraction of a centipoise for molten metals and alkali halides to 10^6 cP and more for organic liquids such as sucrose and glucose. The variation of η with temperature for a given liquid is equally large, and it is generally of an *exponential* nature. For example, the coefficient of viscosity of glycerine falls from 6.71×10^6 to 6.29×10^2 cP, or about 10,000-fold, as the temperature rises from 231° to 303°K, or less than 50%. Such a rapid fall of viscosity is only partially explained by the growing looseness of the aggregate with temperature. It must be sought mainly in the increasing randomness of thermal motion which subjects the passage of a molecule from one layer to another to statistical laws. A more detailed analysis of the temperature dependence of viscosity must therefore be postponed until these laws become available (from thermodynamics, for example).

12-3 Illustrative Example

Determine the coefficient of viscosity η of molten lead at its melting point if $\rho = 11.35$ g/cm³, $M = 207.21$ g/mole and $\nu = 2 \times 10^{12}$/sec.

Solution. According to Eq. (12-11),

$$\eta = \frac{4\nu m}{3a_0}$$

The value of m is given by the following relation:

$$m = \frac{M}{N_A} = \frac{207.21}{6.02 \times 10^{23}} = 3.43 \times 10^{-22} \text{ g}$$

In like manner—see Eq. (12-3)—

$$a_0 = \sqrt[3]{M/N_A\rho} = 3.1 \times 10^{-8} \text{ cm}$$

Hence,

$$\eta = \frac{4 \times 2 \times 10^{12} \times 3.43 \times 10^{-22}}{3 \times 3.1 \times 10^{-8}}$$
$$= 0.030 \text{ g/(sec cm)} = 0.030 \text{ dyn sec/cm}^2 = 3 \text{ cP}$$

The observed value of η is 2.8 cP, in good agreement with the computed value.

12-4 Coefficient of Fluidity. The reciprocal of the coefficient of viscosity η is called the *coefficient of fluidity*. It is often designated by the Greek letter ϕ. Thus,

$$\phi = 1/\eta \tag{12-13}$$

The units of ϕ are cm^2/dyn sec in the CGS system. 1 cm^2/dyn sec is called 1 rhe (from the Greek *rheo*, meaning flow).

12-5 Kinematic Viscosity. In many problems concerned with fluid flow, particularly when the flow is caused by gravity forces, the rate of flow (i.e., the volume of liquid flowing in unit time) depends on the viscosity–density ratio, η/ρ, rather than on viscosity alone (see illustrative example, Section 12-6). The ratio η/ρ is called *kinematic viscosity*. Its units in the CGS system are

$$[\eta/\rho] = \frac{\text{dyn cm}^{-2}\text{ sec}}{\text{g cm}^{-3}} = \frac{\text{g cm}^{-1}\text{ sec}^{-1}}{\text{g cm}^{-3}} = \frac{\text{cm}^2}{\text{sec}}$$

Thus η/ρ is truly a kinematic property, depending only on length and time. (As will appear in later courses, properties having the units of cm^2/sec measure the rate of dissipation of a given quantity—momentum, heat, mass, etc.) The unit of kinematic viscosity in the CGS system, 1 cm^2/sec, is called a *stoke*, from the name of the British physicist Sir George G. Stokes (1845). The one hundredth part of a stoke is called a *centistoke*.

Industrial oils have been rated by the Society of Automotive Engineers (SAE) by specific SAE numbers. Thus, SAE 20 corresponds to about 60 centistokes at 100°F, and SAE 50 corresponds to about 200 centistokes at the same temperature.

12-6 Illustrative Example. Flow in a Capillary

Experiment shows that the flow of a liquid in a circular capillary resembles the sliding of concentric tubes telescoping into each other, Fig. 12-2a. Assume a long capillary and a steady flow of the liquid under its own weight. Since the flow is steady, the force of gravitation P acting on a cylindrical element AB of the liquid, Fig. 12-2b, is balanced by the forces ff resisting the sliding motion of AB within the surrounding liquid. If ρ is the density of the liquid and g acceleration of gravity,

$$P = \pi r^2 l \rho g \tag{12-14}$$

On the other hand, according to Eq. (12-12) the total force F acting on the periphery $2\pi rl$ of the element AB and resisting the sliding movement is

$$F = 2\pi rl\tau = 2\pi rl\eta\dot{\gamma} \tag{12-15}$$

By virtue of equilibrium of forces,

$$P + F = 0$$

or

$$\pi r^2 l \rho g = -2\pi r l \eta \dot{\gamma}$$

Simplifying and rearranging the terms, we have

$$\dot{\gamma} = -\tfrac{1}{2}(\rho/\eta)gr \tag{12-16}$$

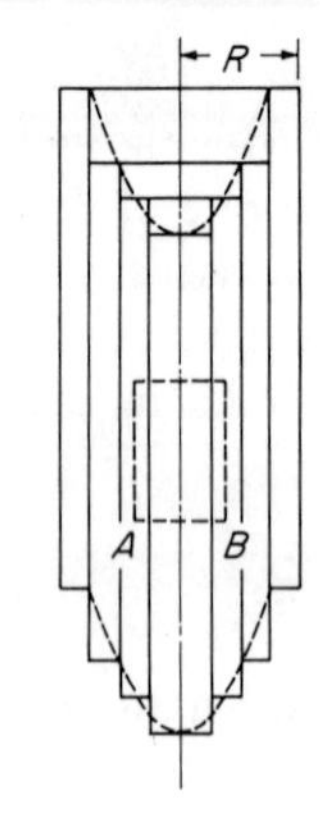

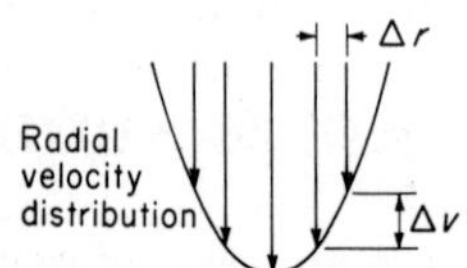

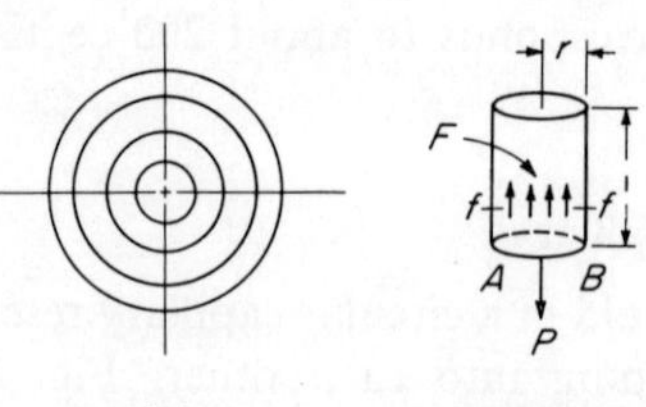

FIG. 12-2 Flow in a capillary. (a) Telescopic flow of concentric laminae. (b) Equilibrium of a lamina

FIG. 12-3 Various types of flow. *OA*, simple Newtonian liquid; *OB*, generalized Newtonian liquid; *OCD*, plastic flow

From Fig. 12-2 we deduce that if the relative velocity of sliding is Δv, then

$$\dot{\gamma} = \Delta v/\Delta r \tag{12-17}$$

and, at the limit for infinitely thin cylindrical shells of the liquid,

$$\dot{\gamma} = dv/dr \tag{12-18}$$

Substitution of Eq. (12-18) into Eq. (12-16) yields

$$dv = -\tfrac{1}{2}(\rho/\eta)gr\,dr$$

and, on integrating,

$$v = -(\rho/\eta)g\frac{r^2}{4} + C \tag{12-19}$$

Since the layer adhering to the wall is stationary, $v = 0$ for $r = R$. Putting $v = 0$ and $r = R$ in Eq. (12-19), we obtain

$$C = \frac{\rho}{\eta}g\frac{R^2}{4}$$

and thence,

$$v = \frac{\rho}{\eta}g\frac{R^2 - r^2}{4} \tag{12-20}$$

The velocity of flow varies as the square of the radius; it is maximum at the center and it reduces to zero at the wall of the capillary.

To obtain the rate of flow Q, we observe that the volume of liquid dQ passing in unit time through an annular section $2\pi r\,dr$ is

$$dQ = 2v\pi r\,dr \tag{12-21}$$

or, with reference to Eq. (12-20),

$$dQ = \pi\frac{\rho}{\eta}g\frac{R^2r\,dr - r^3\,dr}{2}$$

Integration from $r = 0$ to $r = R$ yields

$$Q = \pi\frac{\rho}{\eta}g\left[\frac{R^2r^2}{4} - \frac{r^4}{8}\right]_0^R = \pi\frac{\rho}{\eta}g\frac{R^4}{8} \tag{12-22}$$

We see that for a given capillary the rate of flow varies as the reciprocal of the kinematic viscosity η/ρ of the liquid. Or, to say it differently, the rates of flow of two liquids in a given capillary are inversely proportional to their kinematic viscosities. This relationship provides a convenient method of determining by means of a capillary the kinematic viscosity of one liquid from the knowledge of the kinematic viscosity of another liquid.

12-7 Deviations from Newton's Law. The derivation of Newton's law was based essentially on the premise that in a liquid the molecules can exchange their partners *spontaneously*, that is, without the intervention of an external force. The external force does intervene to either supply or remove the extra momentum produced in laminar flow by the exchange of molecules, but it does not have to sever the bonds between them. This is basically the reason for the observed proportionality between the shear stress and the shear strain rate embodied in Eq. (12-12). A plot of shear stress τ versus shear strain rate $\dot{\gamma}$ is thus a straight line passing through the origin, line OA, Fig. 12-3, and the slope of the line is a measure of the viscosity of the liquid.

If the plot departs from proportionality, we suspect that the exchange of molecules between the lamina of the liquid is not wholly spontaneous. Several instances can be cited.

1. *Generalized Newtonian Liquids.* In some instances the plot of shear stress versus shear strain rate affects the trend depicted by the curve OB, Fig. 12-3. The slope is steep at the origin but it diminishes as the stress is increased, and it often tends to a constant value for very large stresses. A finite, even though steep, slope at the origin indicates that the molecules are still able to transfer momentum from one layer to another, and hence, exchange their partners. On the other hand, the variation of the slope with stress suggests that the molecules themselves undergo certain structural changes in the process, presumably fragmentation, which accounts for the growing ease of flow. The substance is thus a liquid. It is called a *generalized* Newtonian liquid in contrast to a *simple* Newtonian liquid which obeys the law of proportionality embodied in Eq. (12-12). Prominent among generalized Newtonian liquids are organic solutions such as rubber in toluence, cellulose in acetone, or gelatine in water. They have a common tendency to form gels at much lower temperatures.

2. *Plastic Flow.* In other instances the plot of shear stress versus shear strain rate is more complex. It follows the trend shown by the curve OCD, Fig. 12-3. We see that the flow does not begin until the shear stress has exceeded the threshold value OC. Below OC the substance is no longer a liquid, for it is able to sustain a load without flowing, exactly as a solid does. The threshold value of the shear stress which is thus necessary to initiate flow recalls the yield stress in plastic deformation, Chapter 9. Hence the name *plastic flow* is given to the phenomenon described by the curve OCD.

The dual behavior of a substance, below and above the threshold value OC, is not without practical advantages, as is readily attested by the widespread use of toothpastes, paints, mustard, mayonnaise, and cosmetics. All of these more or less follow the trend depicted by curve OCD. To squeeze toothpaste out of a tube we must apply a small initial pressure. Thereafter the paste flows continuously until the pressure is removed. It is the same with paint. The stroke of a paintbrush maintains a steady flow of paint, thereby removing brush marks and producing a smooth surface. Left to its own gravity, the paint ceases to flow and sticks to the wall. The virtues of condiments and cosmetics conceivably lie elsewhere than in the properties of plastic flow, yet without these properties they are not likely to be of much use.

3. *Thixotropy.* Concomitant with the behaviors depicted by curves OB and OCD is a tendency exhibited by some substances to flow under a lower stress once they have been subjected to a higher stress, in particular, once the threshold value OC has been exceeded. Mild vibrations produce a similar

effect. Thus, a suspension of the ceramic material bentonite in water forms a slurry which settles at the bottom of a test tube and does not flow out when the tube is turned over. However, a light tap on the wall converts the substance into a freely flowing liquid. It is as though at a touch the bonds between molecules were severed and a spontaneous exchange of partners was established. The name *thixotropy* is given to this phenomenon (from Greek *thixis*, touch, and *tropē*, change). With the cessation of flow, the substance recovers its initial stability.

Like plastic flow, thixotropy finds useful industrial applications. For example, in oil well operations the thixotropic behavior of drilling mud makes it possible to carry the cuttings up to the surface in the form of a liquid and to extract the tool from the hole without damage. On the other hand, with the cessation of motion the substance congeals, thus preventing the walls of the hole from collapsing.

12-8 Visco-Elasticity. Considerations of the previous section clearly indicate that, depending on circumstances, the same substance can exhibit either stability or instability of molecular configuration. In the first instance, the substance tends to resist a change of *shape* and it manifests elastic behavior. In the second instance, it tends to resist a change of *flow* and it manifests viscous behavior. Yet, there is seldom a sharp transition from one behavior to the other. In the majority of cases the transition is gradual, depending on the length of time one or the other behavior can be brought into prominence. Thus, a piece of pitch deforms elastically and breaks in a brittle manner when struck with a hammer. Under constant pressure, however, it deforms continuously and flows. The behavior of bouncing putty—a plastic material of the silicone family—is even more characteristic in this respect. Rolled into a spherical shape it bounces like a rubber ball. Left to its own gravity it flattens out and spreads like a viscous liquid.

The famous British scientist James Clerk Maxwell (1831–1879) was probably the first to point out that such a dual behavior was to be expected of all substances: gases, liquids, and solids alike. (The ancient Greeks took a somewhat one-sided view by declaring that everything flows.) However, in gases and in most liquids the stability of a given molecular configuration is generally too short-lived to give rise to perceptible elastic effects associated with changes of shape. On the other hand, it may take centuries before the occurrences of flow can be detected in solids. Occurrences of this kind are the sagging of old marble tombstones and the thickening of ancient window panes at the base. Thus the time factor appears to be an essential characteristic of the transition from elastic to viscous behavior in various substances. Maxwell called it the *relaxation time.*

12.9 Relaxation Time of Simple Newtonian Liquids. For liquids obeying the proportionality law, Eq. (12-12), the relaxation time can be defined in terms of the shear modulus G and the coefficient of viscosity η of the material. To derive the pertinent equation we imagine that the liquid has been suddenly subjected to a change of shape, and we inquire as to how long it will be able to resist such a change. Let γ_0 be the shear strain associated with the imposed change of shape. At time equals zero, γ_0 will be wholly elastic. Hence by virtue of Hooke's law, the change of shape will be resisted by a shear stress τ_0 such that, for $t = 0$,

$$\tau_0 = G\gamma_0 \tag{12-23}$$

As time goes on, however, there will be a gradual decrease of the elastic behavior in favor of the viscous behavior. Let $\dot{\gamma}_e (= d\gamma_e/dt)$ be the rate at which the elastic strain decreases with time, and let $\dot{\gamma}_v$ be the rate at which the viscous strain increases with time. Then, since the total strain γ_0 is kept constant,

$$\dot{\gamma}_e + \dot{\gamma}_v = 0 \tag{12-24}$$

We seek to express $\dot{\gamma}_e$ and $\dot{\gamma}_v$ in terms of the corresponding changes of the shear stress, τ. We observe first that, if the elastic strain γ_e changes by an amount $\Delta\gamma_e$, the corresponding shear stress τ, by virtue of Hooke's law, changes by an amount $\Delta\tau$ such that

$$\Delta\tau = G\,\Delta\gamma_e \tag{12-25}$$

Since these changes occur at the same time increment Δt, we can also write

$$\Delta\tau/\Delta t = G\,\Delta\gamma_e/\Delta t$$

and, in the limit,

$$d\tau/dt = G\,d\gamma_e/dt = G\dot{\gamma}_e \tag{12-26}$$

On the other hand, Newton's law, written in the form of Eq. (12-12), requires that

$$\tau = \eta\dot{\gamma}_v \tag{12-27}$$

Substituting for $\dot{\gamma}_e$ and $\dot{\gamma}_v$ the expressions from Eqs. (12-26) and (12-27) into Eq. (12-24), we obtain

$$\frac{1}{G}\,d\tau/dt + \tau/\eta = 0 \tag{12-28}$$

Equation (12-28) can be rewritten to read

$$d\tau/\tau = -(G/\eta)\,dt$$

or, since

$$\frac{d\tau}{\tau} = d(\ln \tau)$$

$$d(\ln \tau) = -(G/\eta)\,dt \tag{12-29}$$

By integrating Eq. (12-29) we get

$$\ln \tau = -(G/\eta)t + C \tag{12-30}$$

The constant of integration C can be determined by observing that for $t = 0$, $\tau = \tau_0$. Hence, substituting $t = 0$ and $\tau = \tau_0$ in Eq. (12-30), we obtain

$$\ln \tau_0 = C \tag{12-31}$$

and, replacing C in Eq. (12-30),

$$\ln \tau - \ln \tau_0 = -(G/\eta)t$$

whereupon

$$\tau/\tau_0 = e^{-(G/\eta)t} \tag{12-32}$$

Alternatively, using Eq. (12-23), we can write

$$\tau = G\gamma_0 e^{-(G/\eta)t} \tag{12-33}$$

Equations (12-32) and (12-33) show that, as time goes on, the substance rapidly loses or relaxes its resistance to changes of shape. The deciding factor here is the ratio G/η. If G is measured in dynes per square centimeter and η is measured in dynes seconds per square centimeter, the ratio η/G is measured in seconds. We put

$$\eta/G = \theta \tag{12-34}$$

and, following Maxwell, we call θ the *relaxation* time. Using Eq. (12-34) in Eq. (12-32), we get

$$\tau = \tau_0 e^{-t/\theta} \tag{12-35}$$

Equation (12-35) shows that the smaller the relaxation time θ, the sooner will the substance lose its resistance to changes of shape and the sooner will it behave like a liquid. On the other hand, as long as t is small compared to

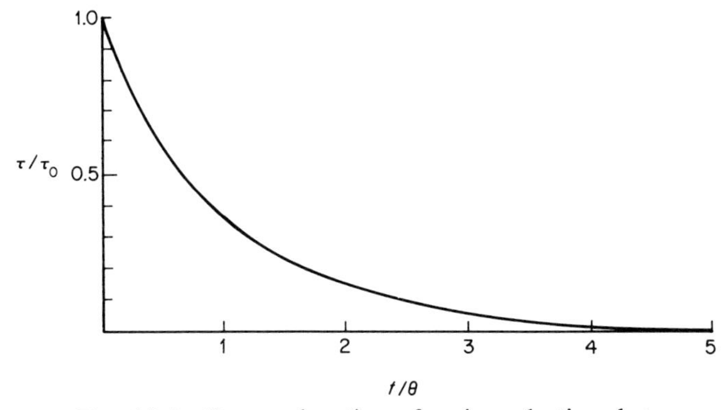

FIG. 12-4 Stress relaxation of a visco-elastic substance

θ, the substance preserves much of its resistance to changes of shape and behaves like a solid. This is also apparent from Fig. 12-4, in which the ratio τ/τ_0 of the actual stress τ to the initial stress τ_0 has been plotted as a function of t/θ. It is seen that it takes a fivefold value of t/θ to reduce τ practically to zero and convert the substance to a liquid. The actual time may be a small fraction of a second or many minutes, depending on θ.

Illustrative Examples

1. For water, η is 0.01 dyn sec/cm^2. The experimental value of G is not available, but it can be surmised to be of the order of 10^{10} dyn/cm^2 from the value of the bulk modulus B, Table 6-3. Thus, the relaxation time $\theta = \eta/G$ is of the order of 10^{-12} sec. A fivefold value of θ is still a vanishing quantity. For all practical purposes, water behaves like a liquid.

2. The viscosity of pitch reaches 10^{13} P at room temperature. The value of G is again not available, but judging from the values of B for polymers, Table 6-3, it can hardly be higher than 10^{10} dyn/cm^2. Thus the relaxation time θ of pitch is no less than 1000 sec. It is therefore not surprising that a piece of pitch when struck suddenly behaves elastically and that it breaks in a brittle manner like glass when the blow is severe enough.

12-10 Creep: Manifestations and Definitions. The examples considered in Section 12-7 and 12-9 involved a more or less gradual transition from an elastic to a viscous behavior of the entire substance. Yet there are numerous cases in which this transition occurs only in isolated regions within the material. In such instances the bulk of the material preserves by and large the properties of a solid, and it maintains some tendency to recover its shape under all conditions of flow. Because of this tendency, it is said to *creep* rather than flow. Creep is exhibited by many materials—such as plastic, glass, and concrete—when subjected to appropriate temperatures and stresses. However, creep is particularly characteristic of crystalline solids, which as a rule maintain the tendency to recover their shape up to the melting point. The recovery is seldom complete, and it decreases as the temperature and stress increase. We are thus led to distinguish between *recoverable* and *permanent* creep. A further distinction is often made between various types of permanent creep depending on whether the rate of creep at constant stress and temperature decelerates, tends to a constant value, or accelerates with time. In the first instance the creep is called *transient*, in the second instance it is said to tend to a *steady state*, and in the third instance it is generally taken as a *forerunner* of impending fracture. These distinctions are not sharp, and they are meaningful only if they can be related to some characteristic changes in the structure of the material or in the mechanism of creep. The behavior of polycrystalline metals is particularly revealing in this respect, and it will be used as an illustration.

12-11 Recoverable Creep. Imperfections of crystal structure, among them dislocations and grain boundaries, are natural sites of instability of molecular and atomic configurations. Even below the yield stress, the grain boundaries may become unstable and generate creep under the influence of an overall shear deformation. This is depicted schematically in Fig. 12-5, a and b, for the case of the boundary AB between grains I and II. The shear deformation in the s direction has produced a rearrangement of atoms a and b. Concomitant with the displacement, there is a change of momentum

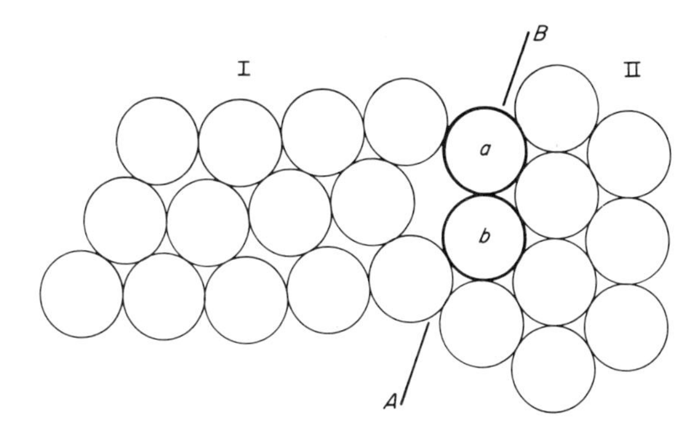

(A) No strain

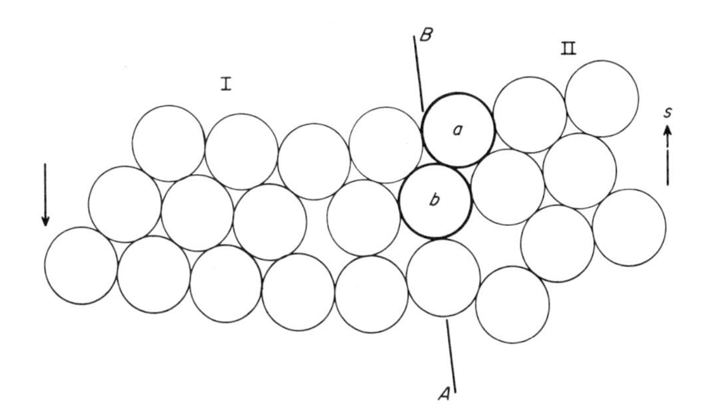

(B) Elastic shearing strain

FIG. 12-5 Schematic representation of grain boundary instability

when the atoms pass from one layer to another. Because of the admittedly local character of this change, Newton's law of viscosity is expected to hold. Thus the grain boundary should behave very nearly like a simple Newtonian liquid with a constant relaxation time θ.

We seek to determine the effect this behavior will have on the change of the overall strain γ of the aggregate with time, i.e., on the creep of the aggregate, under a constant applied shear stress τ_0.

Let α be the fraction of atoms per unit area of the aggregate, undergoing the visco-elastic deformation of the boundary, and let τ be the corresponding, relaxing shear stress. The fraction of atoms undergoing a purely elastic deformation is then $1 - \alpha$. If τ_e is the stress to which this fraction is subjected, the following relation exists between τ and τ_e:

$$\tau_0 = \alpha\tau + (1 - \alpha)\tau_e \tag{12-36}$$

At time zero the whole aggregate behaves elastically, so that $\tau = \tau_e$. It then follows from Eq. (12-36) that for $t = 0$,

$$\tau = \tau_e = \tau_0 \tag{12-37}$$

As time goes on, the stress τ on the grain boundary relaxes and consequently the stress τ_e on the grain increases. By virtue of Eqs. (12-35) and (12-37), we can write

$$\tau = \tau_0 e^{-t/\theta}$$

and, substituting in Eq. (12-36),

$$\tau_0 = \alpha\tau_0 e^{-t/\theta} + (1 - \alpha)\tau_e \tag{12-38}$$

By making use of Hooke's law, namely,

$$\tau_e = G\gamma$$

we can rewrite Eq. (12-38) to read

$$\tau_0(1 - \alpha e^{-t/\theta}) = G(1 - \alpha)\gamma$$

whence

$$\gamma = \frac{\tau_0}{G(1 - \alpha)}(1 - \alpha e^{-t/\theta}) \tag{12-39}$$

Equation (12-39) shows that for $t = 0$ the value of γ is

$$\gamma_0 = \tau_0/G \tag{12-40}$$

whereas for t tending to infinity the value of γ is

$$\gamma_\infty = \frac{\tau_0}{G(1 - \alpha)} \tag{12-41}$$

Obviously γ_∞ is larger than γ_0 in the same ratio as G is larger than $G(1 - \alpha)$. We call G the *unrelaxed* modulus of elasticity, G_u, and $G(1 - \alpha)$ the *relaxed* modulus of elasticity, G_R. Writing that

$$G_R = G_u(1 - \alpha) \tag{12-42}$$

we can eliminate α and τ_0 from Eq. (12-39) and express the relationship between γ and γ_∞ in terms of G_R/G_u and t/θ as follows:

$$\gamma = \gamma_\infty[1 - (1 - G_R/G_u)e^{-t/\theta}] \tag{12-43}$$

Note the analogy and the difference between Eq. (12-43) and Eq. (12-33). Both γ and τ depend on the ratio t/θ. However, to plot γ/γ_∞ as a function of t/θ we must also know the ratio G_R/G_u. For a polycrystalline aluminum aggregate this ratio appears to be close to 0.6.[3] Substituting 0.6 for G_R/G_u in Eq. (12-43) and rearranging terms, we get

$$\gamma/\gamma_\infty = 1 - 0.4e^{-t/\theta} \tag{12-44}$$

According to Eq. (12-44), only 60% of the ultimate strain will occur at time $t = 0$ under a constant stress smaller than the yield stress. The occurrence of the balance of strain will require time. Theoretically the time is infinite, but as with stress relaxation, Section 12-9, almost all the strain will be attained at the fivefold value of the relaxation time θ. This is depicted in Fig. 12-6 by the plot *OAB* of γ/γ_∞ versus t/θ.

The recovery follows a similar trend. At the removal of stress only 60% of the strain is recovered, line *BC*, Fig. 12-6. Full recovery does not occur

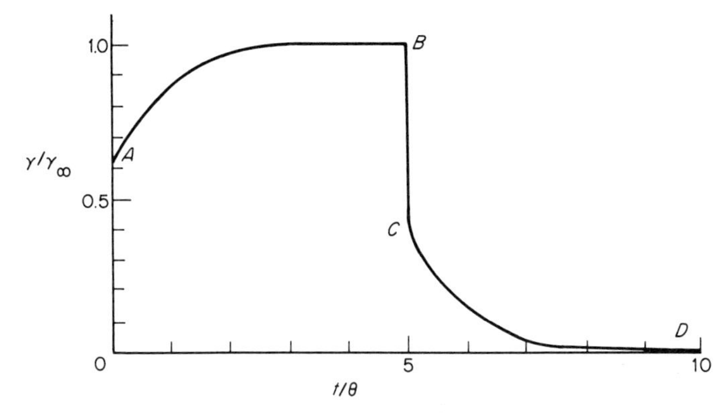

FIG. 12-6 Recoverable creep. Variation of the shear strain ratio γ/γ_∞ versus time ratio t/θ on loading (*OAB*) and unloading (*BCD*)

practically until after a lapse of time at least equal to 5θ, line *CD*, Fig. 12-6. In the final analysis the deformation is elastic, but the strain does not change proportionally to stress. It lags behind, owing to the viscous behavior of the grain boundary. As will be shown in later courses, this behavior is an important cause of energy dissipation in the well-known phenomenon of damping of elastic vibrations in solids—in a tuning fork, for example.

12-12 Permanent Creep. When the yield stress of the material is exceeded, indications of recoverable creep are overshadowed by the appearance of a creep closely associated with plastic deformation. Hence its alternative designation: *plastic creep.*[4] According to the prevailing views, plastic creep,

[3] C. M. Zener, *Elasticity and Anelasticity of Metals*, U. of Chicago, Chicago, 1948.

[4] E. Orowan, "Creep in Metallic and Non-Metallic Materials," *Proc. First Nat. Congr. Appl. Mech.*, A.S.M.E., p. 465, 1952. (Note: Plastic creep is not to be confused with plastic flow, treated in Section 12-7.)

like plastic deformation, is caused by the motion of dislocations; see Chapter 9. That is, at the attainment of the yield stress, and at each subsequent increment of stress, an avalanche of dislocations is pictured to set off and rush through the slip planes of the crystal. This on-rush, however, is readily intercepted and slowed down by various crystal imperfections acting as obstacles. The most important ones are (1) oversized or undersized foreign atoms or *inclusions*, Fig. 12-7, considered in Section 9-7, along with missing

FIG. 12-7 An avalanche of dislocations stopped by an inclusion. (By permission from *Acta Met.*, **4**, 194, "Physical Evidence of Dislocations in Chromium," and courtesy M. J. Fraser, D. Caplan, and A. A. Burr)

atoms at regular sites or *vacancies*, (2) grain boundaries, and (3) other dislocations; cf. Section 9-10. In the absence of any opposing mechanism, the dislocations would end up by piling up before the obstacles. They would build a back pressure that gradually would quench all sources from which further dislocations could generate and spread out under a *constant* stress. This contingency cannot be ruled out, especially at very low temperatures, but experiments[5] conducted on pure aluminum at a temperature as low as 77°K suggest that under appropriate stresses other mechanisms must be at work to partially offset the piling-up process.

The nature of these mechanisms has not yet been fully identified or accepted. Yet as the temperature approaches and exceeds $0.5T_f$, where T_f is the melting

[5] J. E. Dorn, "The Spectrum of Activation Energies for Creep," in monograph, *Creep and Recovery*, p. 255, American Society of Metals, 1957.

point measured on the absolute scale (that is, in degrees Kelvin), one mechanism is generally recognized as being predominant. It consists of a *climb* of a dislocation out of its plane of slip. The climb is ascribed to the thermal agitation of surrounding atoms. Caught in this agitation, the dislocation succeeds in throwing a loop over the obstacle and resumes its forward motion. Conceivably, such a mechanism must operate at all temperatures short of absolute zero; but only beyond $0.5T_f$ is the thermal agitation strong enough to involve more than a negligible fraction of dislocations in the climb and make a significant contribution to the rate of creep.

Dislocations are not the only crystal imperfections affected by the increased agitation of atoms. *Grain boundaries*, too, acquire greater mobility and undergo changes which, in turn, influence the rate and the nature of creep. Prominent among these changes are *sliding* and formation of *fissures*.

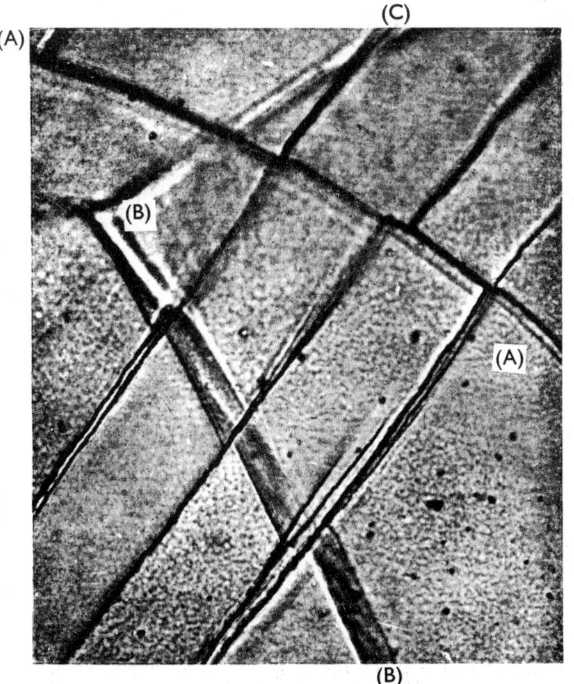

FIG. 12-8 Grain boundary sliding. (From A. H. Sully, "Recent Advances in Knowledge Concerning the Process of Creep in Metals," *Prog. in Metal Phys.*, **6**, 1956, Pergamon, New York, by permission)

Figure 12-8 shows what is meant by grain boundary sliding. Under the action of applied stress the upper grain has slid past the lower grain along the boundary *AA*, as indicated by the cut in the marker *BC*. Similar cuts in the marker *BB* have been produced by the slip mechanism along the slip bands within one of the grains.

A fissure in a horizontal portion of a grain boundary is depicted in Fig.

12-9. Characteristically, the applied force is perpendicular to this portion —an indication that no horizontal component is available to promote local grain boundary sliding.

It is still an open question as to what extent grain boundary sliding and fissures contribute to the ultimate creep failure. However, it is significant

FIG. 12-9 Fissure at a grain boundary. (From A. H. Sully, "Recent Advances in Knowledge Concerning the Process of Creep in Metals," *Prog. in Metal Phys.*, **6**, 1956, Pergamon, New York, by permission)

that many of the alloys used in high-temperature technology fail at operating temperatures by intergranular cracking, i.e., along grain boundaries, and with surprisingly little deformation. For example, Inconel W—an alloy used in the fabrication of gas turbine discs—exhibits up to 25% elongation when tested in tension at room temperature. At 1200°F, however, it fails after 1000 hours of service under a constant stress with as little as 1% elongation, and the fracture is clearly intergranular. Oddly enough, when the stress is raised so that fracture occurs in a few hours rather than in a month, the material shows almost the same elongation as in the tension test at room temperature.

Note. The last remark amounts to an admission of ignorance. It is clear that if the material were a perfect crystal, its properties would be predictable to a considerable extent from the configuration and motion of the elementary particles of which it is made. However, the crystal also contains imperfections, and it is *their* configuration and *their* motion which principally affect the creep properties. Our ignorance stems from two sources: (1) The *configuration* of imperfections is neither regular nor stable; it changes with time, stress, and temperature in a manner that has not yet been fully accounted for. (2) The *motion* of imperfections seldom involves one single mechanism; several mechanisms are generally at work, and only a few of them have been clearly identified. Admittedly, great strides have been made recently in the theory of creep by paying closer attention to factors which affect separately the configuration and the motion of dislocations.[6] Until the theory predicts results more accurately, however, the experiment remains the most reliable source of information for design.

12-13 Strain-Time Diagram. The pertinent experimental information is currently provided in terms of strains obtained as a function of time in axial tension under constant stress and at a constant temperature. A family of such curves drawn for successive temperatures at a given stress, or for successive stresses at a given temperature, enables a systematical study to be made of the influence of each of these factors on creep.

Influence of Temperature. A typical plot of a family of strain-time curves for increasing temperatures at a constant stress level beyond the yield stress is shown in Fig. 12-10. The curves are rated in terms of the ratio T/T_f, where T is the operating temperature and T_f is the melting point, both measured on an absolute scale such as Kelvin. The choice of the parameter T/T_f will be justified later.

It is seen that at all temperatures there is an instantaneous increment of strain OA_1, OA_2, etc., similar to that observed in the recoverable creep, Fig. 12-6. Thereupon the strain increases with time, at first very rapidly,

[6] See, for example, *Mechanical Behavior of Materials at Elevated Temperatures*, monograph, J. E. Dorn, Ed., McGraw-Hill, New York, 1961.

then at a steadily decelerating rate, portions A_1B_1, A_2B_2, etc. These portions correspond to what was called *transient* creep in Section 12-10. If T/T_f is much smaller than 0.5, transient creep may be the only observable component of creep, curve A_1B_1. Around $0.5T_f$, the rate of creep generally slows down

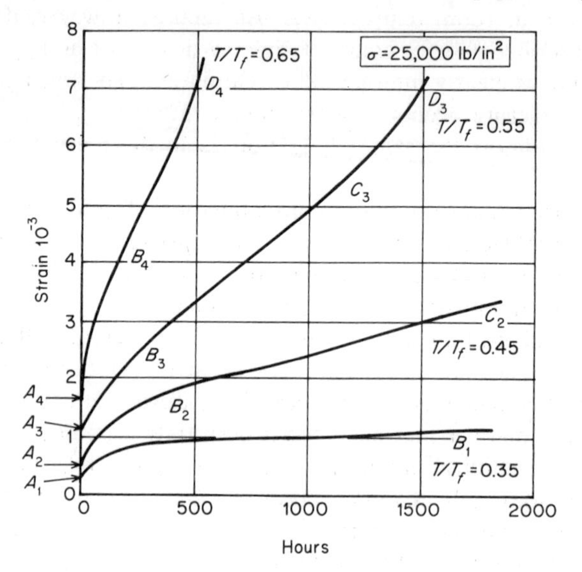

FIG. 12-10 Family of strain–time curves for increasing temperature ratios, T/T_f, at a constant stress beyond the yield stress

to an almost constant value for a certain length of time, portions B_2C_2 and B_3C_3, and the creep reaches a *steady state* according to the definition of Section 12-10. However, if T/T_f is much higher than 0.5, the rate of creep merely slows down to a minimum and it accelerates thereafter, portion B_4D_4. This accelerated stage may also follow the steady state creep, portion C_3D_3. In both cases it is a sign of impending failure.

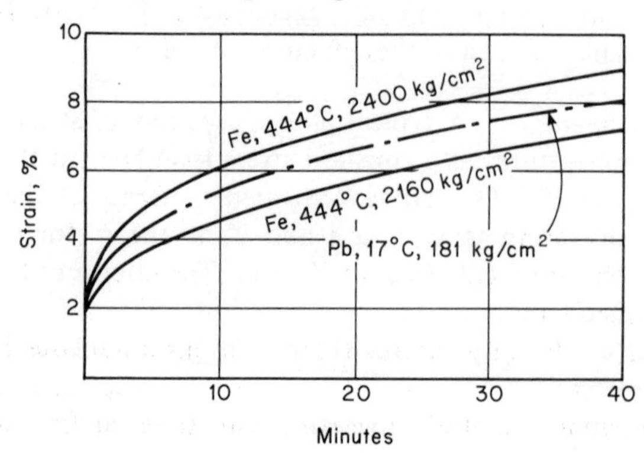

FIG. 12-11 Strain–time curves of lead and iron at comparable T/T_f ratios (after Andrade)

The trends mentioned above are common to all metals provided the ratio T/T_f and not T alone is chosen as a parameter. This is exemplified by Fig. 12-11, where lead at 17°C is seen to exhibit the same type of creep as iron at 444°C. The similarity becomes clear when the temperatures are referred to the corresponding melting points, 600°K and 1800°K, of the two metals. They then read $0.48T_f$ for lead and $0.4T_f$ for iron.

Another common characteristic is the great sensitivity of strain rate to temperature changes. As a rule, the strain rate $\dot{\varepsilon}_s$ at steady state varies exponentially with T/T_f. This is shown in Fig. 12-10, where an almost threefold increase of $\dot{\varepsilon}_s$ results from a barely 20% increase of T/T_f.

Influence of Stress. The influence of stress on strain is similar to that of T/T_f but not nearly as strong. This is illustrated in Fig. 12-12, where strain

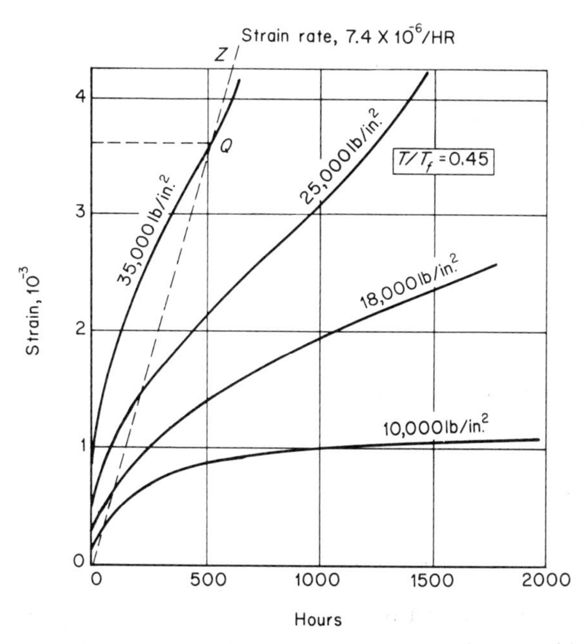

FIG. 12-12 Family of strain–time curves for increasing stresses, at a constant T/T_f ratio

versus time is plotted at a constant $T/T_f = 0.45$ but at various stress levels for a representative high-temperature metal. It is seen that, by raising the stress, the same sequence of creep curves can be obtained at a constant temperature as by raising the temperature at a constant stress, Fig. 12-10. Since the influence of stress on the configuration and motion of dislocations is known to be quite different from the influence of temperature, it follows that the similarity of trends implies merely the same *interplay* of mechanisms rather than the *same kind* of mechanisms. This is even more apparent when comparing the creep behavior of metals and plastics. Under appropriate conditions of stress and temperature, both kinds of materials yield identical types of creep curves. Yet neither the structural changes nor the mechanisms are the same in both cases.

12-14 Stress–Strain Diagrams under Constant Rates. An alternative set of experimental data is provided by a plot of stress versus strain obtained at a constant temperature and at various *strain rate levels.* A typical family of curves in the range of T/T_f below 0.5 is shown in Fig. 12-13. Comparison

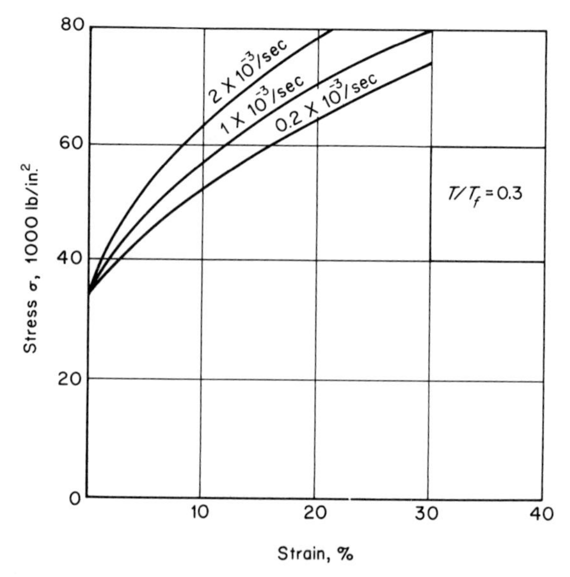

FIG. 12-13 Stress–strain curves at various strain-rates and at a constant T/T_f ratio

of this figure with Fig. 9-20 reveals at once that the true stress-strain curve determined in Fig. 9-20 is but one of the curves of the family of Fig. 12-13. It corresponds to a constant strain rate of 1×10^{-3}/sec. This correspondence emphasizes the fact that a stress–strain diagram beyond the yield stress is not uniquely determined unless the strain rate also is specified. True enough, the importance of the rate of straining is not nearly as great as, say, that of the operating temperature. This follows from the inspection of Fig. 12-13, where the influence of the rate of straining appears to be of a *logarithmic* rather than an exponential nature. Thus, at a given stress level, a tenfold increase of strain rate is seen to barely produce a twofold *decrease* of strain. The influence on stress at a given strain level is understandably much smaller. It hardly amounts to 20% and it is an *increase.*

Note. At first sight, the information provided by the plot, Fig. 12-13, does not seem to contain anything that is not already incorporated in the strain-time curves such as shown in Fig. 12-12. Thus let *OZ*, Fig. 12-12, be a straight line drawn through the origin. It is easy to see that each point on this line, such as point *Q*, corresponds to a constant strain rate, here 7.4×10^{-6}/hr, and that it relates a given stress level, here 35,000 lb/in.^{2}, to a strain measured on the axis of ordinates, here 0.37%. It is thus possible to replot the data of Fig. 12-12 in the manner shown in Fig. 12-13, by drawing a set of straight lines through the origin and noting the pairs of corresponding stresses and strains located on each line (see Problem 12-8). Unfortunately, this procedure leads to erroneous results. Inspection of Fig. 12-12 shows that it exaggerates the effect of larger stresses at the expense of the smaller ones. Not until this effect is properly accounted for can the conversion from one plot to another have true physical meaning. Therein lies the crucial test of any creep theory aimed at providing a reliable basis for design.

12-15 Design for Creep. There is no better way of illustrating the interplay between material properties and design, mentioned in Chapter 5, than to briefly relate the circumstances attending the development of materials for service at elevated temperatures.

Why Elevated Temperatures? Apparently the first concerted demand from industry for metals capable of withstanding temperatures up to 899°K (1000°F) came after World War I, when it was recognized that, by operating steam engines at higher temperatures and pressures, substantial fuel economy could be achieved. It is estimated that from 1920 until 1950 the amount of fuel necessary to produce the same amount of electric energy was cut in half, thanks to the use of heat-resisting alloys. However, higher operating temperatures also entail greater power. With the advent of gas turbines, specifications were accordingly revised to include materials capable of withstanding temperatures as high as 978°K (1300°F). Further revision came about when nuclear fuels and solid propellants for rockets made their appearance. Operating temperatures up to 1367°K (2000°F) were now in order, if only suitable materials could be found. Therein appears to lie one of the most serious problems of modern technology.[7]

Selection Criteria. To understand the nature of the problem, consider, for example, the creep properties of a typical material used in aircraft gas turbines. Two conditions limit the stress to which a part made of this material is subjected in service:

1. The total plastic strain during the lifetime of the part cannot exceed a value set by the allowable tolerances of the design.
2. The stress itself cannot exceed the value leading to rupture within the same lapse of time.

[7] See, for example, *Physics Today*, **13**, 63 (November 1960).

If stress and temperature are selected for peak operating conditions, a total strain of 0.5% in 1000 hours is considered to be a relatively conservative criterion.[8] According to Fig. 12-14, at the peak temperature of 800°K the

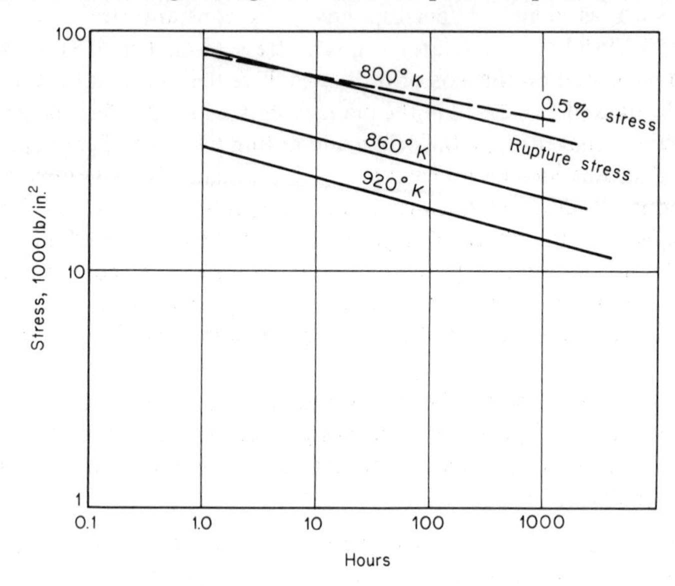

FIG. 12-14 Rupture curves at various temperatures for a typical material used in aircraft gas turbine (dotted line 0.5% creep strain curve at 800°K)

rupture stress, plotted as a solid line, has a smaller value for 1000 hr service than the 0.5% creep stress plotted as a dashed line. The rupture stress is therefore the deciding factor. Both stresses, when plotted on a logarithmic scale, show an almost linear trend versus log time for a given operating temperature. Assuming the rupture stress remains the deciding criterion at all temperatures, it is seen that the allowable stress decreases drastically as the temperature goes up. Since the operating load is not likely to be lower—it tends to be higher—the cross-sectional area of the part must be made larger to offset this decrease of stress, and this in turn entails an increase of weight.

The Density–Strength Ratio. In a conventional type of technology, such as bridge and building construction, excess weight is not always a liability, provided it is compensated by other features of design, a lower production cost, for example. In space technology, where minimum weight is at a premium, every pound that can be saved is vitally important. Therefore, density–strength ratio, rather than strength alone, is often the deciding

[8] H. Hanink and L. Luini, "Criteria in the Selection of Materials for Aircraft Gas Turbines," in monograph *Utilization of Heat Resisting Alloys*, p. 134, American Society of Metals, 1954.

criterion (see Problem 12-12). If we assume that the strength is determined by the stress producing fracture after 1000 hours of service, a diagram, Fig. 12-15, can be constructed by plotting the fracture stress at various temperatures on the abscissae and the density on the ordinates. For alloys

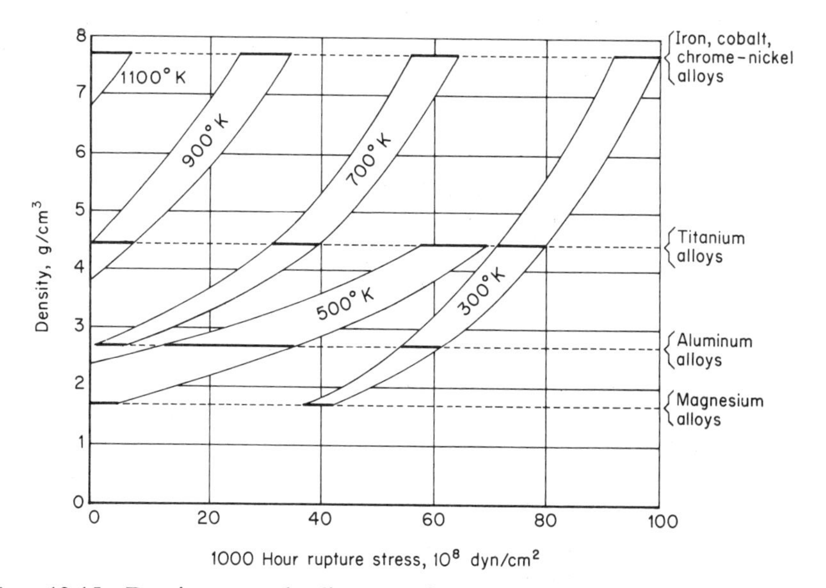

FIG. 12-15 Density–strength diagrams for representative alloys at various temperatures

having nearly all the same density, it has been found more expedient to indicate a range of stress rather than individual values of stress.[9] Likewise, ranges of stresses belonging to the same temperature have been connected by common areas for convenience. Finally, for the sake of comparison, the ranges of ultimate strengths in axial tension at room temperature (rounded off to 300°K) also have been included.

According to Fig. 12-15, the average density–strength ratio at each temperature and each stress range is obtained by measuring the slope of the straight line drawn through the origin to the middle point of the range. The smaller the slope, the lower is the density–strength ratio, and the better is the material suited to the particular temperature. Significantly, if the density is expressed in kilograms per cubic meter, and the stress is expressed in newtons per square meter, the dimensions of the density–strength ratio are kilograms per newton meter or kilograms per joule. We can thus say that the lower the density–strength ratio, the less material is needed to absorb the same amount of work through deformation. Based on this premise, the data

[9] For more exact data see H. C. Cross and W. F. Simmons, "Alloys and Their Properties for Elevated Temperatures," in monograph, *Utilization of Heat Resistant Alloys*, American Society of Metals, 1954.

of Fig. 12-15 show that, as the temperature goes up, the minimum density–strength ratio shifts from the lighter to the heavier metals. Unfortunately, this shift also increases the value of the minimum itself. Thus, the minimum density–strength ratio at 900°K turns out to be roughly eight times greater than at 300°K—a fair warning that parts for high-temperature applications are likely to be much heavier than for use at room temperature. As far as space technology is concerned, this increase of weight is a very serious handicap.

Refractory Materials. At the risk of gross oversimplification—for other factors are no less important—we can rather easily find what is at the core of the problem. The alloys that are best suited to room temperature service (magnesium and aluminum alloys, according to Fig. 12-15) are at a comfortable margin from their melting points. The T/T_f ratio is generally less than 0.35. Contrariwise, the alloys currently available for service at 900°K (iron, cobalt, and chrome-nickel alloys, according to Fig. 12-15) are more than half way toward their melting points. Recalling the exponential effect of T/T_f on creep properties, Section 12-13, it is not surprising that they perform so much less satisfactorily than their counterparts at room temperature. If this is so, the obvious remedy is a recourse to more refractory materials having much higher melting points: refractory metals (molybdenum and tungsten) as well as refractory ceramics (carbides, nitrides, and oxides).

In the current search for better high-temperature materials, oxides of light metals (beryllium oxide and magnesium oxide) have attracted much attention because of their invitingly low density. Taken in bulk, however, they are no better than any other brittle material. Their density-strength ratio is too high, much higher than that of any alloy at room temperature. When suitably processed, these oxides, according to the ideas of Chapter 8, could attain a much greater strength and considerably improve their density-strength ratio. They could thus conceivably be made as strong as the glass fibers mentioned in Chapter 5 at room temperature, and they would assuredly be much stronger than glass fibers at elevated temperatures because of their higher melting points.

It may also turn out, on closer scrutiny, that these oxides are not the best nor even a feasible solution. But whatever the solution, it will not come about unless the designer leaves the conventional tracks and adequately meets the challenge of the new materials. A good illustration of a non-conventional design was provided in Chapter 5 by the spun casings of rocket combustion chambers. This should not remain an isolated case. The sooner the beginning engineer realizes the importance of this fact for space technology, the better will he be able to cope with other "space facts."[10]

[10] See, for example, "Space Facts," Missile and Space Vehicle Department, General Electric Co., Philadelphia.

12-16 Summary. Gain or loss of momentum experienced by molecules in the process of exchange of partners in adjacent layers is responsible for the viscous behavior of liquids, i.e., for the resistance they offer to flow. The flow is laminar if it resembles the sliding motion of a stack of lamellae. In such a flow a spontaneous exchange of molecules between adjacent layers causes the shear stress to increase proportionally to the shear strain rate, in accordance with *Newton's law* of viscosity. The coefficient of proportionality η is called *coefficient of viscosity*, in short, the viscosity of the liquid. In many engineering applications a more convenient measure of the resistance of a liquid to flow is the *kinematic viscosity*, η/ρ, where ρ is the density of the liquid.

The viscosity of common liquids covers a wide range, from a fraction of a centipoise to 10^6 cP and more. The variation of η with temperature is equally large. It is generally of an *exponential* nature.

We distinguish between *simple* Newtonian liquids, obeying the law of proportionality, and *generalized* Newtonian liquids, for which the relation between stress and strain-rate is not a simple proportionality. We speak of a *plastic* flow if the initiation of flow requires a threshold value of stress, as in paints and toothpaste. Finally, *thixotropy* is the tendency of certain substances (e.g., bentonite) to flow under external stimuli (e.g., mild vibrations) and to cease flowing when left to themselves.

A more general property, expected of all substances on theoretical grounds, is *visco-elasticity*: a transition from an elastic to a viscous behavior as a function of time. The characteristic quantity is the *relaxation time*, θ. For simple Newtonian liquids, θ is given by the ratio η/G, where G is the shear modulus of elasticity.

When the transition from elastic to viscous behavior is confined to small regions within the bulk of a solid, the substance is said to *creep*. In the *recoverable* type of creep, nearly all of the original shape of the body is restored when the load is removed, in contrast to a *permanent* creep, where recovery is rather small.

Imperfections of crystal structure, particularly *grain boundaries* in polycrystalline aggregates, are held responsible for a *recoverable* type of creep in metals *below* the yield stress. On the other hand, motion of dislocations appears to cause *permanent* creep *above* the yield stress. The climb of dislocations over the obstacles impeding their motion is considered to be the predominant mechanism when the temperature T exceeds 0.5 of the melting point T_f, both measured on an absolute scale, such as Kelvin. However, at this temperature, grain boundaries likewise acquire sufficient mobility to manifest *sliding* and formation of *fissures*—a plausible explanation of *intergranular cracking* and low ductility of certain alloys used in high-temperature technology.

Creep properties are currently determined in axial tension from *strain-time* diagrams under constant stress and temperature. These diagrams reveal several features common to metals, ceramics, and plastics, but, depending on temperature and stress, one or the other feature may be more prominent. These are

1. instantaneous increase of strain;
2. increase of strain at a decelerating rate, or a *transient* creep;
3. increase of strain at a constant rate, or a *steady state* creep;
4. increase of strain at an accelerated rate—generally a forerunner of impending fracture.

Strain rates are very sensitive to temperature changes. The dependence on T/T_f is of an exponential nature. The influence of stress is less great, following a power law in general.

Another way of determining creep properties of solids is to plot stress versus strain in axial tension at a constant temperature and *strain rate*. This is the same as the stress-strain diagram for plastic deformation discussed in Chapter 9, but with the added—and necessary—specifications of temperature and strain rate. At temperatures below $0.5T_f$, the influence of strain rate is rather small: it is of a *logarithmic* nature.

The strain-time and stress-strain diagrams are not interchangeable, at least not without a proper correction for stress effects, which so far no creep theory has been able to provide. Design for creep is synonymous with design for service at elevated temperatures. In such design, the stress to which a part is subjected during its lifetime must not produce *deformations incompatible* with the imposed tolerances. Nor must it lead to *premature fracture*. Currently available materials can seldom fulfill either condition without imposing *density-stress ratios* that are inacceptable from the point of view of design, particularly in space technology. The use of *light refractory* materials, such as beryllium oxide and magnesium oxide, is a way out of this difficulty, if processing and design follow suit.

References

ELEMENTARY

1. J. P. Frankel, *Principles of the Properties of Materials*, McGraw-Hill, New York, 1957.

ADVANCED

1. E. N. da C. Andrade, *Viscosity and Plasticity*, Chemical Publishing Co., New York, 1951.
2. M. Reiner, *Deformation, Strain and Flow*, H. K. Lewis & Co., London, 1960.
3. L. A. Rotherham, *Creep of Metals*, Institute of Physics, London, 1951.
4. *Creep and Recovery*, monograph, American Society of Metals, Cleveland, 1957.

Problems

12-1 Assuming the validity of Eq. (12-11), compute the frequency of vibration ν of atoms in liquid copper at its melting point from its density $\rho = 7.1$ g/cm^3, atomic weight $M = 52.01$ g/mole, and the measured value of viscosity $\eta = 3.8$ cP.

12-2 In order to maintain a velocity difference $\Delta v = 2$ cm/sec between layers of liquid separated by a distance of 5 cm, a shearing force of 200 dyn must be applied to each square centimeter of the surface of the layers. What is the viscosity of the liquid?

12-3 Explain why a different type motor oil must be used in the crankcase of an engine in summer than in winter.

12-4 Compute the kinematic viscosity η/ρ of a liquid from the known kinematic viscosity of water at 4.0°C (=1.57 centistokes) if the rates of flow of the liquid and water from a given capillary are in the ratio of 1 to 100.

12-5 The rate of flow of a liquid from a capillary 0.15 cm in diameter is 2 cm^3/min. What is the kinematic viscosity of this liquid expressed in centistokes?

12-6 Consider two kinds of paint, *A* and *B*, exhibiting plastic flow according to curve *OCD*, Fig. 12-3. Paint *A* has a higher threshold value *OC* of the shear stress, but a lower slope of the segment *CD* than paint *B*. Which of the two would you prefer? Why?

12-7 Plot a family of strain-time diagrams at a constant temperature using the data given in the table and identify portions of these diagrams in regard to various creep behaviors. Plot the dependence of the minimum strain rate on stress and approximate this dependence by a power law using logarithmic scales.

Time (hr)	*Strain Under Constant Stress* (lb/in.^{2})				
	10,000	15,000	20,000	25,000	30,000
200	0.010	0.022	0.040	0.090	0.168
400	0.018	0.035	0.059	0.130	0.223
600	0.019	0.038	0.070	0.142	0.270
800	0.020	0.039	0.078	0.159	0.380*
1000	0.020	0.040	0.082	0.170	—
1200	0.021	0.042	0.087	0.181	—
1400	0.020	0.041	0.092	0.190	—
1600	0.021	0.042	0.097	0.197	—
1800	0.021	0.040	0.100	0.205	—
2000	0.020	0.041	0.105	0.215	—

* Test discontinued.

12-8 Assuming the validity of cross plotting of information shown in Fig. 12-12 and Fig. 12-13, derive a curve similar to the curves drawn in Fig. 12-13 from the curves shown in Fig. 12-12 for a rate of strain of 2.2×10^{-9}/sec.

12-9 A substance has a value of viscosity $\eta = 10^6$ P and a value of shear modulus of elasticity $G = 10^5$ dyn/cm^2. How long must one wait until this substance exhibits clearly a liquid behavior?

12-10 The substance considered in Problem 12-9 is suddenly sheared by an amount of 0.01 in./in. What stress must be applied at the initiation of shear and after 5 sec to keep it in the deformed state?

12-11 Draw a shear strain-time diagram of a solid subjected to a shear stress $\tau = 5000$ lb/in.^{2} if $G_u = 10^7$ lb/in.^{2}, $G_R = 0.7 \times 10^7$ lb/in.^{2}, $\eta = 10^{12}$ P, and the Y.S. in shear is 7000 lb/in.^{2} (Beware of units.)

12-12 The mass ratio *R* of a rocket, that is, the ratio of mass at takeoff to mass at attainment of escape velocity, is $R = 20$. In this ratio the payload—that is, the part remaining after the casing of the combustion chamber is jettisoned—enters in the amount of 2%. Knowing that the solid propellant has a density $\rho_p = 1.5$ gr/cm^3 and that the combustion chamber is subjected to a pressure p of 60 atm, compute the required density-strength ratio ρ_c/σ of the casing. (Treat it as a thin-walled cylinder under internal pressure completely filled with propellant at the takeoff.)

Is any material at any temperature shown in Fig. 12-15 suitable for the casing?

Hint: If m_p, m_c, and m_l are the masses of the propellant, casing, and payload, respectively, then

$$\frac{m_p + m_c + m_l}{m_c + m_l} = 20$$

also,

$$\frac{\rho_c}{\sigma} = \frac{\alpha \rho_p}{2p}$$

where

$$\alpha = \frac{m_c}{m_p + m_c + m_l}$$

13 / ELECTRICAL PROPERTIES: DIELECTRIC POLARIZATION

Dielectric polarization is a phenomenon characteristic of electrical insulators. It is found in solids, liquids, and gases, and materials in each of these states of aggregation are used for electrical insulation. Like elasticity, dielectric polarization owes its origin to the existence and stability of atomic and molecular forces. This common origin explains the similarity between Hooke's law and the basic dielectric law derived in the present chapter. It also accounts for a certain amount of interaction, or coupling, existing between elastic and dielectric phenomena.

13-1 Manifestations. Dielectric polarization appears whenever electric charges are displaced with respect to each other, and the displacements are reversible. Devices based on this manifestation are numerous. They range from condensers and switch-gear equipment in power and distribution installations to rectifiers, resonators, amplifiers, and transducers—converters of electrical energy to other forms of energy—in communication technology. They include memory devices used for storage of information in modern computers.

In all these manifestations the displacement of electric charges activates restoring forces. The latter either do work or, by resisting, cause external forces to do work on the system. In one case the electrical energy is released; in the other it is absorbed or stored. The release and absorption of energy can be either gradual, as in oscillating circuits and memory devices, or it can be sudden, as in condenser discharge welding and circuit breakers. In both cases a complete analogy exists between dielectric polarization and elasticity. The analogy is further strengthened by considering the nature of the restoring forces.

13-2 Dielectric Polarization and Atomic Forces. The forces acting in inert dilute gases are the simplest to analyze. By dilute, we mean obeying the perfect gas law $pv = RT$ reasonably well. The result of this analysis can subsequently be generalized to include other materials.

The molecule of an inert gas is monatomic, as mentioned in Chapter 1. Because of the symmetry of closed shells, the center of negative charges of the electrons coincides with the location of the positive nucleus. Hence the molecule in the stable state is not only neutral but has no permanent electric dipole. If the nucleus P is displaced from the center of negative charges N, Fig. 13-1, the attraction between N and P will produce restoring forces PP' and NN'. To keep the nucleus in the displaced position, external forces

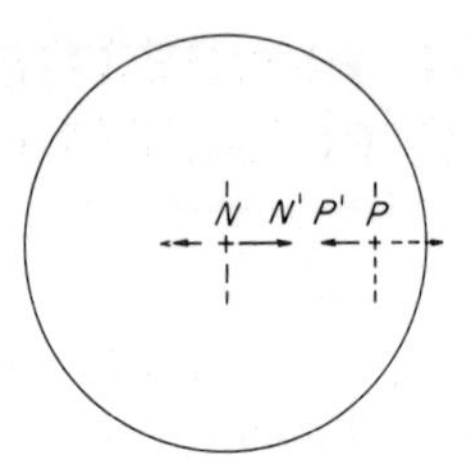

FIG. 13-1 Restoring forces PP' and NN' produced by separation of centers of positive and negative charges

must be applied at P and N opposing PP' and NN'. Forces of this kind can be called to life by placing the molecule in an electric field.

Electric field of a Capacitor. An electric field particularly convenient for the study of dielectric polarization is that existing in a plate capacitor, Fig. 13-2. From elementary physics we know that if two metallic parallel plates are separated by a gap l and are connected to the two poles of a battery, then upon severing the connections with the battery, they will be found to possess a certain amount of electric charge: one of them will have a charge $+q$, the other $-q$. Furthermore, if the gap l is small compared to dimensions of the area A of the plates, an electric field of constant intensity $\mathbf{E}$ exists in the space between the plates.

To recall the meaning of $\mathbf{E}$, we use the analogy with a gravitational field. The intensity of the terrestrial gravitational field is the acceleration of gravity g. A mass m is subjected in this field to a force $f = mg$ downward. In like manner, a positive test charge $\mathbf{q}'$ introduced in the gap l, Fig. 13-2, is subjected to a force $f = \mathbf{q}'\mathbf{E}$ downward. (A test charge is a charge so small that

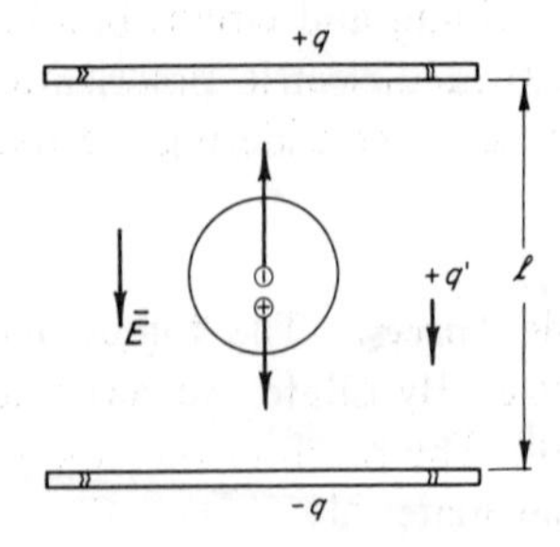

FIG. 13-2 Field created by a plate capacitor

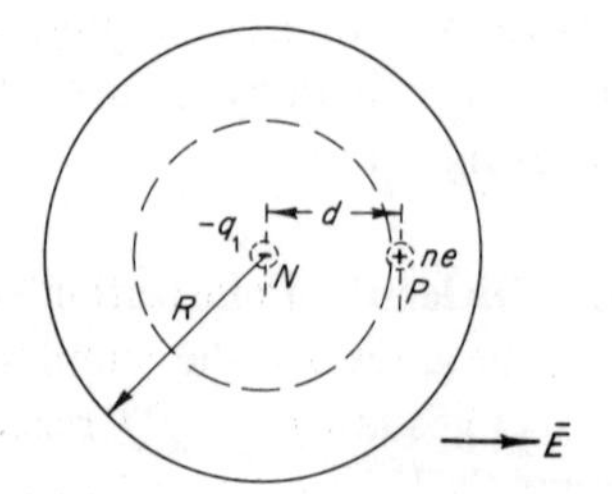

FIG. 13-3 Dipole moment in inert molecule induced by the field of a capacitor

its presence does not disturb the electrical field in its immediate vicinity.) However, at variance with the gravitational field—in which there are no negative masses—a negative test charge $\boldsymbol{q}'$ will be pulled by a force $f = \boldsymbol{q}'\boldsymbol{E}$ upward.

The relation

$$f = \boldsymbol{q}'\boldsymbol{E} \tag{13-1}$$

defines the quantity E as well as it determines its dimensions $[\boldsymbol{E}]$. The latter, as easily seen, are in MKSQ units:

$$[E] = [N/Q] \tag{13-2}$$

We can drive the analogy between $\boldsymbol{E}$ and g closer by recalling another relation, that existing between the charges $\boldsymbol{q}$ on the capacitor plates and $\boldsymbol{E}$ on the one hand and the relation between the terrestrial mass M and the acceleration g on the other. We have, by virtue of Newton's gravitational law,

$$g = \frac{kM}{R^2} = \frac{4\pi kM}{4\pi R^2} \tag{13-3}$$

where R is the radius of the earth and $4\pi R^2$ is surface area. The coefficient k is called the gravitational constant. This is a conversion factor necessary to make the dimensions of acceleration m/sec^2 (meters per second squared) on the left-hand side of Eq. (13-3) consistent with the dimensions kg/m^2 (kilograms per meter squared) on the right-hand side of Eq. (13-3).

In like manner we have, by virtue of Coulomb's electrostatic law,[1]

$$\boldsymbol{E} = \frac{\boldsymbol{q}}{\boldsymbol{\varepsilon}_0 A} \tag{13-4}$$

where A is the surface area of the plate and $\boldsymbol{\varepsilon}_0$ a conversion factor necessary to make the dimensions of $\boldsymbol{E}$ consistent with $\boldsymbol{q}/A$. The dimensions of $\boldsymbol{\varepsilon}_0$, in accordance with Eqs. (13-2) and (13-4), are in MKSQ units

$$[\boldsymbol{\varepsilon}_0] = [Q^2/(Nm^2)] = [Q^2\,sec^2/(kg\,m^3)] \tag{13-5}$$

The value of $\boldsymbol{\varepsilon}_0$ is determined experimentally—like the heat equivalent of work, J. In MKSQ units, the value of $\boldsymbol{\varepsilon}_0$ is approximately

$$\boldsymbol{\varepsilon}_0 = 8.85 \times 10^{-12}\,Q^2\,sec^2/(kg\,m^3) \tag{13-6}$$

Molecular Electric Moment and Electronic Polarizability. In writing Eq. (13-4) we have tacitly assumed that the gap l of the capacitor contains no matter, i.e., that the capacitor is in a vacuum. If now a molecule of an inert gas is introduced in this gap, the electric field will act on the centers N and P of the negative and positive charges by pulling them apart, Fig. 13-3. As

[1] Equation (13-4) is derived in most textbooks of elementary physics. Section 13-16 is given as a refresher.

soon as the centers have been separated, restoring forces caused by Coulomb's electrostatic attraction come into play to pull them back. At the equilibrium distance d, the restoring forces balance the field forces. The centers of charges remain separated, and the monatomic molecule is said to be *polarized.*

To compute the magnitude of the balancing forces, we consider that the nucleus carries its whole charge $+ne$, where n is the atomic number of the element. However, since it remains embedded inside the electron shells, only a fractional charge $-q_1$ of the total electronic charge $-ne$ contributes to the electrostatic attraction f_c. We write, therefore, in accordance with the expression of Coulomb's law in MKSQ units (see Section 13-16), that the electrostatic attraction on the nucleus is

$$f_c = \frac{-neq_1}{4\pi\varepsilon_0 d^2} \tag{13-7}$$

The minus sign indicates that f_c acts in the opposite direction to the force f_P applied by the field of the capacitor. According to Eq. (13-1) the force f_P on the nucleus is

$$f_P = neE \tag{13-8}$$

Hence, at equilibrium,

$$f_c + f_P = -\frac{neq_1}{4\pi\varepsilon_0 d^2} + neE = 0$$

or

$$E = \frac{q_1}{4\pi\varepsilon_0 d^2} \tag{13-9}$$

Small Displacements. The forces that can be applied by the electric field of the capacitor are weak compared to the atomic forces, even at the breakdown field intensity;[2] they are in fact so weak that the displacements d they cause are quite small compared to the radius R of the molecule (see illustrative example, Section 13-5). Under these circumstances, it is permissible to assume that the electrons preserve their original distribution during displacement.

According to the present view, this distribution is continuous rather than discrete, as postulated in the old Bohr model. The electrons are pictured as forming a sort of a cloud inside the atom. The density of the cloud is not uniform. If it were, the value of q_1 (see Problem 13-10) would be

$$q'_1 = ne(d/R)^3$$

Actually, the density is greater near the nucleus; hence the true value of q_1 is larger than q'_1. We can therefore write

$$q_1 = ne(d/\beta R)^3 \tag{13-10}$$

[2] The breakdown field intensity corresponds to loss of insulation and sparking across the gap l.

where β is a fraction characteristic of the actual distribution of electrons in the neutral atom. We expect βR to be a rather large fraction of R; see Section 13-4.

Substitution of $\boldsymbol{q}_1$ from Eq. (13-10) in Eq. (13-9) yields

$$\boldsymbol{E} = \frac{ned}{4\pi\varepsilon_0(\beta R)^3} \tag{13-11}$$

The quantity *ned* is called the *molecular dipole moment* induced by the field $\boldsymbol{E}$. It is generally designated by the Greek letter $\boldsymbol{\mu}$. We therefore put

$$\boldsymbol{\mu} = ned \tag{13-12}$$

whereupon Eq. (13-11) becomes

$$\boldsymbol{E} = \frac{\boldsymbol{\mu}}{4\pi\varepsilon_0(\beta R)^3} \tag{13-13}$$

Since the denominator on the right-hand side of Eq. (13-13) is constant for a given material, the induced molecular dipole moment is *proportional to the applied field intensity* $\boldsymbol{E}$. Equation (13-13) is the expression of the dielectric law, Section 13-3, on the atomic level.

For brevity, we put

$$\boldsymbol{\alpha}_e = 4\pi\varepsilon_0(\beta R)^3 \tag{13-14}$$

whereupon, by transposing $\boldsymbol{\alpha}_e$ to the left side of Eq. (13-13),

$$\boldsymbol{\mu} = \boldsymbol{\alpha}_e\boldsymbol{E} \tag{13-15}$$

The coefficient $\boldsymbol{\alpha}_e$ is called the *electronic polarizability*, since it results from the shift of the electronic cloud with respect to the nucleus.

According to Eq. (13-12), the dimensions of $\boldsymbol{\mu}$ in MKSQ units are

$$[\boldsymbol{\mu}] = [\text{coulombs} \times \text{meters}] = [\text{Q m}] \tag{13-16}$$

Since d is a very small fraction of R ($\approx 10^{-10}$ m) and $e = 1.60 \times 10^{-19}$ Q, $\boldsymbol{\mu}$ is expected to be a very small quantity. Even permanent dipole moments, (see Section 13-8) are seldom larger than 10^{-30} Q m (coulomb meter). A unit equal to 3.33×10^{-30} Q m has been introduced in the study of molecular dipole moments. It is called a *debye* in honor of P. Debye's pioneering work in this field. That is,

$$1 \text{ debye} = 3.33 \times 10^{-30} \text{ Q m} \tag{13-17}$$

In the CGS units and electrostatic esu units of charge,

$$1 \text{ debye} = 10^{-18} \text{ esu} \times \text{cm} \tag{13-18}$$

13-3 Electric Polarization, *P*. As with elasticity, it is desirable to replace the microscopic quantity, here the molecular dipole moment, by a macroscopically describable quantity. To effect this, we consider that the gap l

of the capacitor is filled with the inert gas under normal atmospheric conditions. Let N be the number of molecules per unit volume at a given temperature T and pressure p. Then the volume assigned to one molecule is $1/N$. The volume effectively occupied by one molecule is of the order of $(2R)^3$. Hence the *fraction* of the volume effectively occupied by the molecule is of the order of $8R^3N$. This is a very small number. For example, we know from general chemistry that under standard atmospheric conditions N is close to 3×10^{25} molecules/m^3; on the other hand, R^3 is of the order of 10^{-30} m^3. Hence the fraction of volume effectively occupied by the gas molecules is less than 10^{-3}, i.e., less than one thousandth. Thus, as it were, the space in the capacitor is practically empty of matter.

A test charge q', Fig. 13-4, placed in such a space has little chance of being anywhere so near a molecule as to be aware of its individual action. All it "senses" is the combined action of the whole aggregate. Because of mutual attraction of positive and negative charges, there is a tendency for the molecules to be placed as A and B, Fig. 13-4, that is, in such a way that an

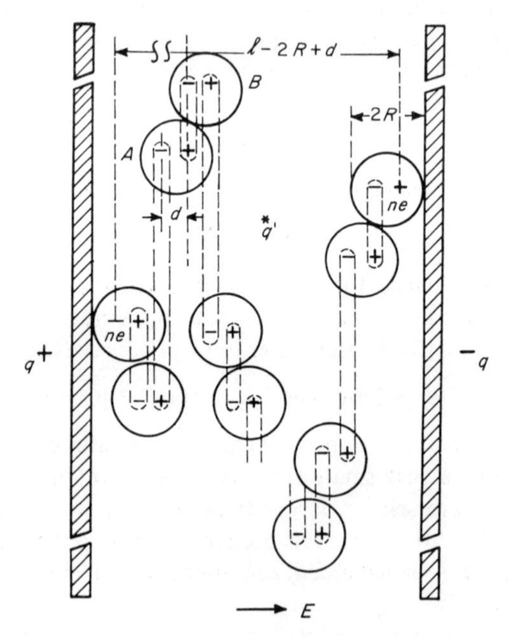

FIG. 13-4 The distribution of molecular dipoles *ned* in a capacitor

equal amount of positive and negative charges lie on the same plane parallel to the plates of the capacitor. However, the distribution of charges in this plane is random. Hence their combined action on the test charge q' is essentially nil. So is the action of charges on other planes parallel to the capacitor's plates. The only exception are the planes adjacent to the plates. Here the charges are all of one sign: negative near the positive plate, positive near the negative plate, Fig. 13-4. Let N' be the number of molecules on each of these planes. To find N' we note that the number of molecules which can be assumed to bridge the distance l in the manner depicted by Fig. 13-4 is l/d on the average. Beginning each time with another molecule adjacent to one of the plates, there are N' of such bridges in volume Al. Hence the total number of molecules in volume Al is $N'l/d$. Alternatively, this number is also equal to NAl. Hence,

$$N'l/d = NAl$$

and

$$N' = NdA$$

The total charge, plus or minus, induced in the molecules adjacent to each plate is thus

$$N'ne = N(ned)A$$

or, using Eq. (13-12),

$$N'ne = N\mu A = \mathbf{P}A$$

where, for the sake of generality, we have put

$$\mathbf{P} = N\boldsymbol{\mu} \tag{13-19}$$

$\mathbf{P}$ is called the dipole moment per unit volume, or the *electric polarization.* It is the macroscopic counterpart of the molecular moment $\boldsymbol{\mu}$.

In terms of $\mathbf{P}$ the test charge $\boldsymbol{q}'$ "senses" an induced charge $-\mathbf{P}A$ opposing $+\boldsymbol{q}$ and an induced charge $+\mathbf{P}A$ opposing $-\boldsymbol{q}$. Thus the *effect of polarization* is to *weaken* the *action* of *charges applied directly* to *the plates.*

In accordance with Eq. (13-4) the field intensity due to the sum $\boldsymbol{q} - \mathbf{P}A$ of the applied and induced charges is

$$\mathbf{E} = \frac{\boldsymbol{q} - \mathbf{P}A}{A\varepsilon_0} = \frac{(\boldsymbol{q}/A) - \mathbf{P}}{\varepsilon_0} \tag{13-20}$$

In this expression $\boldsymbol{q}/A$ represents the charge per unit area of the capacitor plate. It is convenient to introduce a new notation, namely,

$$\mathbf{D} = \boldsymbol{q}/A \tag{13-21}$$

$\mathbf{D}$ is called charge density.[3] It dimensions, as easily seen, are coulombs per square meter [Q/m^2]. Substitution of Eq. (13-21) in Eq. (13-20) and rearrangement of terms yields

$$\mathbf{P} = \mathbf{D} - \varepsilon_0\mathbf{E} \tag{13-22}$$

from which $\mathbf{P}$ can be obtained if $\mathbf{D}$ and $\mathbf{E}$ are determined.

Even though $\mathbf{P}$ has been defined as a dipole moment per unit volume and $\mathbf{D}$ as a charge per unit area, the dimensions of $\mathbf{P}$ and $\mathbf{D}$ are consistent.

[3] In the subsequent course of field theory the charge density is shown to be numerically equal to the normal component of a field vector called electric flux density.

This is seen from Eq. (13-19), in which the molecular dipole moment $\boldsymbol{\mu}$ has the dimensions [Q m] in accordance with Eq. (13-16). There follows

$$[P] = [\mu N] = [\mathrm{Qm/m^3}] = [\mathrm{Q/m^2}] \tag{13-23}$$

13-4 Dielectric Law. We make use of Eqs. (13-19) and (13-15) to obtain a relationship between two measurable macroscopic quantities $\boldsymbol{D}$ and $\boldsymbol{E}$. Substitution of the above two equations in Eq. (13-22) gives

$$\boldsymbol{D} = (\alpha_e N + \varepsilon_0)\boldsymbol{E} \tag{13-24}$$

or, by putting

$$\varepsilon = \alpha_e N + \varepsilon_0 \tag{13-25}$$

$$\boldsymbol{D} = \varepsilon \boldsymbol{E} \tag{13-26}$$

In words, the *charge density* $\boldsymbol{D}$ is *proportional to field intensity* $\boldsymbol{E}$.

The coefficient of proportionality ε depends on the nature of the medium filling the gap l of the condenser. It is called the *dielectric constant*, or *permittivity*.

Obviously $\varepsilon > \varepsilon_0$. With this in mind, assume the capacitor is connected to a source of constant voltage. This implies a constant field intensity $\boldsymbol{E}$ (see illustrative example, Section 13-5). Let $\boldsymbol{D}$ be the charge density when the capacitor is filled with a dielectric, and let $\boldsymbol{D}_0$ be the charge density when the capacitor is in a vacuum. Then, by Eq. (13-26),

$$\frac{\boldsymbol{D} - \boldsymbol{D}_0}{\boldsymbol{D}_0} = \frac{\varepsilon - \varepsilon_0}{\varepsilon_0} \tag{13-27}$$

That is, the charge density is increased in the ratio $(\varepsilon - \varepsilon_0)/\varepsilon_0$. Therein lies the merit of dielectrics having large values of ε. As we shall see below, only liquids and solids possess dielectric constants ε that are significantly larger than ε_0.

The ratio $(\varepsilon - \varepsilon_0)/\varepsilon_0$ is called *electrical susceptibility*. It is designated by the Greek letter χ. That is,

$$\chi = \frac{\varepsilon - \varepsilon_0}{\varepsilon_0} \tag{13-28}$$

Comparison of Eq. (13-28) with Eq. (13-24) shows that

$$\chi = \frac{\alpha_e N}{\varepsilon_0} \tag{13-29}$$

We can also write, by substituting Eq. (13-26) in Eq. (13-22) and making use of Eq. (13-28),

$$\boldsymbol{P} = \chi \varepsilon_0 \boldsymbol{E} \tag{13-30}$$

There is a formal analogy between the dielectric law embodied in Eq. (13-26) and Hooke's law represented by Eq. (6-26). Like the stress σ, the charge density $\boldsymbol{D}$ is a quantity—the electric charge $\boldsymbol{q}$—referred to a unit area. The field intensity $\boldsymbol{E}$, as will appear in the example below, can be viewed as another quantity—the difference of potential V—referred to a unit length, similarly to strain ε. Both laws were established experimentally before having been derived from the same basic Coulomb's electrostatic attraction between charged elementary particles. The only difference between these laws lies in the character of the constants of proportionality. The modulus of elasticity E is a property of the material, whereas the dielectric constant $\boldsymbol{\varepsilon}$ becomes a material property only when $\boldsymbol{\varepsilon}_0$ is subtracted from it. In this respect the law embodied by Eq. (13-30) is more appropriate. However, in practice, the electrical polarization $\boldsymbol{P}$ is determined mostly, if not exclusively, through $\boldsymbol{\varepsilon}$. So Eq. (13-26) is still a correct representation of the experimental dielectric law.

13-5 Illustrative Example[4]

A capacitor with a plate area $A = 0.1\ \text{m}^2$ and a gap $l = 0.01$ m filled with argon under standard atmospheric conditions is connected to a 100-V battery. The charge $\boldsymbol{q}$ on the capacitor measured after the connection with the battery had been severed was found to differ only by 4.8×10^{-12} Q from the charge $\boldsymbol{q}_0$ measured when the capacitor was placed in a vacuum. Determine the electrical susceptibility $\boldsymbol{\chi}$ and the electronic polarizability $\boldsymbol{\alpha}_e$ of argon.

Solution. We recall from elementary physics that 1 V is a potential difference corresponding to work done by the electric field on a charge of 1 Q in a path of 1 m. By moving this charge from the positive to the negative plate of the capacitor over the distance $l = 0.01$ m, the electric field does an amount of work $W = 100$ V. Hence, by calling f the force acting on the charge of 1 Q, we have

$$W = fl$$

or

$$f = W/l = 10^4\ \text{N/Q}$$

But, by Eq. (13-1), a force acting on a unit charge is equal in magnitude to the field intensity $\boldsymbol{E}$. Hence,

$$\boldsymbol{E} = 10^4\ \text{N/Q}$$

On the other hand, the difference in charge density $\boldsymbol{D} - \boldsymbol{D}_0$ between the argon-filled and evacuated capacitor is

$$\boldsymbol{D} - \boldsymbol{D}_0 = \frac{\boldsymbol{q} - \boldsymbol{q}_0}{A} = 4.8 \times 10^{-11}\ \text{Q/m}^2$$

[4] This example has been selected to illustrate the pertinent computations rather than the procedure.

By virtue of Eq. (13-26),

$$\boldsymbol{D} - \boldsymbol{D}_0 = (\boldsymbol{\varepsilon} - \boldsymbol{\varepsilon}_0)\boldsymbol{E}$$

Hence,

$$\boldsymbol{\varepsilon} - \boldsymbol{\varepsilon}_0 = (D - D_0)/E = 4.8 \times 10^{-15}\ [\mathrm{Q^2\ sec^2/(kg\ m^3)}]$$

and finally, by Eq. (13-28),

$$\boldsymbol{\chi} = \frac{\boldsymbol{\varepsilon} - \boldsymbol{\varepsilon}_0}{\boldsymbol{\varepsilon}_0} = \frac{4.8 \times 10^{-15}}{8.85 \times 10^{-12}} = 0.545 \times 10^{-3} \qquad \textit{Answer}^{5}$$

The electronic polarizability $\boldsymbol{\alpha}_e$ is determined by means of Eq. (13-27). Under standard atmospheric conditions ($T_0 = 273°\mathrm{K}$ and $p_0 = 1$ atmosphere) the number of molecules per cubic meter is $N_0 = 2.69 \times 10^{25}$. Hence,

$$\boldsymbol{\alpha}_e = \frac{\boldsymbol{\varepsilon} - \boldsymbol{\varepsilon}_0}{N} = 1.8 \times 10^{-40}\ [\mathrm{Q^2\ sec^2/kg}] \qquad \textit{Answer}$$

Note

1. Using Eq. (13-14) we can also determine the fractional radius βR. There follows

$$(\beta R)^3 = \frac{\boldsymbol{\alpha}_e}{4\pi\boldsymbol{\varepsilon}_0} = 1.6 \times 10^{-30}\ [\mathrm{m^3}]$$

and

$$\beta R = 1.16 \times 10^{-10}\ [\mathrm{m}]$$

If we take for R the value of 1.92×10^{-10} m corresponding to the condensed state of argon at 50°K, then $\beta = 0.6$, which is of the correct order of magnitude as far as the assumption of the theory developed in Section 13-2 is concerned.

2. For the purpose of comparison with the data to be presented later, Section 13-8, we shall also compute the induced molecular dipole moment $\boldsymbol{\mu}$ and the distance of separation d. Using Eq. (13-15) with $\boldsymbol{E} = 10^4$ N/Q and $\boldsymbol{\alpha}_e = 1.8 \times 10^{-40}\ \mathrm{Q^2\ sec^2/kg}$, we have

$$\boldsymbol{\mu} = \boldsymbol{\alpha}_e \boldsymbol{E} = 1.8 \times 10^{-36}\ \mathrm{Q\ m} = 0.54 \times 10^{-6}\ \text{debye}$$

The distance of separation d is computed from Eq. (13-12). Since $n = 18$ for argon, we have

$$d = \frac{\boldsymbol{\mu}}{ne} = 0.62 \times 10^{-18}\ \mathrm{m} = 0.62 \times 10^{-8}\ \text{Å}$$

Even at the breakdown potential of about $10^6\ V/m$, d is still a very small fraction of R, being only 0.6×10^{-4} Å. The assumption of small displacements is thus fully justified.

Of the two quantities $\boldsymbol{\chi}$ and $\boldsymbol{\alpha}_e$, the electronic polarizability $\boldsymbol{\alpha}_e$ is the more

[5] In some handbooks, $\boldsymbol{\varepsilon}/\boldsymbol{\varepsilon}_0$ rather than $\boldsymbol{\chi}$ is listed under the name of dielectric constant. In this example, $\boldsymbol{\varepsilon}/\boldsymbol{\varepsilon}_0 = 1.000545$.

fundamental one since, as shown by Eq. (13-14), it depends only on the electron distribution within the molecule. The electrical susceptibility $\boldsymbol{\chi}$ is also dependent on N and through N on temperature and pressure. This can be seen as follows.

Let N_A be Avogadro's number (the number of molecules per mole), M the mass of the substance in kilograms per mole, and ρ its density in kilograms per cubic meter; then

$$N = N_A \rho / M \tag{13-31}$$

Neither N_A nor M depend on temperature and pressure, but ρ does, and consequently N does too.

13-6 Generalization of the Dielectric Law. Electronic polarizability is but one of the manifestations of dielectric polarization. Reversible displacements of electric charges can activate restoring forces not only within the atom but also among the atoms if the latter are *ionized.* As a rule, however, the most important contribution to the dielectric polarization comes from the presence of *permanent dipole moments* in the molecule, the best example being provided by water. This rule suffers a notable exception in the case of solids, as will be explained below.

In all these manifestations the dielectric constant $\boldsymbol{\varepsilon}$, or the ratio $\boldsymbol{\varepsilon}/\boldsymbol{\varepsilon}_0$, is computed first from the experimental law, Eq. (13-26), in the manner shown in the illustrative example, Section 13-5. Equation (13-29) is then adjusted to take into account the additional contributions due to ionic bonds and permanent dipole moments. Equation (13-29) must also be *corrected* if the state of aggregation is *no longer* that of a dilute gas; see Section 13-9. The procedure is in many respects similar to the procedure used in Section 6-5, when the expression of the modulus of elasticity was generalized to take into account bonds other than ionic.

13-7 Ionic Polarizability. The simplest way of explaining the nature of ionic polarizability is to consider the chain of cations and anions represented in Fig. 6-2. Let z be the valence of the ions. They are redrawn in Fig. 13-5a at their positions of equilibrium, i.e., with a distance of separation equal to the closest approach r_0. Under the influence of an applied electric field, both cations and anions will be displaced: the cations in the direction of the field, the anions in the opposite direction, Fig. 13-5b. If r is the magnitude of the displacement itself, the relative displacement d of, say, an anion with respect to the cations is $-2r$ to the left and $+2r$ to the right in Fig. 13-5b. We can therefore say that the electric field has induced a dipole moment $\boldsymbol{\mu} = ezd$ per cation-anion pair, i.e., per molecule. If the *local* field intensity[6] is $\boldsymbol{E}_1$, the *ionic polarizability* is, by analogy with Eq. (13-15),

$$\boldsymbol{\alpha}_i = \boldsymbol{\mu} / \boldsymbol{E}_1 \tag{13-32}$$

[6] As explained in Section 13-9, in condensed systems this intensity is different from the applied intensity $\boldsymbol{E}$.

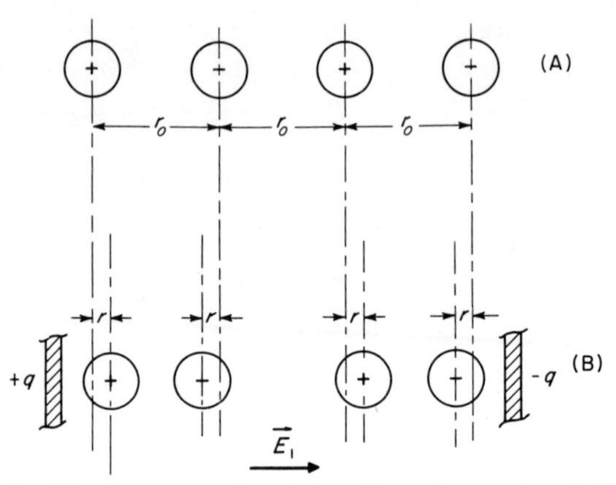

FIG. 13-5 Displacement of a chain of ions in an electric field

As with electronic polarization, restoring forces are called forth by the displacement. They are of the same origin as the forces considered in Section 6-2 in the derivation of the modulus of elasticity of ionic crystals. Knowing the magnitude of these forces we can express the ionic polarizability $\boldsymbol{\alpha}_i$ in terms of r_0 and the repulsion exponent m, Table 6-1, Section 6-2. The same assumption of small displacements is made and the same procedure is followed here as in the case of electronic polarizability, Section 13-2. The details of the procedure are further considered in Section 13-10. We will merely observe here that the ionic polarizability $\boldsymbol{\alpha}_i$ in simple ionic crystals such as sodium chloride, is of the same order of magnitude as the electronic polarizability $\boldsymbol{\alpha}_e$.

13-8 Orientation Polarizability. The molecular dipole moments considered thus far were *induced* by the applied electrical field and they disappeared with the field. There are, however, substances which have an electric dipole moment permanently built into their molecules. This can happen only if the molecule contains at least two different kinds of atoms, i.e., if the substance is a compound. The bonding between different kinds of atoms invariably causes a redistribution of valence electrons and a shift of electric charges. If the new center of negative charges fails to coincide with the center of positive charges, a permanent dipole moment appears. The simplest type of dipole moment is found in a diatomic molecule, Fig. 13-6.

If the bonding were 100% ionic, the permanent dipole moment would be simply ezd_0, where z is the valency and d_0 the distance separating the two

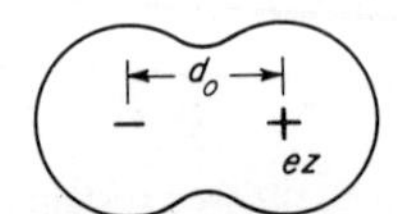

FIG. 13-6 Permanent dipole moment in a diatomic molecule

nuclei. Such an extreme condition seldom exists in real molecules. As we shall see later in the illustrative example of HCl, the bond is only partly ionic, and the actual permanent dipole moment μ_p is much smaller than ezd_0.

Even this amount of dipole moment is not likely to be revealed in the bulk of the material. The reason lies in the thermal agitation of molecules. In the absence of an electrical field, the molecules are randomly oriented in space, and so are their dipole moments. Because of randomness, the contributions of individual dipole moments as a rule cancel each other, and there is no net electrical polarization in the dielectric material itself. This rule applies without exception to gases, and it is generally obeyed in liquids, where free motion of molecules is still largely unhampered. The situation in solids, as we shall see, is more complicated.

When the dielectric material is placed in an electric field, the permanent dipole moment of the molecule does make a contribution to the electric polarization. To find out how much, we observe that if the molecules had a free hand they would end up by aligning themselves parallel to the applied field. Each of them would then have contributed its entire dipole moment μ_p to the electric polarization $\boldsymbol{P}$, and the total contribution according to Eq. (13-19) would have been $N\mu_p$, where N is the number of molecules per unit volume. However, the thermal agitation has an upper hand, so that the contribution is much smaller. Under the competing action of field intensity $\boldsymbol{E}$ and temperature T, the majority of molecules will assume positions that are intermediate between no alignment and full alignment with the electric field. They will oscillate about some average orientation θ, Fig. 13-7. The

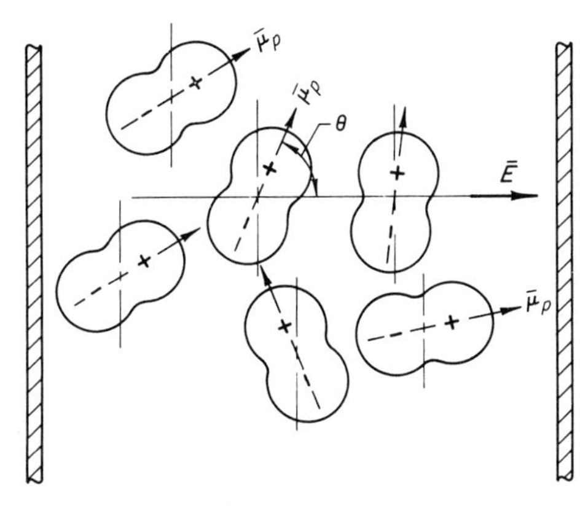

FIG. 13-7 Oscillation of permanent dipole moments about an average orientation θ

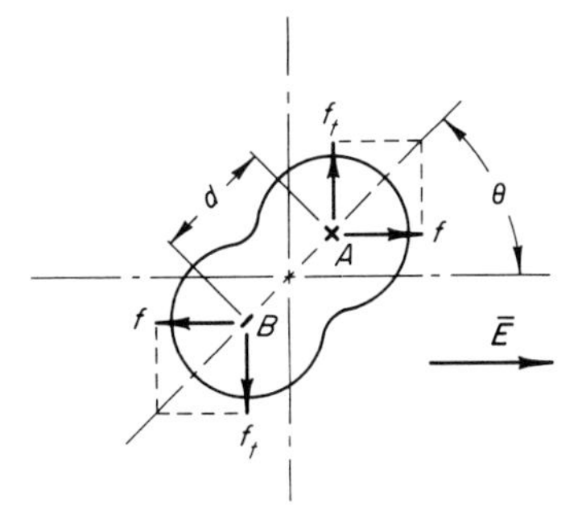

FIG. 13-8 Forces acting on a molecule at the average orientation θ

resulting contribution to $\boldsymbol{P}$ is called *orientation polarization* $\boldsymbol{P}_o$. Its value will be some fraction β of $\mu_p N$. That is,

$$\boldsymbol{P}_o = \beta N \mu_p \tag{13-33}$$

The computation of β is a statistical problem, as all problems involving thermal motion are. Accordingly, its solution must be deferred until the proper tools (thermodynamics) have been made available. A good approximation for practical applications is

$$\beta = \frac{E\mu_p}{3kT} \tag{13-34}$$

where k, the gas constant per molecule, is 1.38×10^{-23} J/deg.

To get a feeling for the origin of β, consider first that with average orientation θ the average dipole moment is

$$\mu_0 = \mu_p \cos\theta = zed \cos\theta \tag{13-35}$$

where d is the separation of charges in the permanent dipole.

This expression can be looked upon as though the separation of charges remained d, but the charges themselves were reduced to $ze \cos\theta$. Repeating the argument of Section 13-3, we shall find that

$$P_o = N\mu_p \cos\theta \tag{13-36}$$

Hence, by Eq. (13-33),

$$\beta = \cos\theta \tag{13-37}$$

Consider now the forces acting on the molecule at the average orientation θ, Fig. 13-8. The forces due to field intensity E are

$$f = \pm zeE \tag{13-38}$$

to counteract which, a force couple f_T must be provided at points A and B by the thermal motion. At equilibrium, as easily derived from Fig. 13-8,

$$\frac{f}{f_T} = \cot\theta \tag{13-39}$$

The couple f_T tends to align the average orientation perpendicular to the direction of the applied field. Such an alignment can be called a random one, since it will make the orientation polarization P_o nil. The maximum work the thermal motion will expend per molecule will occur when the latter turns through ninety degrees, from the direction parallel to a direction perpendicular to the field. The maximum work is easily seen to be $f_T\, d$. According to statistical thermodynamics, it is proportional to the absolute temperature T. That is,

$$f_T\, d = bT \tag{13-40}$$

where b is a constant. Substitution of f_T from Eq. (13-40) in Eq. (13-39) yields

$$\frac{fd}{bT} = \cot\theta \tag{13-41}$$

or, with reference to Eqs. (13-35) and (13-38),

$$\frac{\mu_p E}{bT} = \cot\theta \tag{13-42}$$

In practical applications, the numerator is quite small compared to the denominator; hence, $\cot \theta \approx \cos \theta$ and, by Eq. (13-37),

$$\beta = \frac{\mu_p E}{bT}. \tag{13-43}$$

This is the same as Eq. (13-34), in which b is seen to be $3k$.

Substitution of β from Eq. (13-34) in Eq. (13-33) yields

$$\boldsymbol{P}_o = N \frac{\mu_p^2}{3kT} \boldsymbol{E} \tag{13-44}$$

Hence, by comparison with Eqs. (13-19) and (13-15), we can write

$$\boldsymbol{P}_o = N\boldsymbol{\mu}_0 = N\boldsymbol{\alpha}_0 \boldsymbol{E} \tag{13-45}$$

where $\boldsymbol{\alpha}_0$ is called orientation polarizability. Obviously,

$$\boldsymbol{\alpha}_0 = \frac{\mu_p^2}{3kT} \tag{13-46}$$

In an electrical field, the orientation polarizability $\boldsymbol{\alpha}_0$ is superimposed on the electronic and ionic polarizabilities $\boldsymbol{\alpha}_e$ and $\boldsymbol{\alpha}_i$. Since all of them cause small displacements of centers of charges compared to the dimension of the molecule, their effects on electrical polarization can be considered as additive, i.e.,

$$\boldsymbol{P} = N\boldsymbol{\alpha}\boldsymbol{E} \tag{13-47}$$

where

$$\boldsymbol{\alpha} = \boldsymbol{\alpha}_e + \boldsymbol{\alpha}_i + \frac{\mu_p^2}{3kT} \tag{13-48}$$

And, on generalizing Eq. (13-29),

$$\boldsymbol{\alpha} = \boldsymbol{\alpha}_e + \boldsymbol{\alpha}_i + \frac{\mu_p^2}{3kT} = \frac{\boldsymbol{\varepsilon} - \boldsymbol{\varepsilon}_0}{N} \tag{13-49}$$

Except for a correction to be applied when the dielectric material is in a condensed state (see Section 13-9), Eq. (13-49) is the most general expression of the dielectric behavior of an insulator. This behavior, as we have stressed repeatedly, is due to restoring atomic forces that appear as soon as the applied electric field causes a displacement of charges within the insulator. Conductors of electricity do not exhibit a dielectric behavior, because the displacement of charges in the conductor—like the displacement of molecules in the liquid—is not hampered by any restoring forces.

Equation (13-49) can be rewritten in a more convenient form for computation by dividing both sides by $\boldsymbol{\varepsilon}_0$ and multiplying them by N_0, the number of molecules per cubic meter at standard conditions. There follows

$$\frac{N_0(\boldsymbol{\alpha}_e + \boldsymbol{\alpha}_i)}{\boldsymbol{\varepsilon}_0} + \frac{N_0 \mu_p^2}{3kT\boldsymbol{\varepsilon}_0} = \frac{N_0}{N} \frac{\boldsymbol{\varepsilon} - \boldsymbol{\varepsilon}_0}{\boldsymbol{\varepsilon}_0} \tag{13-50}$$

In this fashion the rather cumbersome units of ε_0 and high negative powers of ten are avoided.

If the ratio $(\varepsilon - \varepsilon_0)/\varepsilon_0$ is measured at various temperatures, the terms on the left side of Eq. (13-50) can be separated, whereupon $\alpha_e + \alpha_i$ and μ_p also can be determined.

Illustrative Example

Given $\varepsilon/\varepsilon_0$ for HCl at atmospheric pressure and at temperatures indicated in Table 13-1, compute the sum of electronic and ionic polarizabilities as well as the permanent dipole moment.

TABLE 13-1

Temperature, t (°C)	*Dielectric Constant Ratio,* $\varepsilon/\varepsilon_0$
−50	1.0067
0	1.0046
100	1.0028
200	1.0019

Solution. We notice from Table 13-1 that $\varepsilon/\varepsilon_0$ decreases with temperature. Since neither α_e nor α_i depend on temperature, we conclude from Eq. (13-50) that the molecule of HCl has a permanent dipole moment, μ_p. We also observe that if the expression on the right-hand side of Eq. (13-50) is plotted against $1/T$, a linear relationship obtains with an intercept equal to $N(\alpha_e + \alpha_i)\varepsilon_0$ for $1/T = 0$. The right-hand side of Eq. (13-50) contains the ratio N_0/N, which, by Eq. (13-31), is equal to the density ratio ρ_0/ρ. Assuming the validity of the perfect gas law, we have

$$N_0/N = \rho_0/\rho = T/T_0 \tag{13-51}$$

where $T = 273 + t$. The plot of $(N_0/N)(\varepsilon - \varepsilon_0)/\varepsilon_0$ versus $1/T$ is shown in Fig. 13-9.

From the intercept of the line with the vertical axis we get

$$N_0(\alpha_e + \alpha_i)/\varepsilon_0 = 0.0013$$

or

$$\alpha_e + \alpha_i = \frac{0.0013 \times 8.85 \times 10^{-12}}{2.69 \times 10^{25}}$$

$$= 4.35 \times 10^{-40}\ \mathrm{Q^2\ sec^2/kg} \qquad \textit{Answer}$$

This value is of the same order of magnitude as α_e computed in the illustrative example, Section 13-5.

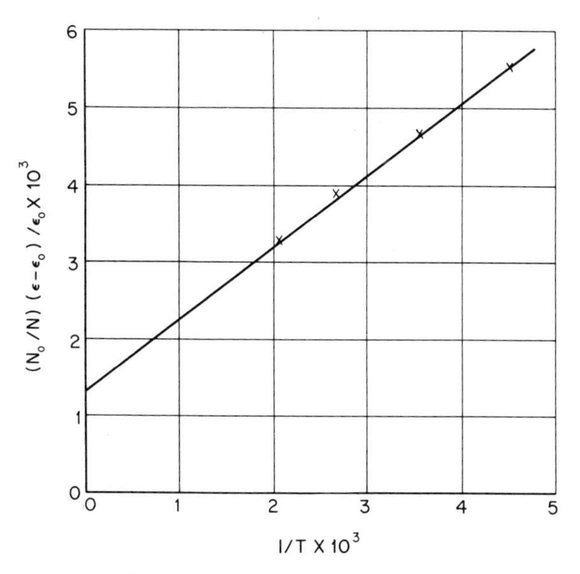

FIG. 13-9 Plot of electric polarizability versus the reciprocal of absolute temperature for HCl

The slope of the line is 0.93°K, or, by Eq. (13-50),

$$\frac{N_0 \mu_p^2}{3k\varepsilon_0} = 0.93°\text{K}$$

whence

$$\mu_p^2 = \frac{0.93 \times 3 \times 1.38 \times 10^{-23} \times 8.85 \times 10^{-12}}{2.69 \times 10^{25}}$$
$$= 12.7 \times 10^{-60} \text{ (Q m)}^2$$

or

$$\mu_p = 3.6 \times 10^{-30} \text{ Q m} = 1.08 \text{ debyes} \qquad \textit{Answer}$$

The permanent dipole moment of HCl is thus at least six orders of magnitude larger than the induced dipole moment computed from the illustrative example, Section 13-5. This figure is typical of the difference in magnitude between the two kinds of dipole moments. Yet, as intimated earlier in this section, the experimentally determined value of 1.08 debyes is still much lower than the value computed on the assumption of a 100% ionic bonding between H^+ and Cl^-. For this type of bonding, the separation of charges is simply the distance d_0 between the nuclei, which is 1.28 Å. Since H^+ and Cl^- are monovalent, the theoretical dipole moment μ' is

$$\mu' = ed_0 = 1.60 \times 10^{-19} \times 1.28 \times 10^{-10}$$
$$= 2.05 \times 10^{-29} \text{ Q m}$$

or about 6 debyes, roughly six times larger than the actual value.

Dielectric Behavior of Water. It will not be amiss to recall here the exceptional ability of water to dissolve ionic salts in considerable amounts. Water owes this property in no small measure to its high dielectric ratio $\varepsilon/\varepsilon_0$, which at 0°C has the value of 88. Another contributing factor is the hydrogen bond. Both are embodied in the peculiarities of the molecular structure of water, Fig. 13-10.

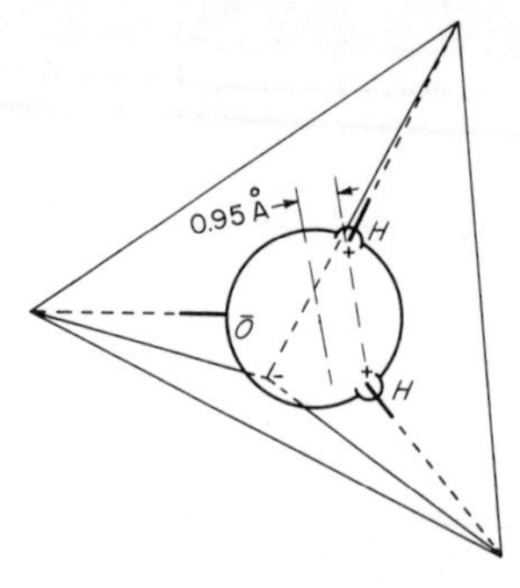

FIG. 13-10 Molecule of water with two hydrogen bonds and two oxygen valence bonds arranged in a tetrahedral configuration

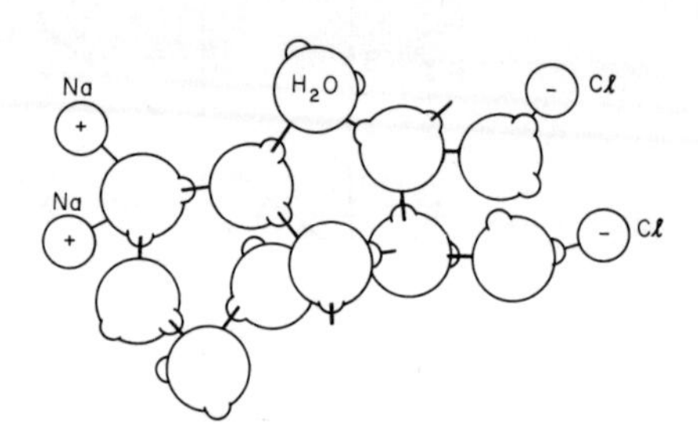

FIG. 13-11 Ions of Na^+Cl^- held apart by a cluster of water molecules

The two hydrogen atoms in the water molecule are located on one side of the oxygen atom and at a distance of 0.95 Å from it. Deprived of their electronic shield, they act as though they were bare protons ready to attract any foreign anion. On the other side of the molecule the electron shell of oxygen, enriched by two extra electrons, manifests an equal readiness to attract two cations.

A molecule of an ionic salt when brought in touch with water is thus subjected to forces which tend to dissociate it in ions. The stage is set for the dissolving action of water.

Once dissociated from each other, the ions of the salt molecule are prevented from recombining by the repulsive action of the permanent dipole moment of the water molecule. There are reasons to believe that more than one dipole moment is involved. That is, the two ions of the salt molecule are kept apart, not by one water molecule, but by an aggregate of molecules held together by the hydrogen bond, as shown schematically in Fig. 13-11. The attraction between the cation and anion of the salt is thereby weakened to such an extent that mere thermal agitation of water molecules is sufficient to keep the ions permanently apart, and the salt remains in solution.

The above conclusion follows from a closer analysis of the dielectric constant ratio of water $\varepsilon/\varepsilon_0$. If we compute this ratio from Eq. (13-50), using the value of the permanent dipole moment μ_p of dilute water vapor, the computed result is lower than the measured value of $\varepsilon/\varepsilon_0$ by a factor of six, in round figures; see Problem 13-4. It is as though the actual dipole moment were six times larger, i.e., as though the cation of the salt molecule were separated from its anion by about six water molecules.[7]

13-9 Polarizability of Condensed Aggregates. We recall that Eq. (13-48) is valid only for dilute gases. It is based on the assumption that a test charge $\boldsymbol{q}'$, placed in the field of a capacitor filled with a dilute gas, has little chance to be affected by the proximity of the polarized molecules. The same is not true when the gas is strongly compressed nor when the dielectric is a liquid or a solid. Here the atoms and molecules practically touch each other. Consequently the test charge $\boldsymbol{q}'$ feels not only the effect of the bulk polarization $\boldsymbol{P}$, already considered in Section 13-3, but also the additional effect of dipole moments induced in the surrounding molecules.

Figure 13-12 depicts schematically the situation in a cubically built aggregate. The test charge $\boldsymbol{q}'$, by replacing one of the molecules at 0, is subjected

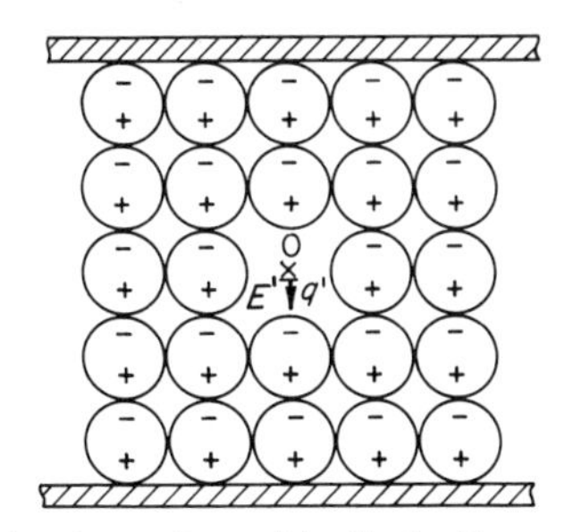

FIG. 13-12 Polarization of a cubically built condensed aggregate

to the action of the surrounding dipole moments, mostly those located in the vertical row below and above it. The field intensity $\boldsymbol{E}'$ produced thereby at point 0 is superimposed on the field intensity $\boldsymbol{E}$ appearing in Eq. (13-22). Both create a *local field* intensity:

$$\boldsymbol{E}_1 = \boldsymbol{E} + \boldsymbol{E}' \tag{13-52}$$

as foretold in Section 13-7.

The field intensity $\boldsymbol{E}_1$, in turn, acts on the molecule at 0 to induce the dipole moment $\boldsymbol{\mu}$. This *feedback* action applies to all dipole moments. We can therefore write, in accordance with Eq. (13-15),

$$\boldsymbol{\mu} = \boldsymbol{\alpha}_1 \boldsymbol{E}_1 = (\boldsymbol{\alpha}_e + \boldsymbol{\alpha}_i)(\boldsymbol{E} + \boldsymbol{E}') \tag{13-53}$$

We have excluded from Eq. (13-53) the contribution of the permanent dipole $\boldsymbol{\mu}_p$, because the role of this contribution to $\boldsymbol{E}'$ is still unsettled.[8]

On multiplying Eq. (13-53) by N, we obtain by Eq. (13-19):

$$\boldsymbol{P} = N(\boldsymbol{\alpha}_e + \boldsymbol{\alpha}_i)(\boldsymbol{E} + \boldsymbol{E}') \tag{13-54}$$

[7] See L. Pauling, *The Nature of the Chemical Bond*, p. 293, Cornell, Ithaca, New York, 1948.

[8] See, for example, C. Kittel, *Introduction to Solid State Physics*, Wiley, New York, 1956.

We seek to express $\boldsymbol{E}$ and $\boldsymbol{E}'$ in terms of $\boldsymbol{P}$ and the dielectric constants ε and ε_0.

By substituting for $\boldsymbol{D}$ its expression from Eq. (13-26) in Eq. (13-22), we have

$$\boldsymbol{P} = (\varepsilon - \varepsilon_0)\boldsymbol{E} \tag{13-55}$$

whence

$$\boldsymbol{E} = \frac{\boldsymbol{P}}{\varepsilon - \varepsilon_0} \tag{13-56}$$

The evaluation of $\boldsymbol{E}'$ in terms of all the induced dipole moments surrounding the molecule at 0 involves summations over rows and layers of molecules, a procedure similar to that indicated in Section 6-2 and no less tedious. For the cubic arrangement of Fig. 13-12 there exists an approximation based on the calculation of a field produced in a spherical cavity in a uniformly polarized continuous medium. This calculation is found in current textbooks on electricity and electromagnetism. In terms of the bulk polarization $\boldsymbol{P}$, the result reads

$$\boldsymbol{E}' = \frac{\boldsymbol{P}}{3\varepsilon_0} \tag{13-57}$$

Substitution of $\boldsymbol{E}$ from Eq. (13-56) and $\boldsymbol{E}'$ from Eq. (13-57) in Eq. (13-54) yields

$$\boldsymbol{P} = N(\alpha_e + \alpha_i)\left(\frac{\boldsymbol{P}}{\varepsilon - \varepsilon_0} + \frac{\boldsymbol{P}}{3\varepsilon_0}\right) \tag{13-58}$$

and, on dividing by $\boldsymbol{P}$ and rearranging the terms,

$$\frac{N(\alpha_e + \alpha_i)}{3\varepsilon_0} = \frac{\varepsilon - \varepsilon_0}{\varepsilon + 2\varepsilon_0} \tag{13-59}$$

The dependence of N on temperature and pressure was noted already in Section 13-5. It is therefore more convenient to substitute for N in Eq. (13-59) its expression from Eq. (13-31). We have, after additional rearrangement of terms,

$$\frac{N_A(\alpha_e + \alpha_i)}{3\varepsilon_0} = \frac{\varepsilon - \varepsilon_0}{\varepsilon + 2\varepsilon_0}\frac{M}{\rho} \tag{13-60}$$

a formula known as the *Clausius-Mossotti equation*, after the names of the German and Italian physicists who derived it.

The expression on the left-hand side is called *molar polarization*. It is sometimes denoted by a special Greek capital letter $\boldsymbol{\Pi}$. Thus, by definition,

$$\boldsymbol{\Pi} = \frac{N_A(\alpha_e + \alpha_i)}{3\varepsilon_0} \tag{13-61}$$

We saw previously that for dilute gases ε differs little from ε_0. By making use of this condition in Eq. (13-59), we fall back on Eq. (13-49) provided μ_p is nil. Thus in the absence of permanent dipole moments, Eqs. (13-59) and (13-60) are further generalizations of the dielectric law, now applicable to all states of aggregation.

Illustrative Example

Compute $\varepsilon/\varepsilon_0$ for solid carbon dioxide CO_2 at $-60°C$, if $\varepsilon/\varepsilon_0$ in the gaseous standard condition is 1.000985. Carbon dioxide exhibits only electronic polarizability. Its density ρ_0 at standard conditions (0°C, atmospheric pressure) is 1.98 kg m³, and the density ρ at $-60°C$ is 1.19×10^3 kg m³.

Solution. Writing Π for the left-hand side of Eq. (13-60), we have

$$\Pi = \left(\frac{\varepsilon - \varepsilon_0}{\varepsilon + 2\varepsilon_0}\frac{M}{\rho_0}\right)_{\text{at } 0°\text{C}} = \left(\frac{\varepsilon - \varepsilon_0}{\varepsilon + 2\varepsilon_0}\frac{M}{\rho}\right)_{\text{at } -60°\text{C}} \tag{13-62}$$

Hence, using the approximation $\varepsilon \approx \varepsilon_0$ for the gaseous state and reducing the terms in Eq. (13-62), we have

$$\frac{9.85 \times 10^{-4}}{3 \times 1.98} = \frac{(\varepsilon/\varepsilon_0) - 1}{(\varepsilon/\varepsilon_0) + 2} \times \frac{1}{1.19 \times 10^3} \tag{13-63}$$

Solving Eq. (13-63) for $\varepsilon/\varepsilon_0$, we get

$$(\varepsilon/\varepsilon_0)_{\text{at } -60°\text{C}} = 1.73 \qquad \textit{Answer}$$

13-10 Ionic Polarizability and Interionic Forces. To bring out more vividly the common origin of dielectric polarization and elasticity, we shall derive the value of ionic polarizability from the relationships of Chapter 6, established for the elastic behavior of the Na^+Cl^- type ionic crystals. For a first-order approximation, the electrostatic interactions will be confined to one unit cell.

The unit cell of a Na^+Cl^- type ionic crystal is represented in Fig. 13-13a. It is a face-centered cubic cell containing four molecules—four cations, and four anions—occupying in succession the corners of eight smaller cubes, into which the unit cell can be subdivided. If a cation is taken arbitrarily as the center of the unit cell, the distribution of ions is that shown in Fig. 13-13a.

To insure neutrality of the unit cell in the absence of external field, the electric chaıges of the ions must be shared with adjacent unit cells in the same way as the ions themselves; see Section 2-4. Accordingly, the charge of the corner ion is shared between eight unit cells, the charge of the ion in the middle of the edge is shared between four unit cells, and the charge in the center of the face is shared beween two unit cells. The cation in the center

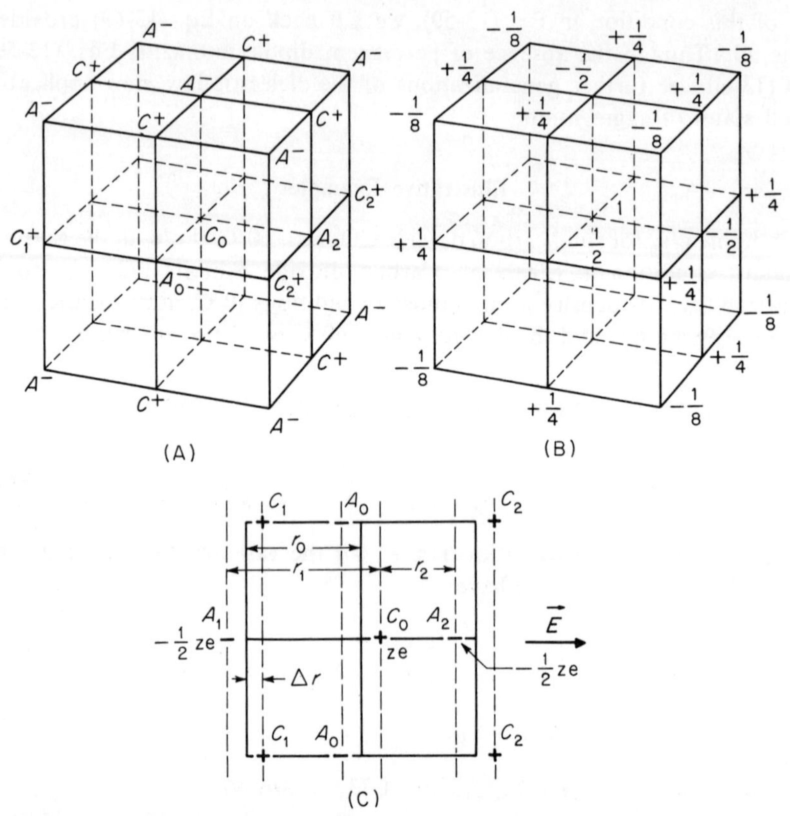

FIG. 13-13 Polarizability of an ionic crystal of the Na^+Cl^- type: (a) distribution of ions; (b) distribution of charges ze per unit cell; (c) displacement of ions in the middle layer

of the unit cell contributes its full charge ze to the cell. The total charge per unit cell is thus (see Fig. 13-13b):

$$-8\frac{ze}{8} + 12\frac{ze}{4} - 6\frac{ze}{2} + ze = 0$$

Under the influence of an electric field, the ions suffer small displacements Δr. The displacements in the horizontal layer containing the cation C_0 are indicated in Fig. 13-13c. We assume that the restoring forces between individual ions obey the law embodied in Eq. (6-9). By virtue of this law, the cation C_0 is attracted to A_1 because r_1 is greater than the equilibrium distance r_0, and it is repelled from A_2 because r_2 is smaller than r_0. These are the major restoring forces. The contributions from the remaining anions are much smaller and will be neglected. The surrounding cations contribute nothing, since their distances to C_0 remain unchanged. Both the attractive force F_1 exerted by A_1, and the repulsive force F_2 exerted by A_2, cooperate to balance the force exerted on C_0 by the electric field. If $\boldsymbol{E}_1$ is the *local* field intensity defined by Eq. (13-52), the equilibrium of forces acting on C_0 reads

$$F_1 + F_2 + ze\boldsymbol{E}_1 = 0 \tag{13-64}$$

The charge contributed to the unit cell by either A_1 or A_2 is $-ze/2$; the charge carried by C_0 is $+ze$. Hence, by rewriting Eq. (6-9) for a pair of ions $+ze$ and $-ze/2$, we have, using MKSQ units,

$$F_1 = -\frac{1}{2}\frac{e^2z^2}{4\pi\varepsilon_0}\left[1 - \left(\frac{r_0}{r_1}\right)^m\right] \tag{13-65}$$

and

$$F_2 = +\frac{1}{2}\frac{e^2z^2}{4\pi\varepsilon_0}\left[1 - \left(\frac{r_0}{r_2}\right)^m\right] \tag{13-66}$$

The signs in front of F_1 and F_2 indicate that both F_1 and F_2 act against the field.

Since the displacement Δr is small compared with r_0, the approximation for small displacements, Section 6-3, applies. In accordance with Fig. 13-13c, we put $r_1 = r_0 + 2\Delta r$ and $r_2 = r_0 - 2\Delta r$. The application of the rule of differentiation used in Section 6-3 leads to a result similar to Eq. (6-14):

$$F_1 = -F_2 = \frac{+z^2e^2\,\Delta rm}{4\pi\varepsilon_0 {r_0}^3} \tag{13-67}$$

Substitution of F_1 and F_2 from Eq. (13-67) in Eq. (13-64) yields

$$-\frac{2z^2e^2\,\Delta rm}{4\pi\varepsilon_0 {r_0}^3} + ze\boldsymbol{E}_1 = 0 \tag{13-68}$$

or, on simplifying and rearranging the terms,

$$\frac{4\pi\varepsilon_0 {r_0}^3}{m} = \frac{2ze\,\Delta r}{\boldsymbol{E}_1} \tag{13-69}$$

The numerator on the right-hand side of Eq. (13-69) is a dipole moment. It refers to one cation and two half-anions, hence to a whole molecule. Denoting as usual the molecular dipole moment by $\boldsymbol{\mu}$, we have

$$\frac{4\pi\varepsilon_0 {r_0}^3}{m} = \frac{\boldsymbol{\mu}}{\boldsymbol{E}_1} \tag{13-70}$$

and, by comparison with Eq. (13-32),

$$\boldsymbol{\alpha}_i = \frac{4\pi\varepsilon_0 {r_0}^3}{m} \tag{13-71}$$

We see that $\boldsymbol{\alpha}_i$, like the modulus of elasticity E_0 in Eq. (6-28), and like the specific surface energy ω in Eq. (7-12), depends on the basic parameters of crystal and atomic structures, r_0 and m.

Comparison with Experimental Data. We rewrite Eq. (13-71) in a form similar to Eq. (13-60). On multiplying both sides by N_A and dividing by $3\varepsilon_0$, we get for the *ionic molar polarizability*,

$$\Pi_i = \frac{N_A \alpha_i}{3\varepsilon_0} = \frac{4\pi}{3m} N_A r_0^3 \tag{13-72}$$

We observe that the volume of the unit cell is $(2r_0)^3$. Since there are four molecules in the unit cell, the volume per molecule is $2r_0^3$. Consequently, N_A being the number of molecules per mole, $N_A r_0^3$ is half of the volume occupied by one mole of the substance. This volume can also be written as M/ρ, where M is the mass contained in one mole and ρ the density. Hence

$$N_A r_0^3 = M/2\rho \tag{13-73}$$

and Eq. (13-72) reduces to

$$\frac{N_A \alpha_i}{3\varepsilon_0} = \frac{2\pi}{3m} \frac{M}{\rho} \tag{13-74}$$

To compare this expression with experimental data, we must subtract from Eq. (13-60) the contribution of the ever-present electronic polarizability α_e. This can be done by making use of the dielectric constant ε_e measured in the same dielectric in high frequency fields. As shown in a more advanced course, the ionic polarizability is not manifest at high frequencies, and α_e alone is operative. Accordingly, Eq. (13-60) reduces at high frequencies to

$$\frac{N_A \alpha_e}{3\varepsilon_0} = \frac{\varepsilon_e - \varepsilon_0}{\varepsilon_e + 2\varepsilon_0} \frac{M}{\rho} \tag{13-75}$$

Subtracting Eq. (13-75) from Eq. (13-60) side by side, we get

$$\frac{N_A \alpha_i}{3\varepsilon_0} = \left(\frac{\varepsilon - \varepsilon_0}{\varepsilon + 2\varepsilon_0} - \frac{\varepsilon_e - \varepsilon_0}{\varepsilon_e + 2\varepsilon_0} \right) \frac{M}{\rho} \tag{13-76}$$

Comparison of Eq. (13-76) with Eq. (13-74) yields finally the expression for the *molar ionic polarizability per unit volume*, $\Pi_i \rho / M$

$$\frac{2\pi}{3m} = \frac{\varepsilon - \varepsilon_0}{\varepsilon + 2\varepsilon_0} - \frac{\varepsilon_e - \varepsilon_0}{\varepsilon_e + 2\varepsilon_0} \tag{13-77}$$

The left-hand side of Eq. (13-77) is known from the theory of ionic crystals, Chapter 6; the right-hand side is determined experimentally. Thus the prediction of the theory can be checked by the experiment.

Such a check has been carried out for representative alkali halides of the Na^+Cl^- type in Table 13-2.[9] The agreement is reasonably good. The more obvious discrepancies can seemingly be accounted for by considering a correction to the local field entering the Clausius-Mossotti Eq. (13-60).[10]

[9] For experimental data see J. Errera, *Zeitschrift fuer Electrochemie*, **36**, 818(1930).

[10] See, for example, A. J. Dekker, *Solid State Physics*, Prentice-Hall, Englewood Cliffs, N.J., 1957.

TABLE 13-2 THEORETICAL AND EXPERIMENTAL MOLAR IONIC POLARIZABILITIES PER UNIT VOLUME, $\Pi_i\rho/M$ OF REPRESENTATIVE ALKALI HALIDES OF THE Na^+Cl^- TYPE

Salt	$\varepsilon/\varepsilon_0$	$\varepsilon_e/\varepsilon_0$	*m*	$\Pi_i\rho/M$	
				Exp.	*Theor.*
LiF	9.27	1.92	5	0.49	0.42
NaF	6.0	1.74	6	0.43	0.35
LiCl	11.05	2.75	6	0.40	0.35
NaCl	5.62	2.25	7	0.32	0.30
KCl	4.68	2.13	8	0.28	0.26
LiI	11.03	3.80	7.5	0.29	0.28
RbI	5.0	2.63	10	0.22	0.21

13-11 Dielectric Properties of Solids. The stability of structure in the solid state accounts for some basic differences in their dielectric properties compared to gases and liquids. Prominent among them is the behavior of *molecular dipole moments.* However, the most recent applications of solid dielectrics derive from a particular feature of ionic polarization called *ferroelectricity.* Both of these behaviors are further reviewed below.

Molecular Dipole Moment of Solids. In the absence of molecular dipole moments, solids behave in an electric field no differently from gases and liquids. However, if the solid contains molecular dipole moments, the stability of structure and the directional character of bonding can impede the alignment of these moments with the electric field. The impediment, when superimposed on thermal agitation, may be sufficient to suppress completely the influence of the molecular dipole moment $\boldsymbol{\mu}_p$ on polarizability. The variation of the dielectric constant below and above the melting point reveals in this case a characteristic trend, Fig. 13-14. The dielectric constant in the solid state is not only much lower than in the liquid state, but it is practically independent of temperature due to the suppression of orientation polarizability $\boldsymbol{\alpha}_0$. The latter reappears abruptly with the onset of melting. It makes itself felt also through the dependence of $\boldsymbol{\varepsilon}$ on temperature, Fig. 13-14.

Ferroelectricity. In all cases considered thus far, the displacement of centers of charges and the ensuing polarization were proportional to the applied electric field, and they disappeared with the latter. Recently a class of ionic crystals has been discovered in which the centers of positive and negative charges, once they have been pulled sufficiently away from each other, remain *permanently* locked in their new positions within the unit cell. The locking mechanism and the ensuing permanent bulk polarization are the

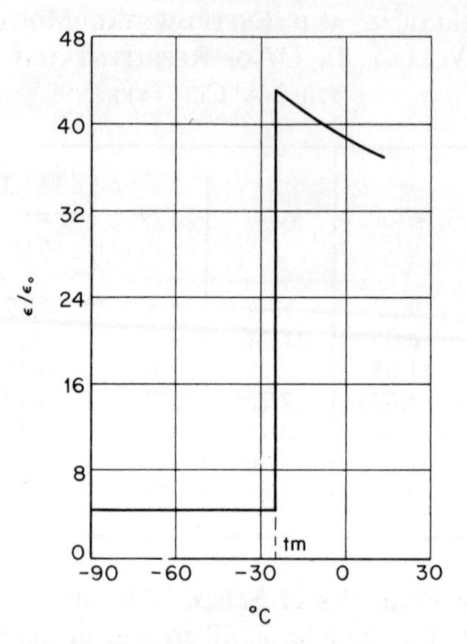

FIG. 13-14 Variation of $\varepsilon/\varepsilon_0$ of nitromethane below and above the melting point t_m. (From C. P. Smyth and W. S. Walls, *J. Chem. Phys.* **3**, 557)

result of cooperative action of individual unit cells within the crystal lattice. Since now the crystal exhibits electric polarization without the help of external field, we say that it is endowed with *spontaneous* polarization. We call this behavior ferroelectricity by analogy with the spontaneous manifestation of

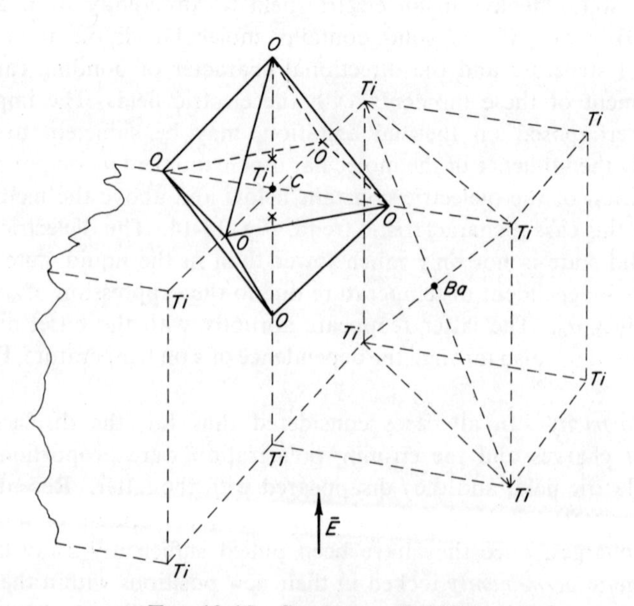

FIG. 13-15 Structure of $BaTiO_3$

magnetism in ferrous materials; see Chapter 14. Like ferromagnetism, ferroelectricity has attracted considerable attention because of its potential applications in modern technology. Of the ferroelectric materials, barium titanate, $BaTiO_3$, has been particularly studied.

We shall focus our attention on a particular feature of the pattern of crystal structure. If we assign to the titanium ion the corner of the unit cell, the oxygen ions will be grouped around the titanium ion on the corners of an octahedron, Fig. 13-15. At and below room temperature, the top and bottom oxygen ions are about 2% further away from the titanium ion than the side oxygen ions. The difference decreases at higher temperatures and it disappears at 120°C. Above 120°C the oxygen ions occupy the corners of a regular octahedron, and the lattice has cubic symmetry. Ferroelectricity is not manifest when barium titanate has this type of symmetry. The inference is that its ferroelectricity is related to the small departure from cubic symmetry below 120°C. The actual situation is far more complex and it defies a summary description. We can, however, get a feel for what happens by visualizing that, due to the slightly elongated form of the octahedron, the titanium ion has not one but two positions of stable equilibrium slightly off center, below and above C, Fig. 13-15. Under the influence of an external field acting upwards, the titanium ion moves toward the upper position of equilibrium. Eventually it becomes locked in this position when the applied field and the field created by the cooperative action of neighboring titanium ions are strong enough to overcome its thermal vibration. The unit cell thus acquires a permanent dipole moment aligned parallel with the applied field.

As the field intensity keeps growing, more and more unit cells become involved. Finally all units cells acquire permanent dipole moments in the direction of the field. The contribution to the electric polarization is then total, at variance with the contribution of molecular dipole moments which, as we saw in Section 13-8, was only partial. This circumstance explains the relatively large values of spontaneous electric polarization of barium titanate. They run into 0.15 Q m/m³. As a basis for comparison, if all water molecules in a given volume were equally aligned so that their molecular dipole moments add up arithmetically, the sum total of the electrical polarization would amount to less than 0.1 Q m/m³. Yet the quality for which barium titanate and its congeners are most remarkable is not so much the large value of the polarizability as the nature of its variation with the field intensity $\boldsymbol{E}$.

For simplicity, a single crystal will be considered, but the behavior is shared by a polycrystalline aggregate into which barium titanate, like any ceramic material, can be cast more conveniently. If a crystal of $BaTiO_3$ is slowly cooled from above 120°C, the titanium ions remain at the dead center C, Fig. 13-15, and there is no spontaneous polarization. A plate of such a crystal when inserted between the two plates of a capacitor will behave at very low field intensities no differently from other dielectric materials. The increment $\Delta \boldsymbol{P}$ will still be recoverable, although its magnitude is much larger than for most of the dielectrics. This is indicated by the value of the slope at the origin (see Fig. 13-16), which amounts to thousands of ε_0.

As the field intensity is gradually raised, however, the titanium ions begin to jump in ever-increasing numbers into one of their more stable positions of equilibrium, say the upper one, and the polarization is no longer recoverable. Also, more and more neighboring titanium ions are being pulled along.

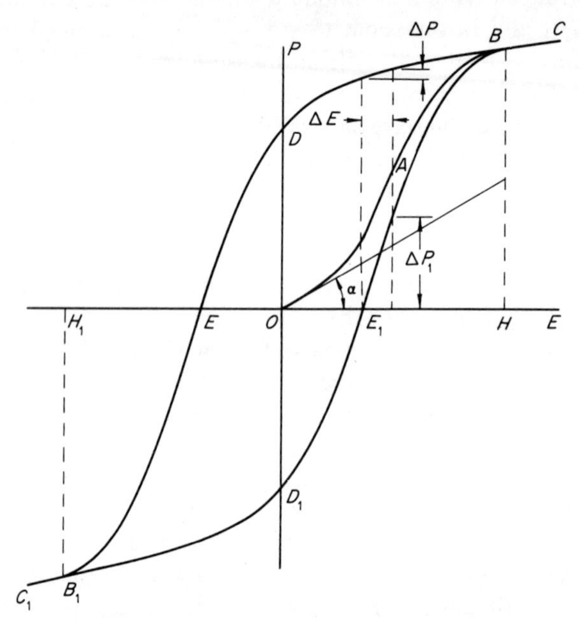

FIG. 13-16 Hysteresis loop of a ferroelectric material

This causes a steep rise of polarization at point A, Fig. 13-16. The rate of rise decreases as less and less titanium ions are left behind. At B, all titanium ions are in the upper equilibrium position. All unit cells in the crystal then contribute to polarization; a point of saturation has thus been reached. True, the electric polarization can still increase beyond point B, but the increase is slow and it is due only to the electronic and ionic polarizabilities, as in other ionic crystals. A more complete description of the hysteresis phenomenon must take into account the existence of ferroelectric domains; see footnote, page 294, Section 14-15.

The attainment of saturation is not the only feature of ferroelectricity. Far more significant is the tendency of the dipoles to *preserve* their common orientation in the unit cells *after* the field intensity has been removed. This is illustrated by the descending branch BD. If the field intensity $\boldsymbol{E}$ is gradually reduced to zero—through insertion of progressively lower resistances between the plates of the capacitor, for example—the polarization $\boldsymbol{P}$ lags substantially behind the field and retains a high value, OD, even after the two plates have been shortcircuited. This phenomenon is called *hysteresis* (from Greek *hysterein*, to come after). OD is called the *remanent* polarization.

To offset the effect of remanent polarization, the external field must now be reversed. When the field intensity reaches the value OE, the bulk polarization is nil. The capacitor behaves as if it were in a vacuum. We can picture this behavior in $BaTiO_3$ as being caused by the titanium ions occupying, under the coercion of the applied field, as many positions below as above the dead center C, Fig. 13-15. If the *coercive* field intensity OE is removed, the remanent polarization OD is restored. However, if the field intensity is increased beyond OE, more and more titanium ions can be pictured as switching from the upper to the lower position of equilibrium, and in so doing, pulling the neighboring titanium ions along. This trend is depicted by branch EB_1, Fig. 13-16. A point of saturation B_1 is thus reached similar to point B. From here on, the trends represented by $BDEB_1$ can be repeated step by step in the reverse direction. The branch $B_1D_1E_1B$ is a centrosymmetrical replica of $BDEB_1$. (This means that every point X_1 on $B_1D_1E_1B$ lies on the extension of the line XO drawn from point X on $BDEB_1$ through the center O at a distance $OX_1 = XO$.)

It is important to note that cycling of the field intensity between H and H_1 will reproduce the loop $BDEB_1D_1E_1B$ over and over again without ever retracing the initial branch OAB. Depending on whether the operating point is on the upper or lower branch of the loop, the increment $\Delta \boldsymbol{P}$ corresponding to the same increment $\Delta \boldsymbol{E}$ will be different. For example, at E_1 the increment ΔE will cause a significant increase of polarization $\Delta \boldsymbol{P}_1$ on the lower branch and almost no change of polarization $\Delta \boldsymbol{P}$ on the upper branch. It is as though the dielectric had *remembered* that its remanent polarization was OD_1 in one case and OD in the other. Because of this property, ferroelectric materials have found use in computers, on a par with ferromagnetic materials described in Chapter 14, to store coded information, e.g., "yes" on the lower branch and "no" on the upper branch.

Other applications of ferroelectric materials derive from the *nonlinear* character of the variation of $\boldsymbol{P}$ with $\boldsymbol{E}$. For example, around point D, equal positive and negative variations of $\boldsymbol{E}$ produce largely different variations of $\boldsymbol{P}$: very small to the right, very large to the left. Devices such as rectifiers and amplifiers are based essentially on this behavior.

The remanent polarization and the width of the hysteresis loop decrease with rising temperature. Beyond 120°C, as expected, they disappear entirely in barium titanate. The temperature varies with other ferroelectric materials, but the trend is the same. By analogy with a similar transition temperature discovered by P. Curie in ferromagnetic materials, the temperature beyond which ferroelectricity vanishes is called the *Curie point*.

Above the Curie point, barium titanate and other ferroelectric materials behave in accordance with the dielectric law. That is, the polarization is essentially proportional to $\boldsymbol{E}$ and it is recoverable. Because of the high value of susceptibility χ—running into thousands—ceramic bodies based on titanates, even though devoid of ferroelectricity, find wide applications in devices such as capacitors for storage and absorption of electrical energy in small volumes. Their refractory behavior makes them also suitable for high-temperature service.

13-12 Electro-Mechanical Coupling. As mentioned in the beginning of this chapter, the common origin of dielectric polarization and elastic deformation accounts for a certain amount of interaction, or coupling, existing between these two properties. We distingush between *electrostriction* and *piezoelectricity*.

Electrostriction is a manifestation common to all dielectric solids. It is a deformation caused by the shift of electron clouds or nuclei in an electric field.

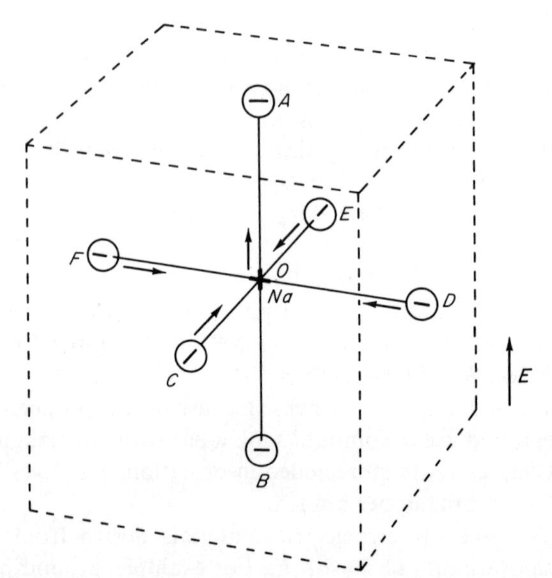

FIG. 13-17 Electrostriction in an Na^+Cl^- type crystal

Consider, for example, sodium chloride, Fig. 13-17. Like Ti^+ in Fig. 13-15, Na^+ is surrounded by six anions, the six Cl^- ions. Similarly, each Cl^- is surrounded by six Na^+ ions. An electric field applied upwards will displace the sodium ion upward with respect to the chloride ions. This, however, is not the only displacement caused by the applied field. The four lateral chloride ions *C*, *D*, *E*, and *F* will move closer to the center *O* to restore the equilibrium distances with regard to the displaced sodium ion. This in turn will cause a small displacement of anions at *A* and *B*, away from the center *O*. The unit cell and the crystal as a whole will thus be deformed. Note that the deformation will have the same sign whether the field is applied upward or downward. More important, there is no *reciprocity* between applied electric field and applied mechanical forces. Specifically, an electric field, by shifting positively charged particles one way and negatively charged particles the other way, will *always* cause deformation. Mechanical forces, by deforming the crystal elastically, will cause no *polarization*, at least not if the crystal has a center of symmetry.

This is readily seen from Fig. 13-18. Since the mechanical forces act only

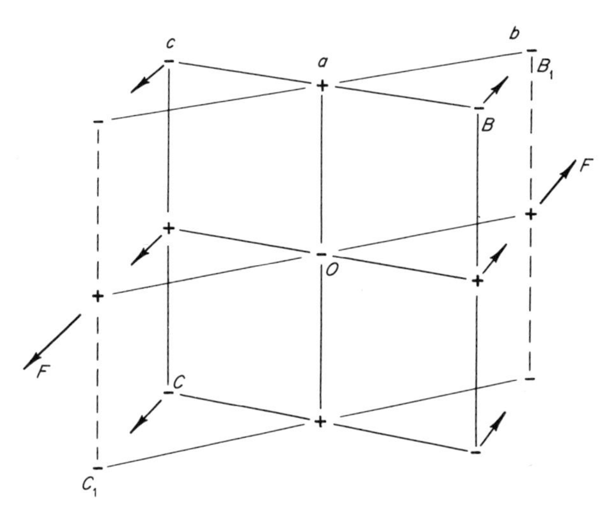

FIG. 13-18 Absence of polarization in a deformed layer of an Na^+Cl^- type crystal

on the mass and take no notice of the charge, the layers c and b will be bodily displaced with respect to layer *a* under the applied force *F*, and there will be no separation of charges. Furthermore, the crystal pattern of Na^+Cl^- has a center of symmetry. Hence, to each displacement such as BB_1 to the right, there corresponds an equal displacement CC_1 to the left but in the opposite direction. Consequently, the center of charges, whether positive or negative, remains at *O*, and there is no net polarization.

The same applies to all crystals endowed with a center of symmetry. Electrostriction is a *one-sided relationship*; polarization deforms the crystal, but deformation does not polarize it. There exists, however, a class of crystals whose pattern lacks the center of symmetry and which do exhibit electric polarization under external forces, under applied pressure, for example. This effect is called *piezoelectricity* (from Greek *piezein*, to press).

The nature of piezoelectricity can be best explained with reference to the cubic variety of ZnS crystal, called zinc blende. The lack of a center of symmetry in the crystal pattern was already mentioned in Section 2-4. Zinc blende has a face-centered cubic lattice. That is, the unit cell contains four lattice points or molecules: four atoms of sulphur and four atoms of zinc.

For clarity, only one atom of zinc is shown in Fig. 13-19. The four atoms of sulphur occupy the corner of the cube and the centers of the three adjacent faces, respectively. They form a regular tetrahedron with the zinc atom placed in the center. The bonds are only partly ionic, but we shall assume for simplicity that we have one zinc cation surrounded tetrahedrally by four sulphur anions.

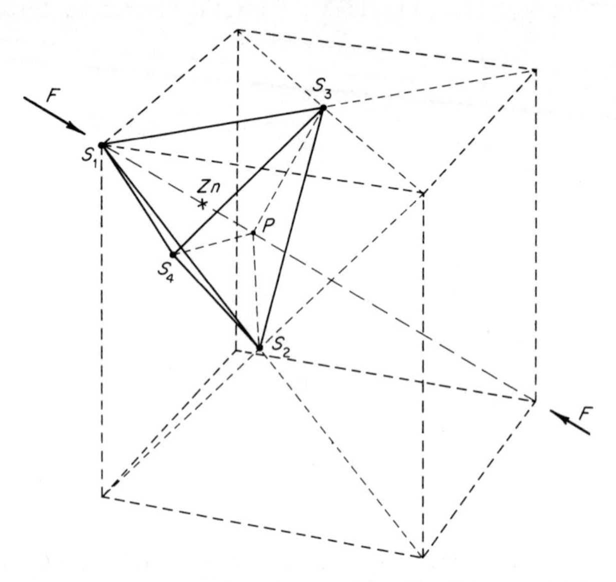

FIG. 13-19 Polarization in a deformed ZnS (zinc blende) crystal (piezoelectricity)

In the absence of external forces, the centers of negative and positive charges coincide, and the polarization is nil. If now the crystal is compressed along the S_1Zn direction, the cation Zn^{++} will be repulsed by the anion S_1^{--}, because they will be closer to each other than their distance of equilibrium r_0. The anions S_2^{--}, S_3^{--}, and S_4^{--} will also come closer to Zn^{++} than r_0. However, the repulsion here will be smaller because the compression along S_1Zn is accompanied by lateral expansion in the directions PS_2, PS_3 and PS_4; see Poisson's ratio, Section 6-4. As a result there will be an unbalance of forces on the Zn^{++} in the S_1Zn direction. The zinc cation will thus be compelled to seek a new position of equilibrium by moving closer to the three anions S_2, S_3, and S_4. This displacement will cause separation of the centers of charges, and it will produce a dipole moment and electrical polarization. The extension along S_1Zn will reverse the direction of displacement and the sign of polarization.

Unlike electrostriction, piezoelectricity is a two-sided relationship, a true linear coupling: the elastic strain ε changes proportionally to the applied field intensity $\boldsymbol{E}$, and the electric polarization $\boldsymbol{P}$ changes proportionally to the applied stress σ. It is customary to express the electric changes in terms of the field intensity $\boldsymbol{E}$, rather than polarization. We symbolize the changes by the customary Greek letter Δ,

$$\Delta\varepsilon = \mathbf{d}\,\Delta \boldsymbol{E} \text{ (for constant } \sigma) \tag{13-78}$$

and

$$\Delta \boldsymbol{E} = \mathbf{g}\,\Delta\sigma \text{ (for constant } \boldsymbol{D}) \tag{13-79}$$

The coefficient $\boldsymbol{d}$ is called the *piezoelectric modulus*; the coefficient $\boldsymbol{g}$ is called the *voltage output coefficient* (implying that the field intensity is rated in volts per meter). In Table 13-3 the magnitude of these coefficients is indicated for two representative piezoelectric materials along with their dielectric constant ratios.

TABLE 13-3 PIEZOELECTRIC CONSTANTS

Material	*Piezoelectric Modulus*	*Voltage Output Coefficient*	$\varepsilon/\varepsilon_0$
	10^{-12} m/V	$\dfrac{\text{V/m}}{\text{N/m}^2}$	
Quartz	2.3	0.058	4.5
Barium titanate ceramic	78	0.0052	1700

It is seen that the barium titanate ceramic will deform more readily under an applied electric field, whereas quartz will produce higher electric fields under an applied stress.

A piezoelectric crystal will respond to a mechanical stimulus by sending an appropriate electric signal along the circuit into which it is inserted. In turn, it will reproduce the stimulus when acted upon by the electric signal. Devices based upon this electromechanical coupling are quite numerous. They range from microphones and loud-speakers in the audio-frequencies to sonars—underwater sounding equipment—and various devices for agitation of solutions, destruction of bacteria and, more recently, as a means of abrasion, in the ultrasonic range. They also find extensive use as frequency standards and filters. In all these applications they convert elastic energy into electric energy and vice versa. Devices endowed with the property of converting one kind of energy into another are called *transducers*.

Influence of Frequency. The dielectric and elastic behavior of solids are greatly influenced by the frequency of the stimulus. The frequency response involves thermal vibration of atoms and molecules, and it must be treated on a statistical basis. This treatment, as others of its kind, must be postponed to a more advanced course.

13-13 Dielectric Breakdown. According to the dielectric law, the higher the field intensity, the wider is the separation of centers of charges on the atomic level, and the greater is the magnitude of the restoring forces produced by electrostatic attractions and repulsions. We anticipate from the elastic behavior of solids, Chapters 7 and 8, that the restoring forces will reach a maximum at some critical separation distance. Beyond this distance the applied field intensity will overcome the restoring action, and the charges will begin to move apart under the influence of the electric field. The dielectric will cease to be an insulator. The corresponding field intensity is designated as the *dielectric strength*, or *breakdown strength*, of the insulator.

In gases, the separation of charges produces free electrons and ions. Both acquire sufficient momentum from the applied field to ionize, in turn, the remaining atoms and molecules by collision. The phenomenon rapidly takes on the aspect of a chain reaction and culminates in a discharge. The accompanying manifestations vary from a simple glow, as in neon lamps, to sparks in capacitors and lightning in thunderstorms, Fig. 13-20. The corresponding dielectric strength increases with pressure, i.e., with the degree of condensation. At atmospheric pressure, the dielectric strength of air in homogeneous fields is about 3×10^6 N/Q or, what amounts to the same thing as far as dimensions are concerned, about 3×10^6 V/m.

If the governing laws of insulation breakdown in gases are extrapolated to liquids and solids, breakdown strengths between 10^9 and 10^{10} V/m should be expected.[11] This expectation is also borne out by an order of magnitude computation in which the restoring forces are taken to correspond to the theoretical tensile strength of ionic crystals (see Problem 13-10). Dielectric strengths of almost this order of magnitude are found in molecular solids such as impregnated papers and plastics. In ceramics, the experimental values are generally two orders of magnitude lower. There is good presumption that here, as with elasticity, crystal imperfections in the form of cracks, vacancies, and dislocations contribute to the loss of strength. Their existence would also explain the much greater complexity of the phenomena accompanying dielectric breakdown in solids than in gases. Liquids occupy an intermediate position.[11]

13-14 Electric Energy Stored in Dielectrics. The recoverable nature of dielectric polarization makes the dielectric a suitable medium for storage and release of electric energy under controlled conditions. As we did for elastic energy, Section 6-5, we shall evaluate the maximum amount of energy which can thus be stored.

Following the line of thought of Section 6-5, we compute the amount of work necessary to separate the plates of a charged capacitor containing the

[11] For more detail, see A. R. von Hippel, *Dielectrics and Waves*, Chapter 32, Wiley, New York, 1954.

FIG. 13-20 Formation of sparks of intricate design in a condenser discharge. (From Arthur R. von Hippel, *Molecular Science and Molecular Engineering*, Wiley, New York, 1959, by permission)

dielectric, Fig. 13-21. In the absence of gravitational forces, the attraction exerted by the positive charge of the upper plate on the negative charge of the lower plate must be balanced by an externally applied force F. The magnitude of this force can be computed by observing that a test charge

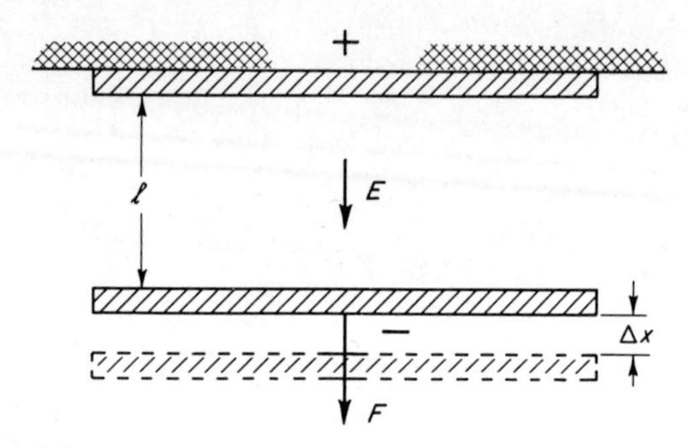

FIG. 13-21 Storage of electric energy in a plate capacitor

located on the lower plate is subjected to only half of the field intensity $\mathbf{E}$. (This follows from the illustrative problem, Section 13-17.) Accordingly, if the actual charge is $\mathbf{q}$, the force F is

$$F = \mathbf{q}\mathbf{E}/2 \tag{13-80}$$

The amount of work ΔW done by this force in the displacement Δx is then

$$\Delta W = \mathbf{q}\mathbf{E}\,\Delta x/2 \tag{13-81}$$

As long as the gap between the plates is kept narrow—and replenished with the dielectric while the plates are being pulled apart—the field intensity $\mathbf{E}$ and the charge $\mathbf{q}$ remain practically unchanged. Thus Eq. (13-81) is valid for any amount of displacement Δx. When at first the plates are almost, but not quite, in touch and thereupon the gap is widened to l, the corresponding amount of work W is obtained by putting $\Delta x = l$:

$$W = \mathbf{q}\mathbf{E}l/2 \tag{13-82}$$

This amount of work is now converted into electric energy and stored in the dielectric. By decreasing the gap—and removing the excess of dielectric—the stored energy is gradually released. It is finally reduced to zero when the plates come in contact, and the electric charges cancel each other. The same result, of course, is achieved when the condenser, originally charged with the amount of electricity $\mathbf{q}$ under a field intensity $\mathbf{E}$ and with the plate separation l, is thereupon discharged through a gradually decreasing resistance or an electric motor connected to the two plates.

We now seek to modify Eq. (13-82) and to derive an expression for the amount of electric energy per unit mass. By Eq. (13-21),

$$\mathbf{q} = \mathbf{D}A \tag{13-83}$$

where $\boldsymbol{D}$ is the charge density and A the cross-sectional area of the plates. Making use of Eq. (13-26) in Eq. (13-83) and noticing that Al is the volume v of the dielectric filling the gap, we have, on substituting the above results in Eq. (13-82),

$$W = \tfrac{1}{2}\boldsymbol{\varepsilon}\boldsymbol{E}^2 v \tag{13-84}$$

Of particular significance in Eq. (13-84) is the dielectric constant $\boldsymbol{\varepsilon}$. It is seen that by changing from air, with $\boldsymbol{\varepsilon}$ hardly greater than $\boldsymbol{\varepsilon}_0$, to a barium titanate ceramic, where $\boldsymbol{\varepsilon} = 1000\boldsymbol{\varepsilon}_0$, the energy stored under the same conditions can be increased one thousandfold.

By proceeding further along the lines of Section 6-5, we obtain the electric energy u stored per unit mass of the dielectric. There follows

$$u = \tfrac{1}{2}\boldsymbol{\varepsilon}\boldsymbol{E}^2/\rho \tag{13-85}$$

where ρ is the density. The similarity between Eqs. (13-85) and (6-54) referring to the elastic energy per unit mass is noteworthy.

The similarity is further strengthened by considering the maximum amount of energy u which can be stored in a dielectric under the most favorable conditions. We take as an example a barium titanate ceramic with $\boldsymbol{\varepsilon} = 1000\boldsymbol{\varepsilon}_0$ and compute u under the assumption that the dielectric strength is as high as 10^8 V/m. There follows, with $\rho = 4.5 \times 10^3$ kg/m^3,

$$u_{\text{max}} = \frac{1}{2} \times 10^3 \times \frac{8.85 \times 10^{-12} \times 10^{16}}{4.5 \times 10^3} \text{ J/kg}$$

or approximately

$$u_{\text{max}} = 10^4 \text{ J/kg}$$

This is of the same order of magnitude as the maximum elastic energy computed in Section 6-5.

13-15 Summary. Like elasticity, dielectric polarization has its origin in the stability of electronic and atomic configurations. The application of an external electric field polarizes an insulator by causing *separation* of positive and negative centers of charges within the atoms and molecules as well as *orientation* of the already existing permanent molecular dipole moments. The dipole moments so *induced* are proportional to the applied field intensity. The coefficient of proportionality is called *polarizability*. The same relationship can be expressed as a proportionality between charge density and field intensity in a plate capacitor. The corresponding coefficient of proportionality is then called *dielectric constant*. By eliminating the contribution of the charge density to the electric field in vacuum, a proportionality between electric polarization and field intensity is obtained. The relevant coefficient of proportionality expressed as a multiple of the dielectric constant in vacuum $\boldsymbol{\varepsilon}_0$ is called the *electrical susceptibility*.

Depending on the origin of the restoring forces acting on the charges, we distinguish between the *electronic*, *ionic*, and *orientation* polarizabilities. Of these, the orientation polarizability alone is temperature dependent.

Unlike polarizability, the dielectric constant $\boldsymbol{\varepsilon}$ is greatly influenced by the state of aggregation. The ratio $\boldsymbol{\varepsilon}/\boldsymbol{\varepsilon}_0$ differs little from one for dilute gases but can easily reach values of ten and higher in the liquid and solid state. Particularly important for the solvent action of water is its relatively high dielectric constant ratio of 88. Values exceeding 100 and even 1000 are found in ceramics based on barium titanate.

Barium titanate also belongs to a class of ionic crystals that manifest spontaneous electric polarization called *ferroelectricity*. Like ferromagnetism, ferroelectricity disappears above a critical temperature called the *Curie point*. Below the Curie point, ferroelectricity is responsible for the phenomenon of *hysteresis* and for the *nonlinear* behavior of the electric polarization in electric fields. Both manifestations have important applications in modern technology.

The common origin of dielectric polarization and elasticity is responsible for *electrostriction*—an elastic deformation caused in solid dielectrics by an electric field. The converse phenomenon of *piezoelectricity* is manifest only in a special class of crystals. Piezoelectricity is a true electromechanical coupling: the induced strain is proportional to the applied field intensity, and the induced field intensity is proportional to the applied stress. The coupling coefficients are called *piezoelectric modulus* and *voltage output coefficient*, respectively.

A dielectric ceases to be an insulator at the attainment of a critical field intensity called its *dielectric strength* or *breakdown strength*. A representative figure for gases under standard conditions is 10^6 V/m. In liquids and solids the values may range from 10^6 to 10^9 V/m, depending—in solids—on the nature of bonds and degree of imperfection of crystal structure.

The recoverable nature of dielectric polarization makes it possible to store electric energy in the dielectrics and to release it under controlled conditions. The amount of energy stored in a given volume and under given field intensity is proportional to the dielectric constant. The amount of energy which thus can be stored in a unit mass, however, is no larger than in an elastic deformation. Dielectrics, like elastic materials, do not provide enough energy to compete with fuels as prime movers.

13-16 Illustrative Problem

Compute the field intensity $\boldsymbol{E}$ in a circular plate capacitor, given its dimensions and the charge $\boldsymbol{q}$ on the plates.

Solution. If A is the area of the plate, the charge density $\boldsymbol{D}$ is $\boldsymbol{q}/A$. Hence the charge comprised in the area $2\pi r\,dr$ of Fig. 13-22 is

$$d\boldsymbol{q} = \boldsymbol{D}2\pi r\,dr \tag{13-86}$$

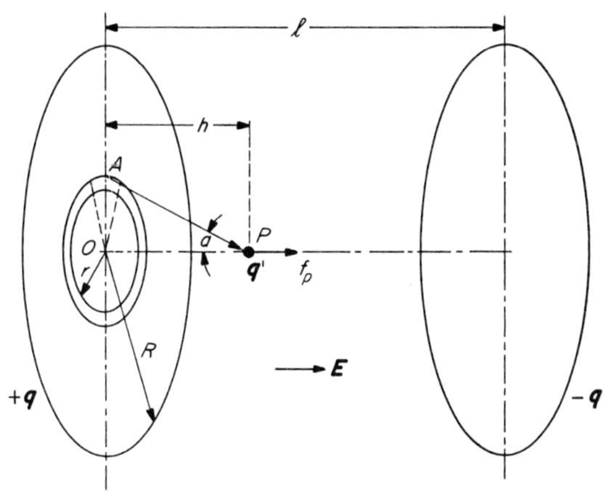

FIG. 13-22 Computation of the field intensity $\boldsymbol{E}$ in a circular plate capacitor

The contribution of $d\boldsymbol{q}$ to the force f_p acting on charge $\boldsymbol{q}'$ placed at P is, by virtue of Coulomb's law,

$$df'_{\text{p}} = \frac{\boldsymbol{q}'\boldsymbol{D}2\pi r\,dr}{4\pi\boldsymbol{\varepsilon}_0\overline{AP}^2}\cos\alpha$$

$$= \frac{\boldsymbol{q}'\boldsymbol{D}2r\,dr OP}{4\boldsymbol{\varepsilon}_0\overline{AP}^3} = \frac{\boldsymbol{q}'\boldsymbol{D}}{4\boldsymbol{\varepsilon}_0}\frac{h\,d(r^2)}{(h^2+r^2)^{3/2}} \tag{13-87}$$

On integrating for the whole area A from $r = 0$ to $r = R$, we get

$$f'_{\text{p}} = -\frac{\boldsymbol{q}'\boldsymbol{D}}{2\boldsymbol{\varepsilon}_0}\left|\frac{h}{(h^2+r^2)^{1/2}}\right|_{r=0}^{r=R}$$

or, if the distance of separation l is small compared to R,

$$f'_{\text{p}} = \frac{\boldsymbol{q}'\boldsymbol{D}}{2\boldsymbol{\varepsilon}_0} \tag{13-88}$$

Repeating the same procedure for the negative plate, we have, likewise,

$$f''_{\text{p}} = \frac{\boldsymbol{q}'\boldsymbol{D}}{2\boldsymbol{\varepsilon}_0}$$

Hence, adding the two contributions f'_{p} and f''_{p}, the total force acting on P is

$$f = f'_{\text{p}} + f''_{\text{p}} = \frac{\boldsymbol{q}'\boldsymbol{D}}{\boldsymbol{\varepsilon}_0}$$

and, since $f/\boldsymbol{q}' = \boldsymbol{E}$,

$$\boldsymbol{E} = \frac{\boldsymbol{D}}{\boldsymbol{\varepsilon}_0} = \frac{\boldsymbol{q}}{\boldsymbol{\varepsilon}_0 A}, \quad \text{q.e.d. Eq. (13-4)}$$

Notes:

1. We have assumed a circular shape of the plate. However, the smallness of h/R makes it obvious that Eq. (13-4) holds for any shape of the plate.

2. Equation (13-4) holds for any point between the plates of the capacitor sufficiently removed from the edges so that the distance of the projection O from the nearest edge is large compared with l.

3. If the charge is on one of the plates, there is no contribution from this plate, and the field intensity acting on the charge is then only $\boldsymbol{E}/2$.

References

ELEMENTARY

1. F. Bitter, *Currents, Fields and Particles*, Wiley, New York, 1956.

ADVANCED

1. C. Kittel, *Introduction to Solid State Physics*, McGraw-Hill, New York, 1959.
2. A. R. von Hippel, *Dielectrics and Waves*, Wiley, New York, 1954.
3. C. P. Smyth, *Dielectric Behavior and Structure*, McGraw-Hill, New York, 1955.

Problems

13-1 Using the dielectric constant of water in Coulomb's law, show that the interionic force between cation and anion of a salt will decrease roughly ten times when the salt is dissolved in water.

13-2 Derive the dielectric constant of neon by assuming the same electron density distribution as in argon. Take $R = 1.5$ Å for neon.

13-3 Compare the result of Problem 13-2 with the actual value of the dielectric constant of neon. The reported value of ϵ/ϵ_0 is 1.000127 at 0°C. Explain the discrepancy if there is any.

13-4 Compute the dielectric constant of water at 0°C from the dipole moment of the water molecule = 1.87 debyes. Neglect the contribution of electronic and ionic polarizabilities and assume the validity of Eq. (13-50) for condensed systems.

13-5 Compute the dielectric constant of solid argon using Eq. (13-60) and the value of electronic polarizability of 1.8×10^{40} Q^2 sec^2/kg (the only polarizability present in inert gases). Solid argon builds a FCC crystal lattice with $a_0 = 5.43$ Å. (Hint: Compute the density from Eq. (2-4).)

13-6 A piezoelectric quartz 2 in. long has been compressed with a stress of 1000 lb/in.^{2} Compute the change of voltage produced between its two ends.

13-7 Compute the amount of electric energy stored in a capacitor charged by a battery of 100 V. The area of the condenser is 0.3×0.3 m^2 and the two plates are separated by a wafer of quartz 0.02 m thick (take $\epsilon/\epsilon_0 = 4.5$).

13-8 How much change in electric energy has been produced in the capacitor described in Problem 13-7 by compressing the wafer of quartz 0.1%?

13-9 Compute the magnitude of the electric field necessary to disrupt the bond between a cation and an anion of a Na^+Cl^- molecule. (Hint: Use Eq. (7-5) to compute the maximum cohesive force. Beware of MKSQ units and the dielectric constant ε_0.)

13-10 Prove that an electron cloud filling uniformly a sphere of radius R, Fig. 13-3, and having a total charge $-ne$ attracts a concentrated + charge at a distance d ($< R$) from the center as though its total charge had been reduced to $-ne(d/R)^3$. (Hint: Since the concentrated plus charge is on the inside of the spherical shell $R - d$, it feels, according to the laws of electrostatics, no attraction from the electron cloud filling this shell.)

14 / ELECTRICAL PROPERTIES: MAGNETIZATION

Like electric polarization, magnetization owes its origin to the phenomena of interaction between electric charges on the atomic scale. However, magnetization appears only when the electric charges move with respect to each other. In atoms the relative motion of charged particles (of electrons, for example) assumes a steady state and depends on the atomic structure. Hence, as a rule, magnetic properties of most materials can be explained by and predicted from the particulars of the atomic structure, without a detailed analysis of the motion of each charged particle. An outstanding example is the magnetic properties of ceramic materials, described in Section 14-18. It is this dependence on structure that justifies the inclusion of magnetic properties in the present volume.

14-1 Manifestations. The first recorded application of magnetic properties of materials antedates the applications of their dielectric properties by several centuries. The property of a magnetized iron needle to assume a fixed orientation in the terrestrial field was used in navigation as early as the 12th century. Engineering applications, however, were not made until magnetism and electricity had been reduced to the same basic phenomenon of interaction of electric charges. The simulus came from the pioneering works of Ampère in France and Faraday in England, in the first half of the 19th century. Since then, the close relationship between magnetic and electric properties of materials has been manifest in many applications, although probably nowhere was the relation as close as in the generation of electric power. The insertion of a magnetized iron core in the rotor of an electric generator increased considerably the supply of electric energy and more than any other factor contributed to an almost universal use of electric power in industry and domestic life. Magnetism has played an equally important role in the distribution of electric energy, mainly through the use of magnetic cores in high-tension transformers. The most recent applications of magnetism in communication engineering are no less noteworthy. Magnetic amplifiers, modulators, and rectifiers in combination with transistors, described in Chapter 15, are competing successfully with similar electronic devices based on vacuum tubes. Yet nothing appears to rival, in efficiency or compactness, the magnetic memory devices built for digital computers. The use of magnetic ceramics deserves special mention here, for it has increased considerably the speed of operation and storage of information. The change from magnetic metals to magnetic ceramics is significant from another point of view. It focuses our attention on the *orderly* motion of *bound* electrons rather than the *disorderly* flow of *free* electrons found in metals. Depending on the degree of orderliness, the manifestations of magnetism vary. Some of the most characteristic manifestations will be described below. In all of them the concept of magnetic moment plays a central and fundamental role. We begin, therefore, by recalling the origin of this concept as well as of the related concepts of magnetic induction $\boldsymbol{B}$ and magnetic field intensity $\boldsymbol{H}$.

14-2 Magnetic Moment. To recall first the concept of magnetic moment we make use of a model. Consider, in Fig. 14-1, a small rectangular test

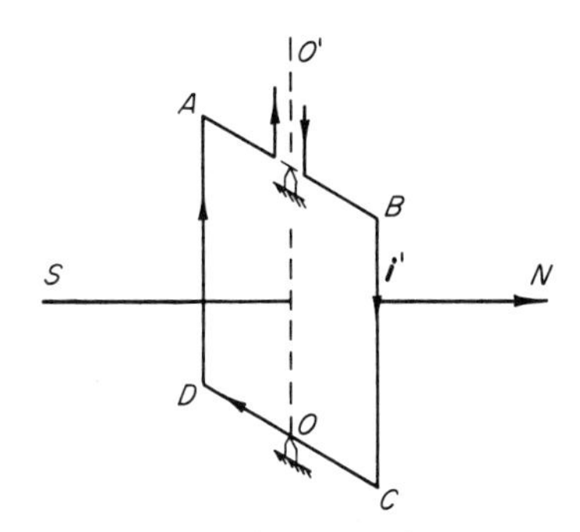

FIG. 14-1 A loop of current in a terrestrial field

loop of wire, free to rotate about the OO' axis and passed by an electric current, $\boldsymbol{i}'$. (Like the test charge in dielectric polarization, Chapter 13, the test loop is considered to be so small that its presence does not disturb the magnetic field in which it is placed.) According to Ampère's circuital law, taught in elementary physics, such a loop will assume a fixed and stable orientation in the terrestrial field. The plane $ABCD$ will be perpendicular to the SN direction, with the current in the loop flowing clockwise when viewed from south to north. The loop will return to this orientation whenever deflected from it by a certain angle, and it can be kept in the deflected position only if an external torque T is applied. We seek to evaluate the magnitude of this torque in terms of the electrical parameters characterizing the behavior of the loop.

The use of terrestial field is not very suitable for such an evaluation. It is too weak and it does not provide the proper electric parameters. A more convenient field is provided by a solenoid—a tightly wound long coil of wire passed by an electric current $\boldsymbol{i}$, Fig. 14-2a. The loop $ABCD$, when placed inside the solenoid, behaves exactly as if it were in a terrestrial magnetic field. A stable configuration is obtained when the plane $ABCD$ is perpendicular to

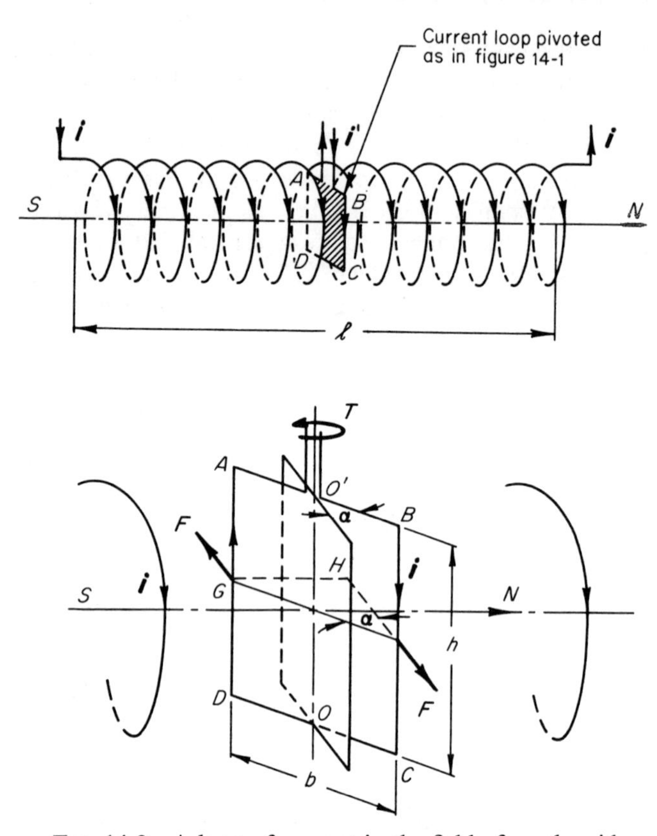

FIG. 14-2 A loop of current in the field of a solenoid

the axis *SN* of the solenoid and when both currents, $\boldsymbol{i}$ and $\boldsymbol{i}'$ are flowing in the same direction, when viewed from the same side.

Basically, this behavior can be predicted from Coulomb's law by making due allowance for the motion of charged particles. The pertinent relationships are derived in a more advanced course of electromagnetic theory. For our present purpose, it is sufficient to follow the method adopted in elementary physics and to establish the needed relationships experimentally.

By analogy with the terrestrial magnetic field, we assign to the magnetic field of the solenoid the direction *SN* in Fig. 14-2b. When the loop is deviated from its equilibrium position by the torque T, the field acts on the loop *ABCD* by means of a force couple *F-F* and tends to restore the original orientation. To maintain the loop at an angle α to this orientation, the torque T must balance the restoring couple. According to Fig. 14-2b, we have

$$T = F \times GH = Fb \sin \alpha \qquad (14\text{-}1)$$

where b is the width of the loop. We find experimentally that F is proportional to the current $\boldsymbol{i}'$ and the height h of the loop. We therefore write

$$F = \boldsymbol{B}\boldsymbol{i}'h \qquad (14\text{-}2)$$

where $\boldsymbol{B}$ is a coefficient of proportionality yet to be determined. Substitution of Eq. (14-2) in Eq. (14-1) yields

$$T = \boldsymbol{B}\boldsymbol{i}'hb \sin \alpha \tag{14-3}$$

We notice that hb is the area A' of the loop. Resorting again to experimentation, we find that the same torque obtains for a circular loop and a loop of any shape, provided the area A' is kept constant. Thus, the governing factor of the loop behavior is the product $A\boldsymbol{i}'$. We put

$$\boldsymbol{m}' = A\boldsymbol{i}' \tag{14-4}$$

and call $\boldsymbol{m}'$ the magnetic moment of the loop. Since the current $\boldsymbol{i}'$ is measured in coulomb per second and the area A' is measured in square meters, the dimensions of $\boldsymbol{m}'$ are

$$[\boldsymbol{m}'] = \left[\frac{\text{Q m}^2}{\text{sec}}\right] \tag{14-5}$$

In vector notations, the area A' is represented by a vector $\vec{A'}$ normal to the plane of the loop and equal in magnitude to A. Accordingly, the magnetic moment becomes also a vector quantity. We write, since the current is considered to be a scalar,

$$\vec{\boldsymbol{m}'} = \boldsymbol{i}'\vec{A} \tag{14-6}$$

14-3 Magnetic Induction. Substitution of Eq. (14-4) in Eq. (14-3) yields

$$T = \boldsymbol{B}\boldsymbol{m}' \sin \alpha \tag{14-7}$$

whence

$$\boldsymbol{B} = \frac{T}{\boldsymbol{m}' \sin \alpha} \tag{14-8}$$

Since all quantities on the right-hand side of Eq. (14-8) can be measured, we can use this equation to define $\boldsymbol{B}$. We call $\boldsymbol{B}$ the *magnetic induction*. According to Eqs. (14-7) and (14-5), the dimensions of $\boldsymbol{B}$ are

$$[\boldsymbol{B}] = \left[\frac{\text{N m}}{\text{Q m}^2/\text{sec}}\right] = \left[\frac{\text{N sec}}{\text{Q m}}\right] \tag{14-9}$$

or, substituting kg m/sec^{-2} for N,

$$[\boldsymbol{B}] = \left[\frac{\text{kg}}{\text{Q sec}}\right] \tag{14-10}$$

In electromagnetic theory it is more convenient to define $\boldsymbol{B}$ as a vector quantity referred to unit area. In order to introduce the units of area in Eq. (14-9), we rewrite $\boldsymbol{B}$ to read

$$[\boldsymbol{B}] = \left[\frac{\text{N sec m}}{\text{Q m}^2}\right]$$

But

$$[\text{N m}] = [\text{V Q}]$$

hence,

$$[\boldsymbol{B}] = \frac{\text{V sec}}{\text{m}^2} \tag{14-11}$$

The product volt second is called a *weber*, in honor of the German physicist and mathematician W. E. Weber (1804–1891). We write, accordingly,

$$1\,\boldsymbol{B} = 1\,\frac{\text{Wb}}{\text{m}^2} \tag{14-12}$$

We shall see later that this is a rather large unit. For example, the earth magnetic induction is of the order of 10^{-5} Wb/m^2. The values of ***B*** attainable in the laboratory are much larger, but they do not exceed 10 Wb/m^2.

The vectorial character of ***B*** becomes apparent when we introduce the vectorial representation of the torque. As explained in mechanics, the torque T is a vector aligned with OO', Fig. 14-2b. It is thus perpendicular to $\vec{m}'$, and it will also be perpendicular to ***B*** if the magnetic induction is represented by a vector aligned with *SN*. Equation (14-7) can then be rewritten in a more concise vector form to read

$$\vec{T} = \vec{\boldsymbol{B}} \times \vec{\boldsymbol{m}}' \tag{14-13}$$

since by definition the numerical value of this vector product is $\boldsymbol{B}\boldsymbol{m}' \sin\alpha$.

14-4 Magnetic Field Intensity. The magnetic induction **B** was introduced in Eq. (14-2) to account for the proportionality existing between the magnetic moment $\boldsymbol{m}'$ and the force F acting on the loop $ABCD$, Fig. 14-2b. This particular action obviously comes from the current $\boldsymbol{i}$ passing through the solenoid. It is, therefore, natural to expect that the coefficient ***B*** should depend in some known manner on the characteristics of the solenoid. The quantitative dependence can be established experimentally, but it is generally derived in elementary physics from the law of Biot and Savart.[1] If n is the number of coils evenly spaced over the total length l of a tightly wound solenoid, then the magnetic induction ***B*** in the central portion of the solenoid, far from both ends (e.g., at a distance equal to 20 times, or more, the diameter of the coil), is found to depend only on the product $\boldsymbol{n}\boldsymbol{i}/l$ of the current $\boldsymbol{i}$ and the *number of coils* or *turns* n/l per unit length. However, since ***B*** is measured in webers per square meter, and the units of $\boldsymbol{n}\boldsymbol{i}/l$ are amperes per meter, a conversion factor is necessary to establish the correct relationship. We write, accordingly,

$$\boldsymbol{B} = \frac{\hat{\mu}_0 \boldsymbol{n}\boldsymbol{i}}{l} \tag{14-14}$$

[1] See, for example, F. W. Sears, *Principles of Physics II, Electricity and Magnetism*, Addison-Wesley, Reading, Mass., 1947.

where $\hat{\mu}_0$ is the required conversion factor. To avoid confusion with the symbol $\boldsymbol{\mu}$, used in Chapter 13 for the molecular dipole moment, we write $\hat{\mu}$. The dimension of $\hat{\mu}_0$ are obviously

$$[\hat{\mu}_0] = \frac{[B]}{\left[\frac{ni}{l}\right]} = \frac{\text{Wb/m}^2}{\text{amp-turns/m}}$$

or, reverting to the fundamental MKSQ units,

$$[\hat{\mu}_0] = \left[\frac{\text{kg/(Q sec)}}{\text{Q}^2\text{/(m sec)}}\right] = \left[\frac{\text{kg m}}{\text{Q}^2}\right] \tag{14-15}$$

The numerical value of $\hat{\mu}_0$ is[2]

$$\hat{\mu}_0 = 1.25 \times 10^{-6} \text{ kg m/Q}^2 \tag{14-16}$$

The magnetic field intensity $\boldsymbol{H}$ of the solenoid can now be defined in terms of the quantities figuring on the right-hand side of Eq. (14-14). We write by definition,

$$\boldsymbol{H} = ni/l \tag{14-18}$$

whereupon

$$\boldsymbol{B} = \hat{\mu}_0 \boldsymbol{H} \tag{14-19}$$

Since $\boldsymbol{B}$ is a vector quantity and $\hat{\mu}_0$ is a scalar, $\boldsymbol{H}$ must also be a vector. A more correct form of Eq. (14-19), therefore, is

$$\vec{\boldsymbol{B}} = \hat{\mu}_0 \vec{\boldsymbol{H}} \tag{14-20}$$

Note: By multiplying the numerator and denominator of Eq. (14-18) by the cross-sectional area A of the solenoid and noticing that Al is the volume v of the solenoid, we have

$$\boldsymbol{H} = nAi/v \tag{14-21}$$

The product Ai is the magnetic moment of a single loop of the solenoid. Writing $\boldsymbol{m}$ for Ai, we can say that $n\boldsymbol{m}$ is the magnetic moment of the whole solenoid. The expression on the right-hand side of Eq. (14-21) is then the

[2] In a more advanced course of electromagnetic theory the conversion factor $\hat{\mu}_0$ is derived from Coulomb's law by making due allowance for the relativistic correction brought about by the relative motion of (negative) charges with respect to a common frame of reference, e.g., the positive ion cores in the conductor. The pertinent relationship is

$$\hat{\mu}_0 \varepsilon_0 c^2 = 1 \tag{14-17}$$

where c is the speed of light in vacuum; i.e., 3×10^8 m/sec. Substituting the value and units of ε_0 from Eq. (13-6), Chapter 13, in Eq. (14-16), we have

$$\hat{\mu}_0 = \frac{1}{\varepsilon_0 c^2} \frac{\text{sec}^2}{\text{m}^2} \frac{\text{kg m}^3}{\text{Q}^2\text{sec}^2} = 1.25 \times 10^{-6} \frac{\text{kg m}}{\text{Q}^2}$$

in agreement with Eq. (14-16).

magnetic moment per unit volume of the solenoid. Denoting this quantity by $\boldsymbol{M}^*$, we see that in the particular case of the solenoid the field intensity $\boldsymbol{H}$ is numerically equal to the magnetic moment of the solenoid per unit volume. That is,

$$\boldsymbol{H} = \boldsymbol{M}^* \tag{14-22}$$

and

$$\boldsymbol{B} = \hat{\mu}_0 \boldsymbol{M}^* \tag{14-23}$$

Since $\boldsymbol{m}$ is a vector quantity, the same is true of $n\boldsymbol{m}/v$ or $\boldsymbol{M}^*$, and we can rewrite Eq. (14-23) in vector notation to read

$$\vec{\boldsymbol{B}} = \hat{\mu}_0 \vec{\boldsymbol{M}}^* \tag{14-24}$$

To simplify the notations, the arrow over the symbol will not be used subsequently unless there is a need for stressing the vectorial nature of the quantity.

14-5 Magnetic Dipole Moments. In possession of the governing relationships—Eqs. (14-7), (14-19), and (14-23)—we can now study the behavior of atoms and atom aggregates in a magnetic field, such as the field of a solenoid, Fig. 14-2b. According to the older atomic model, the Bohr atom, each electron is pictured as describing a closed orbit around the nucleus. If e is the charge and ν is the number of revolutions per second, then the product νe is a charge passing through each point of the orbit in one second, or a current $\boldsymbol{i}' = \nu e$. Furthermore, if A' is the area enclosed by the orbit, the product $A'\boldsymbol{i}'$ can be viewed by analogy with Eq. (14-4) as the magnetic moment of the orbiting electron, or as its *orbital magnetic moment.* It follows that an atom placed with its orbiting electrons in a magnetic field, as in the field of a solenoid, should be subjected to a torque, like the small current loop *ABCD* of Fig. 14-2b. This conclusion has been confirmed experimentally, as we shall see in Section 14-7. A more careful analysis of the data, however, disclosed that to account numerically for the already known features of the atomic model, it was necessary to postulate the existence of an additional magnetic moment in the electron. This is the *spin magnetic moment* ascribed to the rotation or spinning of the electron around its own axis, not unlike the spinning of the earth and other planets of the solar system. The spin magnetic moment appears as an essential property of the electron. Its value measured in the direction of applied magnetic field is 9.27×10^{-24} Q m²/sec. This value is the same as the *unit* of magnetic moment derived in Section 14-6 from the orbital magnetic moment of the electron in the hydrogen atom. The unit is called *Bohr magneton*, and it is represented by the symbol $\boldsymbol{m}_{\mathrm{B}}$. That is,

$$1\boldsymbol{m}_{\mathrm{B}} = \text{one Bohr magneton} = 9.27 \times 10^{-24}\ \mathrm{Q\ m^2/sec} \tag{14-25}$$

Since the magnetic moment is a vector quantity, one might expect that the total magnetic moment of an atom is the vector sum of the orbital and spin magnetic moments of its electrons. There are, however, restrictions imposed on this sum by the same quantum mechanical rules that preside over the building of the atoms. Some of these restrictions will be briefly considered.

We recall that in the closed shells the number of electrons is even. Half of these electrons spin one way, half the other way. In addition, the closed shells possess spherical symmetry. This means the electrons are as likely to orbit clockwise as counterclockwise. On both counts then, the contributions of closed-shell electrons to the magnetic moment of the atom cancel each other. As a result, only the unfilled shells need to be considered. Even here, the first two electrons can be ruled out on the ground that they have opposite spins and don't have any prescribed orbit. The situation of the remaining electrons in the unfilled shells is more complicated and will not be analyzed, except later in relation to ferromagnetism; see Section 14-12. One thing appears certain: A spin that is not paired with an opposite spin will, as a rule, make a contribution to the magnetic moment of the atom.

Thus, in the case of hydrogen and elements of Group I of the periodic table—Li, Na, K, Rb, and Cs—the magnetic moment of the atom is different from zero, since the valence shell of the atom contains only one unpaired spin. On the other hand, the atoms of the Group II—Be, Mg, Ca, Sr, and Ba—and, of course, the atoms of all inert elements—He, Ne, A, etc.—have no magnetic moment, since here the electron spins are everywhere paired. We say that the atoms of the first kind have a *permanent magnetic dipole*, whereas the atoms of the second kind have none. The word "dipole" is used here to emphasize the fact that these permanent moments, when placed in a magnetic field, behave in the same way as the molecular *electric dipoles* do when placed in an electric field—a point to be further considered in Section 14-7. It is not meant to imply that two distinct poles appear, since magnetic isolated poles do not exist in nature.

Nuclear Magnetism. Although the orbiting and spinning of electrons are the major contributions to the magnetic moment of the atom, they are not the only ones. The nucleus provides a weak but significant component to this moment. Nuclear magnetism is caused by the spin of protons and *neutrons.*

That spinning of protons would produce a magnetic field is not altogether surprising, since protons, like electrons, are electrically charged particles. They are about 2000 times heavier than the electrons; hence, they are expected to spin that much slower and cause a correspondingly weaker magnetic moment. This expectation has been borne out by experiments on solidified hydrogen, whose nucleus, we recall, is reduced to only one proton.

That the neutron, too, has a magnetic moment has been shown by studying the penetration of a neutron beam through iron. There was a marked difference, depending on whether the iron sample was magnetized or not.

This would not have happened had the neutrons themselves not been magnetized. What is the cause of their magnetism? The neutron is electrically neutral, but so is the atom. Yet, owing to its particulate structure, the atom we saw can have a permanent magnetic moment. The inference is that the neutron, too, is made up of smaller particles. This seems to be the case, although the details of the neutron's structure are still an object of investigations.

14-6 The Bohr Magneton. The orbital magnetic moment of the hydrogen atom in the Bohr model is the simplest to compute. It is also used as a unit to measure the magnitudes of permanent magnetic dipoles of other atoms, as well as other magnetic moments on the atomic scale.

To carry out the computation, we assume, in accordance with the Bohr model, that the single electron of the hydrogen atom moves in a circular

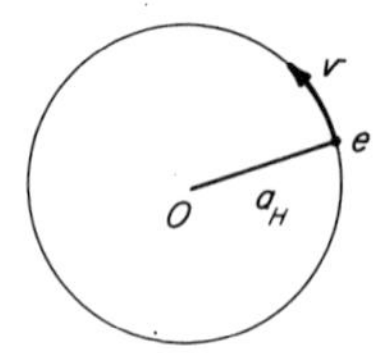

FIG. 14-3 Magnetic moment of an orbiting electron of the hydrogen atom (schematic)

orbit of radius a_{H} about the nucleus, Fig. 14-3. If ν is the number of revolutions per second, the orbital magnetic moment $\boldsymbol{m}_{\mathrm{B}}$ is, according to Section 14-5,

$$\boldsymbol{m}_{\mathrm{B}} = -\pi a_{\mathrm{H}}{}^2 e\nu \tag{14-26}$$

The minus sign signifies that the motion of the electron is in the opposite direction to the accepted direction of current.

Instead of ν, we introduce in Eq. (14-26) the circumferential velocity v of the electron, by noticing that v is equal to the path covered by the electron in ν revolutions, i.e.,

$$v = 2\pi a_{\mathrm{H}}\nu \tag{14-27}$$

Elimination of ν from Eqs. (14-26) and (14-27) yields

$$\boldsymbol{m}_{\mathrm{B}} = -\tfrac{1}{2}ea_{\mathrm{H}}v \tag{14-28}$$

Both a_{H} and v are subject to the restrictions imposed by the postulates of quantum mechanics. First, an electron of mass m moving with a speed v interacts with an electromagnetic field as though it were itself a radiation of wavelength λ. The magnitude of λ is governed by a postulate of quantum mechanics which says that

$$\lambda = \frac{h}{mv} \tag{14-29}$$

where h is the universal, Planck's constant equal to 6.62×10^{-34} J sec. Next, the motion of the electron in its orbit represents a steady state. Therefore, the interactions between the electron and the electromagnetic field must reveal the periodicity of the circular motion. To say it differently, the circumference of the circle must contain a whole number of wavelengths, so that the same amplitude of radiation is repeated at each turn. The simplest and the most stable condition occurs when the circumference corresponds to only one wavelength. That is,

$$2\pi a_{\mathrm{H}} = \lambda \tag{14-30}$$

Substitution of λ from Eq. (14-30) in Eq. (14-29) yields, after rearrangement of terms,

$$a_{\mathrm{H}} v = \frac{h}{2\pi m} \tag{14-31}$$

whereupon Eq. (14-28) becomes

$$\boldsymbol{m}_{\mathrm{B}} = -\frac{eh}{4\pi m} \tag{14-32}$$

Substituting in Eq. (14-32) the values of e, h, and m expressed in MKSQ units, we obtain

$$\boldsymbol{m}_{\mathrm{B}} = -\frac{eh}{4\pi m} = \frac{1.60 \times 10^{-9} \times 6.62 \times 10^{-34}}{4\pi \times 9.11 \times 10^{-31}} \frac{\text{Q J sec}}{\text{kg}}$$
$$= 9.27 \times 10^{-24} \text{ Q m}^2/\text{sec}$$

—a unit called one Bohr magneton, as mentioned in Section 14-5.

14-7 Magnetization and Magnetic Susceptibility. We have indicated in Section 14-5 that the computation of permanent dipole moments in atoms is a complex and difficult problem. This is due to the fact that not only the orbital and spin magnetic moments of the contributing electrons in unfilled shells must be added vectorially, but also the addition itself must comply with the rules of quantum mechanics. The situation in polyatomic molecules is even more complicated. However, for monoatomic and molecular dilute gases and for many condensed systems, the permanent magnetic dipole can be determined experimentally, that is, by placing the substance in the field of a solenoid. Each of the magnetic dipoles, if it were free, would be expected to behave in such a field as the loop of Section 14-2 and to align itself parallel to the vector $\vec{\boldsymbol{B}}$ of the magnetic induction. In dilute gases the intermolecular forces are practically nil, so there is no interference from neighboring magnetic dipoles. The same appears to be true of many condensed systems, with the notable exception of ferromagnetic materials, to be taken up in Section 14-12. However, there is another interference which comes from the thermal agitation of molecules. As in the case of electric dipole moments studied in Section 13-8, thermal agitation hampers a complete alignment of the permanent magnetic dipoles with the vector $\vec{B}$. Outwardly the substance behaves as if only a fraction of its magnetic dipoles succeeded in aligning themselves with this vector. Thus, let $\boldsymbol{m}_p$ be the magnitude of the magnetic dipole of a molecule and N the number of molecules per unit volume. Then the vector sum of the individual magnetic dipoles aligned with vector $\vec{B}$ will not be $N\boldsymbol{m}_p$ per unit volume, but $\beta N\boldsymbol{m}_p$, where β is a fraction.

In Section 14-4 we introduced a special symbol $\boldsymbol{M}$ to denote the magnetic moment per unit volume of the solenoid. In like manner we shall put

$$\boldsymbol{M} = \beta N\boldsymbol{m}_p \tag{14-33}$$

to represent the magnetic moment per unit volume of the substance. By analogy with polarization $\boldsymbol{P}$, defined in Section 13-3, we call $\boldsymbol{M}$ the *magnetization.*

Because of the overriding influence of thermal agitation, the magnetization $\boldsymbol{M}$, as a rule, is a rather small fraction of $N\boldsymbol{m}_p$. Exceptionally, and then only in very strong magnetic fields, $\boldsymbol{M}$ can approach the saturation value equal to $N\boldsymbol{m}_p$, as in gadolinium sulfate, $Gd_2(SO_4)8H_2O$ (see footnote [3]).

In all circumstances the presence of thermal agitation reduces the computation of β to a statistical problem similarly to the case of the orientation polarization treated in Section 13-8. Here, as there, the thermal agitation produces a force couple, or a torque, which keeps the magnetic dipoles oscillating about an average position making an angle θ with $\vec{B}$. The computation of β must here, too, be postponed to a more advanced course, but the approximate value of β is of the same form as in Eq. (13-34), Chapter 13,[4] namely,

$$\beta = \frac{\boldsymbol{B}\boldsymbol{m}_p}{3kT} \tag{14-34}$$

Substitution of β from Eq. (14-34) in Eq. (14-33) yields

$$\vec{M} = \frac{N\boldsymbol{m}_p{}^2}{3kT}\vec{B} \tag{14-35}$$

For reasons which will appear below, it is more convenient to express $\boldsymbol{M}$ in terms of field intensity $\boldsymbol{H}$ rather than magnetic induction $\boldsymbol{B}$. Using Eq. (14-20), we have

$$\vec{M} = N\frac{\hat{\mu}_0\boldsymbol{m}_p{}^2}{3kT}\vec{H} \tag{14-36}$$

[3] A. R. von Hippel, *Dielectrics and Waves*, Wiley, New York, 1954.

[4] In fact, the computation of β was first carried out for the case of magnetic dipoles by P. Langevin in 1905. Only later was it adapted by P. Debye, in 1912, to the case of the electric dipole moments.

According to Eq. (14-36), a substance containing permanent magnetic dipoles, on being placed in a magnetic field, acquires a magnetization $\boldsymbol{M}$ proportional to the field intensity $\boldsymbol{H}$. In gases and amorphous materials, the directions of vectors $\vec{\boldsymbol{M}}$ and $\vec{\boldsymbol{H}}$ coincide, but in crystalline materials, they may differ, as a more involved computation shows.

The coefficient of proportionality in front of $\boldsymbol{H}$ is called *magnetic susceptibility*. Like its dielectric counterpart, Eq. (13-29), magnetic susceptibility is represented by a Greek letter χ, but with a subscript m. Thus,

$$\chi_{\mathrm{m}} = \frac{N\hat{\mu}_0 \boldsymbol{m}_{\mathrm{p}}^{\,2}}{3kT} \tag{14-37}$$

whereupon

$$\vec{\boldsymbol{M}} = \chi_{\mathrm{m}}\vec{\boldsymbol{H}} \tag{14-38}$$

In accordance with Eq. (14-22), the dimensions of magnetization are the same as those of the field intensity $\boldsymbol{H}$, that is, ampere-turns per meter if the MKSQ system is used. Alternatively, we can express $\boldsymbol{M}$ as the magnetic moment per unit volume—as Q/sec m, in accordance with Eq. (14-5). The two expressions are, of course, equivalent. Since $\boldsymbol{M}$ has the same dimensions as $\boldsymbol{H}$, the magnetic susceptibility χ_{m}, like its electrical counterpart χ, has no dimensions. This can also be seen by examining the units of the quantities figuring on the right-hand side of Eq. (14-37).

Considering that $\boldsymbol{m}_{\mathrm{p}}$ seldom exceeds 3 Bohr magnetons, the value of χ_{m} at room temperature is a small fraction even for a very condensed state of aggregation, the ferromagnetic materials excepted. This can be seen by substituting in Eq. (14-37) 10^{30} molecules per cubic meter for N and 300°K for T. There follows, with $\boldsymbol{m}_{\mathrm{p}}$ equal to 3 Bohr magnetons and the other quantities being universal constants,

$$\chi_{\mathrm{m}} = 10^{30}\,\frac{1.25 \times 10^{-6} \times 3^2 \times 9.27^2 \times 10^{-48}}{3 \times 1.38 \times 10^{-23} \times 300}$$

or about 0.08.

14-8 The Law of Magnetization. The proportionality between the field intensity $\boldsymbol{H}$ and the induced magnetization $\boldsymbol{M}$ embodied in Eq. (14-38) has been derived so far only for the case of permanent magnetic dipoles and for a dilute gas placed in a field of a solenoid. We shall see, in Section 14-11, that a similar law of proportionality exists for substances devoid of permanent magnetic dipoles. Experimentally, the law of proportionality has been found to apply to many condensed systems as well. The only notable exceptions are the already-mentioned ferromagnetic substances, whose behavior is discussed in Section 14-12.

Despite its generality, Eq. (14-38) is seldom used to represent the law of magnetization experimentally. The reason is that the magnetization $\boldsymbol{M}$—like its electric counterpart, the polarization $\boldsymbol{P}$—cannot be measured directly.

To express the law of magnetization in terms of directly measurable quantities, we imagine a solenoid fitted into a receptacle which contains the gas to be studied. We seek to evaluate the magnetic induction $\boldsymbol{B}$ from the combined action exerted on a test loop L by the field intensity $\boldsymbol{H}$ and the magnetization $\boldsymbol{M}$ of the gas, Fig. 14-4, using the procedure outlined in Sections 14-2 to 14-4.[5] The direction of magnetization $\vec{\boldsymbol{M}}$ coincides here with the

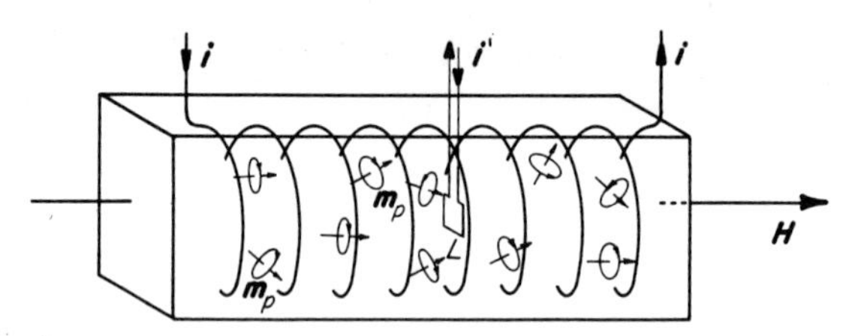

FIG. 14-4 Action exerted on an elementary current loop L by the field intensity $\boldsymbol{H}$ and magnetization $\boldsymbol{M}$ due to permanent magnetic dipoles $\boldsymbol{m}_p$ of a gas

direction of the field intensity $\vec{\boldsymbol{H}}$, and both vectors represent the same physical quantity, namely the magnetic moment per unit volume. We conclude that their action on the loop must also be the same.[6] That is, they both produce force couples opposing the applied torque. Because of the smallness of $\boldsymbol{M}$ compared to $\boldsymbol{H}$, their actions may be considered as additive.[7] Hence, by following the arguments of Section 14-4, we can write

$$\vec{\boldsymbol{B}} = \hat{\mu}_0(\vec{\boldsymbol{H}} + \vec{\boldsymbol{M}}) \tag{14-39}$$

or, using Eq. (14-38),

$$\vec{\boldsymbol{B}} = \hat{\mu}_0(1 + \chi_m)\vec{\boldsymbol{H}} \tag{14-40}$$

We shall not attempt to extend the validity of Eq. (14-39) to condensed aggregates. The difficulties here are similar to those encountered previously in the case of polarization, Section 13-9.[8] However, we shall adapt this

[5] This procedure has been imagined solely for the sake of demonstration. For actual experimental procedures see, for example, an article by D. J. Epstein in A. R. von Hippel's *Dielectric Materials and Applications*, Wiley, New York, 1954.

[6] Like the test charge q' in Fig. 13-4, the loop L placed in a dilute gas has little chance to be anywhere so near a molecule as to be aware of its individual action. All it senses is the global effect of the magnetized aggregate.

[7] This can be shown as follows: By virtue of Eq. (14-38) and from the subsequent computation of χ_m, the action of $\boldsymbol{M}$ can be taken as equivalent to that of a small increase of field intensity $\boldsymbol{H}$. We therefore write

$$\boldsymbol{M} = \Delta \boldsymbol{H} = \chi_m \boldsymbol{H}$$

and, by an argument similar to that used in Section 6-3,

$$\boldsymbol{B} = f(\boldsymbol{H} + \Delta\boldsymbol{H}) = f(\boldsymbol{H}) + f'(\boldsymbol{H})\Delta\boldsymbol{H} = \hat{\mu}_0\boldsymbol{H} + \hat{\mu}_0\boldsymbol{M}$$

[8] See, for example, F. Bitter, *Currents, Fields and Particles*, Wiley, New York, 1956.

equation later in Section 14-12 to the behavior of ferromagnetic materials. By putting

$$\hat{\mu} = \hat{\mu}_0(1 + \chi_m) \tag{14-41}$$

and observing that $\hat{\mu}$ is constant for a given material *at a given temperature*, we get from Eq. (14-40)

$$\boldsymbol{B} = \hat{\mu}\boldsymbol{H} \tag{14-42}$$

That is, the *magnetic induction* $\boldsymbol{B}$ is *proportional to the field intensity* $\boldsymbol{H}$. The coefficient $\hat{\mu}$ depends on the nature of the medium filling the inside of the solenoid. It is called the *magnetic permeability of the medium.*

There is a close analogy between the law of magnetization embodied in Eq. (14-42) and the dielectric law represented by Eq. (13-26). Like the dielectric constant $\boldsymbol{\varepsilon}$, the magnetic permeability $\hat{\mu}$ is not, strictly speaking, a material constant. It becomes a material property only when the conversion factor $\hat{\mu}_0$—called the permeability of the vacuum—is subtracted from it.

In practice the value of $\boldsymbol{B}$ is measured by placing the unknown substance in a field of given field intensity $\boldsymbol{H}$. The ratio $\boldsymbol{B}/\boldsymbol{H}$ supplies the value of $\hat{\mu}$. The magnetic susceptibility χ_m is then computed from the relation

$$\chi_m = \frac{\hat{\mu} - \hat{\mu}_0}{\hat{\mu}_0} \tag{14-43}$$

14-9 Illustrative Example

A solenoid 0.5 m long and containing 500 turns of wire is passed by a current of 10 amp. When placed in an atmosphere of oxygen at $t = -150°C$, it exhibits an increase of magnetic induction of $\Delta B = 1.04 \times 10^{-8}$ Wb/m^2 above that measured in a vacuum. Compute the magnetic susceptibility of oxygen at $-150°C$ and the magnetic dipole moment of the molecule.

Solution:

1. From Eq. (14-40) we conclude that

$$\Delta \boldsymbol{B} = \boldsymbol{B} - \hat{\mu}_0\boldsymbol{H} = \hat{\mu}_0\chi_m\boldsymbol{H}$$

whence

$$\chi_m = \frac{\Delta \boldsymbol{B}}{\hat{\mu}_0\boldsymbol{H}}$$

The value of $\boldsymbol{H}$ is

$$\boldsymbol{H} = \frac{in}{l} = \frac{10 \times 500}{0.5} = 10^4 \text{ amp-turns/m}$$

Hence, the magnetic susceptibility of oxygen at $-150°C$:

$$\chi_m = \frac{\Delta \boldsymbol{B}}{\hat{\mu}_0\boldsymbol{H}} = \frac{1.04 \times 10^{-8}}{1.25 \times 10^{-6} \times 10^4}$$

$$= 0.83 \times 10^{-6} \qquad \textit{Answer}$$

2. From Eq. (14-37) we deduce that

$$\boldsymbol{m}_{\mathrm{p}}^{2} = \frac{3kT\chi_{\mathrm{m}}}{N\hat{\mu}_{0}}$$

In this equation,

$$T = 273 + t = 123°\mathrm{K}$$

and

$$N = \frac{N_0 T_0}{T} = \frac{2.69 \times 10^{25} \times 273}{123} = 6.0 \times 10^{25} \text{ molecules/m}^3$$

Hence,

$$\begin{aligned}\boldsymbol{m}_{\mathrm{p}}^{2} &= \frac{3 \times 1.38 \times 10^{-23} \times 123 \times 0.83 \times 10^{-6}}{6.0 \times 10^{25} \times 1.25 \times 10^{-6}} \frac{\mathrm{J}}{1/\mathrm{m}^3} \frac{\mathrm{kg\,m}}{\mathrm{Q}^2} \\ &= 56.5 \times 10^{-48}\ \mathrm{Q}^2\ \mathrm{m}^4/\mathrm{sec}^2\end{aligned}$$

or

$$\boldsymbol{m}_{\mathrm{p}} = 7.5 \times 10^{-24} = 0.81 \text{ Bohr magneton} \qquad \textit{Answer}$$

14-10 Curie's Law. On dividing χ_{m} by N, we obtain from Eq. (14-37)

$$\frac{\chi_{\mathrm{m}}}{N} = \frac{\hat{\mu}_0 \boldsymbol{m}_{\mathrm{p}}^{2}}{3kT} \tag{14-44}$$

a quantity called the *molecular magnetic susceptibility*. χ_{m}/N is measured in cubic meters per molecule and is independent of the state of aggregation. A corresponding macroscopic quantity can be obtained by multiplying both sides of Eq. (14-44) by Avogadro's number, N_{A}. There follows

$$\frac{\chi_{\mathrm{m}} N_{\mathrm{A}}}{N} = \frac{N_{\mathrm{A}} \hat{\mu}_0 \boldsymbol{m}_{\mathrm{p}}^{2}}{3kT} \tag{14-45}$$

But, according to Eq. (13-31), the ratio

$$\frac{N_{\mathrm{A}}}{N} = \frac{M}{\rho} \tag{14-46}$$

is the magnitude of the volume occupied by one mole. Hence, substituting for N_{A}/N in Eq. (14-45) from Eq. (14-46), we get

$$\frac{\chi_{\mathrm{m}} M}{\rho} = \frac{N_{\mathrm{A}} \hat{\mu}_0 \boldsymbol{m}_{\mathrm{p}}^{2}}{3kT} \tag{14-47}$$

a quantity called the *molar magnetic susceptibility*, measured in cubic meters per mole.

In handbooks, another macroscopic quantity is listed, the *specific magnetic susceptibility*. It is obtained on dividing both sides of Eq. (14-47) by the mass M of one mole. There follows, for the expression of the specific magnetic susceptibility,

$$\frac{\chi_m}{\rho} = \frac{N_A \hat{\mu}_0 \boldsymbol{m}_p^2}{3kTM} \tag{14-48}$$

The dimensions of χ_m/ρ are, of course, m^3/kg.

We notice that the molecular, molar, and specific magnetic susceptibilities vary as the reciprocal of the absolute temperature. We can, therefore, write

$$\frac{\chi_m}{N} = \frac{C_m}{T} \tag{14-49}$$

$$\frac{\chi_m N_A}{N} = \frac{C_M}{T} \tag{14-50}$$

$$\frac{\chi_m}{\rho} = \frac{C_\rho}{T} \tag{14-51}$$

where C_m, C_M, and C_ρ are material constants independent of the state of aggregation. The above three equations are all expressions of the same law that P. Curie discovered experimentally in 1895.

For oxygen, using the values of the illustrative example, Section 14-8, we obtain

$$\frac{\chi_m}{N} = \frac{\hat{\mu}_0 \boldsymbol{m}_p^2}{3kT} = \frac{1.71 \times 10^{-30}}{T} \text{ m}^3/\text{molecule}$$

$$\frac{\chi_m M}{\rho} = \frac{\chi_m N_A}{N} = \frac{1.03 \times 10^{-6}}{T} \text{ m}^3/\text{mole}$$

and

$$\frac{\chi_m}{\rho} = \frac{1.03 \times 10^{-6}}{32 \times 10^{-3} \times T} = \frac{32.3 \times 10^{-6}}{T} \text{ m}^3/\text{kg}$$

The latter value is in reasonable agreement with the value of $33{,}700 \times 10^{-6}/T$ cm^3/g, determined by P. Curie in 1895.

14-11 Diamagnetism and Paramagnetism. In Section 14-8 it was pointed out that the law of proportionality between the field intensity $\boldsymbol{H}$ and magnetization $\boldsymbol{M}$ holds not only for substances endowed with permanent magnetic dipoles but also for substances devoid of permanent dipoles. What is then the origin of their magnetization?

To answer this question, we consider again an electron moving in a circular orbit, Fig. 14-5. For the sake of simplicity we will assume that the plane of the orbit is perpendicular to the magnetic induction $\boldsymbol{B}$ and that the electron is immersed in the magnetic field by a downward motion. Let the speed of the motion be set at such a pace that the whole orbit ABA has penetrated in the magnetic field, from point A to point B, by the time the electron has made one full turn.

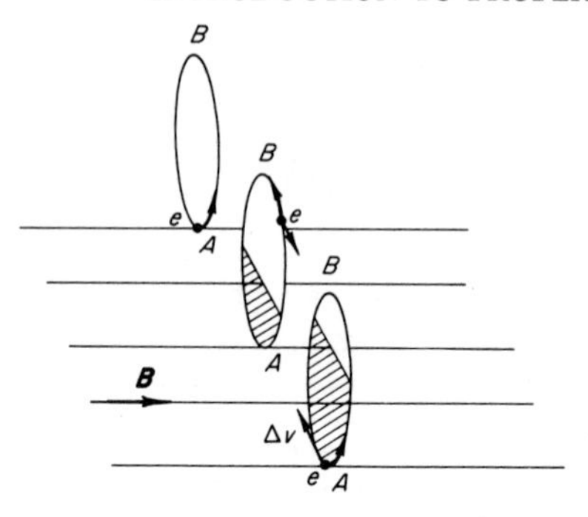

FIG. 14-5 Schematic representation of the origin of diamagnetism in a loop of an orbiting electron immersed in a magnetic field

By virtue of Faraday's law of electromagnetism, taught in elementary physics, the electron is subjected during the downward motion to a force resulting from the induction of an emf, or of a difference of potential, in the circuit ABA.

If we denote by $\mathbf{\Phi}$ the product of $\boldsymbol{B}$ by the cross-sectional area A of the orbit, then, by virtue of Faraday's law,

$$\text{emf} = \frac{d\mathbf{\Phi}}{dt} = \dot{\mathbf{\Phi}} \tag{14-52}$$

$\mathbf{\Phi}$ is called the magnetic flux. In vector notation,

$$\mathbf{\Phi} = \vec{\boldsymbol{B}} \cdot \vec{A} \tag{14-53}$$

Since $\boldsymbol{B}$ is constant,

$$\text{emf} = \dot{\mathbf{\Phi}} = \frac{d\mathbf{\Phi}}{dt} = \frac{d(\boldsymbol{B}A)}{dt} = \frac{\boldsymbol{B}dA}{dt} = \boldsymbol{B}\dot{A} \tag{14-54}$$

We seek to evaluate the change of momentum which this emf has produced in the motion of the electron and derive from there the change of the magnetic moment. In accordance with our initial assumptions, the impulse corresponding to the change of momentum acts during a time interval Δt, during which the electron has completed one single turn $2\pi r$. On the other hand, the force f contributing to the impulse is given by the expression

$$f = e\boldsymbol{E} \tag{14-55}$$

where e is the charge of the electron and $\boldsymbol{E}$ is the average intensity of the electric field. The field intensity $\boldsymbol{E}$, in turn, results from the application of the emf across the circuit $2\pi r$. Hence,

$$\boldsymbol{E} = \frac{\text{emf}}{2\pi r} \tag{14-56}$$

However, we can also write, with reference to Eq. (14-54),

$$\boldsymbol{E} = \frac{\boldsymbol{B}\dot{A}}{2\pi r} \tag{14-57}$$

hence, the expression for f becomes

$$f = \frac{e\boldsymbol{B}\dot{A}}{2\pi r} \tag{14-58}$$

The equality between the change of momentum and the impulse can thus be written as follows:

$$m\,\Delta v = f\,\Delta t = \frac{e\boldsymbol{B}\dot{A}\,\Delta t}{2\pi r} \tag{14-59}$$

where m is the mass of the electron and Δv is the change of its circumferential velocity.

Equation (14-59) can be further simplified by observing that $\dot{A}$ is the rate at which the area of the circuit is being immersed in the magnetic field, and Δt is the time corresponding to a full immersion. Hence,

$$\dot{A}\,\Delta t = A = \pi r^2 \tag{14-60}$$

Also, if ν' is the change of frequency of the orbital motion of the electron, then $1/\nu' = \Delta t$ and

$$\Delta v = \frac{2\pi r}{\Delta t} = 2\pi r\nu' \tag{14-61}$$

Finally, an electron orbiting ν' times per second is equivalent to a current induced in the circuit $2\pi r$ of a magnitude

$$\boldsymbol{i} = e\nu' \tag{14-62}$$

Eliminating Δv, $\dot{A}\,\Delta t$, and ν' from Eqs. (14-59) to (14-62) and rearranging the terms, we find that

$$\boldsymbol{i} = \frac{e^2}{4\pi m} \cdot \boldsymbol{B}$$

The corresponding induced magnetic moment $\boldsymbol{m}_i$, according to Eq. (14-4), is

$$\boldsymbol{m}_i = \boldsymbol{i}A = -\frac{e^2}{4m}\,r^2\boldsymbol{B}$$

or, since $\boldsymbol{B} = \hat{\mu}_0 H$,

$$\boldsymbol{m}_i = -\frac{e^2\hat{\mu}_0}{4m}\,r^2\boldsymbol{H} \tag{14-63}$$

The minus sign in Eq. (14-63) indicates, in accordance with Faraday's law, that the induced magnetic moment $\boldsymbol{m}_i$ opposes the magnetic field intensity $\boldsymbol{H}$. (Equation (14-64) has been derived by assuming for simplicity that the time of immersion of the circuit ABA in the magnetic field was $1/\nu'$. It is clear, however, that the validity of the derivation does not rest on this restriction.)

Equation (14-63) can be generalized to include all Z electrons of an atom. The radius r must then be averaged over all positions of all electrons—a procedure implying the knowledge of the density distribution of electrons in the atom. Let R be the radius of the atom and α a fraction depending on the density distribution. We can then write, by analogy with Eq. (13-15),

$$\boldsymbol{m}_{\mathrm{d}} = -\frac{Ze^2\hat{\mu}_0}{4m}(\alpha R)^2\boldsymbol{H} \tag{14-64}$$

That is, the induced magnetic moment is proportional to the magnetic field intensity.

The same relationship of proportionality, but with appropriate changes in the values of Z and α, holds for polyatomic molecules of gases. It is also a valid approximation for the condensed systems. In all these instances the induced magnetic moments of individual electrons can be computed independently of each other, and the combined magnetic moment can be obtained by simple superposition. It is thus possible to pass from the atomic to macroscopic quantities by summing up the magnetic moments of all molecules or atoms contained in a unit volume. Let N be their number. Then, from Eq. (14-64), we have

$$\boldsymbol{M}_{\mathrm{d}} = N\boldsymbol{m}_{\mathrm{d}} = -\frac{NZe^2\hat{\mu}_0}{4m}(\alpha R)^2\boldsymbol{H} \tag{14-65}$$

As in the case of permanent magnetic dipoles considered in Section 14-7, the product $\boldsymbol{M}_{\mathrm{d}} = N\boldsymbol{m}_{\mathrm{d}}$ is called magnetization. However, this magnetization has a negative sign. It opposes the action of the magnetic field, in contrast to the magnetization due to permanent magnetic dipoles, which support the action of the magnetic field. The dissimilarity of the two actions becomes apparent when we seek to evaluate again the combined effect of the field and magnetization on the magnetic induction $\boldsymbol{B}$, in the manner described in Section 14-7 and represented by Eq. (14-39). Here $\boldsymbol{M}_{\mathrm{d}}$ will subtract from $\boldsymbol{H}$, thus weakening the effect of the applied field. It is for this reason that the phenomenon associated with the induction of magnetic moments is called *diamagnetism*, whereas the phenomenon associated with the orientation of permanent magnetic dipoles is called *paramagnetism*, the Greek prefixes *dia- and para-* meaning across and along, respectively.

By analogy with Eqs. (14-36) and (14-37), we can write for the diamagnetic susceptibility, using Eq. (14-65),

$$\chi_{\mathrm{m}} = -\frac{NZe^2\hat{\mu}_0}{4m}(\alpha R)^2 \tag{14-66}$$

Unlike paramagnetism, diamagnetism occurs regardless of whether the molecule does or does not have a permanent magnetic dipole. However, in paramagnetic substances its effect is masked by the effect of paramagnetism, which is about two orders of magnitude larger.

This follows from the comparison of the related values of susceptibilities. We put, as in Section 14-7, $N = 10^{30}$ molecules/m^3. Since α^2 decreases rapidly as Z increases, an upper limit for the product $\alpha^2 Z$ can be set at 10. Hence the maximum value of diamagnetic susceptibility, according to Eq. (14-66), with $R = 10^{-10}$ m, is

$$\chi_m = -\frac{10^{30} \times 10 \times 1.60^2 \times 10^{-38} \times 1.25 \times 10^{-6} \times 10^{-20}}{4 \times 9.7 \times 10^{-31}}$$
$$= -0.00082$$

as against 0.08 for the paramagnetic susceptibility given in Section 14-7.

14-12 Spontaneous Magnetization. Ferro-, Ferri-, and Antiferromagnetism. Like dielectric polarization, the phenomenon of magnetization in solids is greatly affected by the stability of crystal structure. Prominent in this respect is the behavior of the transition elements, particularly of iron and its compounds. The close interaction which exists between the neighboring atoms in solids hampers considerably the freedom of orbital motions of their electrons. As a result, the spins become the only major contributors to the permanent magnetic dipoles. Depending on the configuration of spins in the atom and on the orientation of the magnetic dipoles in the unit cell, we may have a total cooperation of the individual magnetic dipoles, a partial cooperation, or a total cancellation. (This point is taken up later in Section 14-14.) Total cooperation is characteristic of metallic iron and its alloys; hence the name of *ferromagnetism* given to this manifestation. Partial cooperation is found in many natural minerals containing the ferric ion Fe^{+3}; hence the name of *ferrimagnetism*, under which it is presently classified.

Most prominent among natural ferrimagnetic minerals is the ferrous ferric oxide $FeO.Fe_2O_3$, whose name, magnetite—derived from Magnesia, an ancient city in Asia Minor near which it was mined—has become a hallmark of the property itself.

Both ferromagnetism and ferrimagnetism produce a net magnetization in the bulk of the material. The magnetization persists even in the absence of an applied magnetic field. Hence it is called *spontaneous*, at variance with the magnetization derived from diamagnetism and paramagnetism which is induced by the applied field and which disappears with the latter. Finally, the total cancellation of effects of individual magnetic dipoles, which results in no bulk magnetization whatsoever, as in MnO, is called *antiferromagnetism*, to contrast it with the type of magnetism existing in iron.

The technical importance of ferromagnetism has been stressed at the beginning of this chapter. The growing importance of ferrimagnetism has also been implied by making reference to ceramic magnetic devices. In both instances a better evaluation of the potential uses can be made by taking a closer look at the origin of magnetic dipoles and the nature of magnetization in the transition elements.

14-13 Spin Configuration of the Third Shell. We begin by recalling that the simple rules for the formation of elements considered in Chapter 1 come to naught with the onset of the fourth period. To obtain a better understanding of the ensuing behavior of the electrons, we must temper their quest for greater stability with the quantum traffic restrictions imposed on their motion. We recall that the first two electrons entering a new shell are subject to no traffic regulations, but they must have opposite spins if they are to be paired. They are called s-electrons, and the part of the shell they occupy is called the s *subshell.* The letters s, p, and d refer to the nature and intensity of the spectral lines to which these electrons give rise upon ionization: s for sharp, p for principal, and d for diffuse.

Thus, the eleventh electron of sodium enters the 3s subshell, and so does the twelfth electron of magnesium. The remaining six electrons of the third period enter successively the 3p subshell, for which the quantum rules in a free atom prescribe three directions of motion perpendicular to each other. With the completion of the 3p subshell, a second octet of electrons of extra stability is formed in the inert atom of argon. There are, however, five additional possibilities of restricted motion left to the electron in the third shell. They are obtained by spelling out in quantum language the available five orientations for the orbital magnetic moment of the electron. The corresponding portion of the shell is the 3d subshell of our present interest. Yet, on receiving its nineteenth electron, potassium avails itself of none of the openings in the 3d subshell. Instead, it places the valence electron in the 4s subshell, where freedom of motion insures, apparently, a greater stability of structure to the whole potassium atom. The atom of calcium follows suit, and so it has two valence electrons in the 4s subshell. Unfortunately, no more than two electrons can enjoy the liberalities of the 4s subshell. Accordingly, the twenty-first electron of scandium when confronted with the restrictions of the 4p subshell, prefers the greater stability of the still unfilled 3d subshell. That is, beginning with scandium and ending with nickel, the interrupted process of filling the third shell resumes in the transition elements of the fourth period. While this is going on, the two valence electrons are marking time in the 4s subshell. The situation reverts to normal with copper, which, on receiving a ninth electron in the 3d subshell pulls down one of the valence electrons and completes the decade of electrons in the 3d subshell. It thus becomes the first regular element of the fourth period. The above sequence of events is conveniently summarized in Table 14-1.

Table 14-1 shows that, barring the intervention of orbital magnetic moments, the only major contributors to the magnetization of transition elements are the unpaired spins of the 3d subshell. Since each unpaired spin counts for

TABLE 14-1 NUMBER AND CONFIGURATION OF ELECTRONS IN SOME OF THE ELEMENTS OF THE FOURTH PERIOD

Element	*Shells and Subshells*							*Remarks*
	1	2		3			4*	
	1s	2s	2p	3s	3p	3d	4s	
K	2	2	6	2	6		1	Transition elements
Ca	2	2	6	2	6		2	
Sc	2	2	6	2	6	1	2	
Ti	2	2	6	2	6	2	2	
V	2	2	6	2	6	3	2	
Cr	2	2	6	2	6	4	2	
Mn	2	2	6	2	6	5	2	
Fe	2	2	6	2	6	6	2	
Co	2	2	6	2	6	7	2	
Ni	2	2	6	2	6	8	2	
Cu	2	2	6	2	6	10	1	Normal elements
Zn	2	2	6	2	6	10	2	

* Other subshells not shown.

TABLE 14-2 3d ELECTRONS AND SPIN DIPOLE MOMENTS OF SOME ELEMENTS OF THE FOURTH PERIOD

Element	*Number of 3d Electrons*	*Spin Dipole Moment in Bohr Magnetons*			
		Per Free Atom	*Per Ion in Solid*		
			Divalent	*Trivalent*	*Metallic**
Cr	4	4			0.4
Mn	5	5	5		0.5
Fe	6	4	4	5	2.2
Co	7	3	3		1.7
Ni	8	2	2		0.6
Cu	10	0	1		0
Zn	10	0	0		

* Experimental values. Source: A. R. von Hippel, *Dielectrics and Waves*, p. 220, Wiley, New York, 1954.

one Bohr magneton, the magnitude of the dipole moment, $\boldsymbol{m}_{\mathrm{p}}$, per atom can be computed simply by counting the number of the unpaired spins. This has been done for some elements of the fourth period in column 3, Table 14-2. We see, for example, that of the total of six electrons contained in the 3d subshell of iron, four are unpaired, since the indicated value of $\boldsymbol{m}_p$ is 4 Bohr magnetons, etc.

In the solid state, the computed value of the dipole magnetic moment may change depending on the nature of bonding. When the bonds are wholly ionic and bivalent, no change is anticipated, since only the two 4s electrons are removed. This is indicated in column 4, which repeats the values of column 3, Table 14-2. However, a trivalent ionic bond requires the removal of a third electron, and in the case of iron this happens to be one of the paired electrons of the 3d subshell. Consequently, the magnitude of the dipole moment $\boldsymbol{m}_p$ is increased by one Bohr magneton in the trivalent ionic bonding of iron, as indicated in column 5 of Table 14-2.

The situation in the metallic state is a great deal more complicated. The relatively high values of the moduli of elasticity, plotted in Fig. 6-9, Chapter 6, seem to indicate that at least some of the 3d electrons contribute to the cohesion of the transition elements. They are also believed to participate in the conduction. On both counts then, their share in the magnetic dipole moment $\boldsymbol{m}_p$ is expected to be smaller. This expectation is borne out by the experimental values shown in column 6, Table 14-2. However, a satisfactory theoretical computation is still lacking. The same is not true of the values indicated in columns 4 and 5. These are theoretical values and are well substantiated by experimental measurements as explained in Section 14-18.

14-14 Curie and Néel Points. Magnetostriction. The values of the elementary magnetic dipole moments listed in Table 14-2 offer little clue to either the nature or the magnitude of the spontaneous magnetization found in the transition elements. Thus, the elementary magnetic dipole of metallic nickel is smaller than the magnetic dipole of the paramagnetic oxygen molecule in the ratio of 0.6 to 0.81, according to the illustrative example, Section 14-9. Yet, even in the solid state and under field intensities as high as 10^6 amp-turns/m, the magnetization $\boldsymbol{M}$ of oxygen remains but a small fraction of the spontaneous magnetization of nickel.

This conclusion follows from the perusal of representative values of $\boldsymbol{M}$ listed in Table 14-3, column 2, for the three ferromagnetic metals: iron, cobalt, and nickel. The corresponding value for oxygen in a field of 10^6 amp-turns is about 10^6 orders of magnitude smaller, as can be inferred from the value of the susceptibility χ_m computed in the illustrative example, Section 14-9.

What is the reason for such a large discrepancy? We get an idea of the underlying cause by determining the fraction β of the elementary magnetic dipoles contributing to magnetization in both cases. According to Eq. (14-33),

$$\beta = \frac{\boldsymbol{M}}{N\boldsymbol{m}_p} \tag{14-67}$$

TABLE 14-3 REPRESENTATIVE VALUES OF MAGNETIZATION, $\boldsymbol{M}$, AT ROOM TEMPERATURE, NUMBER OF ELEMENTARY MAGNETIC DIPOLES PER CUBIC METER, N, AND CURIE POINTS θ OF IRON, COBALT, AND NICKEL

Element	$\boldsymbol{M}$ amp-turns/m *in* 10^6	N *per* m^3 *in* 10^{28}	θ (°K)
Iron	1.61	8.5	1043
Cobalt	1.3	9.0	1400
Nickel	0.51	9.2	631

where N is the number of either molecules, atoms, or ions per unit volume, depending on the state and nature of aggregation. For cubic crystals

$$N = \frac{n}{a_0^{\,3}} \tag{14-68}$$

where n is the number of atoms per unit cell and a_0 is the length of the edge of unit cell. The values of N computed from Eq. (14-68) are listed in column 3, Table 14-3. Substituting the values of $\boldsymbol{M}$, N, and $\boldsymbol{m}_p$ from Tables 14-2 and 14-3 in Eq. (14-67), we find that β is close to unity for all three ferromagnetic metals. This means that nearly *all* elementary magnetic dipoles contribute here to magnetization. At variance with the above result, the fraction β of the elementary dipoles which contribute to magnetization in paramagnetic materials is negligibly small.[9] We are, therefore, justified in saying—as we did in Section 14-12—that there is complete cooperation between the elementary magnetic dipoles in the case of ferromagnetism. To put it differently, all elementary dipoles are here aligned and they all point the same way, so their individual values add up arithmetically. We will see in Section 14-16 that in the case of ferrimagnetism some of the elementary dipoles point the other way, so the total contribution to magnetization, although still substantial, is much smaller. Finally, in the case of antiferromagnetism, half the elementary dipoles point one way, half the other way, and there is complete cancellation of effects. Not only the spontaneous, but also the induced (paramagnetic) magnetization is here all but missing, at least so long as the elementary dipoles remain perfectly aligned. What

[9] This follows from Eq. (14-36). On dividing both sides of the equation by $N\boldsymbol{m}_p$, we have

$$\beta = \frac{\boldsymbol{M}}{n\boldsymbol{m}_p} = \frac{\hat{\mu}_0 \boldsymbol{m}_p \boldsymbol{H}}{3kT} \tag{14-69}$$

Even if $\boldsymbol{m}_p$ is as large as 5 Bohr magnetons and $\boldsymbol{H}$ as high as 10^6 amp-turns/m, β is still a small fraction, being close to 0.5% at room temperature. The situation near absolute zero is more complicated, and it will not be considered here.

ultimately destroys the alignment is the growing thermal agitation as the temperature is raised. Like the spontaneous dielectric polarization described in Section 13-11, the spontaneous magnetization—and its counterpart, the antiferromagnetism—disappear above a certain critical temperature, and the substance becomes paramagnetic.

In ferromagnetic and ferrimagnetic materials this temperature is called the Curie point, after Pierre Curie, who pioneered most of the research in this field. In antiferromagnetic materials it is sometimes referred to as the Néel point, T_c, in honor of Curie's compatriot, the contemporary French physicist, L. Néel, who did much to elucidate their nature. The Curie points for iron, cobalt, and nickel are shown in column 4, Table 14-3. They all lie above room temperature. At room temperature, thermal agitation still causes a slight misalignment of elementary dipoles, a misalignment which ultimately disappears at the approach of absolute zero. On the other hand, thermal agitation takes over completely above the Curie point, so that even the partial alignment normally associated with paramagnetism is not possible without assistance from an applied magnetic field.

The change of magnetization from spontaneous to paramagnetic, which a ferromagnetic material experiences at the Curie point, is somewhat reminiscent of the change of density a substance undergoes at the boiling point. Below the boiling point, the molecules are more or less in close contact. The substance is a liquid, and its density is primarily dependent on the size of the molecules. Above the boiling point, the thermal agitation disrupts the contact between molecules. The substance is a gas, and its density cannot be specified unless the magnitude of the applied pressure is known.

The above analogy suggests that the alignment of magnetic dipoles in a ferromagnetic state, like the condensation of molecules in a liquid state, is due to forces of interaction between close neighbors. On the present view this interaction is also of an electrostatic nature. Its rare occurrence in the metallic state is explained by the severe restriction which the pairwise coupling of opposite spins imposes on the incidence of parallel alignments. The restriction is less severe for ferrimagnetism, and even less for antiferromagnetism, presumably because here there is partial fulfillment of pairing by the oppositely aligned dipole moments. This would explain the more frequent occurrence of ferrimagnetism and antiferromagnetism in nature among minerals.

A further analogy exists between the condensation of molecules during liquefaction and the alignment of elementary dipoles during spontaneous magnetization. In both instances there is a release of heat and a change of volume. However, for magnetization the changes are rather small and they are gradual. The change of volume may be a contraction or an expansion. In either case the change spreads over a range of temperatures, so that its occurrence cannot be detected unless the simultaneous thermal contraction due to cooling is subtracted from it, for example, by using as a reference a paramagnetic substance having a comparable coefficient of thermal expansion. Concurrently with a change of volume, spontaneous magnetization causes a slight distortion of crystal structure. In iron, both manifestations culminate in a contraction, hence the name of *magnetostriction*, under which they are known.

We distinguish between *spontaneous magnetostriction*, caused by the spontaneous magnetization itself, and *forced magnetostriction*, an additional elastic deformation produced in magnetic materials by the application of an external magnetic field. Like electrostriction, which was described in Section 13-12, magnetostriction is a one-sided manifestation. A magnetic field deforms the sample, but an elastic deformation does not magnetize it.

Despite this one-sided character, magnetostriction has found important applications in the field of ultrasonic transducers. High-frequency oscillations of the magnetic field can induce in selected magnetic substances mechanical vibrations of sufficient power to warrant the use of these substances as cutting tools or drills for brittle materials. They also find applications in sonar equipment. Nickel is the most widely used metal in all magnetostrictive devices. Under proper conditions it can develop pulses of strain amounting to 5% of the yield strain. Much larger changes of strain have recently been found in some ferrimagnetic minerals (e.g., $CoFe_2O_4$), which mark them as potentially new materials for future magnetostrictive uses.

14-15 Generalization of Curie's Law. The approximate relationship between the magnetization $\boldsymbol{M}$ and the temperature T embodied in Eq. (14-36) implies, similarly to Eq. (13-44), that the individual magnetic dipoles $\boldsymbol{m}_p$ behave independently of each other. Such an assumption is obviously invalid in spontaneous magnetization. So long as the temperature is different from absolute zero, however, the behavior of the dipoles is still statistical, but the statistics reflect the quantum mechanics restrictions to which these elementary dipoles are subjected. Accordingly, the relationship between $\boldsymbol{M}$, T, and $\boldsymbol{H}$ is not as simple as that given by Eq. (14-36). The appropriate derivation must be deferred to a more advanced course, but it will prove instructive at this stage to analyze the final result. The pertinent relationship can be put in the following form:

$$\frac{\boldsymbol{M}_s}{\boldsymbol{M}_0} = \tanh\left(\frac{C\boldsymbol{H}}{\boldsymbol{M}_0 T} + \frac{\theta \boldsymbol{M}_s}{\boldsymbol{M}_0 T}\right) \tag{14-70}$$

where

$$\boldsymbol{M}_0 = N\boldsymbol{m}_p \tag{14-71}$$

is the ultimate magnetization attained at absolute zero, $\boldsymbol{M}_s$ is the maximum (the saturation) magnetization attained at temperature T, θ is the Curie point, $\boldsymbol{H}$ is the applied field intensity, C is a constant having the value

$$C = \frac{\hat{\mu}_0 N \boldsymbol{m}_p{}^2}{3k} = \frac{\hat{\mu}_0 \boldsymbol{m}_p \boldsymbol{M}_0}{3k} \tag{14-72}$$

and tanh stands for the operation

$$\tanh a = \frac{e^{a} - e^{-a}}{e^{a} + e^{-a}} = \frac{1 - e^{-2a}}{1 + e^{-2a}} \tag{14-73}$$

We can simplify Eq. (14-70) by observing that in the case of spontaneous magnetization $\boldsymbol{H} = 0$. By expressing further $\boldsymbol{M}_s$ as a fraction x of $\boldsymbol{M}_0$ and T as a fraction ϕ of θ, i.e., by putting

$$s = \frac{\boldsymbol{M}_s}{\boldsymbol{M}_0} \tag{14-74}$$

and

$$\phi = \frac{T}{\theta} \tag{14-75}$$

we have

$$x = \tanh \frac{x}{\phi} = \frac{1 - e^{-2x/\phi}}{1 + e^{-2x/\phi}} \tag{14-76}$$

This is a transcendental equation in x and ϕ, which can be solved, e.g., for x given the values of ϕ, either graphically or by trial and error.

We observe that for a spontaneous magnetization ϕ varies between 1, when $T = \theta$, and zero, when $T = 0$. We have, directly from Eq. (14-76), that

$$\text{for } \phi = 1, \qquad x = 0$$

and

$$\text{for } \phi = 0, \qquad x = 1$$

That is, spontaneous magnetization disappears at the Curie point, and it attains its ultimate value of $\boldsymbol{M}_0$ at absolute zero, as expected. The variation of x with ϕ between these two limits is shown in Fig. 14-6. The three sets of symbols represent experimental points for iron, cobalt, and nickel, respectively. It is seen that Eq. (14-76) predicts reasonably well the variation of $\boldsymbol{M}_s$ with T for all three metals.

Above the Curie point the magnetization is no longer spontaneous and it has a very small value compared to $\boldsymbol{M}_0$. Since T is also larger than θ, the second term in the parentheses of Eq. (14-70) is a very small fraction. So is the first term, as can be seen on substituting for C its value, Eq. (14-72). There follows

$$\frac{C\boldsymbol{H}}{\boldsymbol{M}_0 T} = \frac{\hat{\mu}_0 \boldsymbol{m}_p \boldsymbol{H}}{3kT}$$

which is identical with the expression of β, Eq. (14-69), and which has been shown to be less than 0.5%. For small values of the argument,

$$\tanh a \approx a$$

With these approximations, Eq. (14-70) becomes for the case of paramagnetic materials, by reverting to $\boldsymbol{M}$ instead of $\boldsymbol{M}_s$,

$$\frac{\boldsymbol{M}}{\boldsymbol{M}_0} = \frac{C\boldsymbol{H}}{\boldsymbol{M}_0 T} + \frac{\theta \boldsymbol{M}}{\boldsymbol{M}_0 T}$$

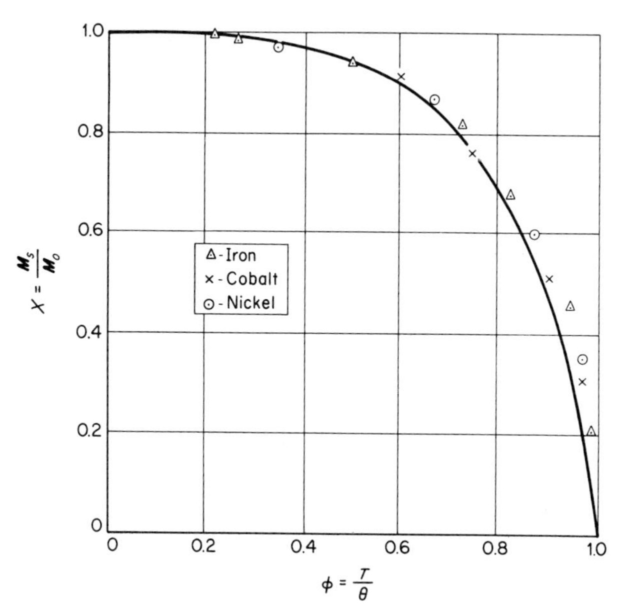

FIG. 14-6 Variation of fractional saturation magnetization M_s/M_0 with fractional temperature T/θ

and, on simplifying and rearranging the terms,

$$\boldsymbol{M} = \frac{C}{T - \theta}\boldsymbol{H} \tag{14-78}$$

We fall back on the proportionality between $\boldsymbol{M}$ and $\boldsymbol{H}$ derived in Section 14-7 under more simplified assumptions.

We can write with reference to Eq. (14-38) a new expression for the paramagnetic susceptibility, namely,

$$\chi_m = \frac{C}{T - \theta} \tag{14-79}$$

or, taking into account Eq. (14-72),

$$\chi_m = \frac{N\hat{\mu}_0 \boldsymbol{m}_p^2}{3k(T - \theta)} \tag{14-80}$$

If the substance remains paramagnetic down to a very low temperature we can put approximately $\theta = 0$, and Eq. (14-80) becomes identical with Eq. (14-37).

By rewriting Eq. (14-79) in terms of the reciprocal of χ_m, we obtain

$$\frac{1}{\chi_m} = \frac{T - \theta}{C} \tag{14-81}$$

a linear relation valid for $T > \theta$. The line has an intercept $T = \theta$ if plotted in the coordinate system T and $1/\chi_m$, Fig. 14-7, line 1. This relation becomes a simple proportionality for purely paramagnetic substances with $\theta = 0$,

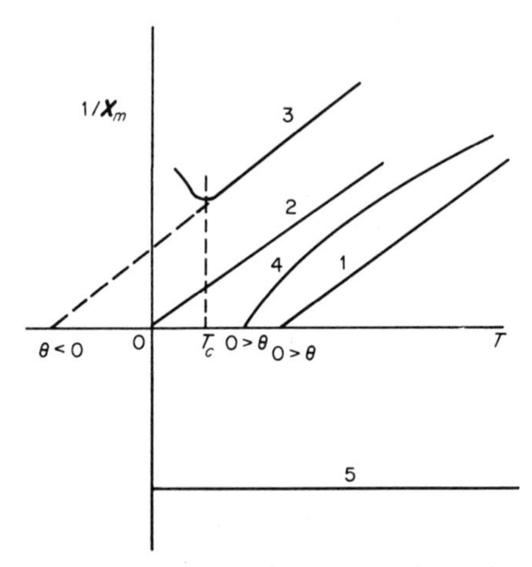

FIG. 14-7 Graphical representation of the variation of the reciprocal of susceptibility above the Curie and Néel points, θ and T_c, for various magnetic substances: 1. ferromagnetic, 2. paramagnetic, 3. antiferromagnetic, 4. ferrimagnetic, 5. diamagnetic (schematic)

line 2. For antiferromagnetic substances the onset of spontaneous magnetization is marked by a rather sudden decrease of χ_m below the critical temperature, or the Néel point T_c. On the other hand, the substance is paramagnetic above T_c; hence χ_m also decreases for $T > T_c$. That is, the magnetic susceptibility reaches its maximum at T_c, Fig. 14-8. The reciprocals $1/\chi_m$ can generally be fitted above T_c by an expression of the same form as Eq. (14-81) but with a negative value of θ, line 3, Fig. 14-7. The trend of the reciprocal of magnetic susceptibility above the Curie point in ferrimagnetic substances cannot be fitted by a straight line. The lines are generally curved downwards, line 4, Fig. 14-7.[10] Finally, the reciprocal of magnetic susceptibility becomes a large negative constant in diamagnetic substances, line 5, Fig. 14-7.

The variation of $1/\chi_m$ with temperature offers thus a convenient means of classifying all known aspects of magnetization.

14-16 Magnetic Domains. Hysteresis. One point so far has been left out of our considerations, and it must now be included. Since the Curie point of iron is so much above room temperature, why is a piece of ordinary iron devoid of magnetism? Why does it become a strong magnet only when placed in the field of a solenoid, as anyone familiar with the functioning of a

[10] For more details see *Molecular Science and Molecular Engineering*, p. 311ff., by A. R. von Hippel and contributors, The Technology Press, M.I.T., Cambridge, Mass., and Wiley, New York, 1959.

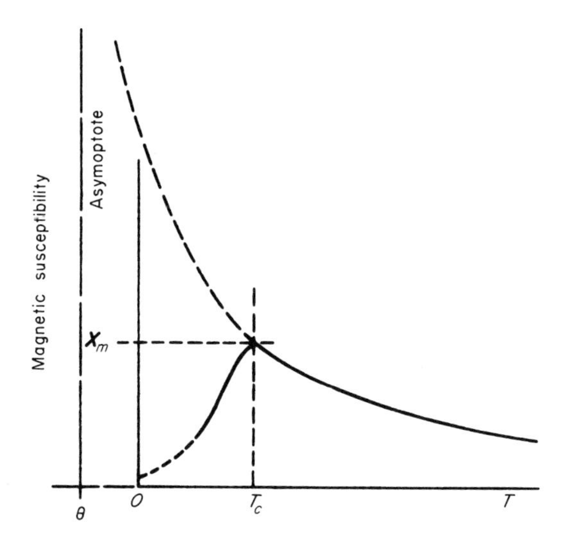

FIG. 14-8 Variation of magnetic susceptibility with temperature in a substance exhibiting antiferromagnetism (schematic)

doorbell assuredly knows? Yet the necessary current, which can conveniently be drawn from a flashlight battery, is beyond reasonable doubt much too weak to originate the forces of interaction which are responsible for ferromagnetism! To find a way out of this dilemma, the French physicist P. Weiss conceived in 1907 the notion of magnetic domains. Like the concept of dislocations, the concept of magnetic domains has since been proved to correspond to physical reality.[11] It has been shown that in the absence of an applied field, a single crystal of iron as well as grains in a polycrystalline aggregate are subdivided in several regions or domains. The elementary dipole moments are aligned parallel in each domain—as they should in a ferromagnetic state—but the directions of magnetization vary from domain to domain in such a way that the bulk magnetization is nil. This is shown schematically in Fig. 14-9a. The existence of domains can be revealed by coating a carefully polished surface of a sample with a suspension of fine particles of magnetite. The particles collect at the boundaries or walls between the domains, as indicated by an actual photograph taken under a microscope, Fig. 14-10. The collection of the particles is due to attraction produced by the magnetic field emerging from the sample along these boundaries. In an annealed single crystal of iron, the direction of magnetization coincides with one of the three cube axes. Since the vector of magnetization can point either way along each of these axes, there are six possible orientations. Four are indicated in Figs. 14-9a and 14-10. The domains are of plate-like shape. They are about 10^{-5} m thick for a crystal 10^{-2} m long. The small triangular domains at each end, Fig. 14-9a, are called closure domains. Their role will

[11] F. Bitter, *Physical Review*, p. 528, **38** (1931).

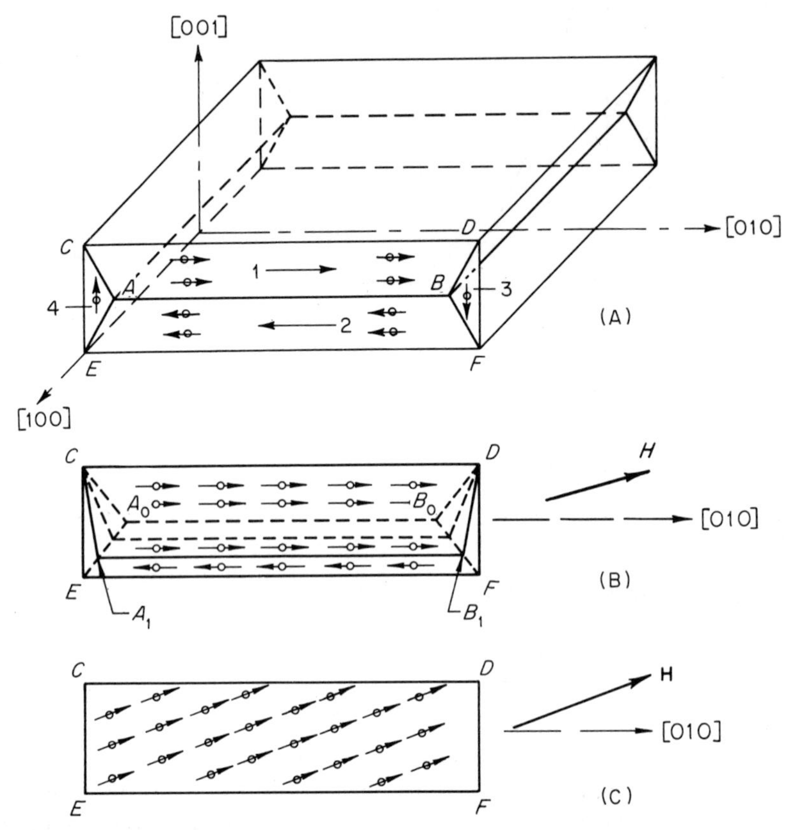

FIG. 14-9 (a) Magnetic domains in single crystal of iron. (b) Motion of domain walls *AB*, *AC*, *BD*, *AE*, and *BF*, and growth of the favorably oriented domain 1 in the initial stages of magnetization. (c) Rotation of the overgrown domain 1 at the final stage of magnetization (schematic)

become clear when we discuss the attraction exerted by a magnet on a piece of iron, Section 14-17. In an annealed polycrystalline aggregate the domains are also generally, but not necessarily, oriented in the directions of the cube axes of the grain.

The existence of domains not only explains why there is no bulk magnetization in the absence of an external field, but it also shows how magnetization is building up when the field is gradually applied. It also accounts for the nonlinear relationship between $\boldsymbol{M}$ and $\boldsymbol{H}$ during this buildup and for the appearance of hysteresis.[12]

Consider first the idealized case of a perfect single crystal, Fig. 14-9a. Let the field intensity make the smallest angle with the magnetization of domain 1.

[12] Domains have also been found in ferroelectric materials, and they contribute to the phenomenon of hysteresis, as pointed out on page 250, Section 13-11.

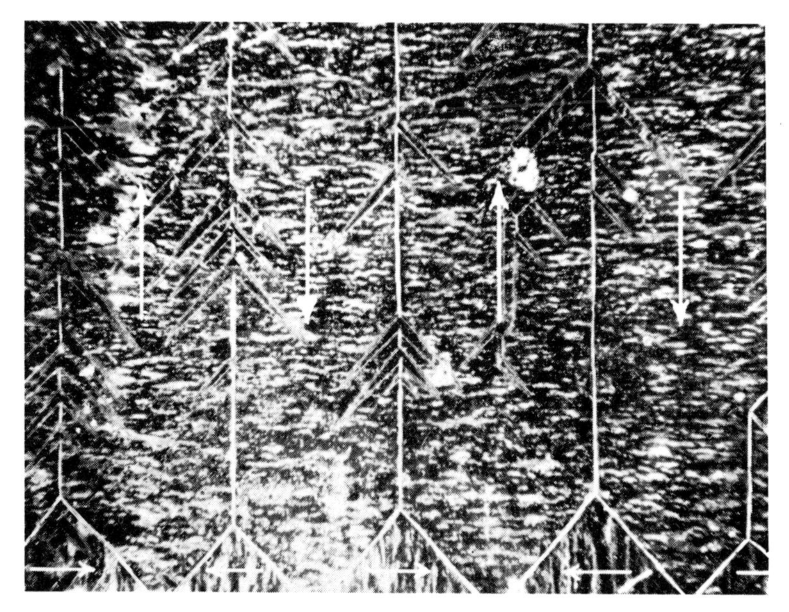

FIG. 14-10 Magnetic domains in iron observed under a microscope using Bitter's technique. (From "Magnetic Properties of Metals and Alloys," American Society for Metals, Cleveland, Ohio, 1959, by permission)

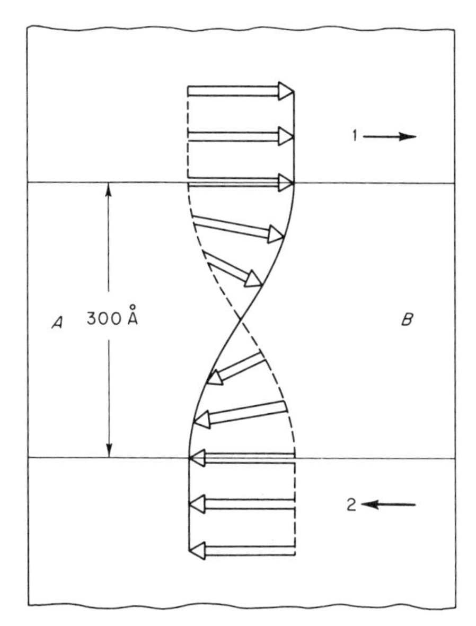

FIG. 14-11 Reorientation of elementary dipoles across a domain wall (after Kittel)

Then, on gradual application of the field intensity ***H***, the domain 1 will grow at the expense of other domains as shown in Fig. 14-9b. The phenomenon of growth can be best understood when we assume that the elementary magnetic dipoles in a wall separating two domains are passing from one orientation to another progressively rather than abruptly, Fig. 14-11. Since the field ***H*** has its largest component in the direction coinciding with the magnetization of domain 1, it will force the elementary dipole moments to align themselves with this magnetization, one after another. As a result, the wall will be pushed back, and domain 1 will grow at the expense of its neighbors. So will its own magnetization. In the ideal case, only a small and constant value of ***H*** would be necessary to keep this process going, and the process itself would be perfectly reversible. In reality, the motion of the wall is accompanied by an elastic deformation due to magnetostriction, and there are nonmagnetic inclusions and imperfections in real crystals. As a result, the field intensity ***H*** must be continuously increased if the process of magnetization is to be kept going. There is, furthermore, unavoidable dissipation of energy in overcoming the obstacles to motion, put up by the inclusions, so the process is no longer reversible. Yet, as domain 1 grows in size, the net magnetization of the crystal increases faster than the applied field, and the same is true of a polycrystalline piece of iron, where several domains, more favored by the field than their neighbors, grow simultaneously in size.

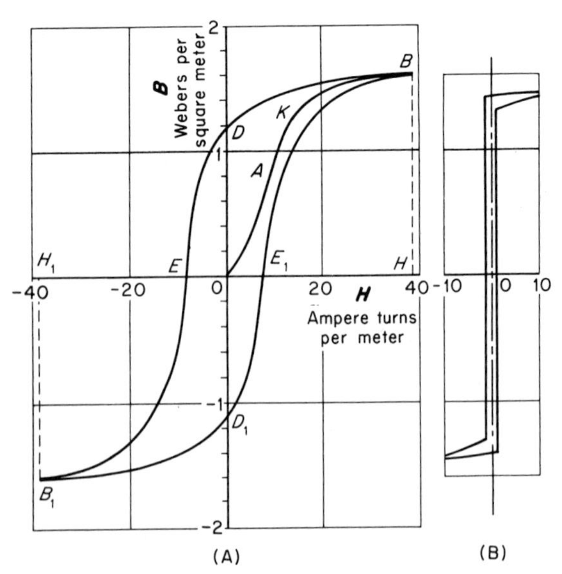

FIG. 14-12 Typical hysteresis loop: (a) for pure iron; (b) for 65 Permalloy annealed with field present

In Fig. 14-12a this stage of magnetization is represented by the segment *OA*. In making actual measurements, it is more convenient to plot the directly measurable quantity $\boldsymbol{B}$ rather than $\boldsymbol{M}$. The latter can be obtained from the former by means of Eq. (14-39), namely,

$$\boldsymbol{M} = \frac{\boldsymbol{B}}{\hat{\mu}_0} - \boldsymbol{H} \tag{14-82}$$

At the approach to knee K, Fig. 14-12a, the process of growth in the favored domains is essentially finished. There are now several large domains in the polycrystalline sample and one single domain in the single crystal. An additional increase of induction $\boldsymbol{B}$ and bulk magnetization $\boldsymbol{M}$ in the polycrystalline sample can occur only if the magnetizations in the favored domains are forced to rotate away from their preferred cube directions and align themselves with the field intensity $\boldsymbol{H}$. Such a coercion requires a substantial increase of $\boldsymbol{H}$, as will be explained below. The attainment of the induction $\boldsymbol{B}_s$ corresponding to the saturation magnetization $\boldsymbol{M}_s$ is thus characterized by the appearance of a knee and by a considerable decrease of slope in the $\boldsymbol{B}$-$\boldsymbol{H}$ diagram, portion AKB, Fig. 14-12a.

If now the field intensity $\boldsymbol{H}$ is reversed, the $\boldsymbol{B}$-$\boldsymbol{H}$ curve does not retrace its initial path $OAKB$. The induction $\boldsymbol{B}$ lags behind $\boldsymbol{H}$ just as the polarization $\boldsymbol{P}$ lagged behind the electric field intensity $\boldsymbol{E}$, Section 13-11. This is the phenomenon of hysteresis, which has been known to exist in ferromagnetism long before it had been revealed in ferroelectricity. When the field intensity $\boldsymbol{H}$ falls back to zero, there is still more than 80% of the induction $\boldsymbol{B}_s$ left in the sample, point D, Fig. 14-12a. To reduce the induction to zero during the process of demagnetization, a coercive field OE must be applied. The single crystal and the grains in the polycrystalline sample are now split again into several conflicting domains, each of them realigned in the direction of one of the cube axes of the crystal. The configuration is not necessarily, and most likely is not, the same as at point O, since the process itself is irreversible. It is also conceivable that some of the domains favored by the reverse sign of the field intensity have already begun to grow before the total magnetization had been reduced to zero. These domains will continue to grow, and eventually they will end up by aligning themselves with the field intensity as $\boldsymbol{H}$ reaches the value OH_1. The saturation point B_1 will thus be obtained—a centrosymmetrical replica of point B. The hysteresis curve can now be completed by reversing the field again in its initial direction, branch $B_1D_1E_1B$, Fig. 14-12a. The general shape of the hysteresis loop can be retraced several times by alternating the magnetizing current, and the field intensity $\boldsymbol{H}$, without ever falling back to point O.

Although the above picture gives only the most salient features of the magnetization process,[13] it is sufficient to describe the behavior and properties of some important ferromagnetic materials. As will appear below, the

[13] For more detail consult, for example, J. J. Becker, "Metallurgical Structure and Magnetic Properties," in monograph *Magnetic Properties of Metals and Alloys*, American Society of Metals, Cleveland, 1939.

concept of hysteresis loop plays indeed a major role in the differentiation of these materials.

14-17 Demagnetization. Ferromagnetic Materials. According to Fig. 14-12a, a fully magnetized piece of iron should retain about 80% of its saturation magnetization when it is removed from a magnetic field, namely, at points D and D_1 of the hysteresis loop. Actually, the remanent magnetization of pure iron is rather small. We infer that the specimen has reverted spontaneously to a configuration of several conflicting magnetic domains akin to the arrangement depicted in Fig. 14-10. The inference is correct but by no means obvious. From the considerations of Section 14-14, we would rather expect a single domain to be more stable by virtue of the cooperative action of all elementary magnetic dipoles. These considerations, however, overlook the conditions at the boundary of the domain. There is no simple way to account *quantitatively* for the conditions existing at the boundary of a magnetized body without drawing in the general concepts of the field theory developed in standard textbooks on electricity and magnetism. For our present purposes such an approach is not warranted, and a qualitative description will suffice. We see that in the special case of Fig. 14-13a the magnetic dipoles

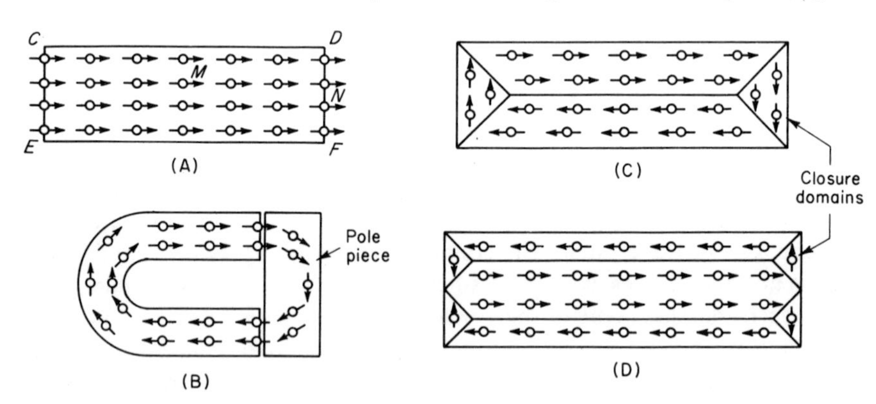

FIG. 14-13 Magnetized (a) and (b) and demagnetized (c) and (d) states of a ferromagnetic material (schematic)

are parallel to the faces CD and EF and perpendicular to the faces CE and DF. The magnetic dipoles that are adjacent to the faces CD and EF contribute little or nothing to the field outside the magnetized body. A test loop placed near the boundary will hardly be aware of their existence. The same is not true of the magnetic dipoles near the faces CE and DF. These dipoles contribute fully to the outside magnetic field. One way to account for the above difference is to consider that a magnetic dipole, such as N, near the faces CE and DF is less favorably surrounded by its neighbors than a magnetic dipole, such as M, near the faces CD and EF. In particular, there are no magnetic dipoles in front of N to offset the action of the magnetic dipoles in the rear of

N. We can surmise that, by being thus less favorably surrounded by its neighbors, the magnetic dipole *N* will be in a less stable state than the magnetic dipole *M* and in an even less stable state than any of the magnetic dipoles embedded in the domain.

To gain greater stability, the magnetic dipole of the *N* variety will tend conceivably to acquire additional neighbors, much like the molecules on the surface of a liquid which tend to satisfy their needs for additional bonding by the process of adsorption and wettability discussed in Section 7-5. This tendency explains the attraction which a magnetized bar of iron exerts on other pieces of iron in its surrounding. On being attached to the faces *CE* and *DF*, these pieces reorient their own domains—by a process of growth and rotation similar to that described in Section 14-16—to match as nearly as possible the orientation of the magnetic dipoles in the bar. If the bar is shaped in the form of a horseshoe, a single piece of iron, called a pole piece, can accomplish the matching at both ends, as shown schematically in Fig. 14-13b. Under these circumstances even a bar of pure iron can conceivably be maintained as a single domain. In practice, pole pieces are used to prevent demagnetization of permanent magnets, caused mainly by thermal agitation of magnetic dipoles near the surface.

In the absence of a pole piece, a magnetized bar of iron can confer greater stability to the magnetic dipoles adjacent to the surface by forming *closure* domains. These are small, triangularly shaped prisms in which the elementary magnetic dipoles have tilted from their original orientation to align themselves parallel to the surface, Fig. 14-13, c and d. As explained below in connection with permanent magnets, such a protective tilting requires expenditure of energy. Furthermore, it must be accompanied by the splitting of the single domain in at least two, and generally more, opposing domains. Additional energy must then be expended to maintain the spiral configuration of the elementary magnetic dipoles, Fig. 14-11, in the wall separating adjacent domains. The result, of course, is a nearly total loss of bulk magnetization, or *demagnetization*, which thus appears to be a more stable condition in pure iron than magnetization. Yet the margin of stability cannot be very large, since even a weak external field suffices to tip the balance. Evidently, it does not take much less energy to build closure domains and domain walls in a demagnetized state than it does to maintain a single domain within the currently prescribed shapes and sizes of magnetized bodies.

Permanent Magnets. The ease with which pure iron can be magnetized and demagnetized is clearly indicated by the small value—less than 10 ampere-turns per meter—of the coercive field intensity, Fig. 14-12a. It is only when the overgrown single domain is to be tilted in the direction of the applied field, Fig. 14-9c, that the value of $\boldsymbol{H}$ has to be substantially increased, reaching about 40 amp-turns/m at points B and B_1, Fig. 14-12a. Even this figure is still a small fraction of the coercive field intensities, of 10,000 amp-turns/m and more, characterizing the behavior of permanent magnets. A high value of coercive field implies, of course, great resistance to demagnetization. It is therefore a desirable feature in permanent magnets. How can it be achieved and what is it due to? There is no simple answer to this question. Much depends on the chemical composition as well as the mechanical, thermal, and magnetic treatments to which the material is subjected during fabrication. In many cases even the basic phenomena are not yet fully understood. In recent years, however, much attention has been given to the production of improved magnets from small particles. Here, at least, the situation is clear in regard to two major factors: the domain structure and directionality, or crystal anisotropy, of magnetization.

To take up the domain structure first, it seems obvious that any piece of iron that has been somehow prevented from splitting in two or more domains becomes automatically a permanent magnet. The governing factors here are shape and size. A long, narrow needle magnetized in the axial direction is little affected by the boundary conditions at both ends. Also, by being sufficiently narrow it can hardly harbor a domain wall of any extent. On both counts then a narrow particle—several microns long—is expected to be a natural, permanent magnet. The problem is not so much how to produce such particles, but rather how to aggregate and compact them so that they all point in the same direction. If this could be done with a degree of compactness approaching only half the density of ordinary iron, permanent magnets could be built apparently only one-fifth the size of the currently available products for the same applications. Also such magnets would exhibit no less than 60% of the saturation induction and would resist coercive fields much in excess of 100,000 amp-turns/m.[14] As explained below, the directionality of magnetization should be the main reason for their high resistance.

To introduce the concept of directionality, we observe that the only way these magnets could be demagnetized would be by having the domain in each particle rotate at least 90° from the common direction of magnetization. In doing so, the magnetic dipoles would have to be aligned successively with various crystallographic directions. If the particle were a single crystal—as it most likely will be—the applied field intensities would be those corresponding to the magnetic saturation $\boldsymbol{M}_s$ in Fig. 14-14. It is seen that these intensities vary considerably with crystallographic directions. The magnetic field intensity is very small, in fact a minimum, in the direction of the cube axis [100], and it is very large in the directions of the face diagonal [110] and the cube diagonal [111]. In the BCC iron, [100] is the easiest and [111] is the hardest direction of magnetization. In the FCC nickel the situation is reversed. Cobalt has a HCP structure, and the easiest magnetization here is in the direction of the height of the unit cell.

[14] R. M. Bozorth, "The Physics of Magnetic Materials," in monograph "*Science of Engineering Materials*," J. E. Goldman, Ed., Wiley, New York, 1957.

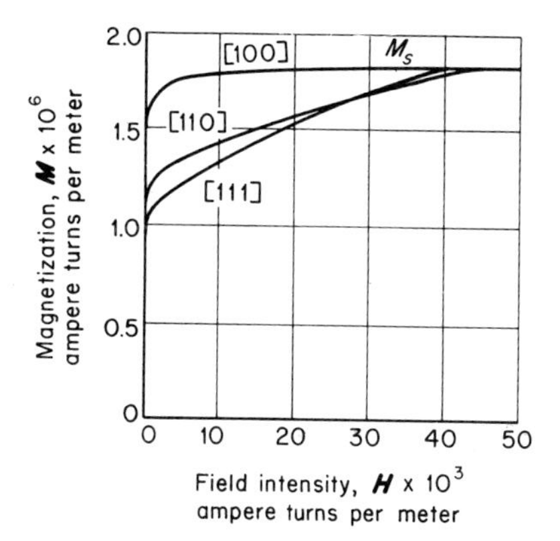

FIG. 14-14 Magnetization of iron single crystal in the [100], [110], and [111] crystallographic directions

It is now clear why a demagnetization of a small-particle magnet would require such large coercive fields. The domains are naturally aligned with the easiest direction of magnetization. To rotate them 90° would mean pushing them past one of the hardest directions of magnetization. This is not likely to occur in any one particle—even near the boundary— without the intervention of a commensurate external field. For all practical purposes a small particle magnet would thus be truly permanent.

Transformer Core Material. Large remanent inductions and high coercive fields have been shown to be attractive features in permanent magnets. However, they also entail large hysteresis loops with the attending dissipation of energy, or hysteresis losses. (In standard textbooks on electricity and magnetism the dissipation of energy is shown to be proportional to the area of the hysteresis loop.) On account of these losses, large hysteresis loops must be avoided in the cores of power transformers. The main function of the core material is to channel the electric power from high-tension windings to low-tension windings by electromagnetic induction. Since alternating current is used, the core material goes at each cycle through a hysteresis loop and dissipates energy. Considering that the annual production of electric power in the United States is estimated to be of the order of 10^{12} kW-hr,[15] a dissipation of even a fraction of 1% in hysteresis losses represents a considerable waste of energy. This explains the sustained effort made by metallurgists over a number of years to produce transformer steels with smaller and smaller hysteresis areas. Considerable progress was achieved in 1930 when, by a special technique of rolling, the easy direction of magnetization was made to coincide in the polycrystalline aggregate of the material with the intended direction of the magnetic field. Compared to the year 1900, the hysteresis

[15] See, for example, Chauncey Starr, *Atomic Energy in Industry*, Section 38, National Industrial Conference Board, New York, 1952.

losses have been thus reduced at least tenfold. Iron-silicon alloys of various compositions have been found to be the most suitable material for this rather exacting treatment.

High-Permeability Material. Another kind of material that has undergone an equally spectacular development during the first half of this century is an alloy of the iron-nickel family used in communication engineering for detection and amplification of weak signals. The desired feature here is a large increment of induction caused by a small increment of the field intensity, more specifically, a high value of permeability $\bar{\mu} = B/H$ in low fields; hence the commercial designation of Permalloys given to this type of material. The narrow, rectangular shape of the hysteresis loop, Fig. 14-12b, is quite typical for this sort of material. The narrowness and steepness of this loop is particularly revealing by comparison with the hysteresis loop of pure iron, Fig. 14-12a.

14-18 Ferrites. Despite their outstanding performances, ferromagnetic materials have one common shortcoming. They are essentially metallic conductors and, as such, are subject to inductive stray currents in variable magnetic fields—the so-called eddy currents. As explained in standard textbooks on electricity and magnetism, eddy currents not only dissipate energy but also dampen mechanical and electrical vibrations. They thus reduce considerably the usefulness of ferromagnetic materials for high-frequency applications: television tubes, memory devices, high-speed switches, etc. Ferrimagnetic materials, and, in particular, ferrites, are basically free of this shortcoming. Ferrites are refractory materials in which nearly all of the valence electrons can be considered as being tied up in an ionic bonding.[16] They are thus unavailable for conduction and unable to generate eddy currents. The chemical structure of a ferrite molecule can be viewed as a compound made up of the ferric oxide Fe_2O_3 and an oxide of a divalent metal M, in accordance with the formula $MO.Fe_2O_3$. Here, M stands for transition elements such as Mn, Co, and Ni, including the divalent Fe and regular elements such as Cu and Zn.

The dependence of ferrimagnetism on the spin dipole moments of the constituent ions and on their configuration in the crystal structure of ferrites is much better understood than a similar dependence of ferromagnetism on the metallic state. It is thus possible not only to make reasonable predictions regarding the bulk magnetization of natural ferrites but also to anticipate improved magnetic properties in artificially made ferrites. This can be shown as follows:

Ferrites belong to a face-centered cubic lattice in which the pattern and the size of the unit cell are determined largely by the configuration of the big

[16] The small fraction that does not contribute to ionic bonding accounts for the phenomenon of semiconductivity, discussed in Chapter 15.

oxygen ions, or cations. Let us focus our immediate attention on the detail of structure represented in Fig. 14-15. It is confined essentially to $\frac{1}{8}$ of the unit cell.

There are two kinds of sites in this structure that are occupied by the metallic cations M^{++} and Fe^{+++}: site *A*, which is surrounded tetrahedrally

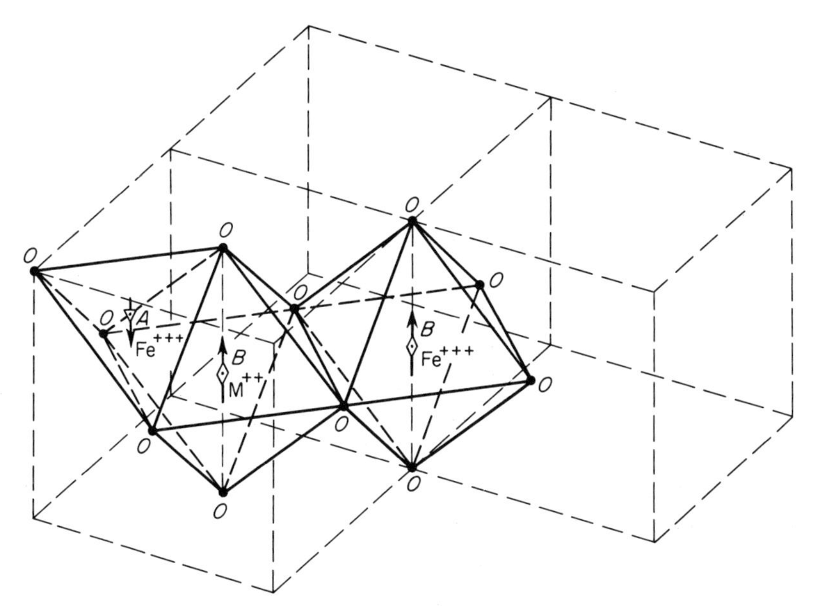

FIG. 14-15 Part of a unit cell of a ferrite $M^{++}Fe_2{}^{+++}O_4{}^{--}$ showing tetrahedral (*A*) and octahedral (*B*) sites of Fe^{+++} with opposite spins, and remainder of octahedral sites (*B*) occupied by a bivalent ion M^{++} with oxygen atoms O in the FCC arrangement

by oxygen ions, and site *B*, which is surrounded octahedrally by oxygen ions. There are two sites *B* occupied for one site *A*.

According to theoretical considerations, which we must omit, the spin dipole moments of ions at sites *A* should be antiparallel to the spin dipole moments of ions at sites *B*. Also, the two ferric ions Fe^{+++} should be antiparallel to each other. These two conditions prescribe that one of the ferric ions be at site *A* and the other at site *B*. Thus, their contributions to magnetization cancel each other, and, as a result, the magnetic dipole of the molecule $MO.Fe_2O_3$ is simply equal to the spin dipole moment of the divalent ion M.

The spin dipole moments of the pertinent divalent ions are shown in column four, Table 14-2. It is of interest to note that these moments decrease by one Bohr magneton as the atomic numbers of the elements increase by one unit. The same, of course, is true of the molecular magnetic dipoles of the corresponding ferrites. Hence, if the molecular magnetic dipoles of various ferrites are determined from their saturation magnetization, they should plot as a straight line against the atomic number of the divalent ions contained in the ferrites. This conclusion has been reasonably well substantiated by experiment Fig. 14-16.

A more practical consequence of the theory bears on the possible improvement of magnetic properties of existing ferrites. According to Fig. 14-15, if

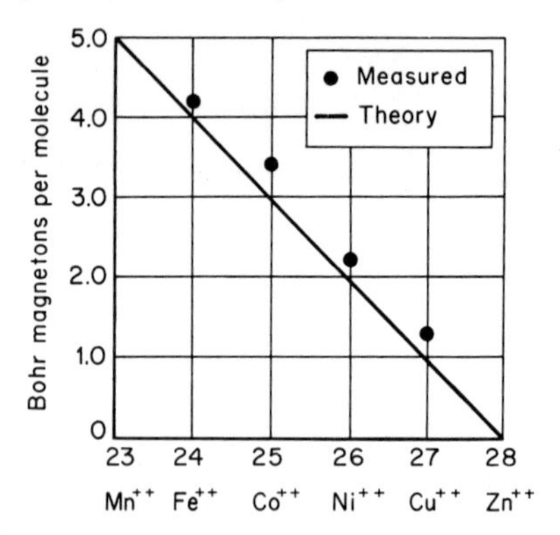

FIG. 14-16 Plot of theoretical and measured molecular moments of ferrites of iron group elements versus the atomic numbers of divalent ions (after R. M. Bozorth)

some of the antiparallel ions at sites *A* could be replaced by ions devoid of any spin magnetic moment, the magnetic dipole of the molecule—and hence the bulk magnetization of the material—should be increased. This conclusion, too, has been confirmed experimentally by mixing the nonmagnetic ferrite $ZnO.Fe_2O_3$ with the magnetic ferrite $MnO.Fe_2O_3$ in the ratio of 1:9 and firing the mixture into a single ceramic body. The spin magnetic moment of Zn is zero, and the divalent zinc ion occupies the *A* sites instead of the *B* sites in zinc ferrite. By replacing 10% of the antiparallel ions at sites *A*, it has thus caused—as foreseen—a 10% increase of the magnetic dipole of the molecule, bringing it from 5 to 5.5 Bohr magnetons. Although not spectacular, this improvement is significant in view of the fact that the bulk magnetization of ferrites is substantially lower than the bulk magnetization of most ferromagnetic materials.

14-19 Summary. Magnetization owes its origin to the orbital motion of electrons around the nucleus and to the spin motion of electrons, protons, and neutrons in the atom. In both instances the response of the matter to an applied magnetic field is determined in terms of a *magnetic moment*—a vector quantity defined by means of an electric current flowing in a closed loop. On the atomic scale, magnetic moments are expressed in *Bohr magneton* units.

The summation of orbital and spin magnetic moments is subject to the restrictive rules of quantum mechanics. As a result, some atoms and molecules have a net magnetic moment and some have not. This moment is called *permanent magnetic dipole*, $\boldsymbol{m}_p$.

Placed in a magnetic field, the permanent magnetic dipole tends to align itself with the *magnetic field intensity*, $\boldsymbol{H}$, and to add its contribution to the action of $\boldsymbol{H}$ on the *magnetic induction*, $\boldsymbol{B}$. This manifestation is called *paramagnetism*. In dilute gases thermal agitation hampers total alignment, and only a fraction β of the N permanent magnetic dipoles $\boldsymbol{m}_p$ per unit volume makes a contribution to $\boldsymbol{H}$. This contribution is called *induced magnetization* $\boldsymbol{M}$—an analog to the induced polarization $\boldsymbol{P}$. $\boldsymbol{M}$ is expressed in the same units as $\boldsymbol{H}$ and it is *proportional* to $\boldsymbol{H}$. The coefficient of proportionality is called magnetic susceptibility, χ_m. Like its dielectric counterpart χ it is a small (dimensionless) fraction for most substances. The proportionality between $\boldsymbol{M}$ and $\boldsymbol{H}$ has been extended experimentally to many condensed states. It also includes the case of the much weaker *diamagnetism*—a manifestation of the emf induced in the substance by the magnetic field and opposed to $\boldsymbol{H}$.

For engineering applications, the proportionality between $\boldsymbol{M}$ and $\boldsymbol{H}$ is converted into *proportionality between* $\boldsymbol{B}$ *and* $\boldsymbol{H}$. The coefficient of proportionality is called here the *magnetic permeability* $\hat{\mu}$. Like the dielectric constant $\boldsymbol{\varepsilon}$, $\hat{\mu}$ is not strictly speaking a material property, since it includes the conversion factor of $\boldsymbol{H}$ to $\boldsymbol{B}$ in a vacuum—called the magnetic permeability in vacuum $\hat{\mu}_0$.

The proportionality between $\boldsymbol{M}$ and $\boldsymbol{H}$ is invalid in the case of *spontaneous magnetization*. Unlike induced magnetization, spontaneous magnetization subsists in the absence of an applied magnetic field. It owes its origin to the interaction of spin *dipole moments* formed by the unpaired spins of inner shells in the transition elements. Depending on the magnitude and sign of interactions, we distinguish between *ferromagnetism*, *ferrimagnetism*, and *antiferromagnetism*. Metallic iron, nickel, and cobalt are typical representatives of ferromagnetic materials; magnetite and closely related minerals called *ferrites* belong to ferrimagnetic materials. Finally, some metals and minerals exhibit antiferromagnetism. Spontaneous magnetization reverts to paramagnetism above a critical temperature called *Curie point*, also referred to as *Néel point* in regard to antiferromagnetism.

Magnetization decreases with increase of temperature. The exact relationship depends on the nature of the magnetization and represents a generalization of the original *Curie's law* for paramagnetic substances.

Like dielectric polarization, magnetization is accompanied by elastic deformation called *magnetostriction*—a property utilized effectively in ultrasonic transducers. However, the most important applications of magnetism are associated with the phenomenon of *hysteresis* in ferromagnetic and ferrimagnetic materials. Permanent magnet materials, transformer core materials, and high permeability materials are clearly differentiated by the size and shape of the hysteresis loop and by the magnitudes of *remanent* induction and *coercive* field intensity. Closely related to hysteresis is the behavior of *magnetic domains*—regions within one grain or several grains in which the permanent magnetic dipoles are aligned with one of the several crystallographic directions of *easy magnetization*. The growth and rotation of magnetic domains are at the heart of the process of magnetization. Conversely, their multiplication with the attending formation of *domain walls* and *closure domains* accounts for demagnetization.

Ferromagnetic materials are endowed with a much higher *saturation* magnetization than ferrites. Yet, by being minerals, ferrites are much less prone to *eddy currents* and on that account they are more adaptable to high-frequency engineering applications. Their magnetic behavior is also more predictable, because the dependence of ferrimagnetism on crystal structure is much better understood than a similar dependence of ferromagnetism on the metallic state.

References

ELEMENTARY

1. F. Bitter, *Currents, Fields, and Particles*, Wiley, New York, 1956.

ADVANCED

1. A. R. von Hippel, *Dialectrics and Waves*, Wiley, New York, 1954.
2. A. R. von Hippel, *Molecular Science and Molecular Engineering*, Wiley, New York, 1959.
3. *Magnetic Properties of Metals and Alloys*, monograph, American Society of Metals, Cleveland, 1959.
4. R. M. Bozorth, "The Physics of Magnetic Materials," *Science of Engineering Materials*, J. E. Goldman, Ed., Wiley, New York, 1957.
5. "Sixth Symposium on Magnetism and Magnetic Materials," *J. Appl. Phys.* (Supplement), **32**, 1S-396S.

Problems

14-1 Assuming the validity of Eq. (14-37) for solid sodium, determine the magnetic dipole moment $\boldsymbol{m}_p$ of the sodium atom from the value of $\chi_m = 0.5 \times 10^{-6}$ at room temperature.

14-2 Assuming the validity of Eq. (14-66) for solid beryllium, determine α in the above equation from the value of $\chi/\rho = -1.0 \times 10^{-9}$ m³/kg at 20°C.

14-3 Compute the fraction β of elementary magnetic dipoles contributing to magnetization of metallic iron, cobalt, and nickel, using data of Tables 14-2 and 14-3.

14-4 Compute the saturation magnetization of nickel at room temperature, using data of Table 14-3 and Fig. 14-6.

14-5 Using the generalized Curie law, Eq. (14-81), compute the magnetic susceptibility of the antiferromagnetic MnO at 200°C if χ_m at 20°C is 4.15×10^{-4} and the "Curie temperature" $\Theta = -610$°K.

14-6 According to Fig. 14-12, 10 amp-turns/m are sufficient to raise the induction B in ordinary iron from 0 to 1.0 Wb/m², whereas more than 30 amp-turns/m are necessary to bring it to the saturation value of 1.3 Wb/m². Why?

14-7 In Fig. 14-13d, let l be the length of the crystal and d the width of the domains. The creation of a domain wall requires an energy W of about 10^{-3} J/m², whereas the creation of a closure domain requires an energy, W, of about 10^4 J/m^3. Show that in order to minimize the energy of demagnetization, i.e., the sum of the energies expended on creation of domain walls and closure domains, the number of domains must be such that

$$d = \sqrt{\frac{2wl}{W}} \approx 0.45 \times 10^{-3} \sqrt{l}$$

(Hint: The energy of demagnetization is $(l - d)hW/d + (hd/2)w$, where h is the thickness of the crystal.)

14-8 What happens if h in Problem 14-7 is smaller than d?

14-9 What would happen to the magnitude of the magnetization if the Zn ion in the nonmagnetic $ZnO.Fe_2O_3$ replaced Mn instead of Fe in the $MnO.Fe_2O_3$ ferrite?

15 / ELECTRICAL PROPERTIES: RESISTIVITY

Motion of charged elementary particles in solids is responsible for the manifestation of electrical resistivity in much the same way as the motion of uncharged particles in fluids is responsible for the manifestation of viscosity discussed in Chapter 12. Here, as there, the statistical nature of the motion calls for a study which in all rigor should utilize methods of thermodynamics and statistical mechanics not available at this level of presentation. Nonetheless, the dependence of electrical resistivity on structure—in the sense indicated in Chapter 5—can be discussed to a large extent independently of the factor of "motion." This discussion provides a useful insight into the origin of electrical resistivity, particularly in the case of semiconductors.

15-1 Manifestations. It is known from elementary physics that a metallic filament connected to the poles of a battery or any other source of electric current becomes hot and incandescent and ends up by melting if the current is high enough. This is one of the simplest and the more obvious manifestations of the resistance materials offer to the passage of an electric current. It is being exploited for heating and illuminating purposes in a variety of domestic and industrial applications: toasters, ranges, furnaces, incandescent lamps, etc. In a broader sense, resistance to an electric current appears whenever the motion of a charged particle in an electric field is being impeded by the motions of or collisions with other charged or neutral particles. Its manifestations then can vary from the glow of neon lamps to the controlling action of photocells, vacuum tubes, and transistors. The more recent manifestations have to do with problems such as direct energy conversion (in solar batteries), stimulation and amplification of one kind of energy by another (in masers and lasers[1]), and control of thermonuclear reactions for peaceful uses (in hydrogen plasma[2]).

In all these manifestations the statistical character of motion of the charged particle plays an important role. However, in solid conductors and semiconductors, with which we are solely concerned here, we can overlook the statistical details and use instead a nonstatistical model which, albeit

[1] Devices whose names derive from the first letters of words: *m*icrowave or *l*ight *a*mplification by *s*timulated *e*mission of *r*adiation.

[2] The word "plasma" was introduced in 1920 by the American physicist Irving Langmuir to denote a collection of electrons and positive ions in a gas discharge such that the bulk electrical neutrality is preserved.

crude, is sufficient for our purposes. This is so because in these solids the carriers of electric current are electrons alone, and their interaction with the relatively stable and rigid ionic lattice can be approximated to some extent by viewing the interaction as a collision between individual small electrons and individual large ions. We begin by applying this concept to metallic conductors and we then extend it to semiconductors.

15-2 Ohm's Law Derived. It was pointed out in Chapter 1 that elements belonging to the first three groups of the periodic table achieve structural stability by letting their valence electrons roam freely through the crystal lattice. Since electrons are negatively charged particles, their motion corresponds to a flow of electricity, or electric current. In the absence of an externally applied potential difference, there are on the average as many electrons wandering through a given cross section of the conductor in one direction as there are in the opposite direction. Hence the net current is zero. However, when a potential difference ΔV is applied to the conductor, the electrons acquire an acceleration. According to the customary sign convention, this acceleration is oppositely directed to the field intensity $\boldsymbol{E}$ produced in the conductor by the difference of potential ΔV. A common drift velocity is thus imparted to all electrons, and as a result there is a net electric current flowing in the conductor. Despite the initial acceleration the current is steady, because lattice interactions impede a gradual buildup of the drift velocity. This can be readily understood in terms of the "collision" approximation referred to previously. If we assume that the electrons, in colliding with the large stationary ions, are scattered in all directions, then on the average the common drift velocity is reduced to zero after each collision. True, the drift velocity can be built up anew before the next collision occurs, since the applied field provides the necessary impulse. After many consecutive collisions, however, it finally settles down to a steady state value. To compute this value we make use of Newton's law of equality between the impulse produced by the applied field and the momentum gained by the electron in the average time interval, the so-called *mean free time*, between collisions. We denote this time by t_c. Let m be the mass of the electron and e its charge. Calling v_c the common drift velocity, we then have the expressions mv_c for the gain of momentum and $e\boldsymbol{E}$ for the force acting on the electron. Since this force acts during the mean free time t_c, the equality of momentum and impulse yields

$$mv_c = e\boldsymbol{E}.t_c \tag{15-1}$$

The mean free time t_c is of the order of 10^{-14} sec for most metals. With the knowledge of m, e, and t_c, the drift velocity v_c can be computed for each value of $\boldsymbol{E}$ using Eq. (15-1). Instead of v_c it is more practical to seek an equivalent expression for the macroscopically measurable electric current $\boldsymbol{I}$.

If N is the number of electrons per unit volume and A is the cross-sectional area of the conductor, then NAv_c is the number of electrons in volume Av_c. This, however, is the same as the number of electrons passing in unit time through the cross-sectional area A. Hence the charge passing through this area in unit time, or the current $\boldsymbol{I}$, is

$$\boldsymbol{I} = eNAv_c \tag{15-2}$$

Substituting in Eq. (15-1) the value of v_c provided by Eq. (15-2), we have

$$\frac{m\boldsymbol{I}}{eNA} = e\boldsymbol{E}t_c$$

or, rearranging the terms,

$$\boldsymbol{I}\frac{m}{e^2NAt_c} = \boldsymbol{E} \tag{15-3}$$

Instead of $\boldsymbol{E}$ we can also write

$$\boldsymbol{E} = \frac{\Delta V}{L} \tag{15-4}$$

where L is the length of the conductor. From this, after another rearrangement of terms, we get

$$\boldsymbol{I}\left(\frac{m}{e^2Nt_c}\right)\left(\frac{L}{A}\right) = \Delta V \tag{15-5}$$

The expressions in parentheses being constant for a given conductor, we see that the voltage drop ΔV is proportional to current $\boldsymbol{I}$—in accordance with the known law from elementary physics, which the German physicist G. S. Ohm (1789–1854) established experimentally.

15-3 Resistivity. Comparison of Eq. (15-5) with the more familiar expression of Ohm's law, namely,

$$\boldsymbol{IR} = \Delta V \tag{15-6}$$

shows that the resistance $\boldsymbol{R}$ of the conductor is defined as follows:

$$\boldsymbol{R} = \frac{m}{e^2Nt_c}\frac{L}{A} \tag{15-7}$$

The dimensions of $\boldsymbol{R}$ in MKSQ units are

$$[R] = \left[\frac{\text{kg m}^3}{\text{Q}^2\text{ sec}}\frac{\text{m}}{\text{m}^2}\right] = \left[\frac{\text{kg m}^2}{\text{Q}^2\text{ sec}}\right]$$

A unit of $\boldsymbol{R}$ is called 1 ohm.

According to Eq. (15-7), the resistance $\boldsymbol{R}$ depends on the dimensions of the conductor, but the quantity

$$\rho = \frac{\boldsymbol{R}A}{L} = \frac{m}{e^2Nt_c} \tag{15-8}$$

does not. ρ is called the *electrical resistivity.* It is a characteristic property of the material of which the conductor is made. The dimensions of ρ are

$$[\rho] = \left[\frac{\text{kg m}^3}{\text{Q}^2\ \text{sec}}\right] = [\text{ohm m}] \tag{15-9}$$

Conductivity. The reciprocal of electrical resistivity is called electrical conductivity. It is frequently designated by the Greek letter σ. Thus

$$\sigma = \frac{1}{\rho} = \frac{L}{RA} \tag{15-10}$$

The dimensions of σ obviously are $\text{Q}^2\ \text{sec/kg m}^3$ or $\text{ohm}^{-1}\ \text{m}^{-1}$.

Range of Variation. Values of electrical resistivity of metallic elements measured at 0°C range from 1.51×10^{-8} ohm m for silver to 109×10^{-8} ohm m for bismuth, Table 15-1, column 2. Significantly, the highest values are exhibited by elements whose metallic behavior, as pointed out in Chapter 1, is at variance with their positions in the periodic table.

Computed values of electrical resistivity for monovalent metals, Ag, Cu, Na, etc., are listed in column 3. They have been obtained from Eq. (15-8), as shown in the illustrative example, Section 15-4. The mean free time t_c figuring in this equation derives from statistical considerations which must be deferred to a later course.[3] It is seen that the agreement between computation and measurement is best for sodium, presumably because in sodium the basic assumption of the theory, to wit that all valence electrons contribute to conduction, is best fulfilled.

Effect of Temperature. According to Eq. (15-8), the electrical resistivity will depend on the temperature to the extent N and t_c do, since neither e—the charge of the electron—nor m—its mass—changes with temperature. Regarding N, the number of valence electrons per unit volume vary in the same way as the number of atoms per unit volume. When caused by a temperature difference this variation corresponds to a volumetric expansion or contraction, which in crystalline solids is small and can be neglected. Not so the change of the mean free time t_c. The higher the temperature, the wider is the thermal oscillations of ions in the lattice, and the more frequent are the collisions between the valence electrons and ions. Thus, the free time t_c between collisions is expected to decrease markedly when the temperature rises. By Eq. (15-8), the electrical resistivity is expected to correspondingly increase. A closer analysis would predict an almost proportional increase of resistivity with temperature for most metals between room temperature and the melting point.[3]

[3] See also C. Kittel, *Introduction to Solid State Physics*, Wiley, New York, 1956.

How well this prediction is fulfilled can be seen from the values of the temperature coefficients of resistivity listed in column 4, Table 15-1. A true proportionality would require that all these coefficients be equal to $\frac{1}{273}$.

This follows from the definition of the temperature coefficient of resistivity. If ρ is the resistivity at temperature T and ρ_0 is the resistivity at temperature T_0, where both T and T_0 are measured in degrees kelvin, then by definition the temperature coefficient of resistivity, α_T reads

$$\alpha_T = \frac{\rho - \rho_0}{\rho_0} \frac{1}{T - T_0} \tag{15-11}$$

Now let ρ_0 be the resistivity at 0°C or at $T_0 = 273$; then, putting

$$\alpha_T = \frac{1}{273} = \frac{1}{T_0} \tag{15-12}$$

we get

$$\frac{1}{T_0} = \frac{\rho - \rho_0}{\rho_0} \frac{1}{T - T_0}$$

or, after rearranging the terms,

$$\frac{T - T_0}{T_0} = \frac{\rho - \rho_0}{\rho_0}$$

whence

$$\frac{T}{T_0} - 1 = \frac{\rho}{\rho_0} - 1$$

and finally

$$\frac{\rho}{\rho_0} = \frac{T}{T_0} \quad \text{q.e.d.} \tag{15-13}$$

Effect of Foreign Atoms. Foreign atoms, or, more exactly, foreign ions, incorporated in the crystal structure of metallic elements disturb the regularity of the lattice in a manner similar to the thermal vibration of ions. That is, they shorten the mean free time between collisions and consequently increase the electrical resistivity. For small amounts of foreign atoms, up to 10%, the increase is generally proportional to the amount added. This is illustrated in Fig. 15-1, which shows the effect of nickel on the resistivity of copper. Significantly, an addition of 10% of nickel suffices to raise the electrical resistivity of copper from 1.56×10^{-8} to about 14×10^{-8} ohm m, or roughly ninefold. A similar increase occurs when copper atoms are incorporated in the crystal structure of nickel. Yet by themselves copper and nickel are good conductors of electricity. We infer that the increase of resistivity is due not so much to the nature of the foreign atom as it is to the degree of disturbance it creates in the lattice. As a rule, the more dissimilar the foreign and the host atoms, the deeper is the disturbance and the greater is the increase of resistivity.

TABLE 15-1 ELECTRICAL RESISTIVITY OF REPRESENTATIVE METALLIC ELEMENTS AT 0°C

Metal	*Resistivity in* 10^{-8} ohm m		*Temperature Coefficient of Resistivity* α_T, T^{-1}
	Measured	*Computed*	
Silver	1.51	0.7	1/243
Copper	1.56	0.6	1/230
Aluminum	2.63	—	1/225
Sodium	4.26	4.35	1/227
Potassium	6.10	5.00	1/180
Lithium	8.45	3.50	1/210
Iron	9.20	—	1/242
Lead	20.2	—	1/236
Antimony	38.0	—	1/279
Bismuth	109.0	—	1/224

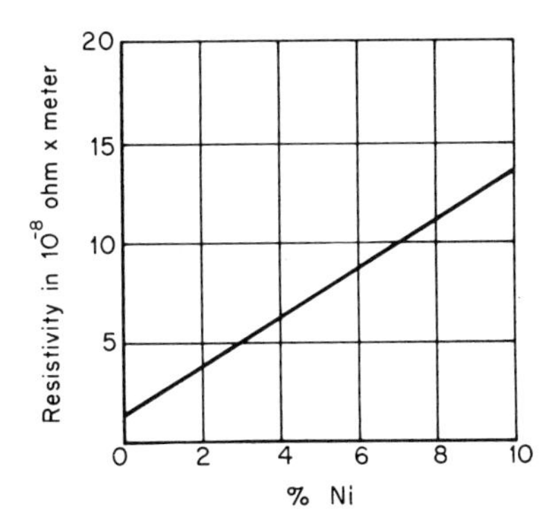

FIG. 15-1 Influence of addition of nickel on the electrical resistivity of copper

15-4 Illustrative Example

Compute the electrical resistivity ρ of sodium at 0°C, if the mean free time t_c at this temperature is 3.1×10^{-14} sec.

Solution. According to Eq. (15-8),

$$\rho = \frac{m}{e^2 N t_c}$$

where m, the mass of the electron, is 9.11×10^{-31} kg, and e, its charge, is 1.60×10^{-19} Q. Sodium being monovalent, the number of valence electrons N per cubic meter is the same as the number of atoms per cubic meter.

Furthermore, sodium builds a BCC lattice with two atoms per unit cell, and the side of the unit cell $a_0 = 4.29$ Å. Hence,

$$N = \frac{2}{(4.29 \times 10^{-10})^3} = 2.56 \times 10^{28} \text{ atoms/m}^3$$

Substitution in Eq. (15-8) yields

$$\rho = \frac{9.11 \times 10^{-31}}{(1.60 \times 10^{-19})^2 \times 2.56 \times 10^{28} \times 3.1 \times 10^{-14}}$$

$$= 4.35 \times 10^{-8} \text{ ohm m} \qquad \textit{Answer}$$

as listed in Table 15-1.

15-5 Resistivity and Permittivity. It is instructive to compare Ohm's law of electric conduction to the law of electric polarization derived in Chapter 13. To this end we substitute for $\boldsymbol{R}$ in Eq. (15-6) its expression in terms of ρ, Eq. (15-8). After rearrangement of terms, we get

$$\rho \frac{I}{A} = \frac{\Delta V}{L} \tag{15-14}$$

The quantity I/A represents the electric current per unit area It is called the current density and is designated by $\boldsymbol{J}$. Reverting to $\boldsymbol{E}$ instead of $\Delta V/L$, see Eq. (15-4), we can also write Eq. (15-14) to read

$$\boldsymbol{E} = \rho \boldsymbol{J} \tag{15-15}$$

That is, the field intensity is proportional to the current density with the resistivity appearing as the coefficient of proportionality. In this form, Ohm's law exhibits a formal analogy with the dielectric law given by Eq. (13-26) and is rewritten as follows

$$\boldsymbol{E} = \frac{1}{\varepsilon} \boldsymbol{D} \tag{15-16}$$

Here $\boldsymbol{D}$ is the charge density, instead of the current density, and ε is the permittivity. More exactly, $\boldsymbol{D}$ is the *surface* charge density, to distinguish it from the *volume* charge density, used in the electromagnetic theory. We note that the laws represented by these equations bear the same relation to each other as Newton's law of viscosity and Hooke's law of elasticity, embodied in Eqs. (12-12) and (6-32), respectively. In particular, the ratio $\frac{\rho}{1/\varepsilon}$ has the dimensions of time, as does the ratio η/G of viscosity over shear modulus of elasticity. This can also be seen by comparing the dimensions of ρ, Eq. (15-9), and ε, Eq. (13-5). There follows

$$\left[\frac{\rho}{1/\varepsilon}\right] = [\rho\varepsilon] = \left[\frac{\text{kg m}^3/(\text{Q}^2 \text{ sec})}{\text{kg m}^3/(\text{Q}^2 \text{ sec}^2)}\right] = [\text{sec}] \tag{15-17}$$

We recall that the ratio η/G represents the relaxation time θ of simple Newtonian liquids. It determines how long a substance resists an initial change of shape under applied shear stress. In like fashion, the product $\rho\varepsilon$ determines how long a medium retains an initial electric charge under an applied field intensity.

15-6 Conductors, Insulators, and Semiconductors. A freely roaming electron in metals can contribute to conduction by moving under any applied field intensity. However, if the electron is tied up in a covalent or an ionic bonding, it offers a resistance to motion too strong to be overcome by the commonly applied electric fields. Molecular bonds are a great deal weaker, but breaking a molecular bond cannot contribute to conduction, since molecules, whether polar or not, have no net electric charge. It follows that aggregates containing only covalent, ionic, and/or molecular bonds cannot conduct electricity and are by definition electrical *insulators*. Such aggregates would be expected to possess an almost infinite electrical resistivity. The electrical resistivity of real aggregates, albeit considerable, is far from infinite. In diamond, the most typical representative of covalent bonding, it attains a value of 10^{12} ohm m at room temperature, but much higher values have been reported for industrial ceramic and plastic insulators (porcelain and mylar). The inference is that even in diamond a small fraction of the valence electrons manages to break away from the covalent bonds and move through the crystal lattice. Because the bond in diamond is one of the strongest, this fraction is truly negligible, and for all practical purposes diamond is an insulator.

As we go down the periodic table, the strength of the bond markedly decreases; as a result, the fraction of valence electrons available for conduction increases considerably. This situation, of course, is reflected in the value of the electrical resistivity, which accordingly becomes much smaller—in fact, several orders of magnitude smaller. Thus in silicon, which is the second element in Group IV after carbon, it is only about 3000 ohm m and in germanium, the third element of the group, it is a mere 0.5 ohm m at room temperature. Both silicon and germanium have the same typically covalent diamond crystal structure as carbon. Hence, the relatively low values of their electrical resistivities cannot be explained by a change in the type of bonding. They can be explained, as we shall see, by assuming defects, or imperfections, in the covalent crystal structure.

Substances deriving their electrical conductivity from the presence of such imperfections are called *semiconductors*, at variance with metallic conductors, whose conductivity is essentially due to the type of bonding. Their function and applications in the electric field are also different. Metallic conductors transport and channel electric energy, whereas semiconductors control its flow and convert electric energy into other types of energy. Depending on the origin of imperfections, we distinguish between *intrinsic* and *extrinsic semiconductivity*. This distinction is basic to the understanding of the semiconductivity itself, as will appear below.

15-7 Intrinsic Semiconductivity. The origin and nature of imperfections responsible for the intrinsic semiconductivity can be best understood by considering the diamond crystal structure of such typical semiconductors as silicon and germanium. This structure, we recall, is characterized by a tetrahedral configuration of the four covalent bonds, sketched in Fig. 1-5. For convenience, the spacial arrangement of bonds has been replaced in Fig. 15-2 by a two-dimensional network, with the atoms located at the nodes of the net. As in Fig. 1-5, the process of sharing of an electron pair has been indicated here by a double link.

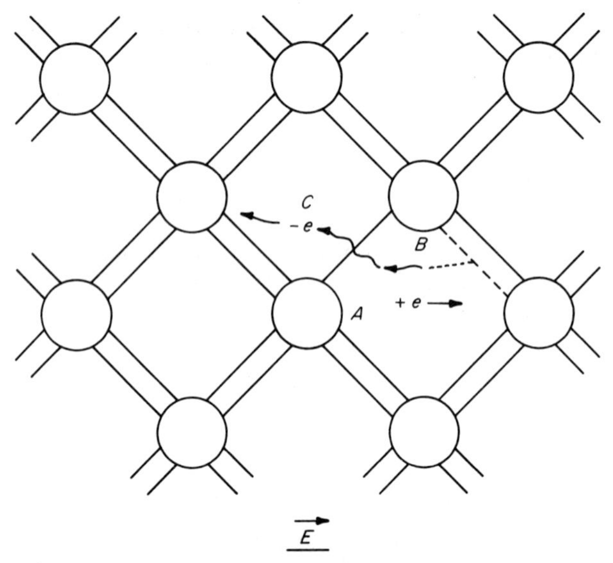

FIG. 15-2 Schematic representation of a diamond crystal structure with a conducting electron at C and a hole at AB

At absolute zero all atoms are at rest, and all electrons are securely held by the covalent bonds. The substance is a perfect insulator. As the temperature rises, the thermal vibration of atoms manages once in a while to impart enough energy to the electron to eject it from the bond. By doing so, it produces a defect, a *hole*, in the bond. Such a defective bond is indicated at AB, Fig. 15-2, by a single link. The ejected electron, at C, is now available for conduction, and it drifts away in the direction of the arrow, if an electric field $\boldsymbol{E}$ is applied to the semiconductor as shown in Fig. 15-2. The hole does not remain stationary either. In time, the missing link is restored through the capture of an electron ejected from a neighboring bond and set adrift in the same direction as the electron at C. The hole has now shifted to the neighboring bond, from there to another bond, and so on.

By thus shifting from bond to bond it drifts in the general direction of the field, rather than against the field, as does the electron. It is easy to see that thereby it contributes to conduction as though it had a positive charge, $+e$. On account of their contribution to conduction, both the hole and the ejected electron are considered to be imperfections of the covalent crystal structure. By producing a defective bond, they make the structure intrinsically imperfect. Hence the name of intrinsic semiconductivity given to the related electrical property.

15-8 Extrinsic or Impurity Semiconductivity. As the name implies, extrinsic semiconductivity owes its origin to factors extraneous to the crystal structure itself. It is due to the presence of foreign atoms, or impurities, incorporated in the crystal structure of an intrinsic semiconductor. For silicon and germanium, the foreign atoms are provided by two distinct groups of elements:

(a) elements like P, As, and Sb of the neighboring Group V of the periodic table;

(b) elements like Al, Ga, and In of the neighboring Group III of the periodic table.

The elements of Group V are called an n (negative) impurity or *donors*; the elements of Group III are called a p (positive) impurity or *acceptors*. The reason for these designations will become clear when we consider the effect these impurities have on the relative amounts of conducting electrons and holes.

An atom of Group V has five valence electrons, one more than the atom of silicon or germanium. It needs only four to share an electron pair with each of the four neighboring silicon or germanium atoms in the covalent diamond crystal structure. There is thus one extra electron or a negative charge which each atom of Group V can *donate* to the semiconductor.

Contrariwise, an atom of Group III has only three valence electrons. It needs one more for the formation of four covalent bonds. It is thus left with one defective bond, or a hole, which it can make available for conduction, as a *positive* charge, by *accepting* an electron from a neighboring bond.

We notice, Fig. 15-3a, that when the extra electron drifts away from the donor, the latter becomes a positive ion. Similarly, Fig. 15-3b, when the hole drifts away from the acceptor, the latter becomes a negative ion. The presence of ions in an otherwise covalent crystal introduces additional imperfections in the crystal structure. These imperfections are superimposed on the holes and conducting electrons which are produced in equal amounts by the semiconductor itself. As a result, depending on whether the impurity is a donor or an acceptor, two different sets of imperfections exist in a semiconductor:

(a) positive ions and an excess of conducting electrons over holes in the case of an n impurity;

(b) negative ions and an excess of holes over conducting electrons in the case of a p impurity.

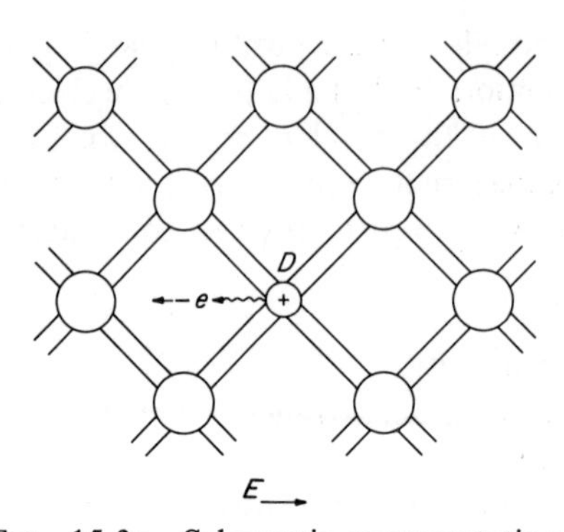

FIG. 15-3a Schematic representation of an n semiconductor with donor's positive ion D embedded in the diamond crystal structure and an excess electron available for conduction

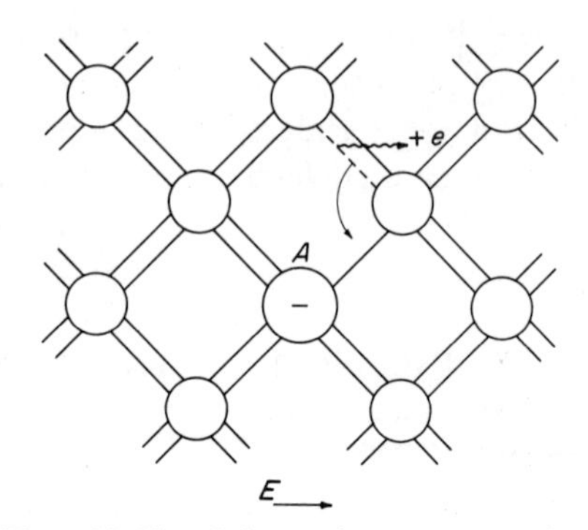

FIG. 15-3b Schematic representation of a p semiconductor with acceptor's negative ion A embedded in the diamond crystal structure and a hole available for conduction

Note. More generally, an n semiconductor is one in which the number of conducting electrons and positive ions exceeds the number of holes *and* negative ions. The converse is true for a p semiconductor. In engineering applications these semiconductors are indistinguishable from those in which there is only one sort of impurity. The presumption is that the presence of positive ions nullifies here the effect of an equal number of negative ions, and vice versa. This simple superposition rule appears plausible in view of the minute amounts of impurities used in semiconductor technology. They seldom exceed 1 part in 10^5 parts of the semiconductor and range ordinarily between 1 part in 10^6 and 1 part in 10^7. Obviously, the degree of purity of the semiconductor itself must be at least one order of magnitude better than this. The attainment of such a high degree of purity, never known before, is one of the most rewarding by-products of the semiconductor technology. It has been made possible thanks to a special technique, zone melting. With this technique, crystals of germanium have been purified to better than one part in ten billions![4]

15-9 Resistivity of Semiconductors. Formally, the analysis of the motion of either conducting electrons or holes under an applied electric field can be carried out in a semiconductor in the same way as in a metallic conductor. However, the meaning of the mass m and the free time t_c figuring in Eq. (15-8) is different. It can be made clear only in terms of quantum mechanics, which is able to account properly for such strange concepts as a "variable" electron mass m_e and a "mass" of a hole m_h. Here we shall merely accept the fact that, if the motions of the conducting electrons and holes are considered separately,

[4] W. G. Pfann, *Zone Melting*, Wiley, New York, 1958.

the corresponding electrical resistivities ρ_e and ρ_h can be written as follows:

$$\rho_e = \frac{m_e}{e^2 n_e t_e} \tag{15-18}$$

and

$$\rho_h = \frac{m_h}{e^2 n_h t_h} \tag{15-19}$$

where m_e and m_h are the "variable" electron mass and the "mass" of a hole, and t_e and t_h are similar to the mean free time t_c of the free electron in a metallic conductor. Finally, n_e is the number of conducting electrons and n_h is the number of holes per unit volume.

In reality, the conducting electrons and the holes contribute *jointly* to conduction. If $\boldsymbol{J}_e$ is the current density due to electrons and $\boldsymbol{J}_h$ is the current density due to holes, the total current density $\boldsymbol{J}$, according to Eq. (15-15), under an applied field intensity $\boldsymbol{E}$ is

$$\boldsymbol{J} = \boldsymbol{J}_e + \boldsymbol{J}_h = \left(\frac{1}{\rho_e} + \frac{1}{\rho_h}\right)\boldsymbol{E} = \frac{1}{\rho}\boldsymbol{E} \tag{15-20}$$

where ρ, the total resistivity of the semiconductor, is, by definition,

$$\frac{1}{\rho} = \frac{1}{\rho_e} + \frac{1}{\rho_h} \tag{15-21}$$

Noticing that $1/\rho$ is the electrical conductivity σ, we can also write

$$\sigma = \sigma_e + \sigma_h = e^2\left(\frac{n_e t_e}{m_e} + \frac{n_h t_h}{m_h}\right) \tag{15-22}$$

Of the quantities figuring in the parentheses, the ratios t_e/m_e and t_h/m_h depend on the particulars of the crystal structure and vary rather moderately with temperature. On the other hand, n_e and n_h depend strongly on temperature and in a manner that is common to all semiconductors. They increase exponentially as the temperature goes up, thus entailing a corresponding increase of conductivity or decrease of resistivity. Therein lies the main difference between the semiconductors and conductors. We recall that in conductors the resistivity *increases* with temperature, albeit only linearly.

15-10 Temperature Dependence of Intrinsic Semiconductivity. The exponential dependence of n_e and n_h on temperature can be explained by treating the conducting electron and hole in an intrinsic semiconductor as *products of dissociation* of a covalent electron. We write symbolically

covalent electron $\rightarrow$ conducting electron + hole

At equilibrium the process depicted by this relationship is balanced by a process going on in the opposite direction, namely, by the regeneration of a covalent electron through capture of a conducting electron by a hole. We can therefore write, as in the case of dissociation of a chemical compound,

$$\text{covalent electron} \rightleftarrows \text{conducting electron} + \text{hole}$$

Like the chemical dissociation, this process shifts more or less to the right, depending on the temperature and the strength of the covalent bond. If the temperature rises, there will be more charge carriers (conducting electrons and holes) compared to the covalent electrons in a given semiconductor, and vice versa. At a given temperature, however, the ratio of the charge carriers to the covalent electrons will remain constant. That is, the dissociation of covalent electrons into conducting electrons and holes is governed by the same *law of mass action* as the ordinary chemical reaction. The number N of all valence electrons per unit volume available for dissociation is the same as the number of atoms per unit volume. The number of conducting electrons is n_e and the number of holes is n_h. Hence, by virtue of the law of mass action,

$$\frac{n_e n_h}{N} = \text{constant} \tag{15-23}$$

or, since N is practically unaffected by the small proportion of dissociated covalent bonds, the product $N \times$ (constant) is also a constant, i.e.,

$$n_e n_h = N \times (\text{constant}) = K \tag{15-24}$$

As intimated before, the constant K depends on the temperature and the strength of the covalent bond. A detailed study of this statistical relationship is the subject of advanced courses, particularly thermodynamics. Here we shall limit our discussion to writing down an approximate expression for K, similar to that given in textbooks of general chemistry,[5] namely,

$$K = K_1^2 e^{-E_g/(kT)} \tag{15-25}$$

where K_1 is a coefficient which can be considered constant for all practical purposes,[6] E_g is the so-called energy gap, measured by the amount of work necessary to pry the electron loose from its covalent bond, T is the absolute temperature (in degrees kelvin) and k is the gas constant already encountered in a similar statistical relationship, Eq. (13-34).

By making use of Eq. (15-25) in Eq. (15-24) and noticing that for an intrinsic semiconductor

$$n_e = n_h \tag{15-26}$$

we obtain, with $n_e = n_h = n$,

$$n = K_1 e^{-E_g/(2kT)} \tag{15-27}$$

[5] cf L. Pauling, *General Chemistry*, Freeman, San Francisco, 1948.

[6] At room temperature K_1 is of the order of $0.1\% N$; see, for example, W. Shockley, *Electrons and Holes in Semiconductors*, Van Nostrand, New York, 1950.

In like fashion, Eq. (15-22) can be simplified to give the following expression for the electrical conductivity $\boldsymbol{\sigma}_i$ of an intrinsic semiconductor:

$$\boldsymbol{\sigma}_i = ne^2\left(\frac{t_e}{m_e} + \frac{t_h}{m_h}\right) \tag{15-28}$$

By combining Eqs. (15-27) and (15-28) and writing $1/\boldsymbol{\rho}_i$ for $\boldsymbol{\sigma}_i$, we finally have

$$\boldsymbol{\rho}_i = Ce^{E_g/(2kT)} \tag{15-29}$$

where for simplicity the practically constant quantities have been consolidated in a coefficient C, such that

$$C = \frac{1}{K_1 e^2[(t_e/m_e) + (t_h/m_h)]} \tag{15-30}$$

In practice, both C and E_g are determined experimentally. Thus, let $\boldsymbol{\rho}'_i$ and $\boldsymbol{\rho}''_i$ be two values of resistivity measured at temperature T' and T''. By substituting these values in Eq. (15-29) and dividing $\boldsymbol{\rho}'_i$ by $\boldsymbol{\rho}''_i$, we have

$$\frac{\boldsymbol{\rho}'_i}{\boldsymbol{\rho}''_i} = e^{E_g[(1/T') - (1/T'')]/2k} \tag{15-31}$$

or, resorting to logarithms,

$$\log \boldsymbol{\rho}'_i - \log \boldsymbol{\rho}''_i = \frac{E_g \log_{10} e}{2k}\,[(1/T') - (1/T'')] \tag{15-32}$$

whence

$$\frac{E_g \log_{10} e}{2k} = \frac{\log \boldsymbol{\rho}'_i - \log \boldsymbol{\rho}''_i}{(1/T') - (1/T'')} \tag{15-33}$$

The right-hand expression is the slope of a linear plot of log $\boldsymbol{\rho}_i$ versus $1/T$. Such a plot is shown in Fig. 15-4 for silicon, line AB and germanium, line CD. The corresponding energy gaps E_g are obtained from the slopes of these lines on dividing their numerical values by $\log_{10} e/2k$. The constants C, if needed,[7] can likewise be determined from the plot by extrapolating AB and CD to the value of $1/T = 0$. For this value the exponent of e in Eq. (15-29) is zero, hence $\boldsymbol{\rho}_i = C$.

In Table 15-2 are listed values of energy gaps E_g for several representative semiconductors. They include not only elements of Group IV, but also elements of Groups V and VI of the periodic table as well as natural and synthetic semiconductive compounds. To avoid cumbersome multipliers of ten, the energy gaps are given in eV units rather than joules. One eV unit, or one *electron volt*, is defined as the work necessary to take one electron over a barrier of one volt. Since the charge of the electron is 1.60×10^{-19} Q, we have

$$1 \text{ eV} = 1.60 \times 10^{-19} \text{ QV} = 1.60 \times 10^{-19} \text{ J} \tag{15-34}$$

[7] As we shall see below, C is less characteristic of the intrinsic semiconductivity than E_g.

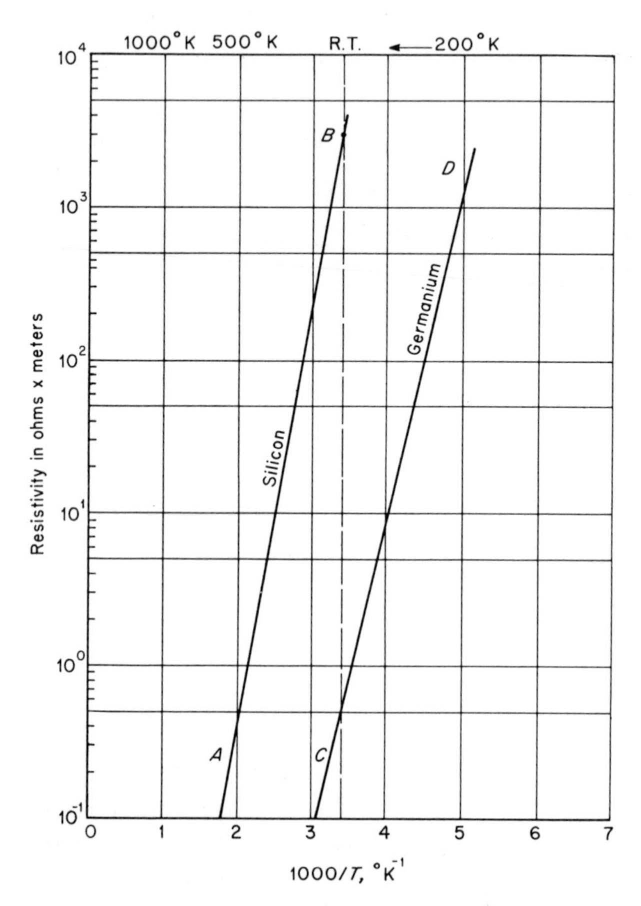

FIG. 15-4 Temperature dependence of resistivity in silicon and germanium

According to Table 15-2, the values of E_g range from 5.2 eV for diamond to about 0.1 eV for alpha, or grey, tin. (Alpha tin has the covalent diamond type structure at variance with beta or white tin, which is metallic. Alpha tin is stable below 13°C; beta tin is stable above 13°C.) Since ρ varies exponentially with E_g (see Eq. (15-29)), the corresponding values of resistivity understandably cover a much wider range. At room temperature they extend from over 10^{12} ohm m for diamond to about 10^{-6} ohm m for grey tin, thus encompassing 18 orders of magnitude! Yet these values and even these orders of magnitude are less characteristic of the intrinsic semiconductivity than E_g. For, unlike E_g, they are subject to large discrepancies because of uncontrollable traces of p or n impurity, which invariably *lowers* the electrical resistance of semiconductors. (Note the difference with the metallic conductors!)

TABLE 15-2 VALUES OF THE ENERGY GAP, E_g FOR REPRESENTATIVE SEMICONDUCTORS IN eV*

Element	E_g	*Compound*	E_g
Diamond	6	Cu_2O	2.1
Silicon	1.1	ZnSe	2.0
Germanium	0.68–0.72	PbS	0.34–0.37
Alpha tin	0.1	PbSe	0.27
Selenium	1.5–1.9	GaP	2.25
Phosphorus	1.4–1.6	AlSb	1.6–1.7
Arsenic	1.2	InAs	0.33
Tellurium	0.4	InSb	0.18

* After K. Lark Horovitz and F. A. Johnson, in monograph, *The Science of Engineering Materials*, Wiley, New York, 1957, and C. Kittel, *Introduction to Solid State Physics*, Wiley, New York, 1956.

15-11 Temperature Dependence of Extrinsic Semiconductivity. The same law of mass action can be invoked here as for intrinsic semiconductivity to explain the dependence of n_e and n_h on temperature. However, in an n semiconductor the accent is mainly on n_e, whereas in a p semiconductor it is mainly on n_h. This is so because the number of the *minority* carriers—n_h in the first case, n_e in the second—is too small compared to the number of the *majority* carriers, n_e and n_h, respectively, to make a significant contribution to conduction. As a result, the resistivity of an extrinsic semiconductor is determined either from Eq. (15-18) or Eq. (15-19). In both cases, the number of the majority carriers is determined to a good approximation from the law of mass action governing the dissociation of the impurity atom into a stationary ion and a wandering charge carrier.

Thus let D stand for a donor atom of Group V incorporated in the crystal structure of silicon or germanium. The process of dissociation can then be written symbolically as

$$\mathrm{D} \rightleftarrows \mathrm{D}^+ + e \tag{15-35}$$

where e is the excess (fifth) valence electron released by the donor and D^+ is the ion left behind. Furthermore, if N_{D} is the total number of impurity atoms per unit volume and $N_{\mathrm{D}}{}^+$ is the corresponding number of ions, then $N_{\mathrm{D}} - N_{\mathrm{D}}{}^+$ is the number of nonionized atoms, and we can write, similarly to Eq. (15-23),

$$\frac{N_{\mathrm{D}}{}^+ \times n_e}{N_{\mathrm{D}} - N_{\mathrm{D}}{}^+} = \text{constant} \tag{15-36}$$

Since $N_{\mathrm{D}}{}^+ = n_e$, Eq. (15-36) can be further simplified to read

$$\frac{n_e{}^2}{N_{\mathrm{D}} - n_e} = \text{constant} = K' \tag{15-37}$$

By analogy with Eq. (15-25), the constant K' can be written in terms of the coefficient K_1 as

$$K' = K_1 e^{E_i/(kT)} \tag{15-38}$$

thus yielding

$$\frac{n_e^2}{N_D - n_e} = K_1 e^{-E_i/(kT)} \tag{15-39}$$

The quantity E_i, which replaces E_g in Eq. (15-25), is called the *ionization energy*. It is a measure of the amount of work necessary to remove the excess electron from the donor and make it available for conduction. The excess electron is tied to the ion core of the donor by electrostatic forces of the same nature as those prevailing in a free atom. However the medium in which these forces are acting is different: it is made up of highly polarizable atoms of the semiconductor material. For example, the dielectric constant $\boldsymbol{\varepsilon}$ of silicon is 12 times as large as the dielectric constant $\boldsymbol{\varepsilon}_0$ of a vacuum. We saw in Section 13-3 that the effect of polarization was to weaken the electric field intensity produced in the dielectric by embedded charged particles. We infer from this that the ion core of the donor has a much weaker hold on the excess electron inside the semiconductor than in the free atom. Accordingly, it should take much less work to make an excess electron available for conduction in an extrinsic semiconductor than to make a covalent electron available for conduction in an intrinsic semiconductor. This conclusion is borne out by experimental data. In Table 15-3 are listed values of the ionization energy E_i of several n impurities in silicon and germanium. Compared to the value of E_g of pure semiconductors, Table 15-2, they are about two orders of magnitude smaller. Characteristically, the nature of the impurity has but little influence on the value of E_i.

The same line of reasoning and the same conclusions apply to a p impurity, except that in this case the majority carriers are holes rather than excess electrons. Equation (15-37), accordingly, reads

$$\frac{n_h^2}{N_A - n_h} = \text{constant} = K' \tag{15-40}$$

where N_A is the number of acceptors and n_h is the number of holes made available for conduction, both per unit volume. Again K' is related to K_1 by Eq. (15-38). Likewise the corresponding ionization energy E_i is more dependent on the nature of the semiconductor than on the nature of the acceptor, Table 15-4.

In both instances the lowering of the energy barrier from E_g to E_i makes a considerably larger number of charge carriers available for conduction than by Eq. (15-27). See the illustrative example, Section 15-12.

As a rule, therefore, the electrical resistivity of n and p semiconductors, at the temperature of their utilization and below, is several orders of magnitude smaller than the resistivity of the related intrinsic semiconductors. At some

TABLE 15-3 VALUES OF THE IONIZATION ENERGY, E_i, FOR REPRESENTATIVE DONORS IN SILICON AND GERMANIUM IN eV*

	P	As	Sb
Si	0.045	0.049–0.056	0.039
Ge	0.012	0.0127	0.0096

* After C. Kittel, *Introduction to Solid State Physics*, Wiley, New York, 1956.

TABLE 15-4 VALUES OF IONIZATION ENERGY, E_i, FOR REPRESENTATIVE ACCEPTORS IN SILICON AND GERMANIUM, IN eV*

	Al	Ga	In
Si	0.057–0.067	0.065–0.071	0.16
Ge	0.0102	0.0108	0.0112

* After C. Kittel, *Introduction to Solid State Physics*, Wiley, New York, 1956.

higher temperature though the number of charge carriers produced by the "dissociation" of covalent bonds manages to catch up with the number of *all* charge carriers provided by the "ionization" of the impurity. Henceforth the "dissociation" process has the upper hand, and the temperature dependence of electrical resistivity becomes that of an intrinsic semiconductor, Eq. (15-29).

This twofold trend is depicted in Fig. 15-5 for a representative range of impurity contents in silicon. The plots of log ρ versus $1/T$ in the *extrinsic* range, lines *EF*, *GH*. . . *MN*, are markedly affected by the impurity content. At room temperature (300°K) and below (to the right) the extrinsic resistivities are several orders of magnitude smaller than the intrinsic resistivity indicated by line *AB*. The two kinds of resistivities become equal at some higher temperature, points *E*, *G*. . . *M*, after *all* impurity atoms have fully contributed to the conduction. The larger the impurity content, the higher is the temperature at which the merger occurs.[8] Beyond this temperature the resistivity follows a unique trend: that of the intrinsic resistivity alone.

15-12 Illustrative Example

Obtain an order of magnitude ratio of two resistivities at room temperature: one exhibited by pure silicon, the other by silicon containing 0.001 atomic percent of phosphorus.

[8] The upward trend before the merger is due to the slight temperature variation of the coefficient *C*, which is on the increase. This variation becomes noticeable when the concentration of impurity charge carriers reaches saturation.

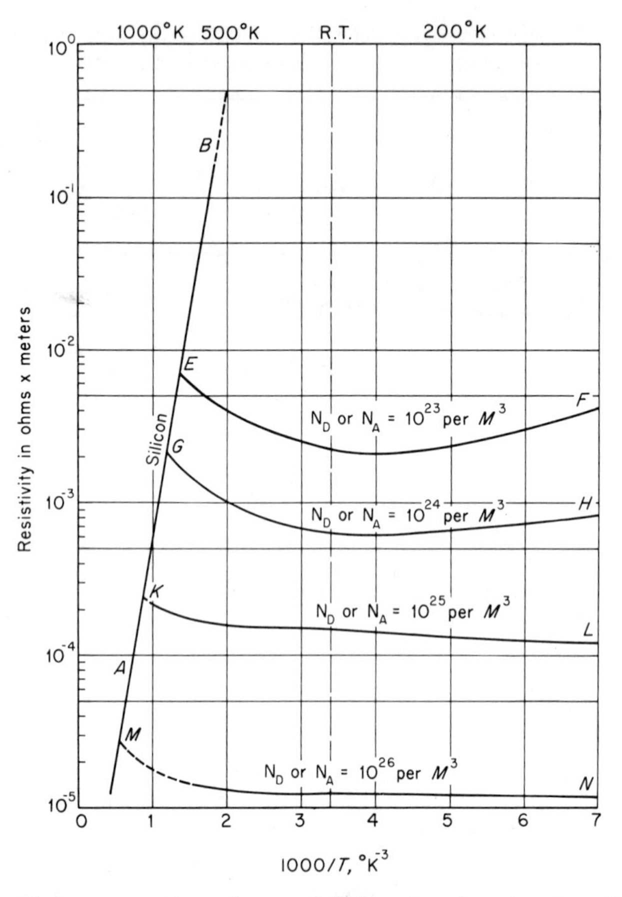

FIG. 15-5 Temperature dependence of silicon for the amounts of donors or acceptors shown

Solution. It will prove more convenient to work with conductivities. Pure silicon being an intrinsic semiconductor, its conductivity is given by Eq. (15-28). The phosphorus-doped silicon is an n semiconductor, hence its conductivity is expressed by the reciprocal of $\boldsymbol{\rho}_e$, Eq. (15-18). We can therefore write

$$\frac{\boldsymbol{\sigma}_i}{\boldsymbol{\sigma}_e} = \frac{n[(t_e/m_e) + (t_h/m_h)]}{n_e t_e/m_e} \tag{15-41}$$

For an order of magnitude computation, we can put approximately

$$\frac{t_e}{m_e} = \frac{t_h}{m_h} \tag{15-42}$$

whereupon

$$\frac{\boldsymbol{\sigma}_i}{\boldsymbol{\sigma}_e} = \frac{2n}{n_e} \tag{15-43}$$

The value of n is given by Eq. (15-27), but to obtain n_e we must solve Eq. (15-40). To this end we rewrite this equation to read

$$N_D - n_e = \frac{n_e^2}{K_1} e^{E_i/(kT)} \tag{15-44}$$

As pointed out in the footnote to Eq. (15-25), K_1 is of the order of 0.1% N at room temperature, where N is the number of silicon atoms per cubic meter. On the other hand, $n_e \leq N_D$, the number of atoms of phosphorus per cubic meter. Hence we can write

$$N_D - n_e \leq \frac{N_D}{K_1} e^{E_i/(kT)} N_D \tag{15-45}$$

N_D/N is given as 0.001%, $E_i = 0.045$ ev according to Table 13-3, and kT at room temperature comes out to be about 0.025 eV. Substitution of these values in Eq. (15-45) yields

$$N_D - n_e < 10^{-2} \times e^{1.73} N_D$$

or, practically,

$$n_e = N_D \tag{15-46}$$

Making final use of Eqs. (15-27) and (15-46) in Eq. (15-43), we get

$$\frac{\sigma_i}{\sigma_e} = \frac{2K_1 e^{-E_g/(2kT)}}{N_D} \tag{15-47}$$

We recall that at room temperature K_1/N_D is of the order of 10^2. Using the value $E_g = 1.1$ eV, Table 15-2, we thus have, with $kT = 0.025$ eV,

$$\frac{\sigma_i}{\sigma_e} = 2 \times 10^2 \times e^{-22}$$

or, approximately,

$$\frac{\sigma_i}{\sigma_e} = 10^{-7.0} \qquad \textit{Answer}$$

The ratio of resistivities is of course a reciprocal of this figure, or 10^7, in fair agreement with the data of Fig. 15-5 obtained by extrapolating AB to room temperature.

15-13 Properties Related to Semiconductivity. Although the basic nature of semiconductivity has not been clearly understood until recently, various manifestations of semiconductivity have been known for some time. As early as 1833 Faraday noticed that the resistivity of silver sulfide fell with rising temperature. He called this behavior "very extraordinary." One of the first manifestations of semiconductivity that appears to have been studied systematically was the response of resistivity to light in various oxides and sulfides. This study laid down the groundwork for future investigations concerned with photoconduction. In like manner, galena (PbS) detectors in the early radio sets can be said to have paved the way to modern solid state rectifiers and transistors. It will prove profitable to indicate briefly the role semiconductivity has played in all these developments, even though the pertinent arguments must by necessity be greatly simplified.

Photoconductivity. Derived from the Greek *photos*, meaning light, photoconductivity characterizes the ability of a substance to conduct electric current when exposed to light. By virtue of its electromagnetic nature, visible radiation interacts with matter in much the same way X-rays do, by setting the electrons in vibration (see Section 4-3). However, the energy thus imparted to the electron is much smaller than for X-rays, in fact, it is so small that as a rule only the valence electrons are involved. On the other hand, the energy contained in visible radiation is much larger than the average energy kT produced by thermal vibration. Additional covalent bonds can thus be "dissociated," thereby increasing substantially the number of conducting electrons and holes in many semiconductors. Prominent among them are Se, Cu_2O, CdS, and ThS. If these semiconductors are connected to a battery, an almost instantaneous increase of electric current takes place when light shines on them. The current drops back to its original low value when light is turned off, although not nearly as fast. The change of electric current is sufficient to actuate relays in various light detectors, such as the "photoelectric eye."

Rectification. The rectification of electric current, that is, the transformation of AC into DC, can be accomplished in various ways and by various means, but none of the devices conceived for this purpose exceeds in simplicity and efficiency the rectifiers based on the *p-n* junction. To obtain such a junction, a single crystal of a pure semiconductor is doped part of its length with a *p* impurity and part of its length with an *n* impurity. In one of the current methods this is accomplished while the crystal is being grown from the melt in the manner described in Section 3-5. The melt is first doped with a *p* impurity, such as gallium. After the solidification has proceeded part way, enough of an *n* impurity, phosphorus, for example, is added to the remaining melt to offset the *p* impurity and transform the balance of the crystal into an *n* semiconductor. The crystal is then cut to a thin wafer containing the *p-n* junction and it is coated on both sides with a metallic layer for the attachment of leads. This is schematically shown in Fig. 15-6a.

The excess of holes on the "*p* side" is indicated by the predominance of plus signs. In like manner, the excess of conducting electrons on the "*n* side" is indicated by the predominance of minus signs. The junction is a natural barrier for both, the holes and the conducting electrons. This follows from the fact that a hole penetrating into the *n* region, from left to right, is repelled by the positive ions of the donor, embedded in the crystal lattice as shown in Fig. 15-3a. Similarly, the conducting electrons are prevented from intruding

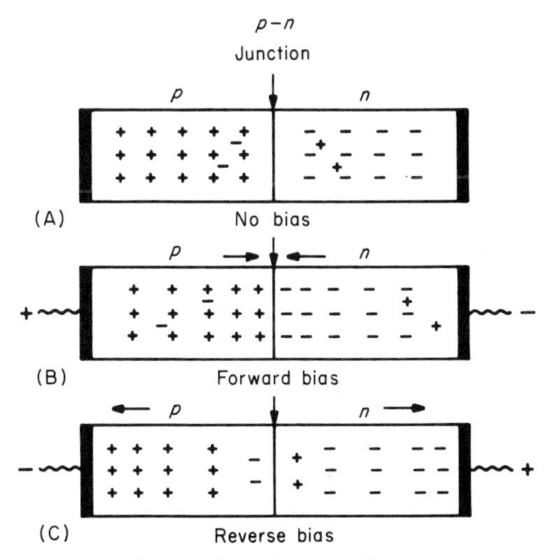

FIG. 15-6 *p-n* junction rectifier (schematic)

from the right into the *p* region by the negative ions of the acceptor, produced in the manner shown in Fig. 15-3b. The situation depicted in Fig. 15-6a corresponds to the absence of an external voltage. When an external voltage is applied, as by connecting the device to a battery, the current flows when the "*p* side" is connected to the plus terminal and the "*n* side" is connected to the minus terminal, but it does not flow when the connections are reversed. The first case is referred to as a *forward bias*, the second as a *reverse bias*. They are schematically represented by Fig. 15-6, b and c.

In Fig. 15-6b the holes of the *p* region behave as positively charged particles. They move away from the plus terminal of the battery and crowd into the junction area. So do the conducting electrons of the *n* region on being repelled by the minus terminal. On both counts, the concentration of charge carriers in the junction area rises momentarily above the equilibrium value governed by Eq. (15-24). Such a rise, however, is tantamount to dissociating more covalent bonds than the thermal vibration of the lattice can handle. So the intruding holes and conducting electrons recombine, and the equilibrium concentration is restored. The way is now open to a second wave of intruders, which meet with the same fate as their predecessors; then a third wave follows, and so on. A steady motion of charge carriers ensues toward the junction: the holes move from the left, the conducting electrons move from the right. In both cases the motion results in an electric current flowing from the plus terminal to the minus terminal of the battery. The higher the voltage, the faster is the motion of the charge carriers, and the larger is the electric current. Thus the forward bias offers no obstacle to a normal flow of electricity. The same is not true when the bias is reversed, Fig. 15-6c. Here the charge carriers tend to move away from the junction toward the now oppositely charged terminals of the battery. However, by doing so they are bound to deplete the junction of its equilibrium quota of carriers, as intimated in Fig. 13-6c. A drift in the opposite direction develops to counteract the attraction of the terminals. The net result is that there is virtually no flow of electric current when the bias is reversed. That is, the device works as a rectifier by letting the current pass in only one direction.

Note. The above conclusion, strictly speaking, applies to the majority carriers alone. The minority carriers behave somewhat differently. They respond to the reverse bias in the same way as the majority carriers do to the forward bias. They move toward the junction. There is one notable difference, however. The junction is *not a barrier* to the minority carriers. The minority carriers can continue moving past the junction. Consequently, they cannot build up the concentration of charge carriers in the junction area beyond a certain saturation value no matter how high the applied voltage. In terms of current density, the saturation value does not exceed 0.1 amp/m^2, which is at least three orders of magnitude less than the current density normally attained in the forward bias.

Photo emf. Closely related to photoconductivity is the ability of a substance to *generate* electric current when exposed to light. The underlying phenomenon is called the photovoltaic effect or photo emf. As is true for rectification, the manifestation of photo emf is particularly simple to visualize in devices based on the *p-n* junction.

Figure 15-7a reproduces the schematic view of the *p-n* semiconductor, Fig. 15-6a, with no outside sources of current. If a narrow beam of light falls on

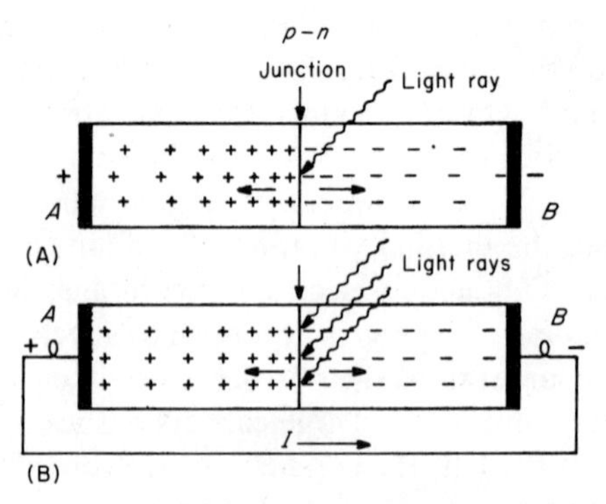

FIG. 15-7 Photo emf produced in a *p-n* junction: (a) no outside connection; (b) outside connection

the *p-n* junction, additional covalent electrons are "dissociated" into holes and conducting electrons, exactly as with photoconductivity. However, since the junction is a barrier to both kinds of majority charge carriers, a concentration of holes builds up to the left of the junction, and a concentration of conducting electrons builds up to the right of the junction. When these concentrations exceed the concentrations of the majority carriers in the corresponding parts of the semiconductor, a drift of excess charge carriers of both sign originates towards ends *A* and *B* and away from the junction. This is indicated by the straight arrows, Fig. 15-7a. In the absence of an external conductor connecting the two ends, the drift stops as soon as the accumulation of charges at these ends builds up a potential difference equal to the emf produced by the difference of the charge concentration. (This is similar to the emf produced in the electrolytic concentration cells, currently treated in the course of thermodynamics.) However, if *A* and *B* are joined by a conductor, Fig. 15-7b, the drift of conducting electrons can continue unchecked through the conductor from the terminal *B* to the terminal *A*. There the excess electrons recombine with the holes, thus opening the way to an uninterrupted flow of conducting electrons, and by the same token to an electric current. The current lasts as long as light keeps shining on the *p-n* junction. By the customary sign convention the electric current flows from *A* to *B*.

The photo emf of semiconductors is currently utilized in light meters. Those based on cuprous oxide, Cu_2O, are particularly common. However, the most promising application of the photovoltaic effect is unquestionably the direct conversion of solar energy into electric energy. Prominent in this respect is the silicon solar battery. Although built on a somewhat different scheme, the silicon battery follows essentially the general pattern of the *p-n* junction, Fig. 15-7, a and b. It can develop up to 0.5 V of potential difference and in current models it can produce up to 1 kWh of power per square meter. Considering the ratio of the energy of 1.1 eV necessary to dissociate a covalent electron to the average amount of incident solar energy per electron, the theoretical efficiency of the device is only 25%. Practically, an efficiency of 14% has been claimed.[9]

Amplification. There is but one step from rectification to amplification by means of a semiconductor. This step has done as much for transistor technology as the insertion of a grid in the diode did for vacuum tube technology. Both advances made it possible to control large amounts of electric power from remote points with exceedingly weak signals. There are, however, differences in detail which make the semiconductor a vastly superior amplifying device to the vacuum tube. We shall use the so-called *junction transistor* as an example.

The junction transistor is an amplifier derived from a *p-n* junction rectifier by forming one more *p-n* junction. Let this be a junction to the right of *n*,

[9] Solar energy is not the only type of energy capable of producing a photo emf in semiconductors. Atomic energy can also be used, but the efficiency is understandably much smaller, since the input energy per electron is so much higher than in the case of solar energy.

Fig. 15-8. We then have a *p-n-p* junction transistor. However, the argument applies equally well to a *n-p-n* junction transistor.

The part of the crystal between the two junctions is called the *base*. With the voltages applied as shown in Fig. 15-8c, the region to the left is called the *emitter*, the region to the right is called the *collector*. That is, the emitter is biased in the forward direction, and the collector is biased in the reverse direction. If no voltage is applied to the transistor, Fig. 15-8a, the holes

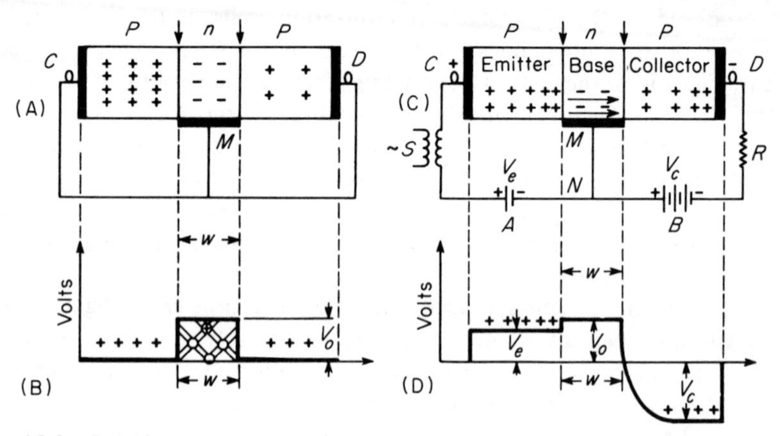

FIG. 15-8 Junction transistor: (a) with no external voltage; (b) corresponding potential barrier for holes; (c) with external voltages; (d) corresponding potential diagram for holes

cannot cross from the emitter to the collector, and vice versa, because a potential barrier V_0, a fraction of a volt, is set up in their path by the donor ions in the *n* region, Fig. 15-8b. We recall that these ions are positively charged when donors make one of their electrons available for conduction on entering the crystal lattice, Fig. 15-3a. By applying external voltages V_e and V_c as shown in Fig. 15-8d, we raise the potential at C and throughout the emitter by approximately V_e and we lower the potential at D and throughout the collector by approximately V_c. If V_e is made slightly smaller than V_0, a weak AC signal slightly in excess of $V_0 - V_c$ at S will suffice to push the holes through the potential barrier V_0. Moreover, if the width w of the base is sufficiently narrow, around 10^{-4} m, practically all holes flowing from the emitter will sail through the base unchecked and enter the collector. There they will combine with the stream of conducting electrons rushing from the minus terminal of the B battery to restore the equilibrium concentration of charge carriers in the collector. If on their way these electrons are made to pass through a resistance R which is much higher than the resistance of the collector, the voltage drop across R will be very nearly $V_0 + V_c$. In practical applications it is possible to lower the potential barrier at the base, Fig. 15-8d, to the order of a millivolt by raising appropriately the voltage V_e. With an ordinary flashlight battery at B, V_c will be of the order of one volt. A signal at S, Fig. 15-8c, in the range of a millivolt and slightly in excess of $V_0 - V_e$, will thus be able to trigger a thousandfold larger voltage variation at R. Since the currents through the emitter and collector are nearly equal, the power output at R will also be one thousand times larger than the power input at S. In the language of communication engineering, the transistor will have a power amplification of the order of 30 decibels—a remarkably high value. One decibel, or 1 db, is defined as the tenfold logarithm of the number. Here, $10 \log 1000 = 30$.

Note. The above reasoning is strictly true only when all current originated at the emitter flows in the collector. Actually, part of the current across the forward biased junction, between the emitter and the base, is also due to the recombination of holes and electrons. This part by-passes the mainstream and returns to the emitter via MN, Fig. 15-8c. There is in addition a current between the collector and the base across the reverse biased junction due to the minority carriers, which also subtracts from the mainstream. Both losses can be reduced to less than 0.1% by making the width w of the base small enough to minimize the chances of recombination and by keeping the concentration of the majority carriers (here the conducting electrons) in the base much lower than in the emitter.

Such a drastic reduction of losses is hardly possible in vacuum tube amplifiers, especially when signals are kept at a very low power level, as in communication engineering. Even in miniature tubes several watts are necessary to heat the filament as against a small fraction of a watt needed to carry the signal. Such a waste of power is—to borrow an apt comparison[10] —like using a two-ton truck to deliver a pound of butter. This is not the only shortcoming. There are also the problems of miniaturization and compactness, Fig. 15-9. All of them make the vacuum tube amplifier quite inferior to the transistor, especially in computer technology.[11]

15-14 Semiconducting Materials. Semiconducting technology is a rapidly expanding field. Its progress is in no small measure due to the theoretical predictions leading to the discovery of the transistor. The diamond type of crystal structure in elements of Group IV (silicon and germanium) played a major role in this discovery. It has also led to the production of artificial semiconductors with a crystal structure of the ZnS type, Fig. 13-19, similar to the diamond type. These aggregates are obtained by combining elements of Group III (Al, Ga, In) with elements of Group V (Sb, As, P). However, semiconductive properties are limited neither to these groups of elements nor to this type of structure. They encompass a large variety of aggregates

[10] W. Shockley, "Transistor Physics," *American Scientist*, **42**, 69(1954).

[11] For further detail see Shockley, *loc. cit.*

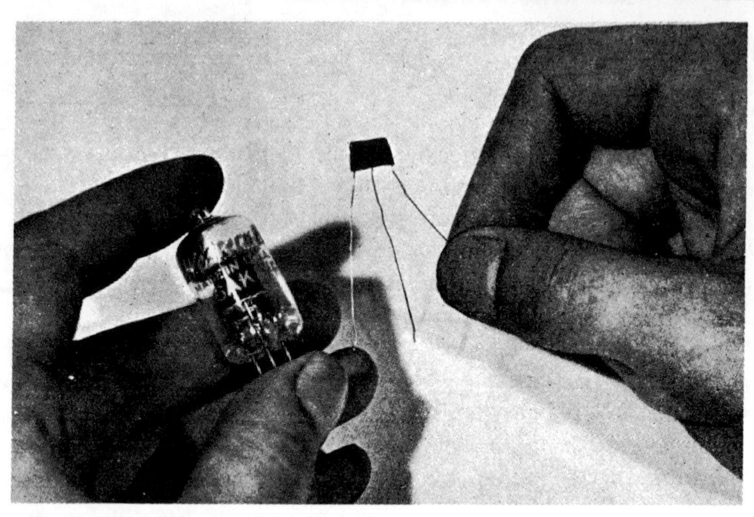

FIG. 15-9 Comparison between a junction transistor and a vacuum tube. (From W. Shockley, "Transistor Physics," *American Scientist*, **42**, 69, by permission)

and compounds containing not only the characteristic "diamond" covalent bonding, but other kinds of bonding, covalent as well as ionic and molecular. Recent studies of the energy conversion problems have drawn attention to metallic compounds, many of which possess definite semiconductive properties (e.g., Mg_2S, Cs_3Sb, etc.). Certain organic dyes (phthalocyanine, methylene blue) also exhibit semiconductivity. And the very fact that there are liquid semiconductors excludes the necessity of a definite crystal structure. More recently a large number of glasses belonging to As-Te-In, T-As-Te and As-Te-Si-Ge systems have also been shown to exhibit semi-conducting properties.[12] In addition, however, they exhibit switching effects, akin to p-n junction rectifiers, and they manifest a "memory" akin to ferro-electric materials. Devices built on these effects are likely to revolutionize the whole transistor technology.[13] The existence of semi-conducting glasses calls for a generalization of the existing theory aimed specifically at the crystalline state. The revision must also take into account the relationship of semiconductivity to other properties of matter (magnetic, thermal, etc.).

15-15 Summary. Electrical resistivity is manifest whenever motion of charged particles in an electric field is impeded by the motions of or collisions with other particles, charged and neutral. The resistivity of *conductors* derives from the metallic type of bonding and is defined by Ohm's law. The resistivity of *semiconductors* derives from imperfections existing or produced in other types of bonding: covalent, ionic, or molecular. This congenital difference is

[12] A. D. Pearson, and C. E. Miller, *Applied Physics Letters*, *14*, 280-282, (May 1, 1969).
[13] See, for example, P. M. Boffey, *Science*, *165*, 673-677, (August 15, 1969).

revealed in the *temperature* dependence: the resistivity of conductors increases linearly, the resistivity of *semiconductors* decreases exponentially with rising temperature. *Impurities* have a similar effect.

Semiconductivity is intrinsic if it is caused by the ejection of an electron from a covalent bond. The ejected electron and the defect, or the *hole*, left in the bond, *both* contribute to conduction: the electron by drifting against the direction of the applied electric field, the hole by drifting in the direction of the field (as though carrying a charge $+e$). Semiconductivity is *extrinsic* if it is caused by an impurity, i.e., by foreign atoms embedded in an intrinsic semiconductor. In the semiconducting elements of Group IV of the periodic table a foreign atom of Group V provides an excess or *conduction* electron by donating one of its five valence electrons. It is called a *donor*, or an *n* impurity, and the intrinsic semiconductor, on being doped with atoms of Group V, becomes an *n* semiconductor. In like manner a foreign atom of Group III provides an excess hole by accepting one valence electron from a neighboring covalent bond. It is called an *acceptor*, or a *p* impurity; the intrinsic semiconductor, on being doped with atoms of Group III, becomes a *p* semiconductor. The amount of foreign atoms seldom exceeds one part in 100,000 parts of the intrinsic semiconductor.

The resistivity of semiconductors varies exponentially not only with temperature but also with the amount of energy needed to make an electron or a hole available for conduction. In intrinsic semiconductors this energy is called the *energy gap*, E_g. It is from one to two orders of magnitude higher than the so-called *ionization energy*, E_i necessary to make an excess electron or an excess hole available for conduction in extrinsic semiconductors. The twofold dependence of resistivity on E_g and E_i can be revealed in an extrinsic semiconductor by varying the temperature. At low temperature, or in the *extrinsic range*, the influence of E_i predominates; at high temperatures, or in the *intrinsic range*, E_g takes over.

Among the properties related to semiconductivity the most characteristic are those having to do with (a) conduction of electric current under the impact of light or *photoconductivity*; (b) generation of electric current under the impact of light or *photo emf*; (c) rectification of electric current, and (d) amplification of electric signals.

Photo emf and rectification are currently achieved in devices based on a *p-n* junction—a junction between a *p*-rich and an *n*-rich portion of a single crystal. Amplifying devices based on a double, *p-n-p* or *n-p-n*, junction are called *junction transistors*. Transistors are superior to vacuum tube amplifiers in wasting no energy on filament heating.

The expanding field of semiconductor technology with new semiconducting materials in existence calls for a generalization of the present theory beyond the crystalline state.

References

ELEMENTARY

1. F. Bitter, *Currents, Fields, and Particles*, Wiley, New York, 1956.
2. W. Shockley, "Transistor Physics," *American Scientist*, **42**, 69(1954).

ADVANCED

1. A. H. Wilson, *The Theory of Metals*, Cambridge U.P., New York, 1958.
2. C. Kittel, *Introduction to Solid State Physics*, McGraw-Hill, New York, 1956.
3. K. Lark Horowitz and V. A. Johnson, "The Physics of Semiconductors," in monograph, *The Science of Engineering Materials*, J. E. Goldman, Ed., Wiley, New York, 1957.
4. W. Shockley, *Electrons and Holes in Semiconductors*, Van Nostrand, Princeton, N.J., 1950.
5. A. F. Ioffe, *Physics of Semiconductors*, Academic Press, New York, 1960.

Problems

15-1 Using the measured value of resistivity for copper at 0°C and assuming that all valence electrons contribute to conduction, compute the mean free time t_c between collisions.

15-2 Assuming the same order of magnitude for t_c in lead as in sodium, i.e., 10^{-14} sec, and using the measured value of resistivity, compute what should be the approximate fraction of valence electrons contributing to conduction. *Note*: For more exact computation, the "variable" mass of electron also must be considered (see Section 15-9).

15-3 A resistor connected to a 6-V battery consumes on the average 3 W in California. How much will it consume on the average in Alaska? Assume an average temperature difference of 80°F and a temperature coefficient of resistivity of $\frac{1}{240}$/°K.

15-4 Compute the resistivity of alpha tin at 200°K, if its conductivity at 13°C is 4×10^5 ohm^{-1} m^{-1}.

15-5 Compute the approximate concentration of n_h holes at 100°K in a germanium semiconductor containing 0.001 atomic percent of gallium.

15-6 Recalling that germanium has a diamond-type crystal structure, compute the fraction of holes at 200°K that can be assigned to each unit cell of the semiconductor considered in Problem 15-5.

15-7 Would you use a transistor in the intrinsic range of semiconductivity? How would your answer affect the limit imposed on the temperature of operation and the concentration of the impurity?

16 / THERMAL PROPERTIES: CONDUCTIVITY AND THERMOELECTRIC POWER

The motion of electrons in metals is responsible for the manifestation not only of electrical conduction but also to a large extent thermal conduction. In insulators, on the other hand, the origin of thermal conduction must be sought in the thermal vibration of atoms. In both instances statistical methods of analysis are needed, even more than for electrical conduction, to derive the pertinent properties from the behavior of elementary particles. This derivation, as well as the treatment of other thermal properties such as specific heat, will not be studied here. As in previous chapters, our main concern is with the dependence of thermal conductivity on structure. We shall find that there is in this respect a striking similarity between thermal and electrical conductivities, culminating in thermoelectricity.

16-1 Manifestations. It is a common experience that heating one end of a bar does not produce instantly a marked rise of temperature at the other end. Depending on the type of material of which the bar is made, it may take from a few seconds to many days to produce such a rise. This time lag is a measure of what may be called the resistance offered by the material to the flow of heat. We are thus led to distinguish, as we did for electricity, between good and bad conductors of heat. Good heat conduction is essential in apparatus such as heat exchangers, which must transfer heat as quickly as possible from one fluid to another, yet keep them in two separate compartments to prevent contamination (e.g., in reactor technology). It is also important in devices such as cooling fins, which must rapidly carry away heat from its point of inception (e.g., from a combustion chamber) to the outside.

Heat insulation is no less important than heat conduction. In domestic applications, in the form of inlays of wood and plastic covering the handles of pots and pans, it provides protection against burns. In industrial applications it insures safe operation of various devices exposed to intense heat. In steelmaking, the walls of the furnace are protected from the direct heat of molten steel by a lining of magnesia bricks, which are rated among the most refractory and best heat-insulating materials.

The more recent and spectacular manifestations of thermal conduction, as with electricity, are associated with semiconductors. The most promising aspects bear on the direct conversion of heat into electricity in thermoelectric piles. This is not the only similarity between electrical and thermal conductivities. A quantitative relationship between these properties can be derived in metals, if heat flow is reduced to the same basic and elementary process as that considered in Section 15-2.

16-2 Fourier's Law Derived. To apply the above process to the case of heat flow we consider, Fig. 16-1, a metallic bar AB of length L whose ends A

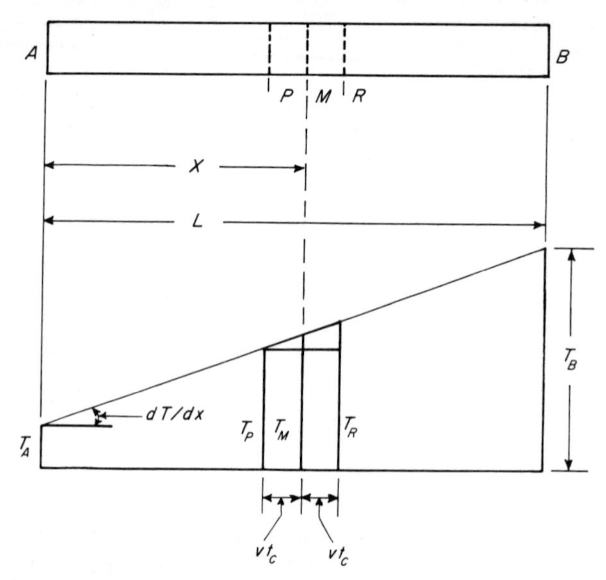

FIG. 16-1 Temperature distribution, with no lateral losses, in a bar subjected to temperatures T_A and T_B, respectively, at both ends

and B are maintained at temperatures T_A and T_B, respectively. Let T_B be greater than T_A. Then, if the bar is free from lateral losses, we will find that a steady state exists in the bar with a temperature gradient $dT/dx = (T_B - T_A)/L$ and a constant temperature prevailing at each section of the bar. Let T_M be the temperature at M, at a distance x from A. The temperatures to the right of M are higher than T_M, and the temperatures to the left of M are lower than T_M. On the atomic scale this situation can be accounted for by considering (1) the energy of vibration which thermal agitation imparts to the ions embedded in the crystal lattice and (2) the kinetic energy which it imparts to the valence electrons moving through the lattice. In both instances the energy is higher to the right than to the left of M. As a result an electron coming from the right will carry across M a higher kinetic energy than that corresponding to M. The converse is true for an electron coming from the left. Since higher kinetic energy also implies greater velocity, there would be in the absence of any interference, more electrons per unit time crossing M with a higher than with a lower kinetic energy, and consequently the temperature at

M should be rising. This of course is not so. Exactly the same phenomenon of collision which prevented the build-up of drift velocity under an applied voltage, Section 15-2, intervenes here to maintain a practically constant temperature at M.

To see why, consider the situation preceding the passing of electrons through M. Most of these electrons are the product of collisions that have occurred previously at some distances upstream and downstream of M, say at R and P, Fig. 16-1. If t_c is the already familiar mean free time between collisions and v is the average velocity of electrons at M, then to a good approximation $PM = MR = vt_c$. The product

$$vt_c = \lambda \tag{16-1}$$

is called the *mean free path* of the electrons. We can also assume that the random nature of thermal collisions has imparted to the electrons leaving P and R an average kinetic energy corresponding to the temperatures T_P and T_R at P and R. However, since λ is known to be less than 1000 Å for most metals, T_p and T_R are very close to T_M. It follows that the average kinetic energy, the velocity, and the number of electrons moving toward M from R are also very nearly the same as those of the electrons moving from P. Therefore any excess of kinetic energy at M coming from the right is compensated, at least in bulk, by an equal deficiency of kinetic energy coming from the left. In conclusion, the average kinetic energy of electrons remains constant at M (and at any other point of the bar), and so does the temperature.

Even though temperature and average kinetic energy at M are kept stationary, there is nonetheless a steady flow of energy through M equal to the difference between the kinetic energy of electrons flowing into the cross section M, *from* the right, and the kinetic energy of electrons flowing out of this cross section, *to* the right. The same of course is true of any other point on the bar. As will appear below, in metals the flow of kinetic energy of electrons is the dominant component of the heat effect associated with the temperature gradient in the bar. Therefore the problem of heat flow here is essentially reduced to the evaluation of this component alone.

Instead of treating the whole problem rigorously, which would require the use of statistics, we shall adopt a mixed procedure. We shall first do the computation as though the whole contribution to inflow came only from the electrons scattered by collision at R, and likewise, as though the whole contribution to outflow came from the electrons scattered by collision at P. We shall then arbitrarily introduce a factor to correct for the inadequacies of our procedure and bring the result in agreement with the more rigorous solution.

On this understanding, we shall write that the average inflow energy $\dot{W}$ is equal to the number $\dot{N}$ of electrons passing through M in unit time, multiplied by the average kinetic energy w_i which each electron has acquired by collision at R. That is,

$$\dot{W}_i = \dot{N}w_i \tag{16-2}$$

On the assumption that all valence electrons in metals contribute to heat conduction, we can write, by making $\dot{N}$ explicit, an expression similar to Eq. (15-2):

$$\dot{W}_i = w_i NAv \tag{16-3}$$

where N is the number of valence electrons per unit volume, A is the cross-sectional area of the bar, and v is the average velocity imparted to the electrons at M by thermal agitation. By analogy, the average outflow energy, $\dot{W}_0$ is

$$\dot{W}_0 = w_0 NAv \tag{16-4}$$

The net flow of the kinetic energy of electrons caused by thermal agitation is thus $\dot{W}_i - \dot{W}_0$. This difference, as pointed out before, accounts for almost the total heat flow $\dot{Q}$ in the bar produced by the temperature gradient. That is, to a good approximation,

$$\dot{Q} = NAv(w_i - w_0) \tag{16-5}$$

We seek to express $(w_i - w_0)$ in terms of the temperature gradient dT/dx. On the so-called free electron model, the average kinetic energy w of electrons caused by thermal agitation is greater the higher the temperature. In fact, from statistical considerations which must be deferred to thermodynamics, we have for this model

$$w = \tfrac{3}{2}kT \tag{16-6}$$

where k is the already familiar gas constant, and T is the absolute temperature (e.g., in degrees Kelvin).

Substitution of w from Eq. (16-6) into Eq. (16-5) yields

$$\dot{Q} = \tfrac{3}{2}NAvk(T_R - T_P) \tag{16-7}$$

Furthermore, from Fig. 16-1,

$$T_R - T_P = 2vt_c\, dT/dx \tag{16-8}$$

Hence,

$$\dot{Q} = (3NAv^2t_ck)\, dT/dx \tag{16-9}$$

Equation (16-9) can be further simplified by observing that on the same free electron model the kinetic energy w of an electron can be written as

$$w = \tfrac{1}{2}mv^2 = \tfrac{3}{2}kT \tag{16-10}$$

where m is the mass of the electron. Substituting for v^2 from Eq. (16-10) into Eq. (16-9) we finally have

$$\dot{Q} = \frac{9Nk^2t_cT}{m} A\, dT/dx \tag{16-11}$$

Here T refers to the temperature T_M at the cross section M. However, the same equation holds for any cross section of the bar. Hence the subscript has been omitted for the sake of generality.

Equation (16-11) must still be corrected for various statistical effects left out from our simplified derivation. For one thing, electrons scattered by collision at other sections than P and R must also be considered. For another, not all valence electrons N contribute to heat conduction. And thirdly, not all electrons scattered at a given point pass through the cross section M. All causes combined change the factor in front of the right-hand term, Eq. (16-11), to $\pi^2/3$, yielding the more exact value for $\dot{Q}$, namely,

$$\dot{Q} = \left(\frac{\pi^2}{3}\frac{Nk^2t_cT}{m}\right)A\,dT/dx \tag{16-12}$$

The expression in parentheses being constant for a given temperature, we see that the heat flow $\dot{Q}$, also called the rate of heat transfer, at a given temperature, is proportional to the cross-sectional area of the conductor and the temperature gradient. This, in essence, is the experimental law that the French physicist and mathematician Jean Baptiste Joseph Fourier proclaimed in 1822.

16-3 Thermal Conductivity. On purely experimental grounds, Eq. (16-12) is written in a more general form as follows:

$$\dot{Q} = \kappa A\frac{dT}{dx} \tag{16-13}$$

where the coefficient κ replacing the expression in parentheses is called the *thermal conductivity*. The dimensions of κ in the MKSQ system are

$$[\kappa] = \left[\frac{\dot{Q}}{A\,dT/dx}\right] = \frac{\text{W}}{\text{m}\,{}^\circ T} \tag{16-14}$$

or κ is equal to watts per meter and per degree Celsius or Kelvin.

The experimental value of κ does not contain only the contribution of the kinetic energy of electrons, κ_e. It also includes the effect of thermal vibration of ions embedded in the crystal lattice, or, in short, the effect of *lattice vibration*, and it comprises the effects of mutual interference between motion of electrons and lattice vibration. However, in pure metals all these effects are of a second order compared to the influence of the kinetic energy of electrons. With this in mind, we can write approximately for pure metals

$$\kappa = \frac{\pi^2 Nk^2t_cT}{3m} \tag{16-15}$$

Thermal Resistivity. The reciprocal of thermal conductivity is called the thermal resistivity. Although a perfectly legitimate and useful concept, the term *thermal resistivity* is less frequently used in the technical literature than thermal conductivity, and certainly less than electrical resistivity. It all seems to be a matter of habit. The dimensions of thermal resistivity in the MKSQ system are, of course, m °K/W.

Range of Variation. Values of thermal conductivity measured at room temperature (around 290°K) vary from about 420 W/(m °K) for silver to about 8 W/(m °K) for bismuth, column 2, Table 16-1. We notice that the values decrease in an inverse order to those of electrical resistivity listed in Table 15-1. This inversion could be more or less anticipated, since conductivity means the opposite of resistivity. The two sets of values, however, are not merely correlated; they are also functionally related to each other. The proof is deferred to Section 16-5. Here we will mention that the experimental support is reasonably good, but it is largely because the ratios of the computed to the measured values are about the same in both cases. This is also borne out by the illustrative example, Section 16-4.

Effect of Temperature. At first glance one might be tempted to conclude from Eq. (16-15) that the thermal conductivity should increase with temperature. Such a conclusion overlooks the factor t_c. It was pointed out in Section 15-3 that the mean free time t_c decreases when the temperature goes up. Between room temperature and the melting point the t_c in pure metals is found to be almost inversely proportional to T. Hence the product t_cT is not expected to greatly vary above the room temperature, and neither is κ by Eq. (16-15). This deduction is well borne out by experimental data; see also illustrative example, Section 16-4. The situation at temperatures approaching absolute zero requires a more refined treatment.

Effect of Foreign Atoms. Foreign atoms embedded in the crystal structure of metallic elements should conceivably affect the thermal conductivity κ through the factor t_c, in the same way they do the electrical conductivity $\boldsymbol{\sigma}$. According to Section 15-3, the electrical resistivity generally *increases* proportionally to small amounts of foreign atoms added. We should therefore anticipate a *decrease* of thermal conductivity in the same ratio—a deduction likewise borne out by experimental data.

16-4 Illustrative Example

Compute the thermal conductivity κ of sodium at 0°C, or 273°K, using the data of the illustrative example, Section 15-4.

Solution. According to Eq. (16-12),

$$\kappa = \frac{\pi^2 N k^2 t_c T}{3m}$$

Making the following substitutions;

$$\begin{aligned} N &= 2.56 \times 10^{28}/\text{m}^3 \\ k &= 1.38 \times 10^{-23}\ \text{J/deg} \\ t_c &= 3.1 \times 10^{-14}\ \text{sec} \\ T &= 273°\text{K} \\ m &= 9.11 \times 10^{-31}\ \text{kg} \end{aligned}$$

we get

$$\kappa = \frac{\pi^2 \times 2.56 \times 10^{28} \times (1.38 \times 10^{-32})^2 \times 3.1 \times 10^{-14} \times 273}{3 \times 9.11 \times 10^{-31}}$$

$$= 150 \text{ W/m °K}$$

as against 140 W/m °K listed in Table 16-1 for 290°K.

TABLE 16-1 THERMAL CONDUCTIVITY OF REPRESENTATIVE POLYCRYSTALLINE METALLIC ELEMENTS AT ROOM TEMPERATURE

Metal	*Thermal Conductivity* κ *in* W/m °K	*Lorenz Number* L *in* 10^{-8} $(V/°K)^2$
Silver	420	2.36
Copper	390	2.30
Aluminum	210	2.05
Sodium	140	2.24
Iron	92	3.10
Lead	35	2.50
Antimony	19	2.64
Bismuth	8	3.25

16-5 The Wiedemann-Franz Ratio and the Lorenz Number. In 1853 two German physicists, G. Wiedemann and R. Franz, formulated an experimental law according to which the ratio of thermal to electrical conductivities $\kappa/\boldsymbol{\sigma}$ was a characteristic constant for metals. This ratio was shown in 1872 by their Danish colleague, L. Lorenz, to be proportional to the absolute temperature T. Both findings can be obtained at once by comparing Eq. (16-15) with Eq. (15-8). Writing $1/\boldsymbol{\rho}$ for $\boldsymbol{\sigma}$, we have

$$\frac{\kappa}{\boldsymbol{\sigma}} = \frac{\pi^2}{3}\left(\frac{k}{e}\right)^2 T \tag{16-16}$$

or, since k/e is constant, the ratio $\kappa/\boldsymbol{\sigma}$ is proportional to the absolute temperature T. On dividing both sides of Eq. (16-16) by T, we obtain the so-called Lorenz number $\boldsymbol{L}$ (in honor of L. Lorenz) such that

$$\boldsymbol{L} = \frac{\kappa}{\boldsymbol{\sigma}T} = \frac{\pi^2}{3}\left(\frac{k}{e}\right)^2 \tag{16-17}$$

The right-hand side expression is a universal constant. Its value in the MKSQ units is

$$\boldsymbol{L} = \frac{\pi^2}{3}\left(\frac{1.38 \times 10^{-23}}{1.60 \times 10^{-19}}\right)^2 \tag{16-18}$$

$$= 2.45 \times 10^{-8} \text{ (V/°K)}^2$$

The agreement between the theoretical value of $\boldsymbol{L}$ and actual measurements can be judged from the data listed in column 3, Table 16-1. These data have been obtained on dividing the figures of κ, column 2, by 290°K and by the reciprocal of the figures listed in column 2, Table 15-1, the latter being corrected for the rise of temperature from 273°K to 290°K. The discrepancy of over 30% shown by bismuth is ascribed to the additional effect of lattice vibration on thermal conductivity. In bismuth this effect becomes comparable to the influence of the kinetic energy of electrons.

It is of importance to note that the experimental values of L are little affected by moderate additions of, say, a few percent, of foreign atoms. This circumstance enables one to determine the effect of impurities on the thermal conductivity of metals from the corresponding electrical conductivity, which is a great deal easier to measure (see Problem 16-2).

16-6 Thermal Conductivity of Solid Insulators. The similarity between electrical and thermal conductivities breaks down when it comes to aggregates devoid of free-moving charge carriers. In principle, such aggregates should exhibit no electrical conductivity, but they can and do exhibit thermal conductivity. As pointed out previously, the contributing factor here is lattice vibration. The covalent, ionic, or molecular bonds holding together atoms, ions, or molecules can be likened to springs connecting discrete masses. A vibration imparted to one of the masses is transferred by means of the springs to other masses and, if kept for a sufficient length of time, it will end up by involving the entire aggregate. In like manner, a more vigorous thermal vibration at the hotter end of a bar will spread to the cooler end, and the transfer mechanism will in many respects be similar to the propagation of elastic waves in a spring mass system. In fact, were it not for the chance lattice disorders created along the bar by local thermal agitation, the excess of vibrational energy transmitted from one end to the other would propagate on the average with the speed of sound—the same as any other elastic disturbance in the lattice. We shall not account quantitatively for the effects of local thermal disorders: this is one of the most complex and intricate problems in physics. We can, however, develop an understanding for the final result by treating these effects on a par with the collisions between free electrons and the lattice, discussed in Section 16-2. Accordingly, we picture that the vibrational energy transferred across a given section M of the bar, Fig. 16-1, is equal, not to the total excess of energy between the hot and the cold ends of the bar, but to a partial excess of energy between points of the bar, such as R and P, separated by what here amounts to twice the mean free path λ' of *lattice vibration.* We can write, by analogy with Eq. (16-1),

$$\lambda' = ct'_c \tag{16-19}$$

where c is the speed of sound and t'_c is the mean free time corresponding to λ'. We can press the analogy further. In fact, we can write similarly to Eq. (16-5)

$$\dot{Q}' = N'Ac(w'_1 - w'_0) \tag{16-20}$$

where $\dot{Q}'$ is the heat flow produced in a bar of an insulating material by a temperature gradient dT/dx, N' is the number of vibrating particles per unit volume, and w'_i and w'_0 are the average vibrational energies per particle at a distance λ' upstream and downstream of a given section. A is the cross-sectional area of the bar and c, as already mentioned, is the speed of sound. From the same statistical considerations as those used in the free electron model,

$$w' = 3kT \tag{16-21}$$

whereupon, by analogy with Eqs. (16-7), (16-8), and (16-9),

$$\dot{Q}' = (6N'c^2t'_ck)A\,\frac{dT}{dx} \tag{16-22}$$

Correcting again for the statistical effects left out of this simplified treatment, we have finally

$$\dot{Q}' = (N'c^2t'_ck)A\,\frac{dT}{dx} \tag{16-23}$$

It follows that to the same degree of approximation as κ_e the thermal conductivity κ_l due to lattice vibration can be written as

$$\kappa_l = N'c\lambda'k \tag{16-24}$$

where for convenience we have substituted the mean free path λ' for ct'_c.

Although only approximate, Eq. (16-24) can be used for an order of magnitude computation of κ_l for most substances between room temperature and the melting point. As is true for metals, the situation at temperatures approaching absolute zero requires a more refined treatment.

With these limitations the value of κ_l is about two orders of magnitude smaller than the value of κ_e in good conductors. This follows from the fact that both the mean free path λ' and the speed of sound c are smaller than the corresponding mean free path λ and the average velocity v of the free electrons in metals. Thus for an order of magnitude computation we can put

$$N' = 10^{28}/\text{m}^3$$
$$c = 5 \times 10^3 \text{ m/sec}$$
$$\lambda' = 10 \times 10^{-10} \text{ m}$$

whereupon the thermal conductivity κ_l turns out to be of the order of 1 W/m °K. Experimental values range from several tens of watts per meter and degree Kelvin for ionic crystals (quartz, alkali halides) to a fraction of a watt per meter and degree Kelvin for molecular structures (plastics, organic compounds). In the glassy state the thermal conductivity of materials is, as a rule, one order of magnitude smaller than in the corresponding crystalline state (e.g., fused silica and crystalline quartz), presumably because of a greater local disorder.

We recall that lattice vibration is also a contributing factor to the heat conductivity of conductors. Compared with the electron motion, this contribution is small and it can be neglected in the case of good conductors like copper, but it becomes significant and it cannot be neglected in the case of poor conductors like bismuth, see Table 16-1.

Note. Gases possess the lowest values of thermal conductivity. This can be readily shown by applying the reasoning of Section 16-2 to the thermal motion of particles in a dilute gas. In fact the whole derivation leading to Eq. (16-15) has been patterned after the statistical kinetics of dilute gases treated in a more advanced course. An expression for κ in all respects identical to Eq. (16-15) obtains—except for the numerical coefficient, which is $\frac{1}{2}$ instead of $\pi^2/3$—namely,

$$\kappa_{\text{gas}} = \frac{Nk^2t_c T}{2m} \tag{16-25}$$

where N is the number of molecules per unit volume and m is the mass of one molecule. For an order of magnitude computation we can put

$$\begin{aligned} N &= 10^{25}/\text{m}^3 \\ t_c &= 10^{-10} \text{ sec} \\ m &= 10^{-27} \text{ kg} \\ T &= 300^\circ\text{K} \end{aligned}$$

whence κ_{gas} turns out to be of the order of 0.01 W/m °K, in good agreement with experimental data. Liquids occupy a position intermediate between solids and gases.

16-7 Thermal Conductivity of Semiconductors. Lattice vibration plays a prominent role in the thermal behavior of semiconductors. Its contribution to thermal conductivity is rather straightforward, at least as far as extrinsic semiconductivity is concerned. Thus, in the case of an n semiconductor, the thermal conductivity κ_l due to lattice vibration simply adds to the thermal conductivity κ_e due to excess electrons.[1] Accordingly the total thermal conductivity reads

$$\kappa = \kappa_l + \kappa_e \tag{16-26}$$

Furthermore, in an n semiconductor the excess electrons *alone* are responsible for electrical conduction. Hence κ_e can be related to the extrinsic electrical conduction σ_e ($= 1/\rho_e$, Eq. (15-18)) by the same Lorenz factor, Eq. (16-1), as for metals. However, the numerical coefficient in front of $(k/e)^2$, Eq. (16-18), is not constant. The statistics of the problem, which are treated in a more advanced course, require that the coefficient be 2 for $n_e < 2 \times 10^{25}/\text{m}^3$ and

[1] A. F. Ioffe, *Physics of Semiconductors*, p. 272, Academic Press, New York, 1960.

$\pi^2/3$ for $n_e > 3 \times 10^{25}/m^3$, with an appropriate transition for intermediate concentrations.[2] Writing A for $\pi^2/3$ to cover all cases and making use of Eq. (16-17) in Eq. (16-26), we get

$$\kappa = \kappa_l + A(k/e)^2 T \boldsymbol{\sigma}_e \tag{16-27}$$

A similar expression obtains for a p semiconductor.

By way of illustration, the values of κ given by Eq. (16-27) are plotted in Fig. 16-2 as a function of $\boldsymbol{\sigma}_e$ at room temperature (R.T.) using data of Fig.

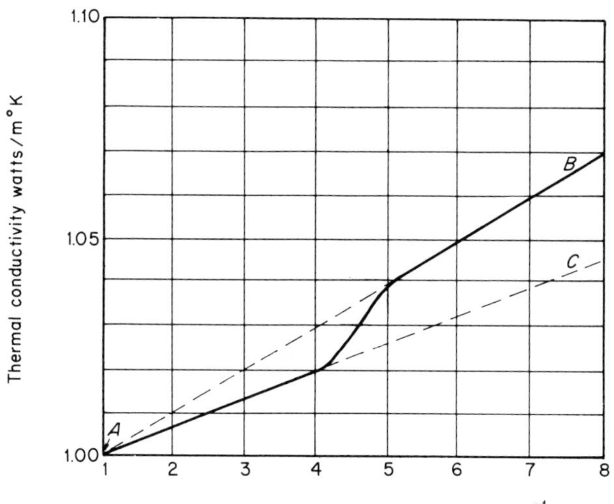

FIG. 16-2 Thermal conductivity versus electric conductivity in a representative extrinsic semiconductor

15-5. The value of κ_l has been arbitrarily taken as 1 W/m °K, merely to account for the right order of magnitude; see Section 16-6. The line AB corresponds to $A = \pi^2/3$, the line AC to $A = 2$. The transition from one line to another should occur somewhere between 4000 and 5000 (ohm m)$^{-1}$, where the concentration n_e changes from 2×10^{25} to $3 \times 10^{25}/m^3$. Experimental confirmation exists, but it apparently needs additional support.[2]

The situation is much more complicated at higher temperatures, when intrinsic semiconduction takes over, Fig. 15-5. Here the holes and the electrons contribute to electrical conduction in equal numbers. Furthermore, by Eq. (15-27), these numbers increase exponentially with temperature. On both counts, then, it is possible for the holes and electrons to participate pairwise and bodily, so to speak, in the transfer of heat from the warmer to the cooler end of the bar. If the holes and electrons remain paired during this transfer, two things happen: (1) the net electric current is nil, as it should be

[2] A. F. Ioffe, *ibid.*, p. 274.

in the absence of an applied voltage, and (2) the holes and electrons recombine in the cooler portions of the bar, liberating an additional amount of heat. As a result more heat is transferred in the intrinsic range of the semiconductor than in the extrinsic range, and the thermal conductivity is correspondingly higher. There is good experimental evidence to support this line of thought, although complete agreement between computation and measurement is still lacking. Figuring prominently among the factors yet to be accounted for is the interaction between lattice vibration and the motion of electron-hole pairs.[3]

16-8 Thermoelectricity. Another thermal property involving interaction with lattice vibration is thermoelectricity. That two pieces of wire AC and BC, Fig. 16-3, made of two different materials, exhibit a voltage difference ΔV

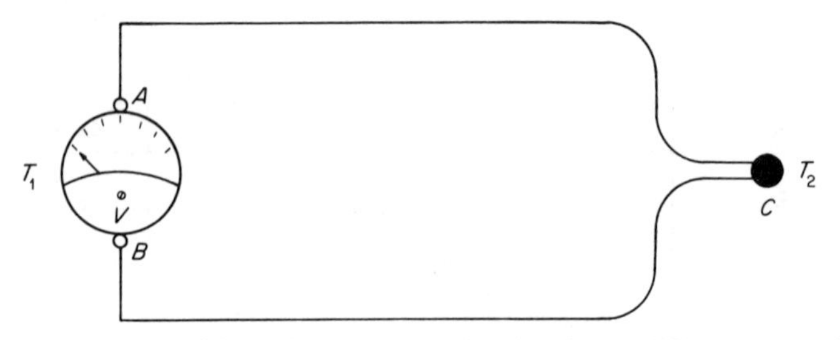

FIG. 16-3 Thermal emf in a thermocouple made of two different materials and subjected to a temperature difference at the junctions C and A-B

between their terminals A and B, when their common junction C is raised to a temperature $T_2 > T_1$, belongs to one of the earliest discoveries in the field of electricity. It was made in 1822 by the German physicist T. J. Seebeck.[4] Significantly, Seebeck showed that thermoelectricity is not only a property of metallic conductors but also of what today we call semiconductors. However, this finding went largely unnoticed until more recently, when thermoelectricity became a potential and promising factor in the attempts at direct conversion of heat into electricity. Heretofore thermoelectricity was utilized almost exclusively in *thermocouples*, as a means of measuring temperature differences, and hence temperatures, by maintaining terminals A and B, Fig. 16-3, at a known, constant temperature.

[3] A. F. Ioffe, *ibid.*, p. 284.

[4] The converse effect, that of generating a temperature difference between the junctions C and A-B by an outside source of electrical current, was discovered 12 years later by a French watchmaker, Jean Charles Athanase Peltier, turned scientist upon inheriting a "modest fortune." Another 28 years went by before William Thomson, better known as Lord Kelvin, had established a quantitative relationship between these two effects. In doing so he stumbled upon a third discovery—called properly "the Thomson effect"—according to which there is an absorption of heat due to electrical conduction in addition to the familiar production of heat, I^2R, discovered by Joule around 1843.

The origin of thermoelectricity can perhaps be best, although rather crudely, explained by referring to extrinsic semiconductivity. Let AB, Fig. 16-1, be made of an n semiconductor. If $v(x)$ is the average velocity imparted to the excess electrons at M by thermal agitation, then the average velocity at R is $v(x + vt_c)$ and the average velocity at P is $v(x - vt_c)$. Since vt_c is small compared to x, we can write approximately (see Eq. (6-12)),

$$v(x + vt_c) = v(x) + \frac{dv}{dx} vt_c \tag{16-28}$$

and

$$v(x - vt_c) = v(x) - \frac{dv}{dx} vt_c \tag{16-29}$$

By a line of thought similar to that used in Section 16-2, the difference of velocity between inflow and outflow, Eqs. (16-28) and (16-29), can be said to give rise to a net flow of excess electrons, $\dot{n}_e$ through section M down the temperature gradient dT/dx. Hence, by analogy with Eq. (16-5),

$$\dot{n}_e = n_e Av(x + vt_c) - n_e Av(x - vt_c) = 2n_e At_c v \frac{dv}{dx} \tag{16-30}$$

The corresponding flow of electricity, or thermoelectric current $\boldsymbol{I}$, is $e\dot{n}$, that is,

$$\boldsymbol{I} = 2en_e At_c v \frac{dv}{dx} \tag{16-31}$$

Corresponding to this current is the voltage drop

$$\boldsymbol{V} = \boldsymbol{IR} \tag{16-32}$$

or, using Eqs. (16-31) and (15-7), with $N = n_e$,

$$\boldsymbol{V} = 2 \frac{mv}{e} \frac{dv}{dx} L \tag{16-33}$$

The right-hand-side expression can be simplified by noting that, according to Eq. (16-10),

$$d\left(\frac{mv^2}{2}\right) = mv\, dv = \frac{3}{2} k\, dT \tag{16-34}$$

and that

$$\frac{dT}{dx} = \frac{T_B - T_A}{L} \tag{16-35}$$

Using Eqs. (16-34) and (16-35) in Eq. (16-33), we get

$$\boldsymbol{V} = 3 \frac{k}{e} (T_B - T_A) \tag{16-36}$$

Statistical effects, which we omit as usual, would reduce the numerical factor in this case to something like $\frac{3}{2}$, although higher values are possible in other cases.[5]

Equation (16-36) has been derived on the assumption that there is an actual flow of electrons $\dot{n}_e$ through section M (or any other section, for that matter). In reality, the first stream of electrons arriving at the cold end A has no further outlet. Consequently it builds up a negative charge and a difference of potential V opposing the *thermal* emf which generates the thermoelectric current, Eq. (16-31). In order to produce a continuous flow of electricity we must close the circuit by an outside connection from A to B. Obviously nothing will be gained by making this connection of exactly the same semiconducting material as AB. However, if we pair a p and an n semiconductor in the manner shown in Fig. 16-4, a steady electric current can be generated by a process of

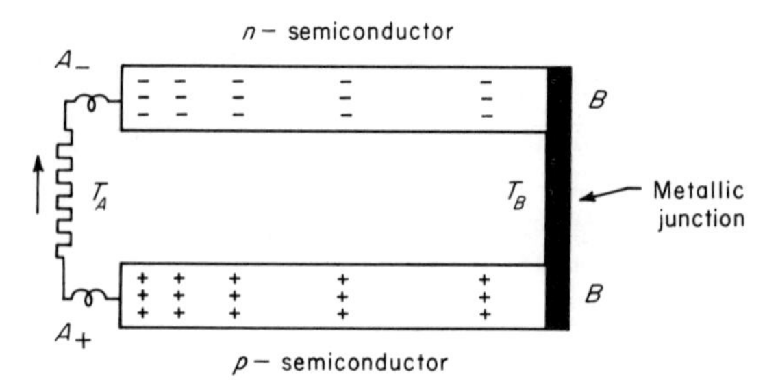

FIG. 16-4 Schematic view of a semiconducting thermoelectric generator

recombination of holes and electrons similar to that occurring in the phenomenon of photo emf, Section 15-12. Also a thermal emf of about the value given by Eq. (16-36) can be expected in this case. Writing V_t for the thermal emf, we thus have approximately

$$V_t = 3\frac{k}{e}(T_B - T_A) \tag{16-37}$$

Hence, to the same degree of approximation, the thermal emf per degree

$$S = \frac{V_t}{T_B - T_A} = 3\frac{k}{e} \tag{16-38}$$

S is called the *thermal emf coefficient*, or the *thermoelectric power*, of the material. Using the data of Section 16-5, we have approximately

$$S = 4 \times 10^{-4}\ \text{V/°K} = 0.4\ \text{mV/°K} \tag{16-39}$$

which is of the right order of magnitude for most semiconductors.

A thermoelectric generator functioning according to the principle of Fig. 16-4 is apparently capable of only 3% efficiency with existing semiconducting

[5] A. F. Ioffe, *ibid.*, p. 303ff.

materials. A thermodynamic analysis shows that considerably higher efficiencies could be achieved by increasing the thermoelectric power S at the expense of the thermal to electrical conductivity ratio $\kappa/\boldsymbol{\sigma}$.[6]

The situation with metals is much less favorable. As with semiconductors, we must couple two different metals A and B in order to generate a continuous electric current.

Calling S_A and S_B their thermoelectric powers, we can write, for the situation depicted in Fig. 16-3,

$$V_t = (S_A - S_B)(T_2 - T_1) \tag{16-40}$$

The value of $(S_A - S_B)$ in metallic thermocouples currently used for temperature measurement does not exceed 0.06 mV/°K or °C. This is one order of magnitude less than for semiconductors. The addition of foreign atoms increases, often substantially, the value of $S_A - S_B$ referred to the pure metallic element. Thus the thermoelectric power of a thermocouple made of copper and constantan (60% Cu, 40% Ni) is roughly 0.04 mV/°C—one of the highest among metals.

It is not easy to account for, let alone predict quantitatively or even qualitatively, the effects of foreign atoms on thermoelectricity. They are often coupled with and complicated by the effects of temperature which at the approach to absolute zero are themselves closely related to lattice vibration. The extreme sensitivity of thermoelectric power to all these effects, in magnitude as well as sign, appears to be one of the most challenging problems in modern physics.[7]

16-9 Summary. Free-moving valence electrons contribute to heat conduction as well as to electrical conduction. This contribution is dominant in the case of *metallic* conductors. It leads to the derivation of the *thermal conductivity* κ from a relationship between heat flow and temperature gradient known as Fourier's law. The close similarity between thermal conductivity κ and electrical conductivity $\boldsymbol{\sigma}$ in metals is embodied in the Wiedemann-Franz ratio $\kappa/\boldsymbol{\sigma}$, which depends only on the absolute temperature T. Alternatively, this similarity is emphasized by the Lorenz number $\boldsymbol{L} = \kappa/(\boldsymbol{\sigma}T)$, a universal constant. Unlike thermal and electrical conductivities taken separately, the ratio $\kappa/(\boldsymbol{\sigma}T)$ is little affected by small additions of foreign atoms. A method is thereby provided to compute one of these properties from the other. Between room temperature and the melting point the thermal conductivity of metallic elements changes but little with temperature.

At variance with their electrical behavior, solids devoid of free-moving charge carriers are not perfect heat insulators. Thermal vibration of atoms, ions, and molecules—in short, *lattice vibration*—also causes heat conduction

[6] A. F. Ioffe, *ibid.*, p. 317.

[7] D. K. C. MacDonald, *Thermoelectricity: An Introduction to the Principles*, Wiley, New York, 1962.

and in the absence of free-moving charge carriers is the only, albeit much weaker, contributor to the thermal conductivity of solids. The poorest heat conductors are gases. Their thermal conductivity of about 0.01 W/m °K is roughly 10,000 times smaller than that of metallic elements. Liquids occupy an intermediate position.

In semiconductors, lattice vibration and free charge carriers contribute in approximately equal amounts to thermal conductivity. In the intrinsic range, additional contributions are possible from electron-hole recombinations and their interactions with lattice vibration.

Lattice vibration is also involved in thermoelectricity: a manifestation of a voltage difference produced in a conductor or semiconductor by a temperature difference. The *thermoelectric power*, or the amount of voltage per degree, is about ten times larger in semiconductors than in metallic conductors where it hardly attains 0.1 mV/deg. Future developments in semiconducting materials are expected to bring about a substantial improvement of the present efficiency of 3% in the generation of electricity by the thermoelectric effect.

References

ELEMENTARY

1. J. B. Austin, *The Flow of Heat in Metals*, American Society of Metals, Cleveland, 1942.

ADVANCED

1. A. H. Wilson, *The Theory of Metals*, Cambridge U.P., New York, 1958.
2. C. Kittel, *Introduction to Solid State Physics*, McGraw-Hill, New York, 1956.
3. A. F. Ioffe, *Physics of Semiconductors*, Academic Press, New York, 1960.
4. D. K. C. MacDonald, *Thermoelectricity: An Introduction to the Principles*, Wiley, New York, 1962.
5. E. H. Kennard, *Kinetic Theory of Gases*, McGraw-Hill, New York, 1938.

Problems

16-1 Using the assumption and the result of Problem 15-1, compute the thermal conductivity of copper.

16-2 The electrical resistivity of copper containing 2% P, the so-called deoxidized copper, is 2.03×10^{-8} ohm m at 20°C. Using data of Table 15-1, page 313, and Eqs. (16-17) and (16-18), compute the corresponding thermal conductivity.

16-3 Assuming the mean free path of lattice vibration λ' to be 8 Å, and taking 6000 m/sec for the speed of sound, compute the thermal conductivity of amorphous silica SiO_2 at 20°C if the density ρ at this temperature is 2.2 g/cm³. (Hint: Use Eq. (13-31) to obtain the number N' of molecules per cubic meter.)

16-4 Compute the heat flow Q through each semiconducting bar, Fig. 16-4, by assuming $\kappa = 1.05$ W/m and °C, $T_B = 200$°C, $T_A = 20$°C, the cross sectional area of each bar $A = 1$ cm² and the length of each bar is 50 cm.

16-5 Compute the electric current $\boldsymbol{I}$ flowing in the thermoelectrical generator, Fig. 16-4, if in addition to the information given in Problem 16-4, the resistance of the wire joining A_+ to A_- is 2 ohms. (Hint: Use data of Fig. 16-2 to obtain the value of $\boldsymbol{\rho}$.)

16-6 Compute the ratio of heat evolved across the wire joining A_+ and A_- in Fig. 16-4 to the heat $\dot{Q}$ flowing through the semiconducting bars. This gives an estimate, albeit too high, of the efficiency of the process. (For further details consult, for example, M. Tribus, *Thermostatics and Thermodynamics*, Van Nostrand, Princeton, N.J., 1961.)

III / ALLOYS, CERAMICS AND POLYMERS

"Engineers and Metallurgists have always been forced to try things empirically with nothing but a general background of theory to guide them." **C. S. Smith**

17 / POLYMORPHISM AND PHASE TRANSFORMATION

In Part II we showed how the properties of materials depended upon the internal structure of matter. We stressed in particular the dependence of the so-called structure insensitive properties, like bulk modulus of elasticity and electrical polarization, on the stability of this structure. We showed in effect that, as long as the response of the material to the imposed stimuli tended to restore the original configuration of atoms, the properties were predictable. That is, they could be expressed in terms of the quantities which characterized the behavior and position of the individual atoms with respect to each other.

To round off the picture we must now determine under what conditions, external and internal to the material, a given behavior and configuration of atoms remain stable, and conversely what changes, if any, are to be expected if these conditions are modified. Alternatively, we may wish to impart new properties to the material by deliberately altering its internal structure. In both instances the outcome will depend on the interplay of the external factors and the nature of the material itself. In this chapter the interplay of the external factors is called upon to explain two main aspects of structural changes: the polymorphism and phase transformation. The succeeding chapters are devoted to the study of the effect of these changes upon the properties of specific types of materials: alloys, ceramics, and polymers.

17-1 Manifestations and Definitions. Carbon, we saw in Chapter 1, exists in two crystal forms: one is called diamond, the other is called graphite. Tin, as mentioned in Chapter 15, also has two types of crystal structure. We say that carbon and tin exhibit *polymorphism* (plurality of forms) meaning they possess two (or more) types of crystal structure.[1] While in no way universal, polymorphism is rather common among elements, especially among metallic elements. No less than twenty metals have been found to exhibit polymorphism. We will mention lithium and sodium in Group I, beryllium and calcium in Group II, titanium manganese, and, above all, iron among the transition elements. The polymorphism of iron has wide metallurgical and industrial significance which is further emphasized in Chapter 18.

Nor is polymorphism restricted to elements alone. Thus silica, SiO_2, exists

[1] Allotropy, from *allos*, other, and *tropos*, direction, is another named used for this type of transformation.

in three major crystal forms known as quartz, tridymite, and crystobalite. Of these quartz and crystobalite have two, and tridymite has three minor modifications. In addition, silica exhibits a glassy or amorphous state. The details of all these structural changes are further described in Chapter 19. Another example of polymorphism among minerals is calcium carbonate, $CaCO_3$, which exists in two crystal forms known as aragonite and calcite. Finally, as will be pointed out in Chapter 20, polymers can be made more glassy or, conversely, more crystalline by appropriate physical and chemical treatments.

In all these instances, which characterize polymorphism, the changes of crystal structure are accompanied by no changes of chemical nature. This, of course, is obvious of elements but it is also true of compounds such as silica. In all its modifications silica is represented by the same chemical formula, namely SiO_2. The glassy and crystalline states of polymers are likewise represented by an identical chemical formula.

At variance with polymorphism we shall designate as heterogeneous phase transformations or simply phase transformations those changes of structure which also involve changes of the chemical composition of the phases. Perhaps the simplest example of phase transformation is the well-known separation of the salt solution of Na^+ and Cl^- in water into crystals of ice (H_2O) *and crystals* of sodium chloride (NaCl) upon solidification. The solution is called the liquid phase while ice and sodium chloride are called the solid phases.[2] Except for the amorphous state a solid phase is always identified with a certain type of crystal structure. Thus ice has a well defined hexagonal crystal structure, and sodium chloride has an equally well defined FCC structure. While the liquid phase contains molecules of water and ions of sodium and chlorine, the solid phases are almost pure water in the case of ice, and pure salt in the case of NaCl. Thus the transformation from liquid to solid has involved here not only a physical change of state, but also a change of chemical nature; a separation of the constitutive elementary particles in two distinct solid phases. Understandably the process of separation must have carried the elementary particles over many atomic distances. Such considerable transfer of atoms and molecules is easily conceivable in liquids, because here lack of structural stability coupled with thermal agitation produces an incessant interchange of close neighbors in the whole body of the liquid. However, as we will see in Chapter 18, a similar transfer of atoms is also feasible in solids even though on a much more reduced scale. This circumstance explains the occurrence of phase transformations not only between liquids, or between liquids and solids, but also between solids alone. Several instances of such transformations will be found in subsequent chapters.

Compared to a phase transformation, polymorphism calls only for local and relatively small displacements of atoms, as will appear below. These

[2] For a more precise definition of phase, see Section 17-5.

displacements as a rule are insufficient to cause a marked redistribution of the constitutive elementary particles. Therein perhaps lies the main distinction between the two types of transformations. Large scale atom movements and the resulting chemical changes play a dominant role in phase transformation, while they are only of secondary importance in polymorphism. This distinction will become more clear if we bring in the influence of three major factors: the temperature, the pressure, and the chemical composition. In the case of polymorphism, obviously only temperature and pressure need to be considered.

17-2 Effect of Temperature. It is well known that temperature rise brings about increased thermal agitation of elementary particles. Ultimately the thermal agitation is strong enough to destroy the stability of a given atomic or molecular arrangement, and the solid is converted into a liquid. In a few instances the loss of stability is accompanied by loss of cohesion. The solid then sublimes directly into a gas. Such is the familiar case of iodine. We will see below that the stability of a given atomic or molecular arrangement can also be upset by inclusion of foreign atoms and that loss of cohesion (and stability) can be prevented by application of hydrostatic pressure. It follows that to account for the effect of temperature alone both the chemical composition and the applied pressure must be kept constant. Unless otherwise stated atmospheric pressure will be assumed henceforth.

With this restriction in mind the response of a crystalline solid to a rise of temperature can be viewed as an adaptation of the internal structure to increasing thermal agitation of atoms. We picture the ensuing configuration of atoms as a sort of a compromise between two opposing trends. On the one hand the potential energy of inter-atomic attractions and repulsions tends to keep the atoms in their position of stable equilibrium; on the other hand the kinetic energy of thermal motion seeks to displace them from this position. The final outcome is an oscillatory motion of atoms with equal amplitudes of vibration in the forward and backward directions. In such motion the average configuration of atoms is obtained by simply locating the centers about which the atoms oscillate. As a rule these centers do not coincide with the equilibrium position of atoms at absolute zero.

To see why, consider the case of ionic crystals. Let r_o, Fig. 6-4, Chapter 6, be the equilibrium distance between ions at absolute zero. When the temperature is raised, each ion begins to oscillate an equal amount about its position of equilibrium. In doing so it approaches its nearest neighbor on the average as often as it moves away from it. However, according to the trend of the restoring force $f = f_a + f_r$ shown in Fig. 6-4, the repulsion caused by approaching the neighbor is greater than the attraction caused by moving the same amount away from the neighbor. To equalize the average magnitude of the restoring forces of both signs, the center of thermal vibration of the ion must be displaced from its initial position of equilibrium. The distance between the centers of vibration becomes thereby greater than r_o, and it keeps growing as the temperature is increased. This, of course, is the familiar phenomenon of thermal expansion, which the ionic crystals share with most, if not all, crystalline solids.

Like all phenomena associated with motion of elementary particles, thermal expansion has a statistical character. That is, its magnitude fluctuates on the atomic scale, and for a brief period of time it may substantially depart from its average value in isolated spots of the aggregate.

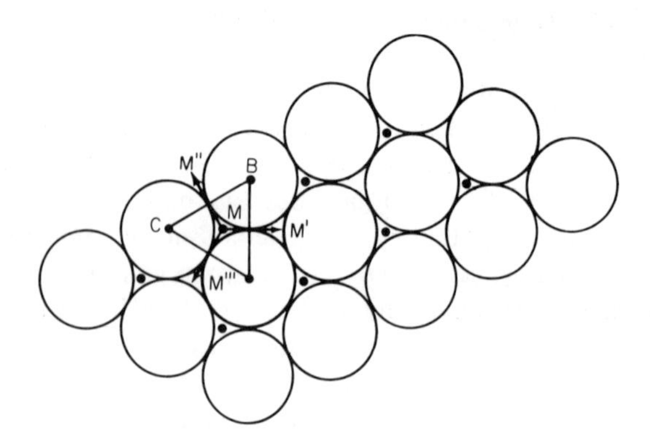

FIG. 17-1 Free slip of atoms over the lowest barriers formed by the underlying layer of atoms in an FCC aggregate expanded 4.5%

Melting. It is of interest to examine how this statistical behavior affects the incidence of melting. To simplify the discussion we resort to the close-packed model of a FCC aggregate depicted in Fig. 9-11, Chapter 9, and reproduced in Fig. 17-1. The atoms symbolized by the dots find the lowest barriers to slip in the directions MM', MM'', and MM'''. Accordingly, as shown in the illustrative problem, Section 17-6, they could freely slip past these barriers as soon as the linear thermal expansion reckoned from absolute zero exceeds locally the value of 4.5 percent. However, for the slip to actually occur, the aggregate must also lose its structural order and stability; it must cease to oppose changes of shape and become a liquid.

Most metals—FCC, HCP, and BCC—as well as many minerals begin to melt long before the average linear expansion exceeds 4.5 percent. Rather consistently they reach their melting point when the average value of linear thermal expansion, reckoned from absolute zero, is in the neighborhood of 2.5 percent.[3] The inference is that at this juncture sufficiently large clusters of atoms have attained locally the required 4.5 percent of thermal expansion and

[3] C. Zwikker, *Physical Properties of Solid Materials*, Interscience, New York, 1954.

become sufficiently disordered to nucleate melting.[4] Yet to keep the process of melting going, additional energy is needed. It is supplied in the form of heat of fusion familiar from general chemistry.

Therein lies the key to most of the structural changes produced by temperature variation. As a rule the rise of temperature favors those structural forms which increase the randomness of thermal motion of atoms by virtue of their less ordered configuration. This rule is but a corollary of a more fundamental principle, the second principle of thermodynamics, whose precise formulation in all propriety must be left to the course of thermodynamics. Nevertheless the most restricted rule offered here suffices to show that the change from the solid to the liquid state is an inescapable consequence of the rise of temperature.

17-3 Effect of Pressure. The *p-T* Phase Diagram. As explained in Chapter 6, the application of hydrostatic pressure produces a decrease of volume but leaves the shape of the body unchanged. However, the decrease of volume caused by atmospheric pressure is too small to affect significantly any of the phenomena described in Section 17-2. Accordingly, these phenomena were treated as though the substance were in a vacuum. Yet the study of the rock formation in the depth of the earth proves that hydrostatic pressure when high enough can produce considerable change in crystal structure, e.g., transformation of graphite into diamond. Many of these changes since have been reproduced in the laboratory, thanks to the progress of the high pressure technique pioneered by P. W. Bridgman. Moreover many new transformations have been discovered.[5] Therein lies the importance of this new technique for future engineering applications.

As far as the *known* transformations are concerned, the effect of pressure on the melting point is a phenomenon quite familiar from general physics. Experiment shows that the increase of pressure raises the melting point of substances which *expand* on melting and lowers the melting point of substances which *contract* on melting.

A classical example is provided by the melting point of ice. It is well known that ice contracts on melting. If a loop of wire is passed over a block of ice supported at both ends, and a weight is suspended from the loop, the pressure under the wire produces local melting at a temperature which is lower than 0°C, the melting point at atmospheric pressure.[6]

Theoretically the dependence of the melting point on pressure can be

[4] It is of interest to note that, in the FCC aluminum and lead and in the HCP cadmium, the additional thermal expansion caused by melting brings the total linear thermal expansion, reckoned from absolute zero, to about 4 percent, or reasonably close to the theoretical value of 4.5 percent.

[5] W. Paul and D. M. Warschauer, *Solids Under Pressure*, McGraw-Hill, N.Y. 1963.

[6] The process of melting continues through the thickness of the block thanks to the supply of heat of fusion provided by refreezing or *regelation* of the quantity of water squeezed out from under the wire.

derived in a straightforward way from the basic principles of thermodynamics. Here we shall develop the pertinent relationship in a more roundabout and approximate way. We first examine what happens to a substance which expands on melting when the external pressure is nil. We then re-examine the situation when the external pressure is different from zero.

In the first instance all of the supplied heat of fusion goes into disordering of the atomic structure, as explained in Section 17-2. In the second instance additional amount of heat must be supplied to do work against external pressure which opposes volume expansion on melting. This work is of the same nature as the work of plastic deformation considered in Section 9-14, Chapter 9. There are, however, two main differences: (1) the work is done not only in the direction of length l but also in the direction of width a and thickness b; (2) the conventional stress σ_o is here replaced by a stress equal and opposite to the external pressure p, which is constant.

With this in mind we first rewrite the expression for the work of deformation W' per unit volume, Eq. (9-49), by replacing σ_o by p (a constant) and ε by ε_l. There follows

$$W' = \int_o^{\varepsilon_l} p d\varepsilon = p\varepsilon_l \tag{17-1}$$

We then add to this work the work done in the directions of width and thickness. If the corresponding strains are ε_a and ε_b, the work of deformation W'_v per unit volume in all three directions is

$$W'_v = p(\varepsilon_l + \varepsilon_a + \varepsilon_b) \tag{17-2}$$

By Equation (6-36), Chapter 6, this is the same as

$$W'_v = p\varepsilon_v \tag{17-3}$$

where ε_v is the volumetric strain. Here, however, ε_v is the volumetric expansion per unit volume caused by melting. Therefore the work W'_v is equal to the additional amount of heat of fusion needed to carry out the process of melting under pressure. Denoting by H'_p and H'_o the heats of fusion per unit volume of the substance melted under external pressure p and under no external pressure we can accordingly write

$$H'_p - H'_o = p\varepsilon_v \tag{17-4}$$

To make the units consistent, the heats of fusion are expressed here in joules per cubic meter and the pressure is expressed in newtons per square meter. Of course ε_v has no dimensions.

Consider now a pressure only slightly above its zero value. For such a small increment of pressure the work of volumetric expansion is negligible compared to the work necessary to take the atoms past their "slip" barriers, Fig. 17-1. In other words the mechanism of melting under pressure is essentially the same as without pressure. So is the randomizing process of the vibrational thermal energy described in Section 17-2. Under these circumstances, as proved more conclusively by statistical arguments which we must omit, additional energy to do work can come only from an increase of the average vibrational thermal energy of the atoms. By Eq. (16-21), Chapter 16, such an increase is tantamount to raising the temperature of fusion.

Specifically let ΔT_f be the increase of temperature of fusion T_f caused by an increment Δp of the external pressure above its zero value. Since the mechanism of melting has remained the same, the additional heat of fusion per unit volume $\Delta H'_f$ is shared among the vibrating atoms in the same way as the initial heat of fusion H'_f. It therefore stands in the same relation to ΔT_f as H'_f does to T_f. That is,

$$\frac{\Delta H'_f}{\Delta T_f} = \frac{H'_f}{T_f} \tag{17-5}$$

Substituting Δp for p and $\Delta H'_f$ for $H'_p - H'_o$ in Eq. (17-4) and using Eq. (17-5) we get

$$\frac{H'_f \Delta T_f}{T_f} = \Delta p \varepsilon_v$$

or rearranging the terms

$$\frac{\Delta T_f}{\Delta p} = \frac{T_f \varepsilon_v}{H'_f} \tag{17-6}$$

We can put Eq. (17-6) in a more standard form by referring the heat of fusion not to a unit volume, but to one mole of the substance. If v_m is the volume occupied by one mole and H_f is the corresponding heat of fusion, we have

$$H'_f = H_f/v_m \tag{17-7}$$

and on substituting in Eq. (17-6)

$$\frac{\Delta T_f}{\Delta p} = \frac{T_f \Delta v_m}{H_f} \tag{17-8}$$

where

$$\Delta v_m = v_m \varepsilon_v \tag{17-9}$$

is the volumetric change on melting of one mole of the substance.

Whatever the assumption about the mechanism of melting, the smaller the deviation from the actual temperature of fusion, the more exact becomes the relationship embodied by Eq. (17-8). In the limit this relationship reads for a temperature of fusion at any pressure,

$$\frac{dT_f}{dp} = \frac{T_f \Delta v_m}{H_f} \tag{17-10}$$

The form assumed by Eq. (17-10) is known as the *Clapeyron* equation, from the name of the French physicist, B. P. E. Clapeyron (1832).

Equation (17-10) applies equally well to substances which contract on melting as to those which expand on melting.

If the substance contracts, Δv_m is negative. Hence by Eq. (17-10) an increase of pressure lowers the melting point.

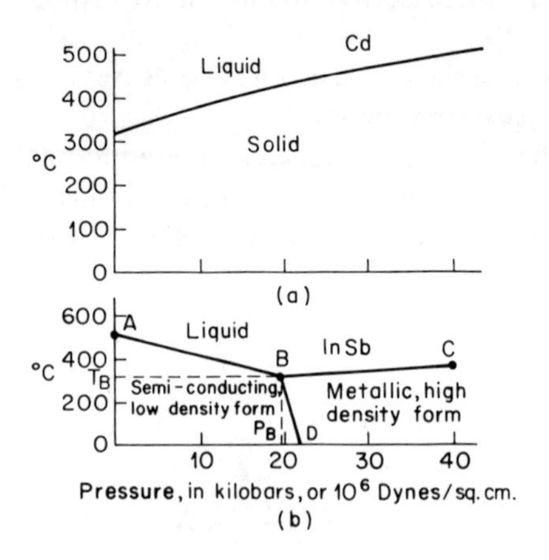

FIG. 17-2 The p-T phase diagrams of (a) Cd and (b) Sb. (After G. C. Kennedy, R. C. Newton, and A. Jayaraman)

Experimentally Clapeyron's equation can be verified by plotting the temperature of melting as a function of pressure. The slope at the origin can then be checked against Eq. (17-10). The check is excellent.[7] In many instances the start of the plot is linear, Fig. 17-2a and b, thereby also substantiating the validity of Eq. (17-8).[8] As the pressure increases, a more or less sharp deviation from linearity can be noted. Yet in all circumstances, as long as the volumetric change on melting Δv_m is of the same sign, the plot has an upward trend when Δv_m is positive, Fig. 17-2a and a downward trend when Δv_m is negative, line AB, Fig. 17-2b. This is so because in Eq. (17-10) neither T_f nor H_f is negative; T_f is positive by definition and H_f must be positive, if the substance transforms from an ordered solid to a disordered liquid. It follows that a change of sign in the slope dT/dp denotes a change of density of either the forming liquid, or more likely, the melting solid. Moreover, if the change of sign is as abrupt as from AB to BC, Fig. 17-2b, we are justified in concluding that the substance has assumed a new, more dense crystal structure under increasing pressure. Clearly the new structure is also denser than the forming liquid, since the trend of BC is upward.

We further notice that the polymorphic transformation from the low to the high density crystal structure under pressure p_B occurs at the highest possible

[7] H. M. Strong. "Melting Temperatures of Metals at Very High Pressures," *American Scientist*, **48**, 58 (1960).

[8] The linearity results from the constancy of the ratio T_f/H_f implied in Eq. (17-6). See Problem 17-3.

temperature, T_B at point B. For pressures smaller than p_B the low density modification melts before undergoing transformation. For pressures higher than p_B it transforms according to Eq. (17-10) at lower temperatures than T_B, provided H_f remains positive. The ensuing functional relationship between p and T then has a downward trend, the same as AB. It is indicated in Fig. 17-2b by the line BD. Point B corresponding to the coexistence of the two crystal forms with the liquid is called a *triple* point.

The preceding discussion is a good illustration of the usefulness of diagrams such as those depicted by Fig. 17-2a and b. Not only does a break in the trend of these diagrams reveal the advent of a new crystal form, but the functional relationship between p and T serves to delineate regions in the p-T field in which one or the other form is stable before melting.

The p-T diagrams have been particularly helpful in clarifying the nature of transformations in semiconducting compounds, such as InSb mentioned in Section 17-2. Even though restricted to polymorphic transformations, the p-T diagrams are called *p-T phase* diagrams in keeping with the usage of general chemistry which indiscriminately applies the word phase to all transformations, polymorphic as well as chemical (see Section 17-5).

17-4 Effect of Composition. Governing Factors. The effects of chemical composition on structural changes have been studied far more extensively than the effects of pressure. They also have been utilized in practice considerably more than the latter. Yet they are much less understood. The reason lies in the complexity of interactions which develop between the admixed, foreign atoms and the existing, host atoms in a given aggregate.

Despite this complexity we can often conceive of the foreign atoms as acting in one of three ways:[9]

1. They can upset and even destroy the fit between closest neighbors by having a larger or a smaller size than the host atoms.
2. They can modify the strength of interatomic bonding, yet leave its nature unchanged, by providing more or less valence electrons for sharing among the same number of atoms.
3. Finally, they can alter the chemical nature of the bond by also changing the spatial distribution of the electrons.

These conceptual differences can be illustrated by the following three examples:

1. Na and K are both monovalent metals, and both form a body-centered cubic crystal structure. However, the atom of potassium is 25 percent larger than the atom of sodium. Experiment shows that despite the identity of crystal structure it is impossible for any significant amount of potassium to remain in the crystal lattice built by sodium, and vice-versa. Yet the valence

[9] W. Hume-Rothery, *Atomic Theory for Students in Metallurgy*, The Institute of Metals, London, 1945.

electrons maintain sufficient cohesion between the two kinds of atoms to keep them aggregated, albeit in a disordered and unstable manner, as a single liquid upon melting.

Since no disparity in valency or in the nature of bonding is involved, we attribute the inability of the two kinds of atoms to build a common *stable* configuration solely to the incompatibility of their sizes, or shortly to the *size factor*.

2. At variance with Na and K atoms, Cu and Zn atoms have nearly the same size, and both copper and zinc are metals. However Zn atom contributes two valence electrons to the metallic bonding while Cu atom contributes only one. This circumstance apparently does not prevent the bivalent ion of zinc to proxy for the monovalent ion of copper in the FCC crystal structure assumed by the latter. In fact almost 40 percent of all copper atoms can thus be replaced by zinc atoms at room temperature without affecting the stability of the FCC configuration. Yet as the number of valence electrons per atom, or shortly the *electron concentration*, reaches the neighborhood of 1.5, a closer analysis which we must omit shows that the FCC structure becomes less stable than the BCC structure. Accordingly, there is a phase transformation from the FCC phase to the BCC phase.

In Cu-Zn alloys an electron concentration of 1.5 corresponds to a 50 percent atomic concentration of Zn and a stoichiometric formula CuZn. X-ray diffraction analysis shows that in agreement with this formula an ordered BCC structure replaces the disordered FCC structure at room temperature, Fig. 17-3.[10] Above 454°C, though, the BCC structure becomes disordered in accordance with the rule stated in Section 17-2a. Phase transformations from FCC to BCC structure at or about a 1.5 electron concentration also occur for other copper alloys as well as for alloys of silver and gold.[11] However, the stoichiometric formula corresponding to the 1.5 electron concentration will vary depending on the valency of the proxying ion. (See problems 17-6 to 17-9.)

3. Finally, consider the effect of admixing Sb atoms to In atoms in the ratio 1:1. Indium is a metal and so is antimony, although the latter shows strong evidence of covalent bonding as explained in Chapter 1. The difference in atomic sizes does not exceed 16 percent, which in similar cases is found to be no obstacle to the formation of a solid aggregate possessing likewise metallic properties. Yet at room temperature and atmospheric pressure InSb is a compound and a semiconductor. It has the same type of crystal structure as ZnS described in Chapter 13. That is, each In atom is surrounded by four Sb atoms placed at the corners of a tetrahedron, and vice versa. This arrangement is in fact identical to the one possessed by elements of Group IV

[10] Since the identity of the atom in the center of the cube, Fig. 17-3, is different from that of the corner atoms, we no longer have a BCC lattice, but rather a crystal structure of the same type.

[11] W. Hume-Rothery, *loc. cit.*

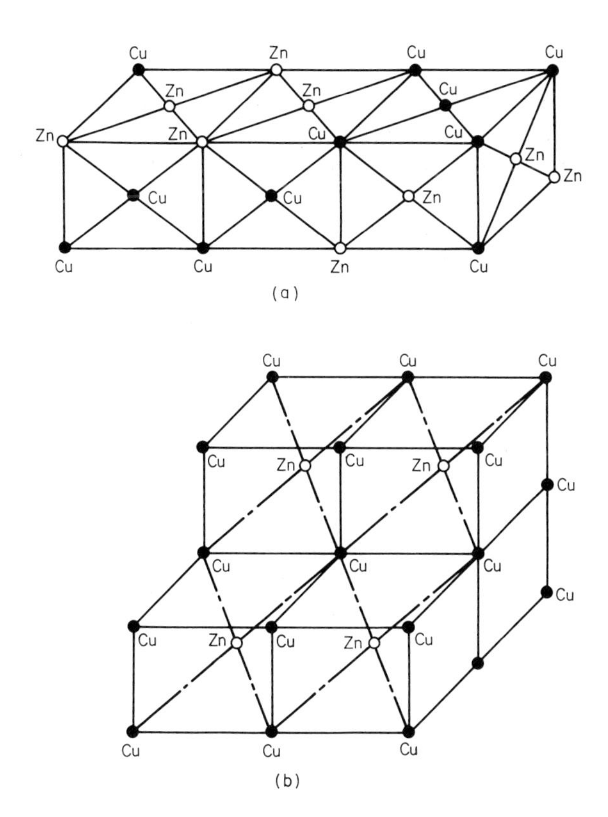

FIG. 17-3 (a) Disordered FCC structure of Cu Zn alloy; (b) ordered BCC structure of Cu Zn alloy

of the Periodic Table under atmospheric conditions, viz. diamond, silicon, and germanium. The inference is that the same type of covalent bonding prevails in InSb as in the latter. Since In has three valence electrons and Sb has five, we picture that the process of sharing is achieved by letting the valence electrons alternate or resonate between the two kinds of atoms. Accordingly each In atom is assumed to borrow five valence electrons from its four closest Sb neighbors in one instant and to lend its own three electrons to them in another instant.[12] Clearly this type of bonding is quite different from the metallic bonding in which all valence electrons are assumed to be equally shared between all atoms of the lattice near and far. Thus, at variance with the two previous effects, here the structural changes are due neither to incompatibility of atomic sizes nor to increased electron concentration. Rather they are caused by a spatial redistribution of electrons and the

[12] An alternative view is to consider that the bond is of an ionic type. According to this view the In atom loses three electrons and becomes In^{+++}, while the Sb atom acquires three electrons thus becoming Sb^{---}. Both views are probably an oversimplification of reality.

ensuing alteration of the chemical bond, in short by the *electrochemical* factor.

The above examples are sufficiently simple so that the role of the particular factor can be easily singled out. However, in many instances no such sharp differentiation is possible. This is particularly true of the electron concentration and electrochemical factors, but it also applies to the size factor. Still, atomic radii when defined in a consistent way[13] do have an important bearing on the geometry of crystal structures built of dissimilar atoms. They lead to predictions based on the ratio of atomic radii which are generally borne out by the structure of alloys, Chapter 18, as well as ceramics, Chapter 19. Likewise, the shape of long chain molecules has an overriding influence on the types of crystal forms assumed by polymers, Chapter 20.

17-5 Terminology. The *c-T* Phase Diagrams. As in the case of pressure, Section 17-3, the structural effects of chemical composition can be better recognized, if not understood, through the effect of composition on the temperature of transformation. For the sake of generality, the effect of pressure also should be included. However, such general study is not warranted at this level of presentation. Besides it is only in its beginning.[14] Consequently a constant atmospheric pressure is implicit in all future discussions. By the argument of Section 17-3, the effects of pressure are thereby all but eliminated. The remaining effects are then adequately and completely depicted by the functional relationship between temperature and composition.

In dealing with this relationship it is well to use the terminology adopted in general chemistry. We first distinguish between a phase and a solution.

A *phase* is defined in general chemistry as a homogeneous part of a system separated from other parts by physical boundaries. The definition holds, whatever the content of the parts. When a phase contains more than one molecular or atomic species, we call it a *solution*.

These definitions offer little ambiguity in the liquid state. In the solid state, though, physical boundaries also exist between grains of the same crystal structure, i.e., of the same phase, if they have different orientations in space (see Chapter 3). For this reason it is more reliable to identify a solid phase by its crystal structure, as we did in Section 17-1, the glassy state being then characterized by lack of structure.

There is less ambiguity in the definition of a *solid solution*. For example, when Cu and Zn atoms build a common FCC structure, it is impossible to determine by physical methods, say by X-ray diffraction, which sites in the unit cells are occupied by one and which by the other atomic species. On the other hand, all a chemical analysis can do is to reveal the average composition of the bulk. As in the case of a liquid solution, our inability to identify a

[13] L. Pauling, *The Nature of the Chemical Bond*, Cornell U.P., Ithaca, 1945.
[14] W. Paul and D. M. Warschauer, *loc. cit.*

given site with a given atomic species stems in part from the steady, albeit slow, interchange of atoms caused by thermal motion. Yet when the structure becomes ordered, as it does in CuZn alloys for the 1.5 electron concentration (Section 17-4), the interchange is no longer haphazard. It is confined to atoms of the same atomic species, very much like in a compound. Hence the name *electronic compound* is suggested for this ordered type of crystal structure.

While on the subject of terminology we may also recall that when one component is present in the solution in much larger amounts than the rest it is called a *solvent*. The other components then become the *solutes*. This nomenclature applies equally well to solid as to liquid solutions.

Finally, in regard to solid solutions, we must distinguish between *substitutional* and *interstitial* solid solutions. In the substitutional solid solutions, the foreign atom merely takes up a site *normally* occupied by the host atom. In the interstitial solid solutions, the foreign atom inserts itself *between* the sites occupied by the host atoms. Obviously, such an insertion is possible only when the size of the foreign atom is compatible with the dimensions of the free space left between the host atoms. A typical example of a substitutional solid solution is the already mentioned CuZn alloy. Iron-carbon alloy exemplifies the interstitial type of solid solutions. As seen from Fig. 18-29, Chapter 18, the face centered cubic (high temperature) variety of iron leaves in the center of the unit cell a space into which an atom can be fitted with a diameter equal to 0.41 of the iron atom diameter. Actually, the ratio of carbon-iron atom diameters, based on the distance of closest approach is 0.56, indicating that an expansion of the unit cell must take place to accommodate the larger carbon atom. This situation is similar to that encountered in substitutional solid solutions and it is taken up later in Section 18-10, Chapter 18, in more detail.

We now turn to the specification of *composition*. In the case of alloys, Chapter 18, it is customary to specify the composition of phases in terms of the constitutive atomic species: Cu, Zn, Al, etc. In the case of ceramics, Chapter 19, the custom is rather to specify the molecular species from which the phases are formed: SiO_2, Al_2O_3, etc. In either case the composition can be expressed in *weight* percent or in *atomic* and *molar* percent, respectively.

Example 1.

An alloy of Cu and Al is made by melting 25 grams of Al with 475 grams of Cu. Specify the weight and atomic composition of the alloy.

Solution. a. The weight percent of Al is

$$100 \times \frac{25}{475 + 25} = 5\%$$

By implication the weight percent of Cu is 95 percent.

b. An atom gram of Al weighs 26.97 grams and an atom gram of Cu weighs 63.57 grams. Hence there are

$$25/26.97 = 0.93 \text{ atom grams of Al}$$

and

$$475/63.57 = 7.5 \text{ atom grams of Cu}$$

or a total of

$$8.43 \text{ atom grams.}$$

The atomic percent of Al is then

$$100 \times \frac{0.93}{8.43} = 11.1\%$$

and by implication the atomic percent of Cu is 89.9 percent.

Example 2.

A ceramic is made by melting 150 grams of Al_2O_3 and 50 grams of SiO_2. Specify the weight and molar composition of the ceramic.

Solution. a. The weight percent of Al_2O_3 is

$$100 \times \frac{150}{200} = 75\%$$

By implication the weight percent of SiO_2 is 25 percent.

b. A mol gram of Al_2O_3 weighs:

$$\begin{array}{lr} Al_2 - 2 \times 26.97 = & 53.94 \text{ grams} \\ O_3 - 3 \times 16.00 = & 48.00 \text{ grams} \\ \hline Al_2O_3 - & 101.94 \text{ grams} \end{array}$$

In the same manner we find the weight of one mol gram of SiO_2 as

$$\begin{array}{lr} Si - & 28.06 \text{ grams} \\ O_2 - & 32.00 \text{ grams} \\ \hline SiO_2 & 60.06 \text{ grams} \end{array}$$

Consequently there are

$$150/101.94 = 1.48 \text{ mol grams of } Al_2O_3$$

and

$$50/60.06 = 0.83 \text{ mol grams of } SiO_2$$

or a total of

$$2.31 \text{ mol grams.}$$

The molar percent of Al_2O_3 is then

$$100 \times \frac{1.48}{2.31} = 64\%$$

and by implication the molar percent of SiO_2 is 36 percent.

The specification of composition by weight percent is probably more convenient, but the atomic or the molecular percent is more revealing of the true relationship between unlike atoms.

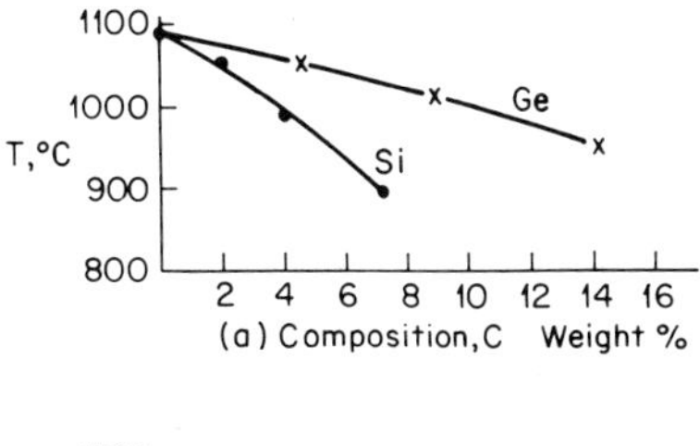

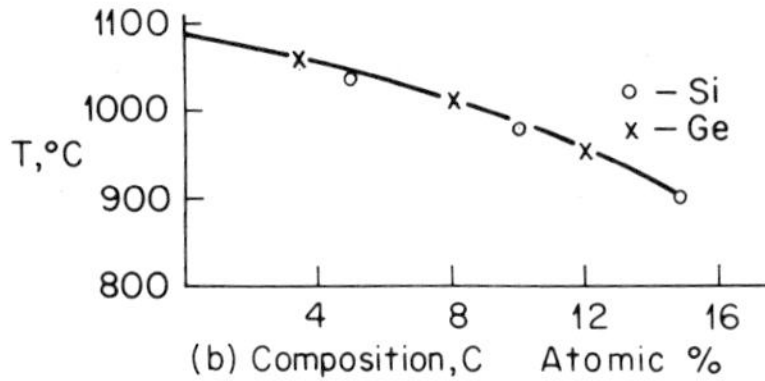

FIG. 17-4 Lowering of the temperature of onset of melting in Cu by admixture of Si or Ge to the melt (a) in weight %; (b) in atomic %. (After W. Hume-Rothery)

Consider, for example, the influence of Si and Ge atoms on the lowering of the melting point in Cu,[15] Fig. 17-4. Expressed in weight percent the influence of Si is stronger, Fig. 17-4a. Yet Ge contributes the same number of valence electrons per atom to the solution as does Si and it has about the same atomic size as the latter. On both counts, then, atom for atom, the effects of Ge and Si are expected to be equivalent. This expectation is borne out by the plot of Fig. 17-4b, in which the amounts of Ge and Si are expressed in atomic per cent instead of weight percent.

For the rest the two types of diagrams are similar. They reveal the same trend between the temperature of melting T[16] and composition C as the diagram, Fig. 17-3, does between the temperature of melting, T and pressure, p. Unfortunately the trend of a c-T diagram cannot be interpreted, let alone derived, as readily as in the case of the p-T diagrams. True, for small admixtures of foreign atoms and molecules, i.e., for *dilute solutions*, a formula for the lowering of melting point can be derived from basic principles of thermodynamics, but the range of its applicability is limited—too limited for

[15] More accurately of the onset of melting. See Chapter 18.
[16] More accurately of the onset of melting. See Chapter 18.

most engineering applications. Still, the temperature-composition, or the *c-T* phase diagrams are far from being useless. Like their *p-T* counterparts, they reveal the advent of new phases by the break or discontinuity of their trends. In addition the *c-T* relationship serves to delineate regions in the *c-T* field where one or more phases are stable. This information alone is sometimes sufficient to select a phase which possesses the desired material property, e.g., a melting point that is considerably lower than that of its components, as in solders. More often, however, additional information is required to make the proper choice. It is obtained by making a systematic study of typical phase diagrams, as explained in the next chapter devoted to alloys.

17-6 Summary. In this chapter, introductory to Part III, attention is focused on the conditions, external and internal to the material, under which a given crystal remains stable. A foundation thereby is provided for the succeeding chapters which consider the occurrences of new crystal structures and study the ensuing changes of properties in three classes of materials: alloys, ceramics and polymers.

A distinction is made between *polymorphism* (or allotropism) involving changes of structure alone, and *phase transformations* entailing also changes of chemical nature. The distinction is essentially based on the absence of large scale atom movements in polymorphism and their presence in phase transformations. In both instances temperature, pressure, and chemical composition are usually the main governing factors.

Rise of temperature favors those forms of aggregation, crystalline or amorphous, which allow the atoms greater randomness, or freedom, of thermal motion. Therein lies the reason for *melting*.

The influence of pressure, p, is best studied through its effect on the temperature of transformation, T. This effect is embodied in Clapeyron's equation

$$\frac{dT}{dp} = \frac{T\Delta v_m}{H}$$

where Δv_m is the change of molar volume and H is the molar heat accompanying the transformation. Experimentally the same effect can be investigated by means of *p-T phase diagrams*.

The influence of chemical composition on phase transformation is less predictable than that of pressure. At least three factors can be recognized in the interaction between host atoms and foreign atoms during transformation

(a) the ratio of the atomic sizes, or the *size* factor,
(b) the number of valence electrons per atom, or the *electron concentration* factor and
(c) the alteration of the chemical bond, or the *electrochemical* factor.

In a few simple cases one single factor prevails. For example, the size factor governs the process of solidification of the solution containing Na and K atoms. Similarly the electron concentration factor plays a major role in the modifications of crystal structure of Cu-Zn alloys. Finally the electrochemical factor presides over the formation of a semi-conducting InSb compound from metallic In and Sb. More often, however, the contributions of the three factors cannot be sharply distinguished.

Like the influence of pressure, the influence of chemical composition, c, on phase transformations is best understood through its effect on the temperature of transformation, T. Experimentally this understanding is gained from the study of *c-T phase diagrams* at constant (atmospheric) pressure.

Unlike liquid phases *solid* phases cannot be identified merely by the existence of physical boundaries separating one homogeneous part of a system from another. Instead each solid phase must possess a different type of crystal structure, or a different size of unit cell in case the two phases have the same type of crystal structure, e.g., Na and K.

On the other hand the meaning of a *solid* solution is not very different from that of a liquid solution. In both cases the word denotes one single phase containing two or more atomic or molecular species that cannot be identified by purely physical means, e.g., by X-ray diffraction. When they can be so identified, e.g., in the ordered CuZn alloy, some authors prefer to call the phase an *electronic compound*, the word electronic recalling the influence of the electron concentration factor on the type of crystal structure.

Solid solutions are called *substitutional* when the solute atom replaces the solvent atom and interstitial when it inserts itself between the solvent atoms.

A composition of a phase is specified either in terms of the constitutive atomic species: Cu, Zn, etc.—mostly in alloys—or in terms of the molecular species from which the phase is made up: Al_2O_3, SiO_2, etc.—mostly in ceramics. In both instances the composition can be expressed in weight percent or in atomic and molar percent, respectively. Weight percentages are more customary, but atomic percentages are more reavealing of the true relationship between unlike atoms.

17-7 Illustrative Problem. Compute the value of the coefficient of thermal expansion enabling atom M in Fig. 17-1 to freely slip into one of the positions marked M', M'', M''' over the lowest barriers formed by the underlying layer of atoms, A, B, C, etc.

Solution. Let α be the coefficient of thermal expansion. If the distance of closest approach AB, BC, AC at absolute zero is r_o then thermal expansion increases this distance to A_1B_1 (Fig. 17-5) such that

$$A_1B_1 = r_o(1 + \alpha)$$

Likewise let d be the distance at absolute zero separating the layer contain-

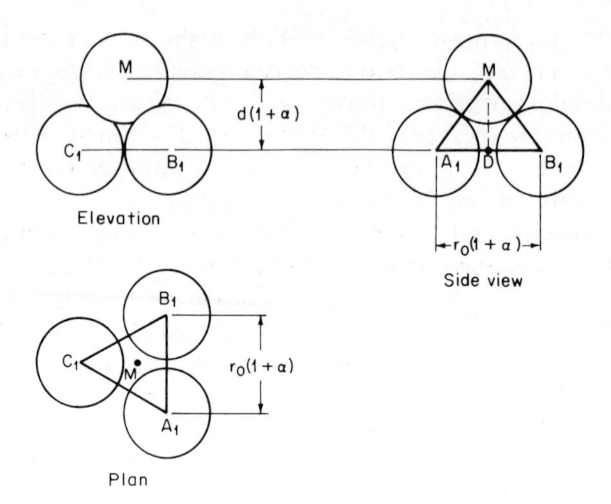

FIG. 17-5 Position of atoms in a close packed structure corresponding to free slip of atom M past the barrier A_1B_1

ing atom M from the layer containing the underlying atoms $A_1B_1C_1$, etc. According to Fig. 9-11, Chapter 9, distance d can be written as

$$d = \sqrt{2/3}\, r_o$$

Taking into account the thermal expansion this distance becomes

$$d_1 = d(1 + \alpha) = \sqrt{2/3}\, r_o(1 + \alpha)$$

On the other hand when atom M is atop the two atoms A and B, its distance MD from the underlying layer becomes (Fig. 17-5)

$$MD = \sqrt{r_o^2 - r_o^2(1 + \alpha)^2/4}$$

Free slip will take place when $d_1 = MD$ or when

$$r_o\sqrt{2/3}(11 + \alpha) = r_o\sqrt{1 - (1 + \alpha)^2/4}$$

Solving for α we get

$$\alpha = 4.5\%$$

References

1. A. Taylor, *X-Ray Metallography*, Wiley, New York, 1961.
2. W. Hume-Rothery, *Atomic Theory for Students in Metallurgy*, The Institute of Metals, London, 1945.
3. W. Paul and D. M. Warshauer, Ed., *Solids Under Pressure*, Monograph, McGraw-Hill, New York, 1963.

Problems

17-1 Show that the polymorphic change depicted by Fig. 17-2b requires that the average amplitude of vibration $a = 0.187\ A'B'$. Also, if $AB \geq r_o$ (r_o corresponding to absolute zero) show that the smallest value of the average coefficient of thermal expansion is about 3 percent.

17-2 Compute the change of volume accompanying the transformation of a BCC lattice to an FCC lattice assuming a hard sphere model and making no allowance for thermal expansion.

17-3 Using Eq. (17-5) prove that T is a linear function of p.

17-4 Show that a 50 atomic percent of Zn in Cu allows for an ordered layer structure in the cube direction in an FCC type of crystal structure.

17-5 What kind of ordered structure can be built in an FCC Cu-Zn alloy containing 25 atomic percent of Zn? Note that this is a hypothetical structure; however, a similar structure does exist in Cu-Au alloys.

17-6 By analogy with the Cu-Zn ordered alloy, what kind of an ordered crystal structure could be assigned to an alloy made up of atoms A and B, of which A is monovalent and B is trivalent, if the electron concentration 1.5 is to be preserved? Give the formula for the compound.

17-7 If A in problem 17-6 is Au and B is Al, what weight percent should be assigned to aluminum?

17-8 Same problem as 17-6 except that A is monovalent and B is tetravalent.

17-9 Give a general formula for a compound satisfying the 1.5 electron concentration, if A has a valency p and B has a valency q.

18 / ALLOYS

Perhaps nowhere have the concentration-temperature, or the *c-T*, phase diagrams described in Chapter 17 proved as valuable as in the study of metallic aggregates called *alloys*. Not only have the *c-T* diagrams enabled the metallurgist to devise a rational classification of the alloys, but they also have provided reliable criteria for anticipating their structural changes and, by inference, their properties. This particular aspect of phase diagrams enhances the role which alloys, and metals in general, have played in the development of technology throughout the ages.

18-1 Importance of Metals. Most of the properties studied in Part II refer to metals. The reason is twofold:

1. Metals have a simple internal structure. Therefore, the relation between properties and structure can be better understood in metals than in other solids.
2. Metals are by far the most important solids in engineering.

The importance of metals, particularly steel, is not so much evidenced by their tonnage, probably the largest of that of any manufactured product.[1] Rather it is reflected in the influence metals have had on the trend of human civilization.

Historians usually distinguish three major periods in our civilization: the Stone Age up to about 3000 B.C., the Bronze Age up to about 1500 B.C., and the current Iron Age. The distinction formally is based on the preponderant use of stone, bronze and iron for making tools, but it implies more than mere changes in raw material. It marks important phases of human endeavor to subjugate and dominate hostile environments. This endeavor would have been impossible without the inherent ability of man to create tools.

Already in their simplest form, as a club or a hammer, tools had enabled primitive man to multiply manyfold the puny force and power on his muscles. However, the true value of the tool came with the cutting edge, with the invention of spearheads, arrowheads, axes, knives, etc. The sharpness of the cutting edge made it possible to pierce, and hence destroy, any obstacle that was less hard than the tool itself. Hence, the sharper and harder

[1] The world production of metals in 1965 exceeded 520 million tons, of which 500 millions of iron alone, with an estimated annual increase of about 6.7 percent for the next three years. (*E/MJ, Engineering and Mining Journal*, McGraw-Hill, January 1967.)

the tool, the better were the chances for the primitive man to gain control over his environment and to adapt it to his needs and desires. Therein lies the main reason why stone—a readily available hard material—was among the first to be used in making tools. The stone tool industry reached a high degree of development between 6000 and 3000 B.C. when flint, a glossy and dense variety of quartz, became the basic raw material. Along with other equally usable forms of silica—chert, obsidian and chalcedony—flint not only was one of the hardest minerals known, but it had even a more desirable property of flaking or chipping with the production of a razor sharp cutting edge. However, the tendency to flaking made flint often less suitable for tools than native copper. Along with gold, which also could be found in the native state, copper initially had been used only for ornamental purposes. It was soon realized, however, that on being hammered it became sufficiently hard to serve as a tool. The trouble with copper, though, was that it was easily blunted.

As a result, the Stone Age did not altogether end with the introduction of native copper. Only when man had discovered the art of smelting—the art of extracting molten metal from ores by heating—had the stage been set for the advent of a new age. For only then was it possible to alloy two or more metals and arrive at a combination of properties, such as hardness and ductility, unattainable in any single pure metal, or in any other solid for that matter.

The Bronze Age was ushered in by a discovery, probably accidental, that copper when alloyed with tin became permanently hardened. The new material, called bronze, proved not only more durable than, but also vastly superior to, stone for making tools and weapons. Thanks to casting, bronze could be shaped in a greater variety of objects and it could be hammered and polished to a better finish. With the advent of the Bronze Age metal has assumed a leading role in the conquest of nature by man, to say nothing of his conquest of fellow men.

To call the succeeding age an Iron Age is something of a misnomer. The first samples containing iron came from meteorites and were alloys of iron and nickel. The iron that was rediscovered by smelting iron ores around 1500 B.C. contained a goodly amount of inclusions (slag) and some carbon picked up from the burning wood. It was soon recognized that this pick-up was essential to convert iron to steel which could then be hardened by quenching.

Whatever the circumstances, the discovery of iron was by far the most important single discovery made by mankind in the field of metals. No other equally great discovery in metallurgy was to be made for the next thirty-four centuries. For iron and its alloys, as we will see in Section 18-11, combine a set and range of properties met by no other metal. In its impact on the trend of civilization the discovery of iron is probably paralleled only by the invention of the liquid steel making process by Bessemer in 1855.

This statement does not imply that important improvements in the making and hardening of tools did not occur in between. Perhaps the best known is the production of the Damascus blade, named after the city in ancient Syria where it was first found by the Europeans. The steel came probably from India. Damascus swords were reputed for their hardness and flexibility. The blade could easily be bent into a circle, yet its cutting edge was as sharp and hard as that of a razor. The characteristic patterns etched on the blade added to its esthetic value.

There were many attempts in the Middle Ages to imitate both the nature and the appearance of the Damascus blade. Apparently the secret was well kept, because the imitations were invariably of poorer quality. There was no way of course to check either the composition or the treatment of the original product, for no such methods were available in the Middle Ages. True, the art of alloying was anything but languishing, particularly in Europe. But its purpose was to find the secret, the famous philosopher's stone, whereby common metals could be transmuted into gold. Quenching of steel was left to the craftsman who operated by the rule-of-thumb and the guidance of superstition. Not until methods of experimental analysis found their way into metallurgy had significant advances taken place in either the production or the treatment of metals.

One such advance was the already mentioned revolutionary process of steelmaking by Bessemer in 1855. Its application has made possible the production of large quantities of steel at low cost. Yet the process would have been doomed to failure had Bessemer not recognized in time the importance of chemical analysis for raw materials. Few metallurgists then appreciated the need for such an analysis. It was Bessemer's faith in experimental methods that saved the process from failure and this inventor from impending ruin.

The ever increasing use of experimental methods is in large measure responsible for the great variety of alloys now prevailing on the market. Their number easily exceeds one thousand, while the number of elements entering their composition hardly reaches forty.

All alloys exhibit to a greater or smaller degree properties that cannot be predicted from the properties of their components, that *defy the law of averages*. Thus, admixture of soft tin to soft copper produces an alloy, *bronze*, that is much harder than either tin or copper. Therein unquestionably lies the great value of alloying.

Yet alloy theory has not advanced to the point where such departures from the law of averages can be reliably predicted from first principles. Pending the arrival of this millenium the metallurgist is thrown back on experimental guides, of which the phase diagrams are probably the most useful, if not the most basic. For, regardless how the phase diagrams are obtained, they embody and reflect one of the principles which constitute the foundation of modern science, the principle of *statistical stability*.

18-2 Alloying and Statistical Stability. As intimated previously, the study of alloys, and of other heterogeneous aggregates as well, can gain considerably in depth and understanding by the use of the principles of statistical stability. To introduce this principle consider the oft cited process of mixing of two mono-atomic gases A and B. The gases are assumed to obey the ideal gas law familiar from General Chemistry. This law implies that the atoms are entirely free, that they have no tendency to aggregate either with their own kind or with foreign atoms. Inert elements discussed in Chapter I approach such a condition rather closely at room temperature.

Let there be N_A atoms A and N_B atoms B. At a given temperature T and pressure p_o gases A and B taken separately occupy volumes V_A and V_B that are prescribed by the ideal gas law as follows.[2]

$$p_o V_A = N_A kT \tag{18-1}$$

and

$$p_o V_B = N_B kT \tag{18-2}$$

where k is the univeral Boltzman constant $= 1.38 \times 10^{-23}$ joule/degree.

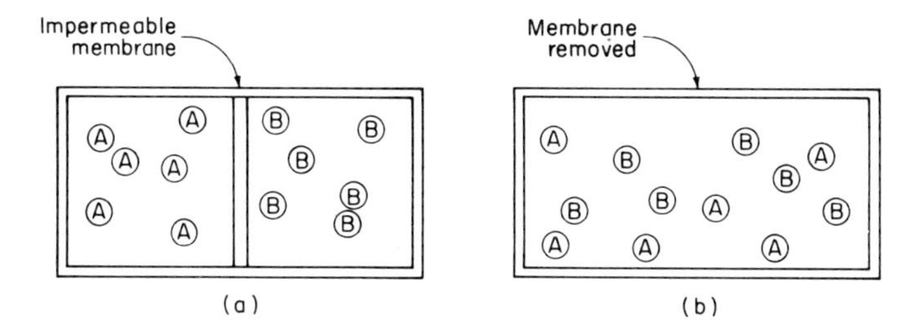

FIG. 18-1 Mixing of ideal gases A and B

We can join the two volumes V_A and V_B in a single volume V, yet keep the gases separated by means of a partition impervious to both kinds of atoms (Fig. 18-1). Since the temperature and pressure are the same on both sides of the partition, gas A will be in thermal and mechanical equilibrium with gas B.

Yet, the system is not stable. If the partition is removed, the gases will not remain confined to their initial volumes. Owing to thermal agitation and the ensuing collisions both kinds of atoms will scatter in all directions, and as a result they both will fill the entire volume V.

In the absence of any other information and for lack of sufficient reason we feel justified in stating that they will fill this volume uniformly. Yet, this statement needs further clarification. For, it can hardly mean that atoms A and B are everywhere arranged in the same regular and repetitive pattern akin, for example, to ions of Na and Cl in the crystal structure of NaCl. Even though such an arrangement could occur momentarily, it will be

[2] See, e.g., L. Pauling, *General Chemistry*, Freeman, San Francisco, 1948.

unavoidably destroyed in the subsequent tumultuous process of collisions. These collisions succeed each other at a rate of about 10^{10} times per second in gases. The word uniform, therefore, must relate to these randomly repeated collisions rather than to an identically repetitive pattern. We say that it must be interpreted statistically.

To put it differently, consider that within the compass of our observations the collisions are so numerous and so random that it is highly improbable, not to say impossible, to detect any differences in the behavior of the aggregate. We will show below that such indeed is the outcome of a spontaneous mixing of the two ideal gases of our present interest. However, the above statement has a much wider implication. It also implies the principle of *statistical stability*. For the process of random collisions makes it equally improbable that differences in behavior, imposed by external stimuli, can be detected once these stimuli have been removed and enough time has been allowed for redistribution of atoms within the aggregate. For all practical purposes then the aggregate on being disturbed by external stimuli behaves as though it tended to recover spontaneously its initial distribution. Reference to such a behavior was already made in Chapter 15, in the derivation of electrical resistivity. There, the electrons were pictured as losing the common drift velocity, imposed by a potential difference after each collision. We will find this statistical approach equally helpful in dealing with alloys.

To return to the problem of mixing, assume first that atoms A and B are randomly mixed, so that collisions occur indistinctly among all N atoms, where $N = N_A + N_B$. Imagine further that the volume V occupied by the mixture is subdivided into N cells, number 1 to N, and that each collision redistributes the atoms among these cells one atom to a cell, akin to a shuffle of N cards in a pack. The total number of possible rearrangements or permutations of the N atoms among the N cells is then given by the factorial

$$N! = N(N-1)(N-2)\ldots 1 \qquad (18\text{-}3)$$

This number also comprises those arrangements which correspond to the umixed situation. How many of such arrangements are possible?

To answer this question imagine now that the N_A atoms A are confined to a separate volume V_A, and correspondingly the N_B atoms are confined to volume V_A. Assigning as previously each atom to a separate cell, we have N_A cells in volume V_A and N_B cells in volume V_B. Consequently there are $N_A!$ possible redistributions or permutations of atoms A among the N_A cells and $N_B!$ possible permutations of atoms B among the N_B cells. In order to include these two sets of arrangements among those given by Eq. (18-3) we must consider them jointly. We note that for each of the $N_A!$ arrangements of atoms A there are $N_B!$ possible arrangements of atoms B, hence the total number of arrangements corresponding to the unmixed situation is $N_A!$ times greater, or

$$N_A!\,N_B! = N_A(N_A-1)\ldots 1 \times N_B(N_B-1)\ldots 1 \qquad (18\text{-}4)$$

What fraction f of the total number of permutations given by Eq. (18-3) do these permutations represent? In other words, what is the magnitude of

$$f = \frac{N_A!\, N_B!}{N!} \tag{18-5}$$

Since factorials are much more difficult to manipulate than sums, we resort to logarithms and with a view to further applications we use natural-logarithms. On this understanding

$$\ln f = \ln N_A! + \ln N_B! - \ln N!$$

or, replacing the logarithm of factorials by the sum of the logarithms of the cofactors

$$\ln f = \sum_1^{N_A} \ln m + \sum_1^{N_B} \ln m - \sum_1^{N} \ln m \tag{18-6}$$

where, e.g.,

$$\sum_1^{N} \ln m = \ln 1 + \ln 2 + \ldots \ln N. \tag{18-7}$$

If N, N_A and N_B are very large numbers, each of the sums in Eq. (18-6) can be approximated by an integral. For example, we can write

$$\ln N! = \sum_1^{N} \ln m = \sum_1^{N} \ln m \,\Delta m$$

where

$$\Delta m = (m + 1) - m$$

When m becomes very large compared to unity, hence to Δm, the summation can be approximated by an integration, thus

$$\ln N! = \int_1^N \ln x\, dx = \Big[x \ln x - x\Big]_1^N = N \ln N - (N - 1)$$

or disregarding unity in the difference $(N - 1)$ when N is large,

$$\ln N! = N \ln N - N \tag{18-8}$$

To see how good the approximation is, put $N = 25$.
There follows

$$\ln N! = 57.96$$

as compared to

$$N \ln N - N + 1 = 56.5$$

or a difference of about 2.6 percent.

Obviously, the approximation improves with increasing N and for all practical purposes it becomes an equality when N is as large as 10^{20}.

Consequently, using Eq. (18-8) in Eq. (18-6) we have

$$\ln f = N_A \ln N_A - N_A + N_B \ln N_B - N_B - N \ln N + N$$

or since

$$N_A + N_B = N$$

$$\ln f = N_A \ln (N_A/N) + N_B \ln (N_B/N) \tag{18-9}$$

Note: Eq. (18-9) can be readily generalized to include several species of atoms and any differences in behavior within the aggregate.

We shall now prove that within the total number of arrangements the fraction of unmixed arrangements f is negligibly small when N is a very large number.

To this end, express N_A and N_B in terms of the atomic concentrations c_A and c_B. By definition

$$c_A = N_A/N \tag{18-10}$$

and

$$c_B = N_B/N \tag{18-11}$$

Substitutions for N_A and N_B in Eq. (18-9) yields after simplification

$$\ln f = N[c_A \ln c_A + c_B \ln c_B] \tag{18-12}$$

Note: Eq. (18-12) can bereadily generalized similarly to Eq. (18-9) to include several atomic species.

In the current theory of alloying we seldom deal with concentrations smaller than 10^{-4}. Considering that the parenthetical expression in Eq. (18-12) is negative, we can therefore write with $c_A = 10^{-4}$ and $c_B = 1 - 10^{-4} = 1$

$$\ln f \leq - N(4 \ln 10) \times 10^{-4}$$

When N is of the order of 10^{20}, f is vanishingly small and so is, by implication, the probability of observing spontaneous umixing of the two gases in the process of random collisions.

Spontaneous random mixing does not preclude, however, the possibility that the gases can again be unmixed by an external agent, much in the same way as electrons in metals can be forced by the applied voltage to rebuild their common drift velocity after each random collision. Yet, in one case as another work must be expended to achieve departure from randomness.

Because of future applications we shall compute the work required to unmix the two ideal gases already considered by setting up the following "thought" procedure.

We imagine that a piston that is permeable to atoms B but impervious to atoms A moves from MN to PQ in the x direction, Fig. 18-2. In its advance the piston will propel forward all atoms A and compress them in a progressively smaller volume while leaving atoms B undisturbed. If the vessel is

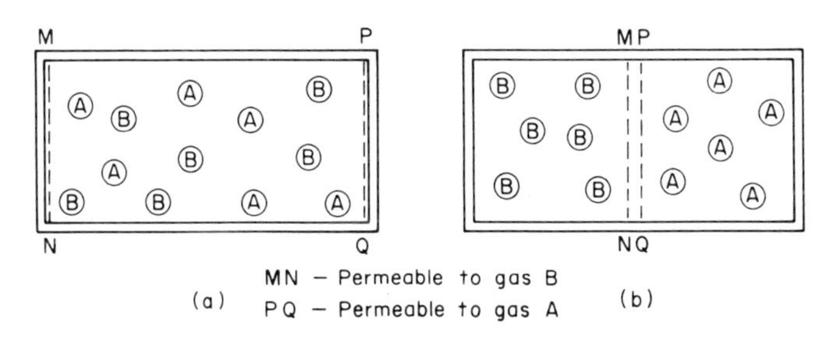

FIG. 18-2 Unmixing of ideal gases A and B

in thermal equilibrium with the surroundings and the piston moves slowly in small increments Δx, the work of compression and the ensuing small increases of the kinetic energy imparted to the A atoms will be dissipated as heat in the surroundings. We can thus confine all atoms A to their original volume V_A without changing their kinetic energy.

We can proceed in the same manner with atoms B, by imagining that another piston permeable to the A atoms but impervious to the B atoms moves in the opposite direction, from PQ to MN. When the two pistons meet at the location of the original partition (Fig. 18-1) the two gases will have been separated from each other and confined to their original volumes V_A and V_B without changing their total internal energy. The combined work of these two pistons will thus have been expended only to achieve the unmixing.

To carry out the actual computation we note that according to the ideal gas law, the gases A and B when allowed to intermix and fill out the whole volume V, each exert a (partial) pressure on the walls of the vessel as though the other gas weren't there. Denoting these partial pressures by p_A and p_B we have by analogy with Eq. (18-1) and Eq. (18-2)

$$p_A V = N_A kT \tag{18-13}$$

and

$$p_B V = N_B kT \tag{18-14}$$

Comparison with Eq. (18-1) and Eq. (18-2) shows that since $V_A + V_B = V$

$$p_A + p_B = p_o \tag{18-15}$$

Thus, compressing gas A from volume V to volume V_A raises its pressure from p_A to p_o and similarly compressing gas B from volume V to volume V_B raises *its* pressure from p_B to p_o.

Let in the course of the compression the partial pressure of gas A rise to a value p comprised between p_A and p_o. Since the piston is impervious to atoms A, all these atoms are in front of the piston and they oppose its motion by exerting a pressure p on its front area. There is no opposition from atoms B to which the piston is permeable. If S is the area of the piston, then the force F opposing its motion in the x direction is

$$F = pS \tag{18-16}$$

A further infinitesimal advance, dx of the piston requires an expenditure of outside work dW_A which, neglecting second order differentials, is

$$dW_A = F\,dx = pS\,dx \tag{18-17}$$

or, denoting by $-dV$ the change of volume which $S\,dx$ represents

$$dW_A = -p\,dV \tag{18-18}$$

But by the ideal gas law

$$pV = N_A kT \tag{18-19}$$

Substituting for p from Eq. (18-19) into Eq. (18-18) we obtain

$$dW_A = -N_A kT \frac{dV}{V} \tag{18-19a}$$

and by integrating from V to V_A

$$W_A = N_A kT \int_V^{V_A} \frac{dV}{V} = N_A kT \ln \frac{V_A}{V} \tag{18-20}$$

Proceeding in the same fashion for gas B the corresponding work W_B is

$$W_B = -N_B kT \ln \frac{V_B}{V}$$

Hence the total work of unmixing

$$W = -kT\left(N_A \ln \frac{V_A}{V} + N_B \ln \frac{V_B}{V}\right) \tag{18-21}$$

The expression in parentheses can be further simplified by observing that $V = V_A + V_B$ and hence by Eqs. (18-1) and (18-2)

$$\frac{V}{V_A} = \frac{N_A + N_B}{N_A} = \frac{N}{N_A}$$

and

$$\frac{V}{V_B} = \frac{N}{N_B}$$

Finally, using Eqs. (18-10), (18-11), and (18-12) we get

$$W = -kTN\,(c_A \ln c_A + c_B \ln c_B) \tag{18-22}$$

or

$$W = -kT \ln f. \tag{18-22a}$$

In words, the work of unmixing at constant temperature and constant overall pressure varies as the negative natural logarithm of the probability of unmixing. The smaller this probability, the larger is the work required to bring about the unmixing. We can therefore use the expression of this work as a measure of the statistical stability of random mixing. It is of interest to note that the higher the temperature, the more stable is the mixture.

The above argument, strictly speaking, applies only to the gaseous state. In liquids, and even more in solids, the molecules and atoms are too close to each other to be unaware of their mutual presence. However, if we assume that in the random exchange of sites occurring in the liquid state (see Chapter 12) the identity of the neighbors can be disregarded, then the probability of observing a spontaneous unmixing of two liquids is as vanishing as that of two gases. Furthermore, if the molecular or atomic concentration of the two liquids is c_A and c_B, respectively, the probability of unmixing is again given by Eq. (18-22a), and *it is still the same when the mixture is solidified.* However, the assumption that atoms are unaware of each other's identity at a range as close at that existing in solids is at best a working hypothesis applicable only to cases where the two species of atoms are quite similar, e.g., Cu and Ni or Ge and Si. In general, the identity of the atoms cannot be ignored, as the subsequent study of alloying amply demonstrates.

Nonetheless, even in solids the concept of statistical stability of mixing implied in the vanishing probability of spontaneous unmixing, Eq. (18-12), remains valid and *so does Eq. (18-22) as a measure of this stability.* The pertinent argument derives from the foundations of Statistical Thermodynamics to which further reference must be made. On this understanding Eq. (18-22) is applicable to the study of alloying in all states of aggregation.

18-3 Alloying and Configurational Stability. As explained previously, lack of interaction between atoms and molecules is the main reason why, as a rule, mixtures of gases are stable at all temperatures, pressures, and concentrations. However, in liquids, particularly near the melting point, and in solids at any temperature this interaction not only exists but is very strong compared, for example, to thermal agitation. In solids it accounts for the order as well as stability of the ensuing configuration of atoms. Configurational stability thus is synonymous with order in the same sense as statistical stability is synonymous with disorder. In what follows we will show that a solute atom inserted in the lattice formed by solvent atoms can upset its stability. Also departure from configurational stability and order in crystals will be seen to require expenditure of work as does departure from statistical stability and randomness in mixtures. However, it will be found that the work so expended is not dissipated in heat as it is in mixtures under constant temperature and pressure. Rather it is stored in the lattice. Consistently with the concepts developed in Section 17-4 we can envision that it is stored in a threefold form:

1. as a *strain energy* owing to changes of interatomic distances produced by the size factor;
2. as an *extra bond energy* owing to changes of electron densities, or to the *electron concentration* factor;

3. as an *alteration in the nature of bond energy* owing to the redistribution of electrons about the solute and solvent atoms, or to the *electrochemical* factor.

The subsequent discussion is limited to the size factor alone. The reason is twofold. For one thing, the effect of the size factor is easy to grasp, though not necessarily to evaluate. Secondly, size factor can conveniently be used to classify common alloys in four distinct groups as shown below. Besides, size factor can be expected to be the only factor when the components belong to the same group of the periodic table, e.g., Na and K. For then, neither the electron concentration nor the nature of bonding are likely to vary from element to element.

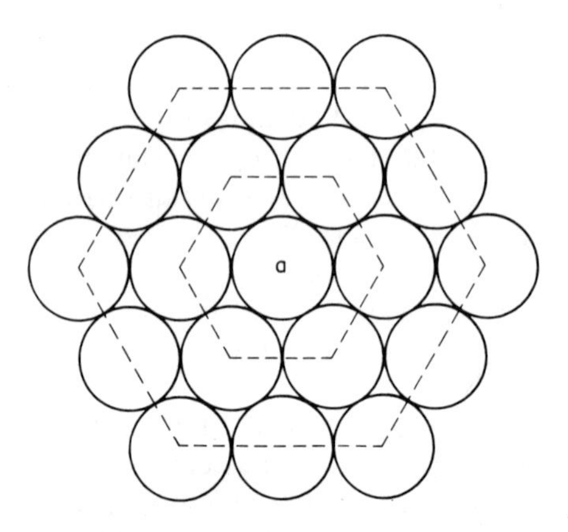

FIG. 18-3 Hexagonal plane packing of balls a about an identical ball a in the center

a. *Stability of the Lattice.* With this in mind consider first a plane close packed lattice made up of elastic frictionless balls, e.g., ping pong balls. We can visualize the formation of such a lattice as a sequential grouping of balls in hexagons of ever-increasing perimeters centered about one single ball, Fig. 18-3. Replace now the ball in the center by a larger ball. This substitution forces the surrounding balls to move outward. In doing so they lose contact with their neighbors along the perimeters of the hexagons, and the lattice ceases to be close packed. It becomes distorted, Fig. 18-4. Both effects, looseness of packing and distortion, are the greatest near the location of the larger ball in the center; they gradually disappear as the distance from the center increases.

To evaluate these effects let the diameter of the larger ball in the center be b and let the diameter of the surrounding balls be a. In the absence of any constraints the outward motion of the surrounding balls will cause a relative displacement along the sides of the hexagons. This displacement varies with

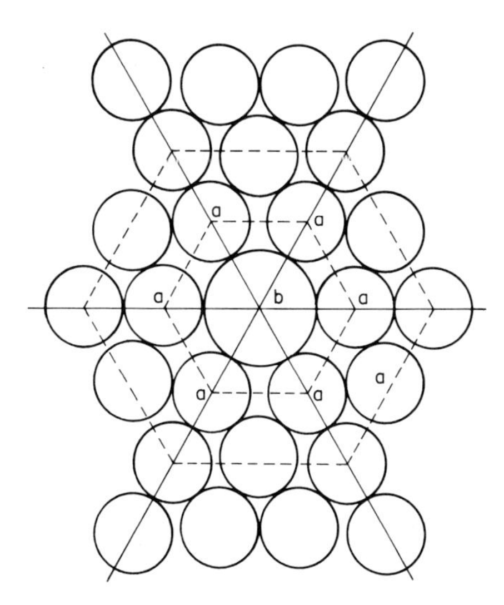

FIG. 18-4 Hexagonal plane packing of balls a about a larger ball b in the center

each successive hexagon in a rather simple manner. It is, in terms of the relative displacements, referred to as *strains*

$$\begin{aligned} &\frac{1}{2}\frac{b-a}{a} \text{ for the first hexagon} \\ &\frac{1}{4}\frac{b-a}{a} \text{ for the second hexagon} \\ &\frac{1}{6}\frac{b-a}{a} \text{ for the third hexagon} \end{aligned} \qquad (18\text{-}23)$$

and more generally,

$$\frac{1}{2n}\frac{b-a}{a}, \text{ for the } n\text{th hexagon.}$$

(See Problem 18-1.)

The above values, however, are markedly reduced when the balls are replaced by atoms A and B that interact with each other. Due to atomic interactions attractive forces come into play whenever the equilibrium distance a is increased, and by opposing the free motion of the atoms they reduce the relative displacements along the perimeters of the hexagons to (tensile) strains ϵ_n appreciably smaller than the unrestricted relative displacements, Eq. (18-23). That is

$$\varepsilon_n < \frac{1}{2n}\frac{b-a}{a} \qquad (18\text{-}24)$$

This reduction of relative displacements forces the A atoms to stay closer to the larger B atom which is in the center of the hexagons. As a result, compressive strains ε'_n and concomitant repulsive forces are generated along the diagonals of the hexagons. The ensuing "strained" configuration about the solute "B" atom becomes stabilized at values of ε_n and ε'_n for which the attractive and repulsive forces acting on each atom are in equilibrium.

A similar, strained configuration of hexagons develops in a close-packed lattice of the B atoms if one of them is replaced by a smaller A atom. However, the signs of ε_n and ε'_n are interchanged. That is, the strains are compressive along the perimeters, and they are tensile along the diagonals of the hexagons. Here too the configuration is stabilized when the resulting attractive and repulsive forces about each atom are in equilibrium.

Although geometrically more involved, the same situation develops about each solute atom in a three-dimensional lattice, regardless of whether the lattice is close-packed or not. In each case the atomic interactions restrict the free displacements of atoms to strains that are proportional to but smaller than $(b - a)/a$. We can therefore write quite generally, using the symbol ε for any strain and denoting the proportionality by the symbol $\sim$

$$\varepsilon \sim (b - a)/a \tag{18-25}$$

The fraction $(b - a)/a$ obviously accounts for the effect of incompatibility of sizes, or the *size factor*.

In conclusion, even though in equilibrium, the configuration resulting from the presence of foreign atoms is *less stable* than the configuration of the pure solvent. The situation is quite similar to that existing on the surfaces of liquids and solids. In both cases the extra energy stored in the medium causes the atoms to depart from their more stable positions of equilibrium. In solutions the extra energy is in the form of strain energy built up by the solute atoms. On the surfaces of liquids and solids the extra energy, according to Chapter 7, appears as the specific surface energy.

b. *Strain Energy of Solutions.* Unlike the specific surface energy, the strain energy of solutions is much more difficult to evaluate, let alone to compute. We know far too little about the exact nature of interactions existing between solute and solvent atoms to expect more than an approximate solution.

If Hooke's law is assumed to be a valid, or at least a first approximation, then by Eq. (6-53), Chapter 6, the strain energy u per unit volume of the solution is proportional to $E\varepsilon^2$, where E is the Young's modulus of elasticity. However, when dealing with liquid solutions it is more meaningful to use the bulk modulus of elasticity, B, instead of E, since liquids as a rule do not have a

Young's modulus. Moreover, bearing in mind that $\varepsilon \sim (b - a)/a$ and that ε decreases rapidly with the distance from the solute atom, we can write more generally that the average strain energy per unit volume is

$$u = \alpha B[(b - a)/a]^2 \tag{18-26}$$

over a volume sufficiently large to neglect the contribution of the cut off portion. Based on further simplifications the coefficient α turns out to be 0.75 for solid solutions.[3] These simplifications cannot be applied to liquids, but the presumption is that for liquid solutions the coefficient is smaller than for solid solutions.[4]

An important feature of the above simplifications is the assumption that the only contributions to the strain energy of solutions come from the interactions between unlike atoms and that these interactions are independent of each other. This limitation reduces the expression for u to a fraction u_i such that

$$u_i = 2\alpha B[(b - a)/a]^2 c_A c_B \tag{18-27}$$

where c_A and c_B are the concentrations of A and B atoms, respectively.

To adduce the necessary proof let there be N_a atoms A and N_b atoms B in a unit volume, so that the total number of atoms per unit volume is $N = N_a + N_b$. Each of the N_b atoms being independently paired to each of the N_a atoms, the total number of unlike pairs is $N_a N_b$. The total number of like pairs is $(N_a^2 + N_b^2)/2$, the factor 1/2 accounting for the twofold appearance of each atom in the like pairs. The fractions of volume contributing to the strain energy being the same as the fraction of unlike atoms, there follows that

$$u_i = \alpha B[(a - b)/a]^2 \frac{N_a N_b}{N_a N_b + (N_a^2 + N_b^2)/2} \tag{18-28}$$

and on simplifying and using Eqs. (18-10) and (18-11)

$$u_i = 2\alpha B[(a - b)/a]^2 c_A c_B \text{ as above in Eq. (18-27).}$$

The same line of thought applies to a solution in which A are the solute atoms and B are the solvent atoms. We can write by analogy with Equation (18-27) that

$$u_i = 2\alpha B[(b - a)/b]^2 c_A c_B \tag{18-29}$$

[3] J. Friedel, "On the Electronic Structure of Primary Solid Solutions in Metals," *Phil. Mag.*, **45** (Supplement), p. 504.
[4] J. Friedel, *ibid.*

Strictly speaking, both equations are valid only for very dilute solutions since the overlap of the hexagons about each solute atom is neglected. The bulk modulus B and the atomic radii a and b in the denominators of the fractions $(a - b)/a$ and $(b - a)/b$ can then be taken as those of the pure solvent. For more concentrated solutions it seems more judicious to use average values $\langle B \rangle$ and $\langle a \rangle$ (or $\langle b \rangle$) weighted in the ratio of the concentrations c_A and c_B.

18-4 Stability of Binary Solutions. We found that on the basis of the size factor alone, the presence of foreign atoms makes the configuration of the aggregate less stable. Consequently, there should be a tendency in the aggregate to acquire greater configurational stability by pushing the foreign atoms out of solution. On the other hand, we saw that short of absolute zero, thermal agitation seeks to keep the foreign atoms *in* the solution. Depending on which tendency predominates the solution is stable or unstable. To ensure stability the strain energy u_i must be smaller than the work *required* for unmixing. If N in Eq. (18-22) refers to the number of atoms per unit volume, the condition of stability reads with reference to Eqs. (18-27) and (18-22)

$$2\alpha B[(a - b)/a]^2 c_A c_B < -kTN(c_A \ln c_A + c_B \ln c_B)$$

and more generally, if B and a are averaged and denoted by $\langle B \rangle$ and $\langle a \rangle$, respectively

$$2\alpha \langle B \rangle [(a - b)/\langle a \rangle]^2 c_A c_B < -kTN(c_A \ln c_A + c_B \ln c_B) \qquad (18\text{-}30)$$

For the sake of the discussion which follows we rewrite Eq. (18-30) to read

$$-\frac{2\alpha \langle B \rangle}{kTN} \left(\frac{a - b}{\langle a \rangle} \right)^2 > \frac{\ln c_A}{c_B} + \frac{\ln c_B}{c_A} \qquad (18\text{-}31)$$

For binary alloys $c_A + c_B = 1$. Hence by putting $c_B = c$ to denote the concentration of the solute, we obtain finally

$$\frac{-2a\langle B \rangle}{kTN} \left(\frac{a - b}{\langle a \rangle} \right)^2 > \frac{\ln(1 - c)}{c} + \frac{\ln c}{1 - c} \qquad (18\text{-}32)$$

The plot, Fig. 18-5, shows the variation of $\ln (1 - c)/c + \ln c/(1 - c)$ as a function of c. It is seen that this expression exhibits a flat maximum $= -2.76$ for $c = 0.5$. Consequently, any value of the expression figuring on the left side of inequality (18-32) that is (algebraically) greater than -2.76 automatically insures the stability of the solution for all concentrations c. To say it differently, the two components A and B are completely soluble in each other. On the other hand, even a slight drop of the value of the left-hand expression in inequality (18-32) below -2.76 is seen to entail a drastic

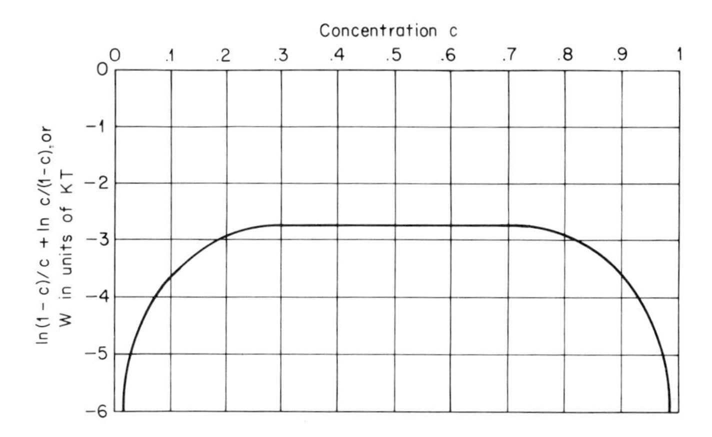

FIG. 18-5 Variation of $\ln(1 - c)/c + \ln c/(1 - c)$, also work of unmixing W, with concentration c

decrease of solubility at both ends of the diagram. Theoretically, the solubility is never nil, no matter how low this value. Practically, if the maximum concentration of the solute falls below, say, 0.1 percent, it is customary to speak of *insolubility*. Although based on simplifying assumptions the trend exhibited by Fig. 18-5 is found in many binary alloys, as will appear below.

18-5 Types of Binary Alloys. According to the foregoing discussion several types of binary alloys may be considered, depending on the magnitude of the size factor $(a - b)/\langle a \rangle$. They are distinguished by the degree of mutual solubility of the two components in each other, to wit: complete solubility, insolubility, and partial solubility.

When the size factor is small enough, so that the left-hand expression in inequality (18-32) is greater than -2.76, the conditions are favorable, *although by no means sufficient*, for the formation of binary solutions at any concentration, in short for continuous binary solutions. In *solid* solutions the restriction imposed by the size factor can be tested by substituting for T in expression (18-32) the maximum temperature at which the metal solidifies, as a rule, the higher of the two melting points of the components. It is clear that if inequality (18-32) is not satisfied at the maximum possible temperature, it cannot be satisfied at any lower temperature, and complete solid solubility cannot be expected.

For an order-of-magnitude computation of the favorable size factor in solid solutions, assume $\alpha = 1.0$, $\langle B \rangle = 10^{11}$ newtons/square meter, $T_m = 1500°K$, and $N = 10^{29}$ per cubic meter. Substitution in inequality (18-32) yields at the maximum value -2.76 of its right-hand expression and with $k = 1.38 \times 10^{-23}$ joule per degree.

$$\frac{a - b}{\langle a \rangle} < 0.17 \tag{18-33}$$

This is reasonably close to the experimentally observed favorable size factor of about 15 percent.[5]

We can likewise compute the minimum value of the size factor for solid *insolubility* by taking $c = 0.1$ percent. There follows (see Fig. 18-5)

$$-\frac{2\alpha\langle B \rangle}{kT_m N}\left(\frac{a - b}{\langle a \rangle}\right)^2 > -8.0 \tag{18-34}$$

or for the same order-of-magnitude computation as above

$$\frac{a - b}{\langle a \rangle} > 28.7\% \tag{18-35}$$

which again is close to the experimentally observed value of 25 percent, e.g., for Na-K.[6]

In *liquid* solutions the size factor for both, the solubility and insolubility limits, is apt to be larger on account of the conceivably smaller values of α and B. Yet near the melting point these values cannot be considerably smaller, particularly when c is as low as 0.1 percent, which is the assumed limit of insolubility. In liquids this limit seems to correspond to a size factor of about 30 percent.

The pertinent argument runs as follows: In dilute solutions, of 0.1 percent and less, the major contributions to the strain energy come from interactions between the solute atoms and the surrounding closest neighbors, which for all practical purposes here are only the solvent atoms. The contributions, therefore, are short range interactions. These are not as likely to depend on the state of aggregation as are the long range interactions. For example, as explained in Chapter 7, specific surface energy has its origin essentially in short range interactions. On that account, the specific surface energy of liquids near the melting point is seen to be almost the same as that of solids, Table 7-1.

Assuming, moreover, that in dilute solutions the long range interactions contribute no more than one-third to the value of the strain energy in solids and nothing at all in liquids, we can write the following two relations for solid and liquid insolubility (see inequality (18-34))

$$-\frac{2a\langle B \rangle}{kT_m N}\left(\frac{a - b}{\langle a \rangle}\right)^2_{\text{solid}} \geqslant -8.0 \tag{18-36}$$

[5] W. Hume Rothery, *Atomic Theory for Students in Metallurgy*, The Institute of Metals, London, 1946.

[6] W. Hume Rothery, ibid.

and

$$-\frac{2}{3} \times \frac{2\alpha\langle B\rangle}{kT_mN}\left(\frac{a-b}{\langle a\rangle}\right)^2_{\text{liquid}} \geqslant -8.0 \tag{18-37}$$

hence,

$$\frac{a-b}{\langle a\rangle}_{\text{liquid}} = 1.5 \times \frac{a-b}{\langle a\rangle}_{\text{solid}} = 33\% \tag{18-38}$$

or approximately 30 percent.

The results of this somewhat lengthy discussion can now conveniently be summarized in one single table, Table 18-1.

TABLE 18-1

Number	*Type of Binary Alloy*		*Size Factor*
	Liquid	*Solid*	
I	Insolubility	Insolubility*	Great than 30%
II	Solubility	Insolubility	Greater than 25%
III	Solubility*	Complete solubility	Less than 15%
IV	Solubility	Partial solubility	Between 15% and 25%

* Self-evident.

We see that based on the limitations imposed by the size factor alone only four types of binary alloys exist.[7] We could also add "Partial Liquid Solubility" to this table. However, the physical properties of such alloys in solid state would not differ appreciably from those characterized by Liquid Insolubility, as will appear more clearly from a detailed discussion of the phase diagrams corresponding to the above four types of alloys.

18-6 Liquid Insolubility. In accordance with Table 18-1, liquid insolubility, in the sense given in Section 18-4, is to be expected whenever the size factor exceeds 30 percent. This expectation is borne out by the example of lead. Having a relatively large atomic diameter of about 3.5 Å, lead is insoluble in most liquid metals. The ensuing phase diagram and properties are well illustrated in Cu-Pb alloys.

Due to their mutual insolubility molten copper and molten lead are separated by a physical boundary, i.e., they form two immiscible liquids. Consequently on cooling, the liquids solidify as pure metals without affecting each other's melting points. Copper builds FCC structure with a lattice parameter of about 3.60 Å; lead builds another FCC structure with a lattice parameter of about 4.95 Å. (Compare Table 2-1, Chapter 2.)

[7] We shall find out later that size factor is not always a reliable criterion for anticipating the type of a binary alloy.

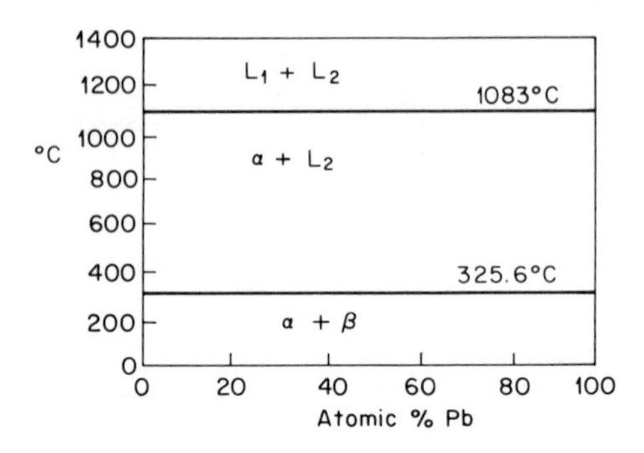

FIG. 18-6 Simplified copper-lead phase diagram

a. *Phase Diagram.* The resulting temperature-composition, or the *T-c* phase diagram (in its simplified form) is made up of two liquid and two solid phases, Fig. 18-6. At all compositions there are two liquid phases L_1 and L_2 above 1083°C (1356°K)—the melting point of copper—and two solid phases, denoted by α and β, respectively, below 325.6°C (598.6°K)—the melting point of lead. In between there is one solid phase, α and one liquid phase, L_2. The *T-c* phase diagram therefore comprises *three* regions separated by two *horizonatal* lines drawn through the melting points of copper and lead, respectively.

b. *Properties and Uses.* Lack of a functional relationship between temperature and composition makes phase diagrams of the type represented by Fig. 18-6 rather trivial from the theoretical point of view. Their practical interest is nonetheless real. With the use of proper emulsifiers droplets of lead can be entrapped and remain in suspension in liquid copper, much like fat does in homogenized milk, see Section 7-5, Chapter 7. On solidification the droplets form finely dispersed inclusions. It has been found that in amounts of about 1 percent these inclusions materially improve the *machining* characteristics of copper, without serious impairment of its properties. They break up the chip and act as a lubricant by preventing the gumming of the tool. Amounts up to 3 percent Pb are incorporated in aluminum and copper alloys to permit their machining at high speed with automatic machines (the so-called free machining alloys). In this case poor thermal conductivity of lead reduces the temperature build-up at the tip of the tool. The same effect is achieved in ferrous alloys by inclusions of MnS—a by-product of steel making. In that sense Liquid Insolubility gives rise to alloys with properties that are shared by neither of the two components, that defy the law of averages.

18-7 Liquid Solubility—Solid Insolubility. In this type of alloy the liquid consists of one single phase: a solution containing both kinds of atoms *A* and *B*. On the other hand, the solid is an aggregate of two distinct phases.

Each solid phase has its own crystal structure and it is made up of only one kind of atom. As shown below, this abrupt transition from liquid solubility to solid insolubility has a profound effect on the inception and mechanism of solidification. Furthermore, the temperature of incipient solidification is strongly dependent on composition in sharp contrast to alloys discussed in Section 18-6.

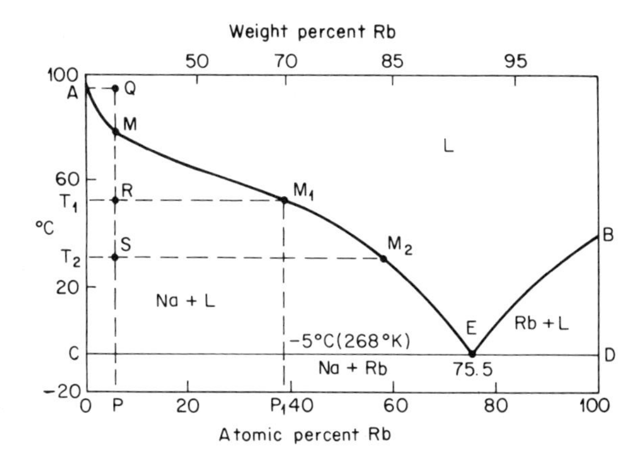

FIG. 18-7 Sodium-rubidium phase diagram

a. *Phase Diagram.* Sodium and rubidium give rise to a phase diagram (Fig. 18-7) that is typical of alloys in this category. Rb belongs to the same IA group of the periodic table as Na. The atomic size factor, based on the distances of closest approach of pure Na and Rb, averages 27 percent, in good agreement with Table 18-1.

According to Fig. 18-7 pure Na solidifies at 97.7°C (370.7°K) point *A*, and pure Rb solidifies at 38.8°C (311.8°K) point *B*. An addition of one of these elements to the liquid formed by the other retards considerably the process of solidification. At the sodium side of the diagram, between 0 and 75.5 atomic percent Rb, a tiny crystal of an almost pure sodium begins to form at a temperature which progressively goes down as the concentration in rubidium increases, line *AE*. At the rubidium side of the diagram the same trend prevails with a precipitation of a tiny crystal of an almost pure crystal of rubidium. Likewise, the temperature of the inception of solidification goes down as the concentration of the solute (here sodium) goes up, line *BE*. It is clear from the trends *AE* and *BE* that there exists a temperature at which both precipitates, Na and Rb are formed side by side, -5°C (268°K), point *E*. This is the lowest temperature of solidification, i.e., the lowest temperature at which the alloy can still exist in the liquid state. Like the melting points A and *B* of the pure components the temperature of 268°K at *E* corresponds not only to the beginning but also the end of solidification of the alloy.

To see why, consider what happens after a tiny crystal of sodium precipitates from the solution. The concentration of rubidium in the solution increases and the composition shifts to the right of point E. However, the temperature 268°K is now lower than the beginning of solidification, so a crystal of rubidium will precipitate. At the same time the composition of the liquid will shift to the left, as a rule, by slightly overshooting point E. Due to overshooting a crystal of sodium in turn is precipitated, and the cycle goes on at a constant temperature until all liquid has been converted to a solid, exactly as for a pure substance.

Because of the alternating nature of the precipitation process, the alloy corresponding to composition E is made up of tiny crystals of sodium and rubidium and possesses a very fine structure. Magnifications beyond 500 times are often necessary to distinguish the two phases. For reasons given below the alloy corresponding to E has been called a *eutectic* (meaning in Greek *easy flowing*).

For any composition other than that of the eutectic, the process of solidification of the alloy is more complicated. For one thing, the process is spread over a range of temperatures instead of being confined to one single temperature. For another, the composition of the solution changes continuously from the beginning to the end of solidification. Both phenomena are related to the fact that in this type of alloy the solidification cannot begin unless the temperature is lowered below the melting point of the precipitate.

The pertinent argument can be derived from thermodynamical consideration and concepts. Under simplifying assumption it is possible to provide a qualitative proof without having recourse to the thermodynamical apparatus. The basic principle involved here is, not surprisingly, that of relative stability.

Consider, for example, an alloy with a small concentration in rubidium, point P, Fig. 18-7. At the melting point of sodium this alloy forms a liquid solution, point Q, which by its very existence is more stable than pure liquid sodium. That is, a drop of sodium deposited on the surface of the liquid will be absorbed by the solution. So will a tiny crystal of (solid) sodium, since by definition liquid and solid sodium have the same stability (they co-exist side by side) at the melting point A. It follows from this argument that pure sodium cannot precipitate from the alloy at point Q. It can, however, precipitate at a lower temperature. The reason is twofold. On the one hand, the stability of solid sodium increases as the temperature is lowered, since the atoms tend thereby to be closer to their positions of stable equilibrium. On the other hand, the stability of the solution decreases, since it is a liquid and lowering the temperature makes the liquid less stable. Therefore a temperature is reached, point M, at which solid sodium is in equilibrium with liquid solution of composition P, and the process of solidification can begin.

Before discussing the next stages of solidification of alloy P we turn our attention to the dependence of temperature of solidification on concentration c. Such dependence can be anticipated from Eq. (18-22). As pointed out previously, the work of deformation represented by Eq. (18-22) measures the degree of stability of gas mixtures. Assuming it also measures the stability of a solution, the plot of W versus c, Fig. 18-5 shows an increase of stability as the concentration c approaches 50 percent from both sides of the diagram, from $c = 0$ and $c = 100$ percent. The departure from the ideal case accounts for the fact that neither the shape of the solidification curve AEB, nor the location of the lowest temperature E in Fig. 18-7 are correctly predicted by Eq. (18-22). Yet, the underlying dependence of stability on concentration remains valid.

With this in mind we now complete the description of the process of solidification of alloy P. At point M the precipitate is as likely to form as it is to disappear. But at a somewhat lower temperature T_1 and point R, the precipitate will remain, since it is more stable than the solution of composition P. How much of the precipitate (of sodium) will form? The answer is that as more and more sodium is removed from the solution, the remaining liquid is progressively enriched in rubidium. The composition of the liquid shifts to the right until it reaches point M_1 where the equilibrium between precipitation and dissolution of sodium is re-established. From this condition the amount of the precipitated sodium can be computed (see Lever Rule below). To precipitate a larger amount of sodium the temperature again must be lowered, T_2 and point S, with the concomitant enrichment of the solution in rubidium and shifting of the composition to point M_2. This process continues until the remaining liquid attains the eutectic composition E, at which point the liquid solidifies with an alternate precipitation of sodium and rubidium crystals.

The same process of solidification occurs for any composition between the pure component and the eutectic E, on both sides of the diagram, except that past point E the first, pro-eutectic precipitate is rubidium instead of sodium, line EB.

In conclusion, alloys characterized by the type of the phase diagram, Fig. 18-7, solidify over a range of temperature between AEB and CED, depending on concentration. Above AEB the alloy is a single liquid phase. Below CED the alloy is a mixture of two solid phases, each made up of a single component. In the triangles AEC and BED there is a mixture of a solid phase and a liquid phase. The solid phase consists of either one or the other pure component depending on the location of the triangle. The liquid phase is an alloy whose composition at a given temperature is read either on AE or EB, also depending on the location of the triangle.

b. *The Lever Rule.* It follows from the above analysis that in the triangles AEC and BED both, the liquid phase and the solid phase have a fixed composition at a given temperature regardless of the initial concentration c of the single liquid solution. However, the initial concentration governs the relative amount, or the ratio, of the liquid to the solid at each temperature.

To see why, imagine a support is placed under line T_1M_1 at point R corresponding to the initial concentration P of the alloy. If line T_1M_1 is thought to be a lever supporting a solid mass at T_1 and a liquid mass at M_1, then the condition of *static* equilibrium requires that the two masses, the liquid and the solid, be in the ratio of RT_1 to RM_1 to each other. It is easy to show that this also is the ratio of the amounts of liquid and solid phases that are in *statistical* or *thermodynamical* equilibrium at temperature T for the overall concentration c of the alloy.

To adduce the necessary proof let x and y be the fractional amounts of the liquid and solid at temperature T_1 so that

$$x + y = 1 \tag{18-39}$$

The initial, overall concentration at point R is c and it is measured by the length OP. That is

$$OP = c \tag{18-40}$$

Similarly, let the concentration of the liquid phase at temperature T_1 be c_1. In turn this concentration corresponds to point M_1 and it is measured by OP_1 so that

$$OP_1 = c_1 \tag{18-41}$$

The solid phase is a pure solvent. Hence its concentration c is zero. By virtue of the law of convervation of mass the total amount of the solute is unchanged; therefore we can write that

$$x0 + yc_1 = c \tag{18-42}$$

Substituting in this Eq. for c and c_1 from Eq. (18-40) and Eq. (18-41) and taking Eq. (18-39) into account we further have

$$yOP_1 = (x + y)OP \tag{18-43}$$

or

$$y(OP_1 - OP) = OPx \tag{18-43a}$$

whence

$$y/x = OP/P_1P = RT_1/RM_1 \quad \text{Q.E.D.} \tag{18-44}$$

c. *Microstructure, Properties and Uses.* Continuous growth of a single phase which precipitates from the liquid over a range of temperatures accounts for the formation of large crystals in those alloys whose composition greatly differs from that of the eutectic, point E, Fig. 18-7. In the final stage of solidification, at the eutectic temperature, point E, these crystals are cemented together by the eutectic—by a fine mixture of crystals of both components, Fig. 18-8. As the composition of the alloy nears that of the eutectic, the fine mixture becomes predominant and finally overtakes the whole microstructure, Fig. 18-9.

FIG. 18-8 Crystals of proeutectic antimony in the matrix of Sb-Pb eutectic. (From Morton C. Smith, *Alloy Series in Physical Metallurgy*, Fig. 2-17b, p. 54, Harper, New York, 1956, by permission)

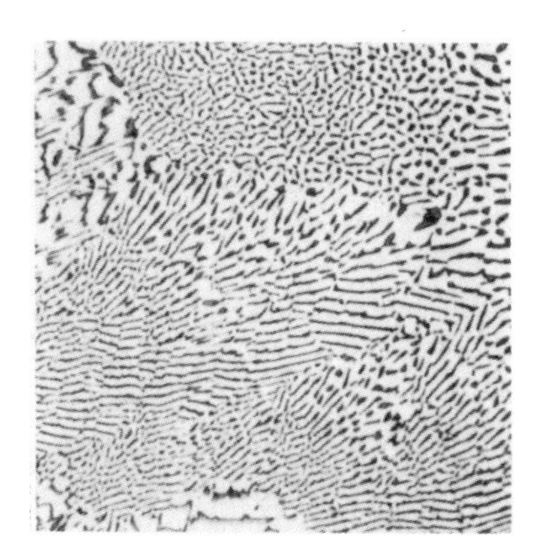

FIG. 18-9 Antimony-lead eutectic. (From Morton C. Smith, *Alloy Series in Physical Metallurgy*, Fig. 2-20b, p. 59, Harper, New York, 1956, by permission)

It is the fineness of the microstructure thus developed rather than the co-existence of crystals of two different species that explains the apparent increase of hardness of the eutectic over that of either of the two components. No such increase, however, is anticipated and found for the structure in-sensitive properties, Section 5-4, such as modulus of elasticity, heat, and electrical conductivities or coefficient of thermal expansion. On the other hand, there is good presumption that a eutectic (composite) material, made up of long mono-crystalline fibers of a harder component imbedded in the matrix of a softer component, can substantially improve the brittle fracture strength of the harder component by altering the statistics of the size effect considered in Section 8-5. To produce such a fibrous structure current attempts are focused on techniques of growth similar to those developed for the production of single crystals, Section 3-5.

Pending these esoteric applications eutectics today find more immediate industrial uses which derive from the peculiarities of the phase diagram, Fig. 18-7. One of such uses is in foundry practice, where eutectics are singled out for their excellent casting properties. Owing to the constancy of the solidification temperature eutectics flow easily and freely in the mold and adapt themselves readily to the most intricate forms of the pattern, thereby justifying their Greek name of *eutectic* (easy flowing). The most widely used and time honored eutectic is *cast iron*, an alloy of iron containing about 4.3 percent carbon in weight. The carbon is in the form of graphite flakes, Fig. 18-10, which act as a lubricant on exposed surfaces, see Section 1-8, Chapter 1. Hence, cast iron is used in sliding contacts to prevent seizure and decrease wear, e.g., in brake shoes. Another eutectic of current application is an *aluminum-silicon alloy* with about 11 percent Si in weight, Fig. 18-11. Its good heat conductivity and light weight, combined with ease of casting, make it a choice material for cylinder heads and pistons in internal combustion engines.

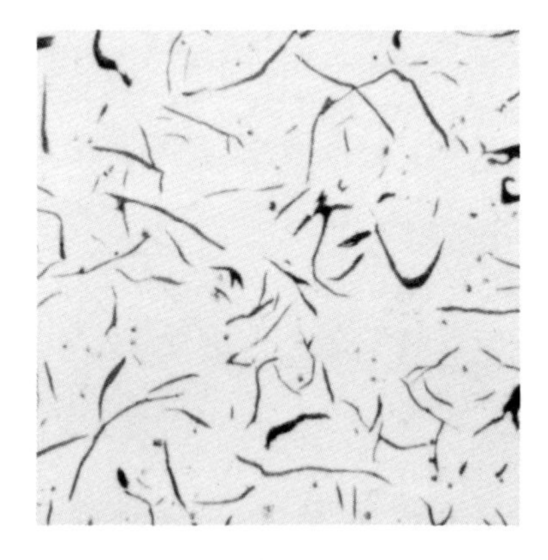

FIG. 18-10 Iron-carbon eutectic. (From Morton C. Smith, *Alloy Series in Physical Metallurgy*, Fig. 8-9a, p. 274, Harper, New York, 1956, by permission)

A companion characteristic of eutectics that finds wide industrial applications is their low melting point. *Solders* which are used for joining metals are essentially eutectics. They enable the operation of joining to be performed at temperatures low enough to prevent distortion of soldered parts. The most common is the *tin-lead* solder with about 60 percent Sn, which combines good wettability, Section 7-5, with low melting point (183°C). *Silver solders* developed during World War II in consequence of tin scarcity are used today in their own right, e.g., to join honeycomb stainless steel structural elements in the aircraft industry. Their melting point, however, is much higher than that of tin solders.

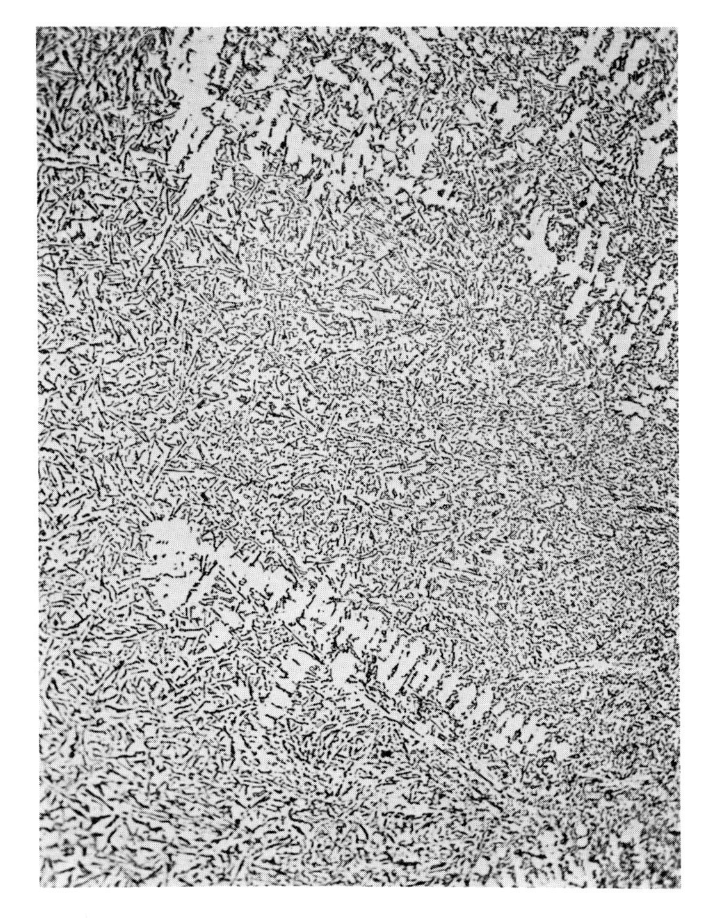

FIG. 18-11 Aluminum-Si eutectic. (Courtesy of George W. Wilcox, Alcoa Research Laboratories)

And last but not least, the low melting point of eutectics combined with their good heat conductivity makes them particularly valuable as circulating fluids in heat exchangers, the most noteworthy example being NaK, the sodium-potassium eutectic, which finds important applications in nuclear reactors.

18-8 Complete Solid Solubility. Diffusion. When the atomic sizes of the two components differ by less than 15 percent, a necessary but by no means sufficient condition is fulfilled for the occurrence of one single solid solution covering the whole range of concentrations from 0 to 100 percent, Table 18-1. Obviously, there is also complete solubility in the liquid phase. To say it differently, the liquid and the solid solutions are more stable than the pure components at both states of aggregation. This condition is presumed to exist in the range of temperatures comprising the melting points of the two components. The range, however, encompasses much higher temperature too (for according to Eq. (18-22) the stability of a solution increases with temperature) and it often extends down to room temperature and below, e.g., Ni-Cu alloys. On this understanding, the occurrence and process of solidification in this type of alloys depends solely on the relative stability of the liquid and solid solutions.

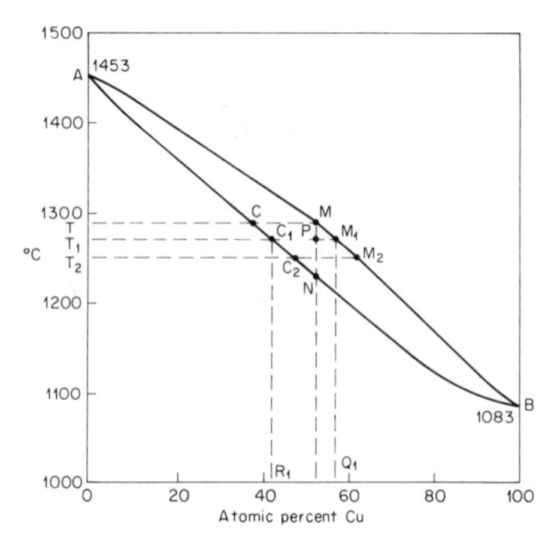

FIG. 18-12 Nickel-copper phase diagram

a. *Phase Diagram.* The Ni-Cu phase diagram is a good illustration of the above dependence. Ni builds a FCC lattice with the side of the unit cell = 3.5238 Å. So does Cu except that the side of the unit cell is 3.6153 Å, Table 2-1, Chapter 2. The solid solution understandably is also FCC with atoms of Ni and Cu indiscriminately and randomly occupying the corners and centers of faces in the unit cells. Because of this randomness not only the identity of atoms at each site but also the relative number of atoms of each kind varies from cell to cell. Therefore, a given atomic concentration of, say, 50-50 percent refers to a composition averaged over a large number of unit cells, 10^6 or more, rather than to a particular cell.

With this in mind consider now what happens if, say, a 47–53 percent Ni-Cu alloy begins to solidify, point M, Fig. 18-12. To initiate the process of solidification at a given temperature a precipitate must be formed that is in *statistical* or *thermodynamical* equilibrium with the liquid. We saw in the example of solid insolubility, Section 18-7, that the precipitate, even though of different composition—in fact a pure component—may co-exist side by side with a liquid solution at a given temperature. The same is true of solid solubility except that here the precipitate, while differing in composition from the liquid, is also a solution.

That liquid and solid solutions may differ in composition, yet co-exist side by side at a given temperature and pressure, i.e., be in thermodynamical equilibrium, derives from the principle of statistical stability embodied in the work of unmixing, Eq. (18-22). Statistical stability requires that in any local transition from liquid to solid solution and vice-versa changes in the works of unmixing be adequately compensated by changes in the heats of fusion akin to those discussed in Section 17-3. It turns out that as a rule this requirement cannot be satisfied unless the compositions of the solid and liquid solutions are different.

The Ni-Cu alloys are no exception to the rule. Therefore, the first precipitate from the 47–53 percent solution has a much lower concentration in Cu than the liquid, point C, Fig. 18-12. However, since M coincides with the beginning of solidification for the 47–53 percent solution, the tiny nucleus of solid is as likely to precipitate from as to dissolve in the liquid. It is therefore necessary to cool the alloy slightly below the temperature T, Fig. 18-12 to stabilize the precipitate. Subsequent to the formation of the stable solid solution at C_1 with a concentration $R_1 < 53$ percent, the concentration of the remaining liquid shifts to $Q_1 > 53$ percent. The corresponding point M_1 denotes again a temperature, T_1, at which the liquid solution of concentration Q_1 is in thermodynamical equilibrium with the solid solution of concentration R_1. As the temperature is lowered, both the liquid and the solid solution are enriched in Cu, C_2M_2, etc. Application of the lever rule, discussed in Section 18-7, shows that such a simultaneous enrichment in Cu is possible only if the amount of the solid phase keeps increasing at the expense of the liquid phase, Problem 18-5. Finally, at the attainment of point N all liquid has been converted to solid, and the process of solidification comes to an end.

It is obvious that the above process applies not only to the 47–53 percent composition but to any composition. The solidification of an alloy begins when its temperature falls below line AMM_1M_2B and it ends when its temperature falls below line AC_1C_2NB. Consequently, a phase diagram corresponding to complete solid solubility contains two types of curves: AMM_1M_2B denoting the dependence of temperature on concentration at the beginning of solidification and ACC_1NN_1B denoting the dependence of temperature on concentration at the end of solidification. The two lines meet at A and B, since for pure substances, the beginning and end of solidification coincide. Line AMM_1M_2B is called the *liquidus* to emphasize the fact that above this line the solution is a single liquid phase. Similarly, line ACC_1NN_1B is called the *solidus*, and accordingly below this line the solution is a single solid phase. The region between the two lines contains both, the liquid and the solid phases.

b. *Microstructure, Properties and Uses.* Since neither the nature nor the location of the different species of atoms can be identified in a solid solution under the optical microscope, the presumption is that the microstructure of (polycrystalline) solid solutions is in no way different from that of pure metals. This presumption is borne out by experiment, provided the solid solution is homogeneous (see below). However, the presence of foreign atoms in the lattice does affect the properties of the alloy. Both structure insensitive and structure sensitive properties are thus affected and both in a manner that cannot be predicted from the law of averages. The effect of alloying on electrical resistivity is perhaps the most spectacular.

As pointed out in Section 15-3 even a small amount of foreign solute atoms sharply increases the resistivity of pure metals. The effect can be compared to the dislocation of traffic caused by cars moving faster or slower than the steady stream of cars. The dislocation results not only from the number of cars out-of-step but also from the randomness of their distribution in the stream. We may anticipate by analogy that electrical resistivity will similarly be affected by the concentration and randomness of mixing of the solute atoms. Furthermore considering the increase of statistical stability with randomness, we are led to expect trends in electrical resistivity similar to those exhibited in Fig. 18-5. This expectation is borne out by the behavior of numerous alloys forming complete solid solutions. That randomness of mixing is a dominant factor in enhancing electrical resistivity of alloys is proved conclusively by the study of Cu-Au alloys. It is found that when the atomic ratio of Cu to Au becomes 3:1 and 1:1 respectively, two types of ordered structures can be formed on slow cooling: one FCC, Fig. 18-13a corresponds to the formula Cu_3Au; the other tetragonal, Fig. 18-13b conforms to the formula CuAu. By analogy with the ordering of Cu-Zn alloys, discussed in Section 17-4, both configurations produce a marked decrease of electrical resistivity, Fig. 18-14, continuous line. On the other hand, when the alloy is maintained in a disordered state by rapid cooling, no such decrease in resistivity is observed, Fig. 18-14 interrupted line. The dependence of electrical resistivity on concentration in the disordered state is quite similar to that of Ni-Cu alloys, Fig. 18-15. However, the almost fiftyfold increase of resistivity of the 55–45 percent Ni-Cu alloy over that of pure components must in part be ascribed to other causes. It is credited to the effect of the unfilled *d* shell in Ni, see Section 14-13. That the unfilled *d* shells of the transition elements do play a part in the enhancement of electrical resistivity is further confirmed by the almost one-hundredfold increase of electrical resistivity in Ni-Cr alloys, Fig. 18-16. The departute from the bell shaped curve of Fig. 18-14 is also attributed to this additional factor.[8]

Whatever the reason, Cu-Ni and Ni-Cr alloys by virtue of their high electrical resistivity find numerous industrial applications. A 25 percent Cr alloy makes an excellent heating element. The one used for flat irons, toasters, and resistors is a triple solid solution of nickel, chromium, and iron. The electrical resistivity of 40 percent Ni-60 percent Cu alloy is little affected by temperature changes in the range of 0° to 200°C. Hence, under the name

[8] See e.g., M. J. Sinnott, *The Solid State for Engineers*, Wiley, 1958, p. 349.

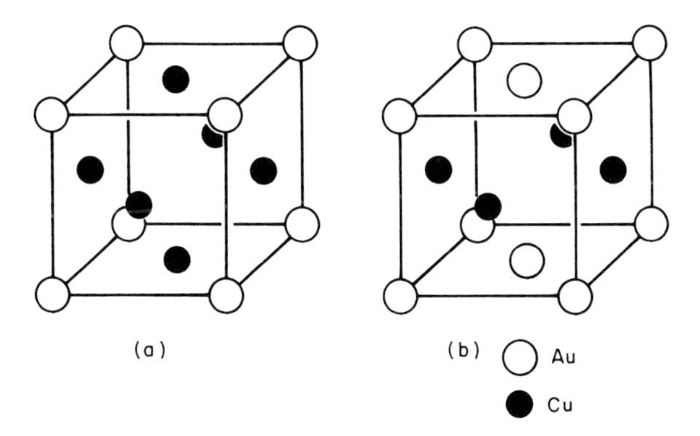

FIG. 18-13 Ordered structures of CuAu alloys: (a) Cu_3Au; (b) CuAu

of *constantan*, it is used for making *standard* electrical resistances. Manganin, an alloy of Ni, Cu, and Mn, has similar applications.

Resistance to corrosion is another property which can be greatly enhanced by the solid solution type of alloying. The 67 percent Ni-28 percent Cu alloy with small amounts of iron, manganese, and cobalt is one representative of this category. Under the name of monel metal it is obtained directly from Canadian ores in the specified composition. It finds applications in hospital and kitchen equipment, but it is being gradually replaced by stainless steel. The basic composition of this alloy is 18–25 percent Cr, 8–20 percent Ni, and the balance iron. The excellent resistance against corrosion is generally coupled with good high-temperature mechanical strength, or creep strength, see Chapter 12.

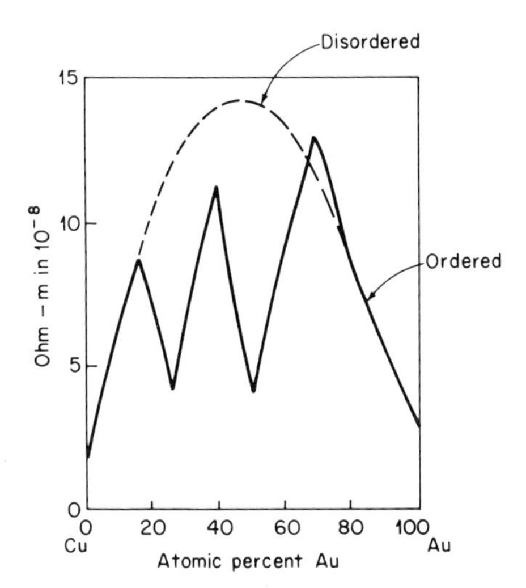

FIG. 18-14 Electrical resistivity of ordered and disordered copper-gold alloys

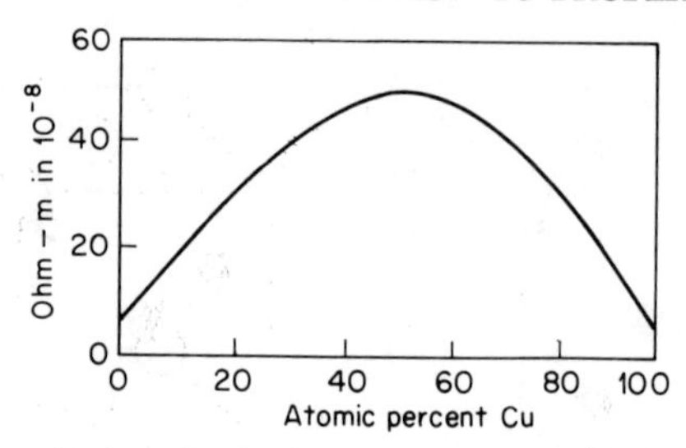

FIG. 18-15 Electrical resistivity of nickel-copper alloys

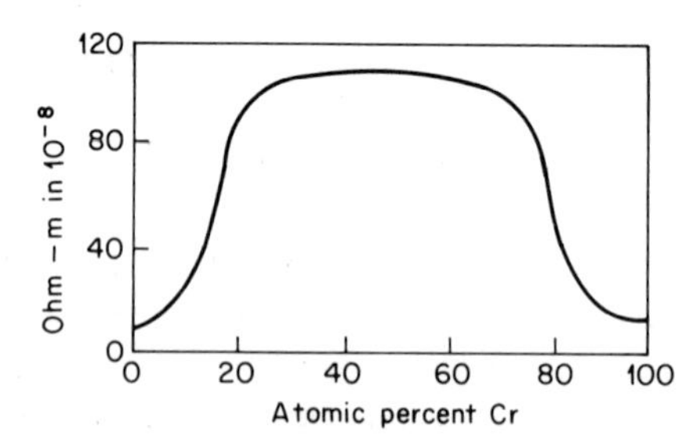

FIG. 18-16 Electrical resistivity of nickel-chromium alloys

In iron-nickel alloys the average coefficient of thermal expansion between 0° and 200°C undergoes a curious and unexpected variation with composition, Fig. 18-17. Its value in the 64 percent Fe-36 percent Ni solid solution is only 0.9×10^{-6} per degree centigrade, or about ten times less than in pure iron or nickel. Because of the ensuing small dimensional changes with temperature, the alloy is called *invar* (from invariable). It finds wide uses in the construction of gauges and precision instruments, where dimensional stability is of prime consideration.

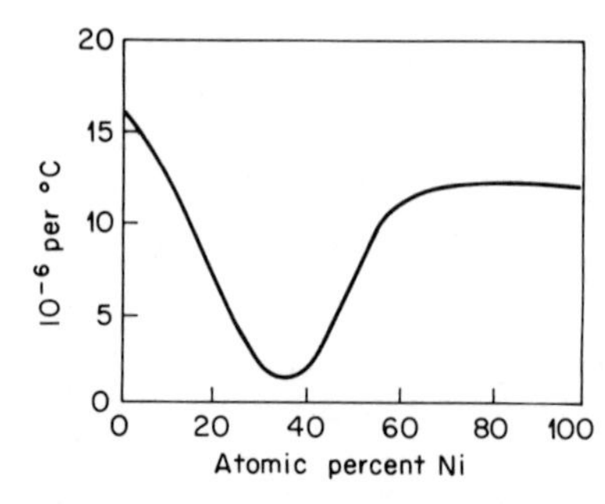

FIG. 18-17 Coefficient of thermal expansion of iron-nickel alloys

c. *Diffusion.* The process of solidification of solid solutions raises an interesting question. According to Fig. 18-12 the composition of the solid phase (and the liquid phase too) continuously changes during solidification.

Thus, at 1330°C the composition of the solid phase is 30 percent Cu. However, at a somewhat lower temperature, e.g., 1300°C the composition of the *whole* solid phase has changed to 35 percent Cu. By what mechanism? To answer this question note that as a result of the temperature drop a new layer of atoms has been precipitated from the liquid onto the already existing crystallites of the solid phase. The new layer must be richer in Cu than the underlying strata, since by Fig. 18-12 the overall concentration of Cu in the solid phase increases on cooling. However, if the composition of the solid is to be uniform—as it must on statistical grounds considered in Section 18-2—a mechanism must be provided for the Cu atoms to migrate from regions of higher concentration to regions of lower concentration. This mechanism is known as *diffusion.*

It is rather easy to conceive how atoms migrate or diffuse through a gas or a liquid. Because both states of aggregation lack dimensional stability, the atoms are more or less free to interchange positions with their neighbors in the wake of thermal agitation. However, in solids dimensional stability precludes such a random process. To preserve the stability of the lattice the atoms are compelled to pass from one site of the lattice to another in single and isolated sequences of jumps. Several mechanisms have been proposed to account for this kind of process. The one most frequently called upon relies on the presence of vacant sites adjacent to the atoms which are about to jump, Fig. 18-18.

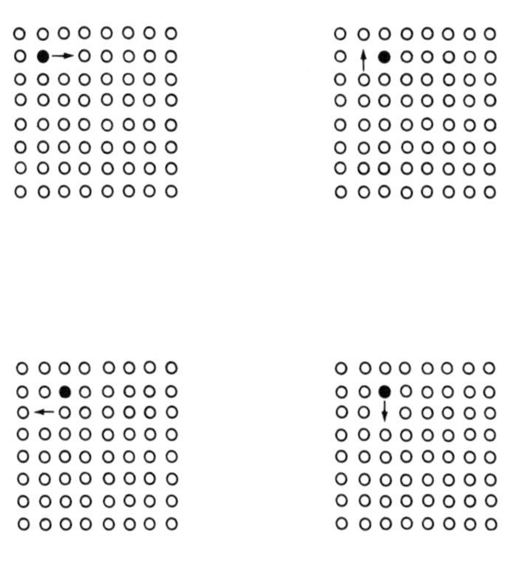

FIG. 18-18 Diffusion of solute atom by means of vacancies

That vacant sites should exist in any lattice and at any temperature short of absolute zero can be justified on grounds similar to those invoked in the theory of mixing, Section 18-2. There also is indirect experimental evidence of their existence.[9] However, it is still an open question whether migration through vacancies is the only and the most frequent way atoms diffuse in solids, especially in substitutional solid solutions.[10]

d. *Heterogeneous Solid Solutions.* Whatever the mechanism of diffusion, it is clear that configurational stability of solids severely restricts the frequency of successful jumps. Accordingly, diffusion in solids is a rather slow process. Even during solidification when the rate of diffusion is the highest, it may take several minutes per degree centigrade to equalize the composition of the solid phase. As the temperature is lowered, less and less atoms have a chance to jump. As with many phenomena that are governed by thermal agitation, e.g., viscous flow in liquids, Section 12-1, the rate of diffusion is strongly temperature dependent. Even a moderate drop in temperature can produce a drastic slowdown in atom movement. At temperatures well below the range of solidification of the alloy it may take years instead of minutes to achieve complete homogeneity of the solid solution. This circumstance emphasizes the importance of very slow rates of solidification. If the alloy reaches room temperature before the composition had time to become uniform throughout the body, the solid solution is heterogeneous, Fig. 18-19. Its properties, particularly ductility, are thereby greatly impaired.

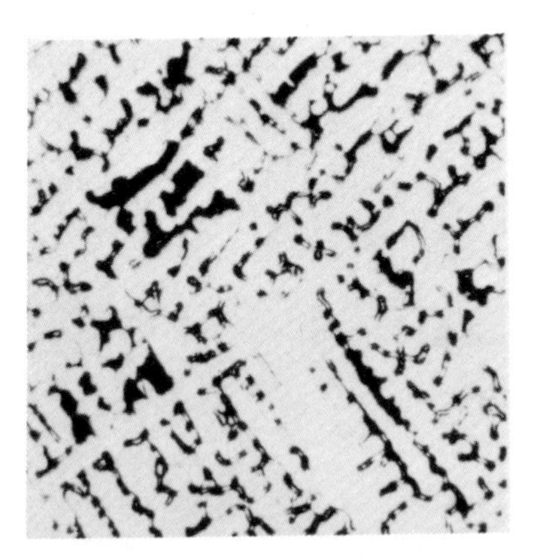

FIG. 18-19 Heterogeneous solid solution. (From Morton C. Smith, *Alloy Series in Physical Metallurgy*, Fig. 3-10, p. 92, Harper, New York, 1956, by permission)

An alternative to a very slow rate of cooling is to solidify the solid solution as rapidly as possible. At first glance this may seem to defeat the purpose. However, if the solidification is rapid enough, then although the local concentration gradients are quite steep, segregation is not too serious, as it can readily be eliminated in subsequent high temperature solid state processing operations. On the other hand, at intermediate solidification rates there is

[9] See e.g., J. A. McComb and M. Meshii, *Sixth International Congress for Electron Microscopy*, Kyoto (1966), p. 347.

[10] See e.g., P. G. Shewmon, *Diffusion in Solids*, McGraw-Hill, New York, 1963.

time for segregation to occur over macroscopic distances, and this is very difficult to eliminate in subsequent treatments. The point is that during solidification the solute can diffuse on the order of 1000 times faster in the liquid than in the solid. Therefore, solute diffuses rapidly through the liquid away from the solid of low solute concentration. After solidification is complete, however, any homogenization treatment occurs in the solid state, so only the relatively slow diffusion rates typical of solids are possible. Therefore, if a homogenization treatment is to be successful, it must require an annealing time on the order of 1000 times the solidification time.

18-9 Partial Solid Solubility, Precipitation Hardening. According to Table 18-1, Section 18-5, solid solubility between two components ceases to be complete when the atomic size factor, $(a - b)/\langle a \rangle$, exceeds 15 percent. We have stated repeatedly that this is not the only limitation imposed on complete solid solubility. Obviously, the two components also must have the same crystal structure. Thus, the atomic size factor for Cu and Zn is about 5 percent, well below the 15 percent limit. Yet, there is no complete solubility, nor can there be any because Cu has a FCC structure and Zn has a HCP structure. The type of crystal structures, as we recall from Section 17-4, is strongly influenced by the electron concentration and the electrochemical factors. Consequently, these two factors likewise impose their own limitation on complete solid solubility.

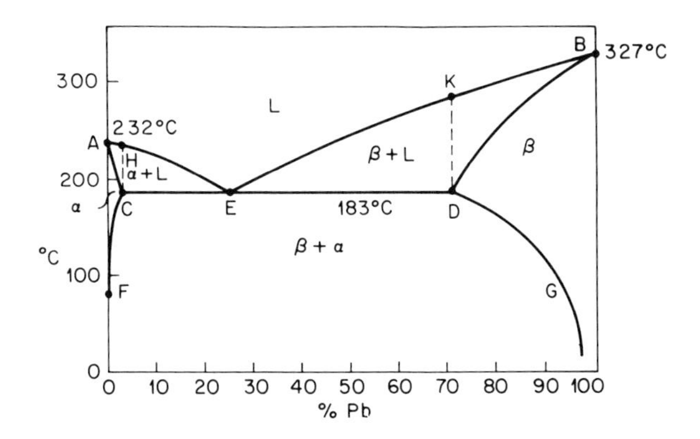

FIG. 18-20 Tin-lead phase diagram

a. *Phase Diagram.* Despite the above mentioned additional restrictions on solid solubility we can still use the general criterion of stability formulated in Section 18-5 to analyze the corresponding phase diagrams. In many cases such diagrams can be looked upon as simply made up of two parts: one related to solid solubility, the other related to solid insolubility.

The tin-lead alloy phase diagram is a typical example, Fig. 18-20. Lead is soluble in solid tin up to 1.45 atomic percent, point *C*, and tin is soluble in solid lead up to 29 atomic percent, point *D*. Accordingly, up to these limits the transformation from the liquid to the solid phase is represented by liquidus and solidus lines that are typical of complete solid solubility: *AH* and *AC* on the tin side, *BK* and *BD* on the lead side. With the onset of solid insolubility the diagram resembles that of Fig. 18-7. It is represented by the liquidus *HEK* and the solidus *CED*, with the formation of a eutectic at point *E*. However, at point *E* the eutectic is made up not of pure elements but of a 1.45 percent lead solution in tin and a 29 percent tin solution in lead, points *C* and *D*. Thereupon, these limits of solubility decrease with temperature as shown by lines *CF* and *DG* in Fig. 18-20.

To summarize, the phase diagram of partial solid solubility in its simplest form consists of six regions, Fig. 18-20. They are

1. Complete liquid solubility and one single phase *L* above *AEB*.

2. and 3. Solid solubility at both ends of the phase diagram, one phase, α at the tin rich side, *ACF*, the other phase, β at the lead rich side, *BDG*.

4. and 5. Mixture of two phases, *L* and α on the hypoeutectic side, *ACE*, and two phases *L* and β on the hypereutectic side, *BDE*.

6. Mixture of two (solid) phases α and β, consisting of α and the eutectic on the hypoeutectic side, and β and the eutectic on the hypereutectic side, *FCEDG*.

b. *Extension to Components Made Up of Compounds.* From the point of view of thermodynamics and statistical stability, a compound in many instances behaves like a pure element. It has a constant melting point and a specific value of heat of fusion. Accordingly, the binary phase diagrams between two compounds or between a compound and an element exhibit the same characteristics and diversity as between two single elements. They vary from (nearly complete) liquid insolubility, as between water and oil, to complete solid solubility, as between MgO and NiO, with intermediate features of (nearly complete) solid insolubility as in NaCl and RbCl aggregates, and partial solid solubility as in MgO-CaO ceramics.[11]

By reversing the argument we can often recognize the existence of a compound between two elements *A* and *B*, by identifying in the phase diagram of these elements the above mentioned features at compositions that are part way between the two terminal compositions of zero and 100 percent. We shall find that as a rule the presence of a compound, say A_nB_m, enables the phase diagram to be split in two parts: one between *A* and A_nB_m, the other between A_nB_m and *B*.

The Cu-Al phase diagram can be used as a typical example (Fig. 18-21). If we limit this diagram to the industrially important region between pure Al

[11] Cf. E. M. Levin, C. R. Robbins and H. F. McMurdie, *Phase Diagrams for Ceramicists*, Am. Ceramic Society, 1964.

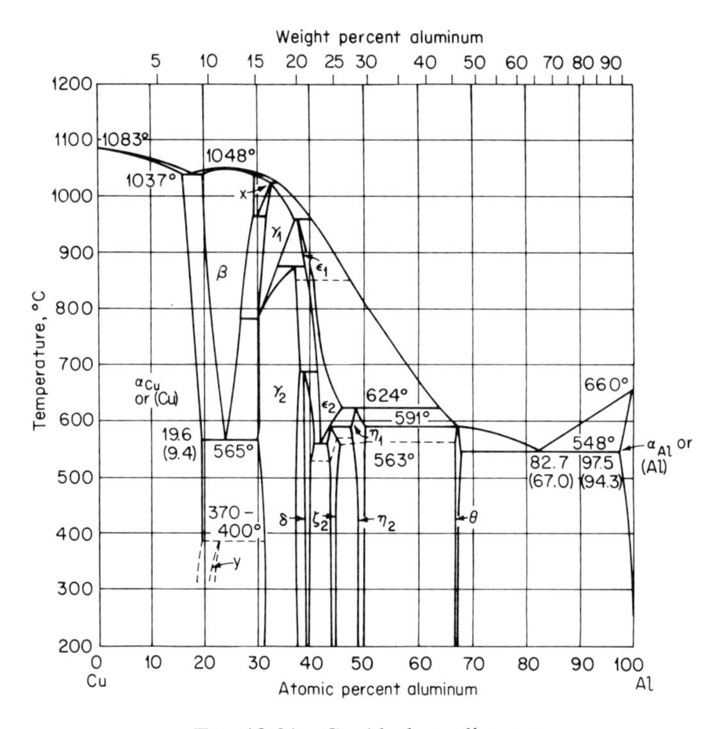

FIG. 18-21 Cu-Al phase diagram

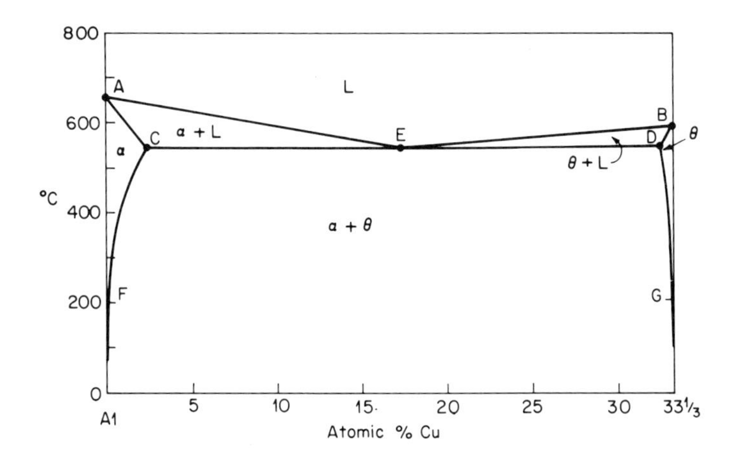

FIG. 18-22 Aluminum rich portion (Al-Al_2Cu) of Cu-Al phase diagram

and Al_2Cu (corresponding to 33.3... atomic percent of Cu), Fig. 18-22, we easily recognize the six characteristic regions of partial solid solubility of Fig. 18-20. It is apparent that the compound Al_2Cu behaves in all respects like one of the components in a binary phase diagram. The existence of an

Al_2Cu compound is also supported by X-ray diffraction analysis. The crystal structure of Al_2Cu is built on a tetragonal lattice, with a body centered unit cell having a square base of 6.054 × 6.054 Å^2, a height of 4.865 Å and containing four Cu and eight Al atoms, Fig. 18-23.

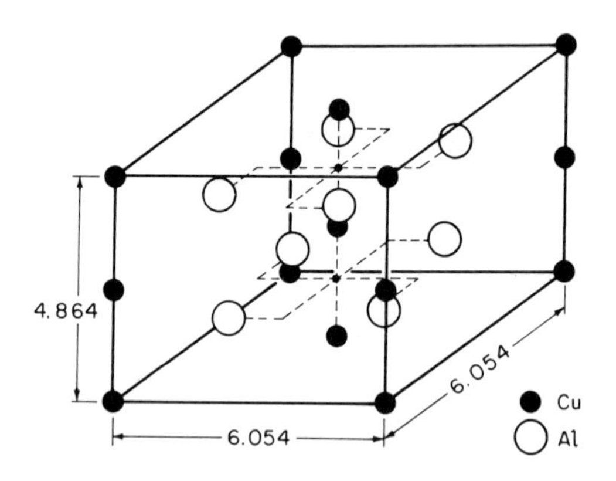

FIG. 18-23 Al_2Cu crystal structure

c. *Precipitation Hardening.* Practical interest in alloys of type IV centers on the decrease of *solid solubility with temperature* represented by line *CF*, Fig. 18-22. This trend is responsible for one of the most important discoveries made in the study of alloys: the *precipitation hardening* heat treatment. The discovery was made by a factory engineer, A. Wilm in Germany in 1906 in the course of a routine heat treatment (annealing) of aluminum-copper alloys. The discovery itself might have been accidental, as most discoveries are believed to be, but it could have remained an isolated fact without the benefit of the corresponding phase diagram, Fig. 18-21. Thanks to this diagram the phenomenon was recognized as a direct consequence of limited solid solubility. It was then readily generalized to many alloys whose phase diagrams showed a similar trend. Thus, the production of a precipitation hardening copper-berylium alloy with a tensile strength of 175,000 psi, as compared to 60,000 psi for the unhardened (annealed) alloy, was no longer a happy accident of a chance discovery. It was the result of a planned program of research based on the knowledge of the Cu-Be phase diagram.

Because of its historical and still widely practical importance the phenomenon of precipitation hardening will be discussed with a particular reference to Al-Cu alloys. The pertinent portion of the Al-Al_2Cu phase diagram, Fig. 18-21, is reproduced on a larger scale in Fig. 18-24.

Consider, for the sake of concreteness, an alloy containing 2 percent Cu, point *M*. At room temperature less than 0.2 percent of this amount is in solution, point *Q*. But at 525°C (798°K) the whole amount of 2 percent Cu is

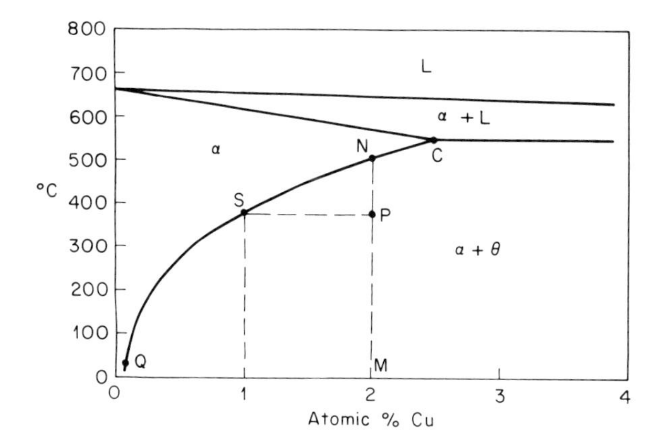

FIG. 18-24 Extended portion of the Al-Al_2Cu phase diagram of FIG. 18-22

dissolved in aluminum, point *N*. The precipitation hardening treatment consists of heating the alloy slightly above *N* and cooling it rapidly (quenching it) to room temperature. If the alloy is held at room temperature for more than five days, it will be observed, Fig. 18-25 curve *B*, that its tensile strength has gradually increased to a maximum value of about 60,000 psi; the alloy is said to have aged. The process of aging can be speeded up by maintaining the alloy at a slightly higher temperature, Fig. 18-25, curve *C*. However, if the temperature is too high, the rapid increase of strength is followed by a drop of strength; the alloy is overaged, curve *D*. Conversely, too low a temperature suppresses aging completely, curve *A*.

The phenomenon of precipitation hardening can be explained by analyzing

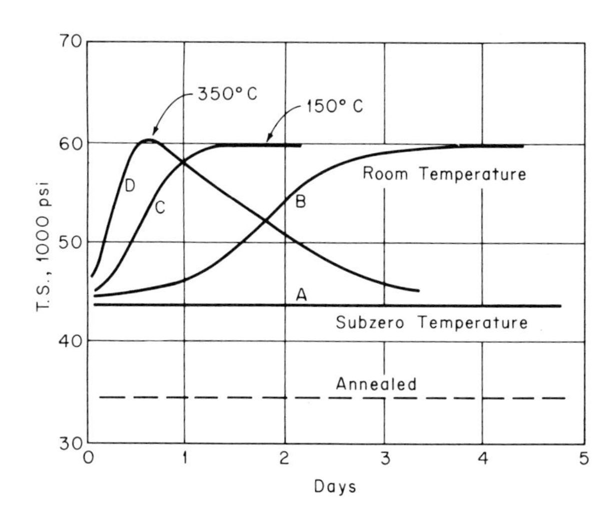

FIG. 18-25 Aging of a heat-treated aluminum-copper alloy

the difference between slow and rapid rate of cooling from above point *N*, Fig. 18-24. On slow cooling the atoms of copper which are in excess of the limit of solubility leave the crystal structure of aluminum along with twice as many aluminum atoms and form a new phase θ. Thus, at 450°C, point *P*, only 1 percent Cu remains in solution, point *S*. The remaining 1 percent Cu has been precipitated from the solution. By what mechanism? Obviously the same mechanism of diffusion which governs the motion of atoms in nickel-copper alloys, Section 18-8c. It will be recalled that this mechanism is slow and that it can almost stop if the temperature is too low. It is the sluggishness of diffusion in the solid state that is at the root of the precipitation hardening phenomenon. To obtain a fully stabilized alloy the rate of cooling must be very low. If the rate of cooling is too high, there is no time for the diffusion to occur, and the solid solution is supersaturated with copper atoms. The next step depends on the temperature. If the temperature is too low, the alloy remains in the supersaturated condition indefinitely. Fig. 18-25 shows that in this condition the alloy is only slightly stronger than in the fully stabilized, or annealed, condition, curve *A*. On raising the temperature a limited motion of copper atoms takes place within the solid solution. X-ray diffraction studies have shown that the copper atoms tend to aggregate, somewhat in the manner suggested by Fig. 18-26 and form platelike clusters with adjacent aluminum atoms, Fig. 18-27. These clusters are known as G.P. zones, after the names of A. Guinier and G. D. Preston who proved their existence in 1938–39 using a special X-ray diffuse scattering technique. At moderate temperatures, i.e., room temperature and 150 °C the clusters appear to be sufficiently thin to maintain continuity, or coherence, with the surrounding matrix. Therein presumably lies their ability to harden the alloy, i.e., to increase its resistance to slip above and beyond that manifested in the "as quenched" condition. The resistance to slip can be expected to grow slowly or rapidly depending on the temperature of aging and the ensuing process of clustering, and it tends to level off as the growth of the G.P. zones themselves slows down, Fig. 18-25, curves *B* and *C*. However, at a still higher temperature the mechanism of diffusion carries the process of clustering beyond its critical stage and leads to an incipient formation of larger precipitates at the expense of neighboring G.P. zones. The fact that now the precipitate is much coarser and that it loses coherence with the matrix appears to account for the ensuing softening and drop of strength, Fig. 18-25, curve *D*.

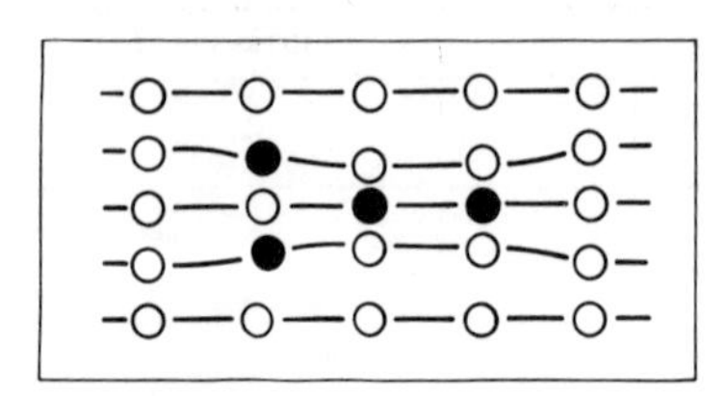

FIG. 18-26 Clustering of Guinier-Preston (G.P.) zones

The above qualitative description can be further refined by considering motion of the dislocations and computing their interactions with the G.P. zones and the precipitates, respectively. These refinements represent useful contributions to the theory, but so far they have not proved to be sufficient to quantitatively predict the outcome of the precipitation hardening process in practical applications.

FIG. 18-27 Precipitates in heat-treated aluminum alloys. (From *Philosophical Magazine*, **3**, 534, Fig. 6, 1958, by permission)

18-10 Diffusivity and Fick's Law. Homogenization of solid solutions and precipitation hardening are but two instances of redistribution of particles by diffusion. To a smaller or greater degree, all phase transformations involve transport of matter. What is then the relation between the microscopic, random mechanism of diffusion caused by thermal agitation and the apparently orderly phenomenon of mass transport on the macroscopic scale? The establishment of such a relationship is important for the control of many industrial processes.

a. *Fick's Law.* There is a close analogy between the relationship we seek to establish and the one which governs the transport of momentum in laminar viscous flow, Section 12-1. Here as there, thermal agitation and random interchange of particles is the underlying mechanism, but *lack* of *macroscopic homogeneity* is the governing factor. In the viscous laminar flow this factor has shown to be the velocity gradient; in the mass transport caused by diffusion the governing factor is the concentration gradient.

To bring out more vividly the analogy between the two processes we resort to a model similar to the one used for the derivation of Newton's law of viscosity, Fig. 12-1.

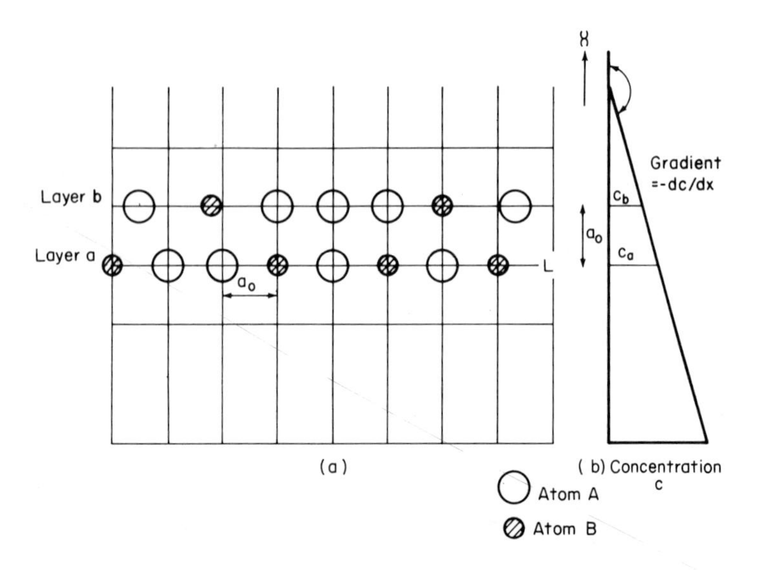

FIG. 18-28 Derivation of Fick's Law, (a) and (b)

We picture that the atoms (or molecules as the case may be) are arranged in parallel layers separated from each other by a distance a_0 and that the average cross sectional area occupied by each atom is a_0^2. Instead of differing in velocity, as in laminar flow, the layers differ in the concentration c of solute atoms. We will assume for simplicity that the concentration decreases linearly in the x direction, Fig. 18-28.

The problem is further simplified by letting the concentration difference $c_a - c_b$ between two adjacent layers a and b be very small compared to the concentration in these layers.

Both the solvent and the solute atom are subjected to random thermal vibration. Let ν be the frequency, i.e., the number of oscillations of the solute atom in unit time. During one oscillation, i.e., during the interval of time $1/\nu$, some of the solute atoms acquire sufficient amplitude to jump from one layer to the other. Let q be the fraction of these atoms. Then, if N is the total number of atoms in unit volume and c_a is the concentration in solute atoms of a particular layer a, the number $\mathring{N}'_x$ of solute atoms per unit area transported in unit time in the forward x direction from layer a to the next layer b is

$$\mathring{N}'_x = \tfrac{1}{2}c_a N a_0 q\nu \tag{18-45}$$

The argument runs as follows:

1. The distance between two adjacent layers a and b is a_0. Hence there are $1/a_0$ layers in unit volume and each layer contains $N/(1/a_0) = Na_0$ atoms per unit area. Of these $c_a Na_0$ are solute atoms.

2. During the time interval $1/\nu$ the number of atoms leaving layer a is $qc_a Na_0$. Hence the number of solute atoms leaving layer a in unit time is $q(c_a Na_0)/(1/\nu) = qc_a Na_0\nu$. Statistically, as many atoms jump in the forward as in the backward direction. Hence the number $\mathring{N}'_x$ of solute atoms jumping in the forward x direction is half the total number of jumping solute atoms or $\frac{1}{2}qc_a Na_0\nu$, q.e.d.

By the same argument, if c_b is the concentration in solute atoms of the b layer, the number $\mathring{N}''_x$ of solute atoms per unit area transported from layer b to layer a in the backward x direction is

$$\mathring{N}''_x = \tfrac{1}{2}qc_b Na_0\nu \tag{18-46}$$

We assume here that neither q nor ν is affected by the small change of concentration. Consequently the net number $\mathring{N}_x$ of solute atoms per unit area transported in the forward x direction from one layer to the other in unit time is

$$\mathring{N}_x = \tfrac{1}{2}qNa_0\nu(c_a - c_b) \tag{18-47}$$

From Fig. 18-28b

$$(c_a - c_b)/a_0 = -dc/dx \tag{18-48}$$

Hence substituting for $(c_a - c_b)$ and rearranging the terms we obtain

$$\mathring{N}_x = -(\tfrac{1}{2}qa_0^2\nu)N\, dc/dx \tag{18-49}$$

Expression (18-49) can be generalized, thus making it applicable to any mass transport, by putting

$$\mathring{N}_x/N = J \tag{18-50}$$

and

$$\tfrac{1}{2}q\nu a_0^2 = D \tag{18-51}$$

J is called the *flux* or the rate of mass transport in the x direction. The dimensions of J are length/time. D is called the *diffusivity* or coefficient of diffusion; its dimensions are area/time. Substitution of Eqs. (18-50) and (18-51) in (18-49) yields

$$J = -D\, dc/dx \tag{18-52}$$

or, in words, the rate of mass transport is proportional to the concentration gradient $(-dc/dx)$—a relationship formulated as a law by the German physicist Adolph Fick in 1855.

b. *Diffusivity D. Range of Variation.* In the cgs system the unit of D is 1 cm^2/sec. Experimentally determined values of D cover a wide range. They spread over several orders of magnitude. The influence of temperature was mentioned previously (Section 18-8d). However, the state of aggregation, nature of the solute and solvent, and even concentration—contrary to the assumption made in the derivation—are also of influence. Moreover, in solids D is vastly different for interstitial and substitutional solute atoms.

Typical orders of magnitude of D in dilute solutions near the melting point of the solvent are:[12]

$D = 10^{-4} - 10^{-5}$ cm^2/sec in liquids,
$D = 10^{-6} - 10^{-7}$ cm^2/sec in interstitial solid solutions,
$D = 10^{-8} - 10^{-9}$ cm^2/sec in substitutional solid solutions.

18-11 Iron-Carbon Alloys. Heat Treatment of Steel. It is fitting to conclude the chapter on Alloys by analyzing the iron-carbon phase diagram which governs the behavior of steel—the most important industrial alloy. The unique position which steel occupies in our civilization appears to result from a combination of properties (and availability) unmatched by any other alloy. Steel can be readily shaped when heated to a high temperature and it can be made extraordinarily hard when quenched subsequently in water or oil. We shall see later that the phenomenon of steel hardening is quite different from the precipitation hardening discussed in Section 18-9. While not unique, the hardening of steel is exceptional in that it is produced by an abrupt change of solubility of carbon in iron following the polymorphic transformation of iron.

The polymorphic changes of pure iron in the solid state have been mentioned earlier in Section 17-2. We shall disregard the high temperature variety appearing immediately after solidification and center our attention on two phases: the FCC phase which is stable above 908°C and the BCC phase which is stable below this temperature. The former, called γ iron, is also known as austenite (after Austen who identified it); the latter, called α iron, is also known as ferrite. Austenite can dissolve carbon up to 2 weight-percent (7.9 atomic percent). On the other hand, ferrite can hold no more than 0.025

[12] W. Jost. *Diffusion in Solids, Liquids, Gases*, Academic Press, N.Y., 1952, and P. G. Shewman. *Diffusion in Solids*, McGraw-Hill, N.Y., 1963.

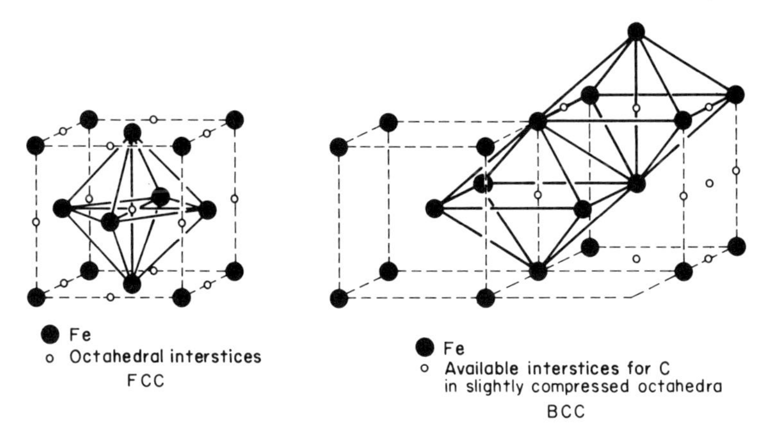

FIG. 18-29 Possible locations of carbon atoms in FCC and BCC iron

weight-percent carbon in solution. The difference in the extent of solubility appears to be closely related to the position of carbon atoms in the crystal structure. We recall that, unlike the solid solutions considered previously, the solid solutions of iron and carbon are not substitutional, but interstitial. The carbon atoms do not replace iron atoms in their sites. Rather they insert themselves between the iron atoms in one of the six voids (per unit cell) formed by six Fe atoms occupying the corners of an octahedron—hence the name of octahedral interstices, Fig. 18-29a. At variance with the FCC structure, the BCC arrangement of iron atoms offers much less room for insertion of carbon atoms in similar interstices, Fig. 18-29b. Hence it is plausible that the BCC ferrite should dissolve much less carbon than the FCC austenite.

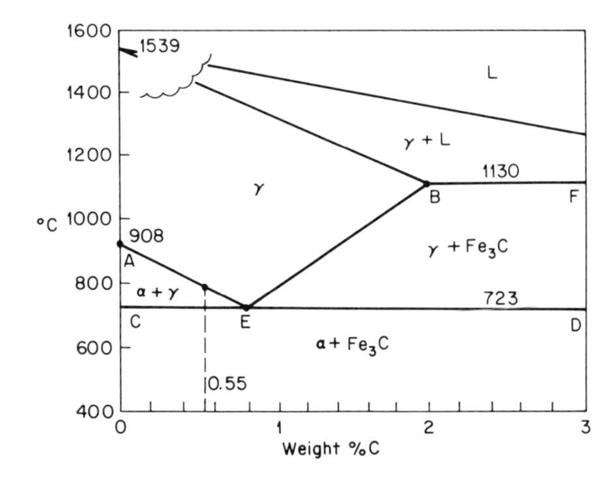

FIG. 18-30 Simplified iron-cementite phase diagram

a. *Phase Diagram.* Depending on the mode of preparation, one of the components in the iron-carbon system may be either carbon itself or an iron-carbon compound Fe_3C, called cementite. The cast iron considered in Section 18-7c is a eutectic of iron and carbon. To distinguish this eutectic from the eutectic of iron and cementite (of the same composition) it is called gray cast iron, after the grayish appearance of its fractured surface. Steel can be called an alloy of iron and cementite. For our present discussion only that part of the phase diagram need be considered which comprises compositions smaller than 2 percent C, Fig. 18-30. We can disregard the upper left corner in this diagram which pertains to the transformation of the high temperature solid phase called δ. With these simplifications the part of the iron-carbon diagram which is above 908°C resembles closely the aluminum-copper diagram of Fig. 18-22. It is seen that the solubility of carbon in austenite decreases with temperature according to the trends shown by *BE*. On slow cooling cementite will precipitate from the solid solution as soon as line *BE* is crossed. At point *E* the process is complicated by the simultaneous transformation of austenite to ferrite. This transformation occurs for pure iron at 908°C, point *A*. However, increasing amounts of carbon in austenite depress the transformation to lower and lower temperatures, line *AE*. This trend is analogous to the solidification of the sodium-rubidium alloys considered in Section 18-7a. The intersection of *AE* with *BE* marks the lowest temperature at which austenite is in equilibrium with its products of decomposition: ferrite and cementite. The situation at point *E*, Fig. 18-30 is in all respects similar to that of point *E*, Fig. 18-7. The decomposition of austenite proceeds here to completion at a constant temperature, and the products of decomposition are extremely fine. The fineness of the structure produces iridescent effects, akin to a grating, when the alloy is etched for microscopic inspection, Fig. 18-31. Hence the name *pearlite* is given to the structure. By analogy with the eutectic of Fig. 18-7 the resulting alloy is called eutectoid. The analogy between the phase diagrams Figs. 18-7 and 18-30 can be pressed further. A composition which is to the left of the eutectoid, e.g., 0.55 percent carbon, transforms through a range of temperatures beginning with 800°C and ending with 723°C. Its structure at room temperature contains an excess of ferrite along with pearlite, Fig. 18-32. Similarly a composition which is to the right of the eutectoid, e.g., 1.1 percent carbon, transforms through the range of temperature 820°C–723°C and forms an end product consisting of pearlite and cementite, Fig. 18-33. In conclusion, the equilibrium phase diagram, obtained by slow cooling, is composed of four regions in the solid state[13]: solid solution γ above the lines *AE* and *EB*, solid solution γ and almost carbon-free iron α in the triangular region *AEC*, solid solution γ and cementite Fe_3C in the trapezoidal region *FBED*, and finally α and cementite below the horizontal line *CED*. Steels having compositions between 0 and

[13] If the δ region is disregarded.

0.8 percent carbon are called hypoeutectoid; those beyond 0.8 percent carbon are called hypereutectoid.

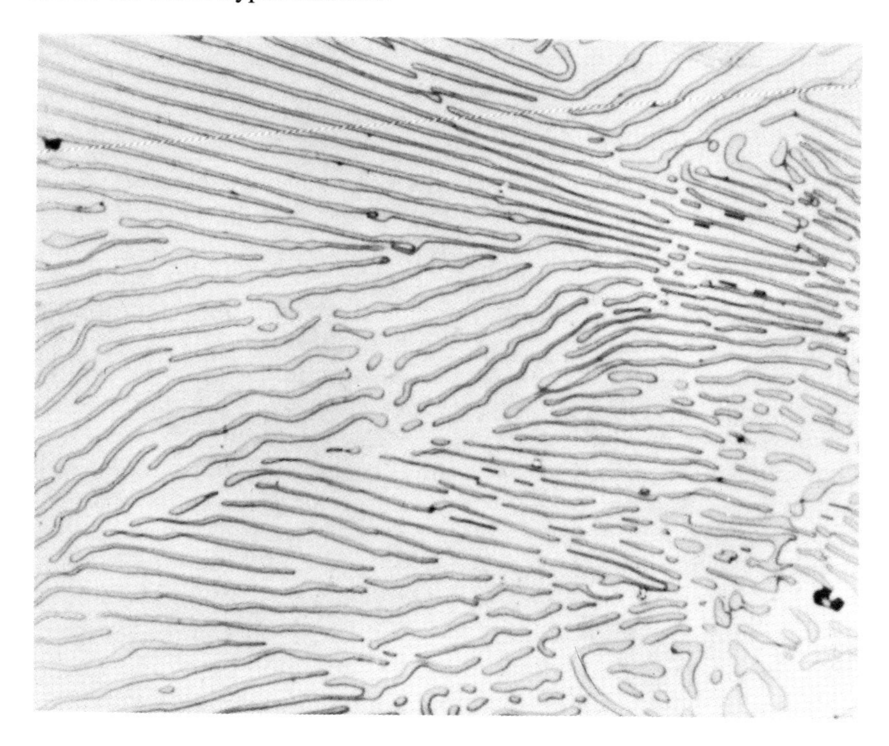

FIG. 18-31 Lamellar structure of pearlite. (From J. R. Vilella, *Metallographic Technique for Steel*, Fig. 11, p. 32, AMS 1938, by permission)

b. *Properties and Uses.* Hot worked and slowly cooled or annealed iron-carbon alloys exhibit the same general trend of properties as alloys of Section 18-8 which are characterized by solid insolubility. They behave more or less according to the rule of averages. Ferrite being soft and ductile and cementite being hard and brittle, the tensile strength increases from about 35,000 psi to 120,000 psi as the carbon content changes from 0 to 0.8 percent. There is a corresponding decrease in elongation. Past the eutectoid composition the results become erratic due to the increased brittleness of the alloy. This wide range of properties produced at almost no extra cost makes the steel one of the most versatile engineering materials. Mild steel with composition varying from less than 0.1 to 0.25 percent carbon is the standard material for deep drawing, sheet metal work in automotive and canning industries and is an important material in the building industry (steel frameworks, bridges). Medium carbon steel from about 0.25 to 0.65 percent carbon is used for shafts, rolling stock, rails, and wires. High carbon steel

FIG. 18-32 Pearlite and ferrite. (From Reed-Hill, *Physical Metallurgy Principles*, Fig. 16-28, D. Van Nostrand Company, Inc., Princeton, 1964, by permission)

from 0.65 to 1.2 percent carbon finds some applications in the annealed conditions, e.g., rails, but serves mostly in the heat treated, hardened condition for the manufacture of tools and cutlery.

c. *Heat Treatment of Steel. Martensitic Hardening*. The hardening of steel is an operation which can be readily described with reference to Fig. 18-30. The metal is heated to a temperature somewhat above that which puts all carbon in solution, i.e., above the lines *AE* and *EB*. It is then cooled at a rate sufficiently high to prevent the precipitation of carbon from the solution, e.g., by quenching the alloy in water. The resulting product (with a high carbon content) possesses a degree of hardness which is exceeded only by a few special types of alloys. X-ray diffraction analysis reveals that at least 90 percent of this product is a new phase called *martensite*, in honor of the nineteenth century metallurgist Martens, the balance being the high temperature polymorph of iron, austenite retained by quenching.

Martensite is built on a tetragonal body centered lattice whose unit cell, Fig. 18-34, can be looked upon as a distorted body centered cube. The distortion is believed to be brought about by carbon atoms retained in the

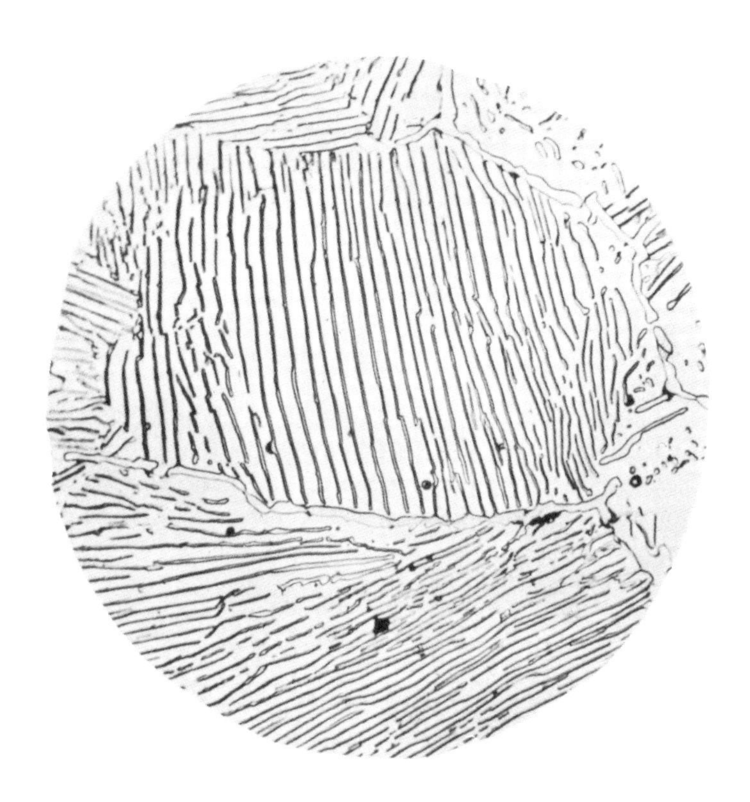

FIG. 18-33 Pearlite and cementite. (From Reed-Hill, *Physical Metallurgy Principles*, Fig. 16-30, D. Van Nostrand Company, Inc., Princeton, 1964, by permission; 1000 × original)

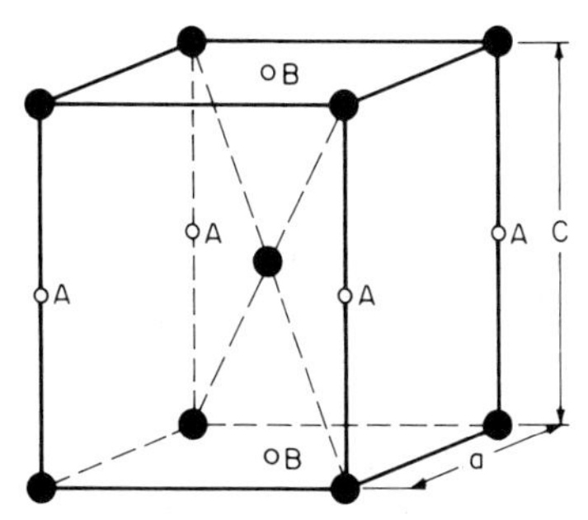

FIG. 18-34 Unit cell of martensite with possible locations of carbon atoms

lattice. However, if the unit cell is to be stretched in the vertical direction, the carbon atoms must settle either in the interstices *A* or *B*, but nowhere else, Fig. 18-34. As seen from this figure, there is only one interstice of each kind per unit cell, at variance with the FCC cubic lattice where there are four equivalent octahedral interstices per unit cell. The degree of distortion thus produced can be conveniently measured by the deviation of the unit cell from a cube, e.g., by the disparity between the height c of the unit cell and the side a of its square base. As expected, this disparity increases with the increased carbon content, Fig. 18-35, as does the volume expansion as measured by the corresponding volumetric strain ϵ_v, caused by the insertion of the carbon atom into the lattice. If terms of order higher than one are neglected, then according to Fig. 18-35 the volumetric strain is proportional to the carbon content, increasing by 3.4 percent for each weight percent, or 0.8 percent for each atomic percent.

The resistance to slip as measured by the magnitude of the Y.S. has also been shown to increase with the carbon content, at least up to 0.6 weight percent. There is thus strong presumption that the lattice distortion caused by the carbon atoms impedes the onset and propagation of plastic deformation in martensite.

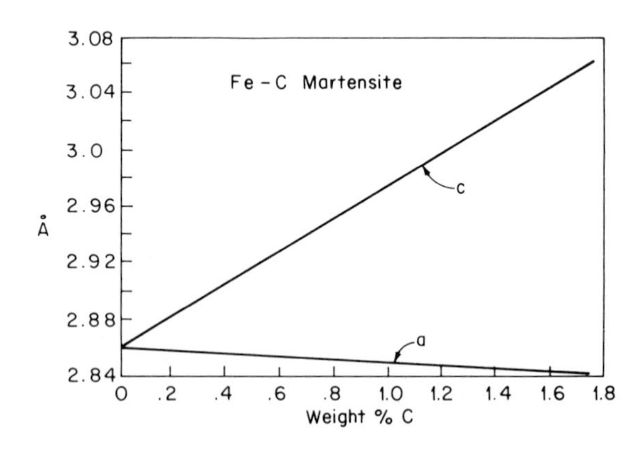

FIG. 18-35 The c/a ratio vs. carbon content in martensite

On this understanding, it seems justified to ascribe the phenomenal hardening of martensite to a lattice distortion caused by the interstitial carbon atoms. The absence of a similar hardening in austenite could perhaps be explained by a much lesser distortion of the lattice due to the more spacious interstices of the FCC structure.

d. *Alloy Steels.* Another proof of the success of experimental methods is the creation of steels that can be hardened with the formation of martensite by letting them simply cool in air. This operation is known as air-hardening. It has been found that an addition of other metallic elements to steel, particularly Mn, Cr, and Mo in amounts varying from a fraction to tens of one percent, considerably reduces the rate of carbide precipitation from a saturated solid solution. Such steel can therefore be hardened even though the rates of cooling are much lower than for ordinary carbon steels. Lowering the rate of cooling has two main advantages:

1. It tends to equalize the rates of cooling through the thickness, thereby causing a deeper penetration of the hardened zone into the core.
2. It minimizes warping and danger of cracking.

Thus, an addition of 12 to 17 percent Cr and about 1 percent Mo to an ordinary carbon steel makes it hardenable in air and almost immune to warping and distortion. Moreover the alloy exhibits excellent wear resistance. It is therefore extensively used for making dies.

It should be noted in all fairness that alloying elements also are added to steel for other purposes than hardening, witness the stainless steel mentioned in Section 18-8b. However, even a partial description of the nature and uses of various alloy steels would take us far beyond the scope of this book.

e. *Tempering*. As with the alloying of steel the heat treatment of steel is not limited to martensitic hardening. However, only in this type of treatment does the metal undergo a truly polymorphic transformation from FCC austenite to BCC tetragonal martensite. All other heat treatments produce phase transformations that entail diffusion and changes of composition from one phase to another. Typical in this respect is tempering.

The operation of tempering is usually applied to reduce brittleness after quenching. The brittleness is reduced at the expense of hardness by reheating the steel to a temperature that lies above the temperature corresponding to the beginning of martensitic transformation of austenite (200°C and up) and below line *CED*, Fig. 18-30, which corresponds to the redissolution of carbon in austenite. Depending on time and temperature, more or less carbides Fe_3C (and hence carbon atoms) are being precipitated from the solution. The martensite formed during previous quenching and the balance of untransformed (retained) austenite are thereby decomposed into products that are less hard and less brittle than martensite. Yet, they confer greater strength to the alloy, without much loss in ductility, than ferrite and pearlite—the equilibrium products of austenitic decomposition along line *CED*, Fig. 18-30. The nature of the phases present is essentially the same in both cases: BCC α-iron and orthorhombic cementite. It is the size and the distribution of the phases, i.e., the *morphology* of the phase transformation, that are being actually affected by the operation of tempering.

The recourse to previous quenching can be avoided by making use of *austempering*. In this operation the alloy is directly quenched from above the *AEB* line, Fig. 18-30, into a hot bath. The temperature of the bath is kept high enough to barely avoid the austenite-martensite transformation, yet it is sufficiently low to impart to the alloy a rate of cooling that prevents premature decomposition of austenite. The actual decomposition takes place in the bath at a constant temperature and relatively low rate. The morphological variety of ferrite and cementite produced thereby is more ductile yet no less strong than the variety obtained by tempering.

To point out the distinction between the diffusive nature of precipitation hardening and the diffusionless formation of hard martensite, we shall add that steels, particularly vanadium alloy steels, can be further hardened, akin to aluminum-copper alloys, by what appears to be clustering or precipitation of carbides in either the martensitic or the ferritic matrix, depending on temperature.[14] This hardening is readily distinguished from the inherent hardness of martensite by its characteristic dependence on time, i.e., by aging or overaging when hardness goes down.

T-T-T Diagrams. The control of heat treatments can be kept to close tolerances thanks to Time-Temperature-Transformation, or T-T-T-, diagrams. These diagrams are established experimentally for each kind of steel by plotting the time that is necessary to initiate a certain stage of tranformation of the austenite at a given temperature below *CED*, Fig. 18-30. Take, for example, 0.8 percent carbon steel, Fig. 18-36. Line *F* indicates the beginning of the transformation of austenite into ferrite and cementite, while line *G* indicates the end of this tranformation. Likewise, M_s is the temperature above which no martensite is formed, whereas M_f is the temperature to which the steel should be quenched to yield the maximum content of martensite. Noteworthy is the noselike shape of curves *F* and *G*. It is at once apparent that, if premature decomposition of austenite is to be avoided in quenching, the rate of cooling indicated by line *RR* must be high enough to miss the tip *T* of the nose. In alloy steel this tip is shifted to the right, thus enabling and justifying the use of the much lower quenching rates mentioned previously. Outcomes of other heat treatments can be similarly predicted and controlled. The *rule of thumb*, hitherto so prevalent in the heat treatment practice, has become a thing of the past.

18-12 Summary. The art of alloying, in which two or more elements are aggregated in one single *metallic* product, has enabled man to achieve a combination of properties, e.g., hardness and ductility, unattainable in either pure elements or any other type of aggregates. Basic to the formation of alloys is the principle of *statistical stability*, manifested by the tendency of different species of atoms to preserve a random distribution within a single phase. This tendency is opposed by several factors of which the *atomic size* factor is, if not the most dominant, at least the most readily accounted for.

In binary alloys made up of components *A* and *B* the atomic size factor is defined by the ratio $(a - b)/\langle a\rangle$, in which *a* and *b* are the distances of closest

[14] E. Tekin and P. M. Kelly, "A Study of the Tempering of Steel Using Transmission Electron Microscopy," *Precipitation from Iron-Base Alloys,* G. R. Speich and J. B. Clark, Ed., Gordon and Breach Science Publishers, New York, 1965.

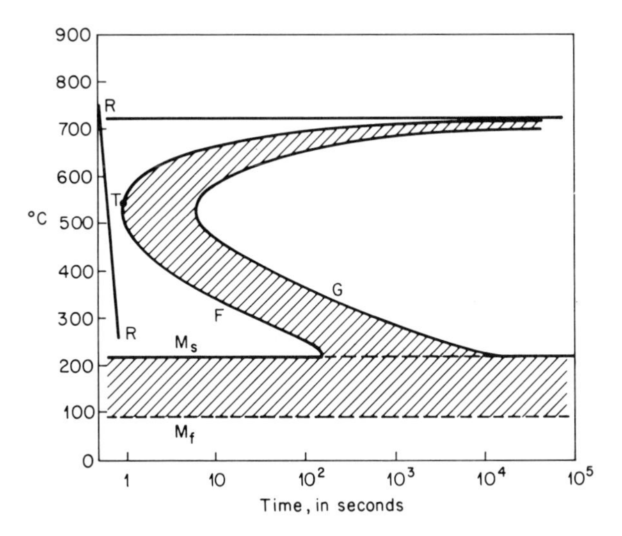

FIG. 18-36 *T-T-T* diagram for 0.8%C steel

approach between atoms in the pure components A and B, respectively; $\langle a \rangle$ is the average between a and b. The incompatibility of atomic sizes measured by this factor creates strains in the lattice, thereby decreasing its stability and opposing the tendency of atoms A and B to remain in the same phase.

Depending on the magnitude of the atomic size factor we distinguish four types of binary alloys: (1) liquid insolubility, (2) solid insolubility, (3) complete solid solubility, and (4) partial solid solubility. Each of these types is identified by a characteristic *c-T*, or concentration-temperature, *phase diagram.* Liquid phases are denoted by capital L: L_1, L_2 etc.; solid phases are identified by Greek letters: α, β, etc.

Liquid insolubility as a rule should be expected when $(a - b)/\langle a \rangle$ is greater than 30 percent. The phase diagram consists of three regions, which depending on the interval of temperatures, contain: (1) two liquids L_1 and L_2, (2) one liquid and one solid, e.g., L_1 and α, and (3) two solids α and β. Lack of liquid miscibility precludes interaction on the atomic scale and explains the lack of interesting combinations of properties. However, emulsified droplets of the minor component, e.g., Pb, can substantially improve the *machining* characteristics of the major component, e.g., Cu.

Solid insolubility generally occurs when $(a - b)/\langle a \rangle$ is greater than 25 percent. Abrupt change from liquid solubility to solid insolubility has a deep effect on the trend and temperature of solidification. The process of solidification is spread over a range of temperatures. The beginning of solidification of one component, say A, is invariably lowered by a greater admixture of the other component, say B. The process of solidification continues on further decrease of temperature, and the ensuing precipitation of component A enriches the liquid in B. The proportion of liquid to solid at each temperature is determined by the *lever rule*. The solidification ends when the composition of the liquid reaches a critical value, that of the *eutectic*, at which both A and B precipitate. The resulting phase diagram contains four regions as follows: (1) one single liquid phase L above the temperature of beginning solidification, (2) two regions $L + \alpha$, $L + \beta$ made up of the liquid phase and one of the solid components (and phases α or β) in the interval of temperatures separating the beginning from the end of solidification, and (3) two solid phases $\alpha + \beta$ below the temperature of solidification of the eutectic.

Solidification of alloys having exact eutectic composition begins and ends at the same temperature which for simple binary alloys is also the lowest temperature of solidification. The products of precipitation are extremely fine. On both counts eutectics find wide application in *foundry* practice, because they melt and flow easily (eutectic in Greek means easy flowing). The low melting point of some eutectics makes them useful as *solders* for joining finished parts or as *circulating fluids* in heat exchangers, e.g., in *nuclear reactors*.

Complete solid solubility cannot be expected unless $(a - b)/\langle a \rangle$ is smaller than 15 percent. The two components obviously must possess the same crystal structure. As in solid insolubility, transition from the liquid to the solid phase is spread over a range of temperatures in which the two phases co-exist in proportions governed by the lever rule. The compositions of the two phases differ, but at a given temperature these compositions are solely determined by *thermodynamic* equilibrium, not by the initial, overall composition of the alloy. The corresponding phase diagram consists of three regions: (1) a region with a single liquid phase L, (2) a closed two-phase region $L + \alpha$ corresponding to the gradual transition of the alloy from the liquid to the solid state, and (3) a region with a single solid phase α. The first and the second regions are separated by the *liquidus* line marking the beginning of solidification. The second and third regions are separated by the *solidus* line marking the end of solidification.

Random and close interaction between dissimilar atoms accounts for some remarkable properties of alloys in this category. Prominent are: the phenomenal increase of electrical resistivity, as in Ni-Cr alloys, low coefficient of thermal expansion, as in Fe-Ni alloys, and high corrosion resistance, as in stainless steel. The attainment of these properties depends in large measure on the degree of uniformity or *homogeneity* achieved during solidification. Thermal agitation provides a mechanism called *diffusion* which evens out the concentration of solid solutions. However, diffusion is much slower in solids than in liquids, presumably because solids possess dimensional stability. Moreover, the rate of diffusion drops drastically when the temperature is lowered. Consequently, if the rate of solidification is too rapid, the solid solution is *heterogeneous*.

Partial solid solubility rather than insolubility theoretically exists in all cases for which $(a - b)/\langle a \rangle$ is larger than 15 percent. Practically, we make a distinction between insolubility and partial solubility to emphasize the effect of *decreasing solid solubility with temperature* on properties of alloys whose atomic size factor is comprised between 25 and 15 percent. The ensuing phase diagram can be shown to be an extension of the phase diagram characterizing complete solid solubility. The extended phase diagram contains six regions as follows: (1) one region with a single liquid phase L above the liquidus line; (2) and (3) two triangular closed regions $L + \alpha$ and $L + \beta$ between the liquidus and the solidus lines, with the regions having a common corner at the eutectic point where the liquidus and solidus lines meet; (4) and (5) two triangularly shaped regions α and β, below the solidus line, one near the left end, the other near the right end of the phase diagram, and (6) one $\alpha + \beta$ region below the solidus line and between the terminal α and β regions.

Similar diagrams are obtained when one or both of the components are compounds instead of pure elements. An industrially important example is the Al-Al_2Cu phase diagram between pure aluminum and intermetallic compound Al_2Cu.

Practical interest centers on one of the regions α or β because of the *precipitation hardening* heat treatment attending the solid solutions in these regions. The treatment takes advantage of the decreasing solid solubility with temperature as well as of the slow rate of diffusion in maintaining the alloy in a supersaturated state on *quenching*. The ensuing clustering of the precipitate in the so called *G.P.* or *Guinier-Preston zones* within the crystal lattice, accounts for the gradual increase of strength or *aging* of the alloy with time.

Most of the features of the above type of alloy are embodied in the Fe-Fe_3C, or iron-cementite, phase diagram of steel. However, the phenomenal hardening of steel is due not to the clustering of a precipitate, but to an abrupt change of the interstitial solubility of carbon in iron at the polymorphic transformation of FCC γ-iron, called *austenite*, into BCC α-iron, called *ferrite*.

On slow cooling the solid solution of carbon in austenite decomposes with the formation of an almost carbon-free ferrite and a eutectic-like, or *eutectoid*, mixture of ferrite and cementite called *pearlite*. Depending on the relative amounts of free ferrite and pearlite, steel can be made soft as in sheet metal, or hard as in rails.

On rapid cooling, rapid enough to prevent formation of ferrite and cementite, austenite is transformed into a body-centered tetragonal variety called *martensite* which keeps all carbon in solution. The atoms of carbon are believed to be sufficiently anchored in their interstitial sites to *harden* martensite, i.e., to considerably increase its resistance to slip. Rapid cooling causes warping and produces a shallow hardened zone. Both shortcomings can be avoided by using *alloy steels* in which elements are incorporated (Mn, Cr, Mo) that retard decomposition of austenite and enable hardening to occur at a much lower rate of cooling.

On quenching ordinary carbon steels become not only harder but also more brittle. The brittleness can be reduced at the expense of hardness by *tempering*, by reheating the steel slightly above the temperature of austenite-martensite transformation. Martensite and the remaining (retained) austenite are thereby decomposed into products—essentially α-iron and carbide—that are much harder but only slightly less ductile than ferrite and pearlite. The same result can be achieved without previous quenching in an operation called *austempering* through a more judicious control of the rate of cooling. Such control is possible thanks to the existence of *T-T-T* or time-temperature-transformation diagrams for each type of steel.

References

1. R. E. Reed-Hill, *Physical Metallurgy Principles*, D. Van Nostrand, New York, 1964.
2. Charles S. Barret and T. B. Massalski, *Structure of Metals*, McGraw-Hill, New York, 1966.
3. J. W. Christian, *The Theory of Transformation in Metals*, Pergamon, London, 1965.

Problems

18-1 Show that the displacement of the *a* balls due to insertion of a *b* ball varies as stated by Eq. (18-23).

18-2 Derive relations similar to Eq. (18-23) when one of the *b* balls is replaced by a somewhat smaller *a* ball.

18-3 Assuming the interatomic forces act according to the law

$$f = \frac{M}{r^2}\left[1 - \frac{r_o}{r}\right]$$

where M is a constant and r_o—the equilibrium distance, compute the strain in the first hexagon of *a* atoms about the *b* atom, Fig. 18-4. Put $\varepsilon_1 = -\varepsilon_1'$ and $b/a \leq 1.15$.

18-4 With the value of ε_1 obtained in Problem 18-3 compute the ε_2 in the second hexagon using the same assumptions as in Problem 18-3.

18-5 Derive the lever rule using Ni-Cu phase diagram, Fig. 18-12.

18-6 What are the atomic percentages of Rb in the equilibrium liquid and solid phases of the Sodium-Rubidium Phase diagram, Fig. 18-7, (a) at 20°C, (b) at −5°C?

18-7 Same question as in Problem 18-6 for the Ni-Cu phase diagram, Fig. 18-12 (a) at 1200°C, (b) at 1100°C.

18-8 Give the temperatures at the beginning and at the end of solidification for a 60 percent Cu in the Ni-Cu phase diagram, Fig. 18-12.

18-9 With reference to Figs. 18-22 and 18-24, what is the maximum content of Cu in solid solution at 500°C?

18-10 Obtain the proportion of α to θ phase in the Al-Al_2Cu phase diagram at the eutectic composition and temperature of solidification, point *E*, Fig. 18-22.

18-11 Consider a composition of 2 percent Cu, Fig. 18-24. List the number and nature of phases through which the alloy goes on slow cooling from 800°C down.

18-12 Rivets made of 4 percent Cu and 96 percent Al alloy are heated to

520°C, quenched in water, and stored in dry ice before use at room temperature. What is the purpose of cold storage?

18-13 Indicate ranges of temperature in which a 0.6 percent alloy consists of (a) γ phase alone, (b) γ and α phase, (c) α phase plus cementite Fe_3C, Fig. 18-30.

18-14 To above what temperature should a 0.55 percent carbon steel be heated to yield maximum hardness on quenching, Fig. 18-30?

18-15 Consider a steel containing 1 percent carbon, Fig. 18-30. List the number and nature of phases encountered on slow cooling from above the melting point.

18-16 Do you have to wait in order to obtain a maximum hardness of steel after quenching? How does this treatment differ from the one applied to an aluminum alloy?

18-17 In the quenching process of a thick walled cylinder, the surface layers cool and undergo the martensitic transformation sooner than the interior. Explain how this circumstance can account for the origin of residual stress after quenching. Show qualitatively the distribution of axial stress across the thickness after the part has reached room temperature.

18-18 Consider a long solid circular bar, one inch diameter made of 0.8 percent carbon steel. The rate of cooling on quenching from 720°C varies parabolically from 700°C per second at the outer surface to 140°C per second at the center. Assuming a uniaxial state of stress and a purely elastic behavior, compute the amount of residual stress and show its radial distribution at the time the outer surface reaches room temperature. Take a value of one percent for the permanent strain (=linear change of dimensions) from austenite to martensite and 3×10^7 psi for the average modulus of elasticity. Neglect the contribution of thermal expansion.
(Hint: The sum of the elastic and permanent strain is a constant, since the cross section must remain plane. Use diagram Fig. 18-36 to compute the relative amounts of martensite and austenite and hence the permanent linear change as a function of the distance from the center of the bar.)

19 / CERAMICS

We saw that the stability and properties of alloys depended in large measure on the average, rather than local, distribution and position of dissimilar atoms. Such statistical dependence can be readily understood, if we recall that alloys are characterized by a *metallic* type of bond—a communal ownership of valence electrons. The situation is quite different in *ceramics*—a category of products obtained through processing of minerals and compounds held together by predominantly covalent and ionic bonds. Here the sharing and/or exchange of electrons occurs chiefly between close neighbors. The local configuration of dissimilar atoms is therefore paramount to the stability and properties of ceramics. Particularly when the bond is ionic, the electrostatic attractions between ions of opposite sign and repulsion between ions of like sign will be seen to lead to a local order and coordination that are as characteristic of ceramics as the orderly arrangement of atoms throughout the whole crystal is of alloys. This does not mean that ceramics cannot build regular crystal structures. Many ceramics do. What it means is that the same local order and coordination are often preserved in spite of the various polymorphic and polyphase transformations which ceramics undergo during processing. The past and present uses of ceramics are largely dependent on this local invariance.

19-1 Role of Ceramics. It may be argued on admittedly sound grounds that ceramics were not nearly as important as metals in getting at the nature of things or in making advances in technology. It would appear indeed that in the first instance they lacked the simplicity of the atomic arrangement so characteristic of metals and in the second instance they lacked the requisite combination of hardness and ductility which made metals so prominent in the conquest of nature (and his own kind) by man.

However, when we look at the cultural rather than the possessive achievements of man, ceramics, for all their relatively modest rank in national economy, occupy a place of distinction secondary to no other material. Not only are ceramics by virtue of their superior resistance to corrosive agents the major, and in some instances the only, surviving evidence of ancient cultures, but they also provide vivid proof that, to use the language of the Scriptures, man does not live by bread alone. From the dawn of civilization to the present times ceramics have embodied man's natural impulse to add beauty to the useful. In that capacity they reveal the creative aspirations of the individual artist no less than the practical needs of the community.

Ceramics and the Individual. It is likely that the plastic quality of clay-water mixtures was recognized and appreciated long before it had been put to utilitarian purposes, e.g., to fashioning pottery. This prepottery era is assigned by radio-carbon dating to the seventh millennium B.C. and earlier. The transition period encompassing the sixth millennium B.C. is characterized by air-dried or crudely fired wares and it probably lasted until the invention of the *kiln*—an enclosure in which fire of sufficient intensity could be built to harden the ware all the way through. Yet, even in this transition period, vestiges of pottery can be found bearing red and brown painted bands—an unmistakable attempt at decoration. Along with painted ware in which banded, zigzagged, and checkerboard motifs predominate, impressed ware made its appearance in the next three millennia, particularly in prehistoric Europe, where the impression in the clay was made by means of a rope (the so called corded ware). In the Bronze Age (*circa* 1500 B.C.) the plasticity of clay inspired the artist to imitate in ceramics the more intricate designs of metal work.[1]

The prehistoric invention of the potter's wheel, in which a lump of clay is imparted a rotary and centrifugal motion, does more than speed up production and render the ware more uniform. It also enables the craftsman to improve upon the form by adding slenderness and grace to the finished product.

An equally important prehistoric invention is *glazing* (*circa* 4000 B.C.). Claywares covered with silica and alkali oxides acquired a vitreous protective layer on firing, which made them more impervious to liquids. However, in the hands of the craftsman glazing also became a widely appreciated form of pictorial art. The ceramic served as a backing—a sort of canvas—for the display of the most exquisite colors and patterns to which glazing lent gloss and permanence. The popularity of glazed ceramics is attested to by the various places throughout the ages in which they attained excellence and fame: China, Japan, Iran, Arab countries, Italy, Spain, etc., beginning with the prehistoric and up to the modern times.[2]

The superior resistance of glazes to chemical attack and their inherent impermeability might also have been one of the factors contributing to *glass making*: the production of molded vitreous objects *without* the supporting backing of clayware, around 2000 B.C. However, the spread of this new technique was slow, and glass objects were mostly imitations of precious stones and often as much treasured.[3]

[1] *Encyclopedia of World Art*, Vol. 3, McGraw-Hill, New York, 1960, pp. 187 and ff.
[2] *Encyclopedia of World Art*, *loc. cit.*
[3] C. Singer, et al. *History of Technology*, Vol. II, Clarendon, Oxford, 1956.

It was not until the first century B.C. that glass making became an independent and rapidly growing industry thanks to the invention of *glass blowing*. The shaping of round objects by blowing air through a metallic can, thrust into a gob of molten glass, did to glass making what the potter's wheel did to clay making: it converted a slow and tedious process into an efficient and precise technique of fabrication. However, it also enabled the artist to make freer use of his inventive talent by producing objects of great originality of form, coloring, and pattern.

The invention of mechanical bottle making in 1903 ushered in the era of mass production and automation of glass industry. However, as long as the art of glass making remains in the hands of individual craftsmen and artists, there is hope of it continuing to contribute to man's cultural needs.

The same can be said of *porcelain*—a rather late invention (*circa* A.D. 200) of Chinese potters who succeeded in producing a white ware on firing above 1200°C a rather moderately plastic clay called *kaolin*, from *kao-ling* (high ridge), the designation of the locality where it was mined. However, the true development and flowering of Chinese procelain dates only from the period of T'ang dynasty (618–906). It was then that the fine thin-walled and translucent ware endowed with a characteristic metallic ring came into prominence. In the succeeding centuries Chinese porcelain became a popular and much sought after article of trade throughout the whole Asian continent. Its great popularity stimulated zealous imitation in Iran and Arab countries with the result that the imitations acquired their own artistic value and were coveted no less than the original. The secluded life of Medieval Europe is perhaps the reason why this celebrated product of Chinese potters remained almost unknown until the thirteenth century. At least it was not previously known to the famous Venetian merchant and world traveler, Marco Polo (1253–1324) who mentioned it under the now accepted name of porcelain in his writings about China, presumably referring to its resemblance to a translucent shell known as *porcellana*.[4] It took, however, several more centuries until the making of porcelain in Europe attained the quality and perfection of the Oriental ware. It began with the Medici porcelain in Italy in the sixteenth century whence it spread to Dresden, Germany in the seventeenth century, to Sèvres in France, to Copenhagen in Denmark, etc., including the famous imitation of the Chinese prototype in Delft, Holland, in the eighteenth century. The characteristic cobalt blue decoration of Delft porcelain—an imitation of the fifteenth century Chinese design—was so highly prized that it in turn became an object of imitation. Interestingly, the trend of imitations brought the Chinese style of decoration of blue on white back to the Far East, to Japan. Thus, there seems to be in art, as in science, an international common ground, on which the rivalry of participating nations builds works of lasting beauty and value.

[4] *Encyclopedia of World Art, loc. cit.*

Ceramics and Society. It is easy to speculate that in the use of ceramics practical needs of the community could have taken precedence over the artistic aspirations of the individual. The ease of shaping, inherent impermeability, and chemical resistance make ceramics ideally suited to building shelters against inclement environment and devising means for channeling and carrying liquids for individual and communal consumption. These endeavors led to the early invention and use of *bricks* and, with the improvement of firing methods, also of *tiles*—two basic building blocks which can be truthfully said to have contributed to communal welfare and stability as much as pottery did to individual comfort and enjoyment. Throughout the ages bricks and tiles served mankind, poor and rich, in a variety of ways: city walls and dwellings, ducts and pipelines, private and public baths, roofs and floors, bridges and viaducts, etc. The obvious utility of their shapes and dimensions, far from clashing, often blended admirably with the esthetic appearance of the finished structure; witness the famous Roman aqueduct near Nîmes, France, dating from the first century A.D. or the brick vaults of the Guildhall at Blakney, England, dating from the fourteenth century.[5]

Characteristically, *concrete*—the leading building material of our day—was either unknown or in small favor in the Middle Ages. Yet, it was much in use in ancient Rome. Roman architects built concrete walls in alternate layers of coarse and fine stone aggregates cemented with a mixture of water, volcanic ash (puzzolane), and lime.

The current resurrection of concrete construction lacks the drama of a single revolutionary invention which characterizes the Bessemer process of steel making in 1855 (see Section 18-1). Rather it seems to be due to several factors: (1) greater availability of ready-made cement, e.g., the Portland cement, (2) more efficient handling equipment, and (3) better quality control. Above all it seems to be the outcome of a happy partnership of concrete with steel known as *reinforced concrete.* This structural symbiosis made reinforced concrete competitive with steel construction not only economically but also esthetically. Thanks to the inner steel skeleton the engineer was able to better exploit the outward monolithic appearance of concrete, particularly in large scale exposed shell structures.[6] As it often happens, a better functional adaptation has brought with it greater esthetic satisfaction.

By and large the same is true of other ceramics, including glass. However, in the history of technology, glass plays a role apart. A fitting beginning is the sixteenth century, when the Venetian glass makers succeeded in producing a flawless transparent glass which they called *cristallo.* Further improvements followed. In particular the refractive index of glass was notably increased by an admixture of lead oxide. A way was thus open to the production of optical glass for lenses. The increased need in the seventeenth century for good spyglasses and telescopes for navigation and warfare did the

[5] C. Singer, *loc. cit.*
[6] Pier Luigi Nervi, *Structures*, F. W. Dodge Corp., New York, 1956.

rest: an important precision tool industry was born, the industry of optical instruments. Beginning with the magnifying glass and ending with the telescope, the optical glass can rightly be credited with having increased our ability to measure distance to the same degree that the pendulum and the hairspring have increased our ability to measure time. This is particularly true of the telescope and the chronometer—two instruments used to determine longitudes at sea: the first by viewing fixed stars, the second by keeping "fixed" time. Not surprisingly these two important inventions came at a time (the seventeenth century) when mastery of the sea belonged to the one who could find his way in the unfamiliar expanse of the Atlantic and Pacific Oceans.

However, gazing at the stars was not the only way by which man gained control over nature thanks to optical glass; it is not even the most important. Peering through the lenses of a microscope proved far more rewarding. It is not hard to imagine what our life would be without this powerful tool. Most of the infectious diseases—typhus, cholera, yellow fever, and malaria—might still be a potential source of epidemics. Without the benefit of image formation at large magnifications, the multiphase and polygranular nature of metals and minerals would have to be deduced second-hand from the more sophisticated diffraction patterns, as explained in Section 4-9, Chapter 4. The whole rich microcosm of life and motion would have been closed to our eye. These facts alone suffice to measure the magnitude of scientific and technological progress achieved thanks to the optical glass.

19-2 The Coordinated Polyhedron and Ionic Radius. Whatever the future modifications the short range order is likely to remain the essential characteristic of ceramics. This characteristic is conveniently embodied in a geometrical figure which represents the distribution and location of ions of like sign about one single ion of opposite sign. The figure is called a coordinated polyhedron. As will appear below the concept of coordinated polyhedron holds even when the bond between dissimilar atoms is not strictly ionic. The generalization is made possible through the introduction of an auxiliary concept, the concept of an ionic radius.

To explain both concepts we consider the oft cited example of Na^+Cl^-, Fig. 19-1. We recall that Na^+Cl^- builds an FCC structure with the side a_0 of the unit cell = 5.62 Å. It follows from Fig. 19-1 that the (shortest) interionic Na^+Cl^- distance is 2.81 Å. Similar interionic distances can be determined in crystals containing one of these ions, e.g., Na^+F^- and Cs^+Cl^-. The question arises: Can each of these ions, and for that matter any other ion, be assigned a constant and specific radius so that the sum of the radii equals the interionic distance in any and all possible cation-anion combinations? The need for a spherical symmetry of closed shell electrons would seem to preclude such a possibility for any type of bonding that is not 100 percent ionic, and this means according to Section 1-7, Chapter 1, the vast majority of bonds between unlike atoms. It is, therefore, both gratifying and significant that the concept of a specific and constant ionic radius can be retained and used to predict the arrangements and to within 5 percent even the (interionic) distances of unlike atoms regardless of their degree of ionization.[7]

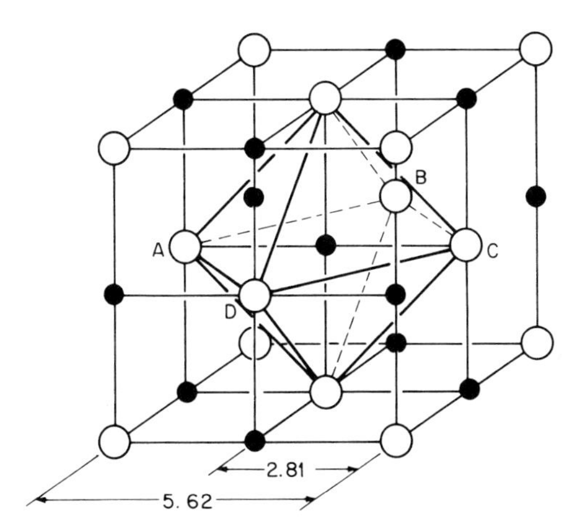

FIG. 19-1 Octahedral grouping of Cl^- about Na^+, coordination number 6

Values of ionic radii of representative elements are indicated in Table 19-1. We see that the ionic radius of a cation, e.g., Na^+, is smaller in the same period than the ionic radius of an anion, e.g., Cl^-. Also, the higher the valency of a cation, i.e., the larger the number of electrons stripped from the valence shell, the smaller is the ionic radius, e.g., Na^+, Mg^{++}, Al^{+++}, and Si^{++++}. The converse is true of anions, e.g., O^- and F^-. All of these findings can be qualitatively explained by considering the build up or scaling down of closed shells and their attraction by the nucleus of the ion (Problem 19-1).

They also provide a rational explanation of the type of coordinated polyhedron formed by the larger anions around a given smaller cation. Thus in the example of $Na^+ Cl^-$, Fig. 19-1, each sodium ion needs only one chlorine ion to neutralize the charge. However, the spherical symmetry of closed shells creates a corresponding spherical field of attraction for negative ions about Na^+. In consequence there ensues a tendency to close packing as in the metallic and molecular bond, Sections 1-5 and 1-8, Chapter 1.

Radii of Complex Ions. Certain groups of atoms, among which NH_4 and OH are prominent, maintain stable configuration and size in various chemical reactions and crystal structures. They approximately behave as

[7] Linus Pauling, *The Nature of the Chemical Bond*, Cornell U.P., 1948.

though they were endowed with a constant charge and constant ionic radius. They are called complex ions. The values of the ionic radii for NH_4^+ and OH^- are listed in Table 19-1.[8]

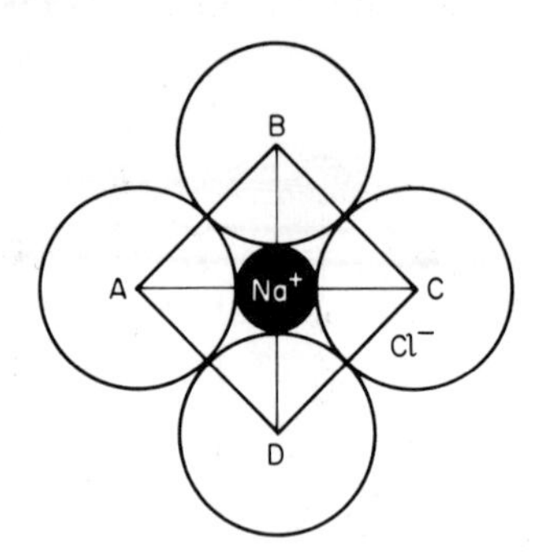

FIG. 19-2 Relation between coordination number and cation-anion radius ratio in Na^+Cl^-

Cation-Anion Radius Ratio r_c/r_a. The number of chlorine ions that can be packed around the sodium ion is not arbitrary. In the first place, all chlorine ions must be in contact with the sodium ion. In the second place, their closed shells must not overlap. Both conditions are fulfilled by writing:

1. $Na^+ - Cl^-$ interionic distance $= r_{Na} + r_{Cl}$ (19-1)

2. $Cl^- - Cl^-$ interionic distance $\geq 2r_{Cl}$ (19-2)

where r_{Na} and r_{Cl} are ionic radii of sodium and chlorine, respectively. These conditions, of course, apply to any kind of ions. In all cases the resulting number of anions around the cation, or the *coordination number of the cation*, as well as the corresponding *shape* of the coordinated polyhedron depend only on the *cation-anion radius ratio*, r_c/r_a.

We shall prove this point by reversing the argument. In Fig. 19-1 each sodium ion is surrounded by *six* chlorine ions forming an *octahedron*. The sodium ion is thus seen to be in the center of a square built by any two opposing ions of chlorine, e.g., *ABCD*. In accordance with requirements (19-1) and (19-2) (see also Fig. 19-2)

$$AC = 2(r_{Cl} + r_{Na}) \tag{19-3}$$

and

$$AB = BC \geq 2r_{Cl} \tag{19-4}$$

From Fig. 19-1

$$AC = a_o \tag{19-5}$$

[8] The value for OH^- refers only to simple compounds, mainly of the *A*OH type, where *A* is mostly a halide, e.g., KOH. The radius of OH^- is quite different in silicates, see Section 19-7.

TABLE 19-1 IONIC RADII OF REPRESENTATIVE ELEMENTS IN ANGSTRÖM UNITS

Period		*I*	*II*	*III*	*IV*	*V*	*VI*	*VII*	*VIII*
1	Ion							H^-	He
	Radius							2.08	
2	Ion	Li^+	Be^{++}	B^{+++}	C^{++++}	N^{---}	O^{--}	F^-	Ne
	Radius	0.60	0.31	0.2	0.15	1.71	1.40	1.36	
3	Ion	Na^+	Mg^{++}	Al^{+++}	Si^{++++}	P^{---}	S^{--}	Cl^-	Ar
	Radius	0.95	0.65	0.50	0.41	2.12	1.84	1.81	
4	Ion	K^+	Ca^{++} Fe^{++}	Sc^{+++} Fe^{+++}	Ti^{++++}	As^{---}	Se^{--}	Br^-	Kr
	Radius	1.33	0.90 0.75	0.81 0.60	0.68	2.2	1.98	1.95	
5	Ion	Rb^+	Sr^{++}	Y^{+++}	Zr^{++++}	Sb^{---}	Te^{--}	I^-	
	Radius								
	a	1.48	1.13	0.93	0.80				Xe
	b					2.45	2.21	2.16	
6	Ion	Cs^+	Ba^{++}	La^{+++}	Ce^{++++}				
	Radius	1.69	1.35	1.15	1.01				
	Special Ions	$NH_4{}^+$						OH^-	
	Radius	1.48						1.53	

* After L. Pauling.

and

$$AB = BC = a_o/\sqrt{2} \tag{19-6}$$

Making use of Eqs. (19-5) and (19-6) in Eqs. (19-3) and (19-4) and eliminating a_o from both we get

$$r_{\text{Cl}} + r_{\text{Na}} \geq \sqrt{2}\, r_{\text{Cl}}$$

from which

$$r_{\text{Na}}/r_{\text{Cl}} \geq 0.414 \tag{19-7}$$

Obviously condition (19-7) does not depend on the identity of the cation or anion. Hence for any cation and anion a coordination number of six and a coordinated octahedron imply a cation-anion ratio, $r_c/r_a \geq 0.414$.

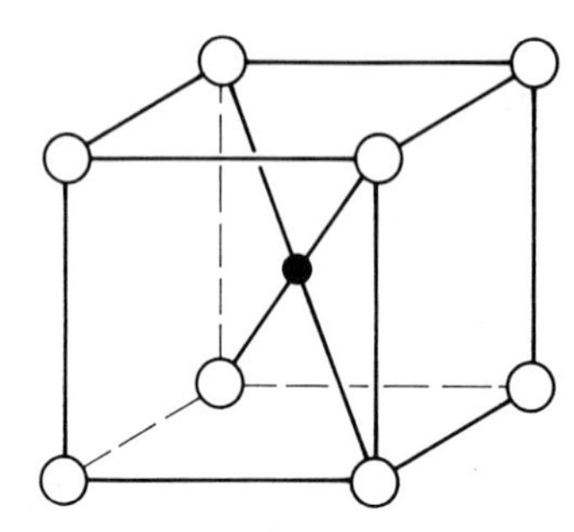

FIG. 19-3 Cubic grouping of Cl^- about Cs^+, coordination number 8

We can generalize the above procedure by first seeking what happens when r_c/r_a becomes increasingly larger than 0.414. We note from Fig. 19-2 that by making $r_c/r_a > 0.414$ we break the contact between the anions. However, the sixfold coordination and the octahedral configuration must remain because of the spherical symmetry of the cation. Not until the ratio r_c/r_a has reached a value of 0.732 can additional cation be inserted and a new configuration found, Problem 19-2. The coordinated polyhedron then is a cube and the coordination number rises to eight. A typical example is Cs^+Cl^-, Fig. 19-3.

The limiting case is $r_c/r_a = 1$. It leads to a cubo-octahedron and the highest coordination number of twelve, Fig. 19-4 and Problem 19-2. Since $r_c = r_a$, here the arrangement of cations about an anion is the same as the arrangement of anions about a cation. Barium and oxygen have such an arrangement in barium titanate, $BaTiO_3$, Fig. 13-15, Chapter 13. The coordination and location of titanium in this more complex structure will be discussed later.

Note: Theoretically it is possible to conceive cases for which $r_c/r_a > 1$. Practically, at least in ceramics, this situation does not occur. Hence, when

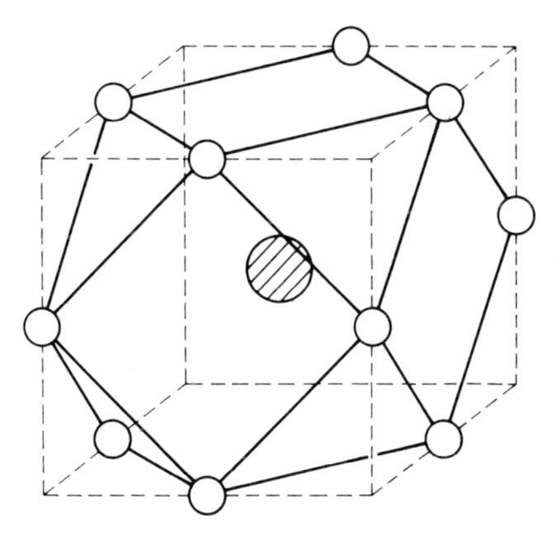

FIG. 19-4 Cubo-octahedron and coordination number 12

we speak of a coordination number or a coordinated polyhedron we always refer to the configuration of anions about a cation and not vice versa.

With this in mind we now complete the sequence for $r_c/r_a < 0.413$. We find, Fig. 19-5 and Problem 19-2, that a coordination number of four and a

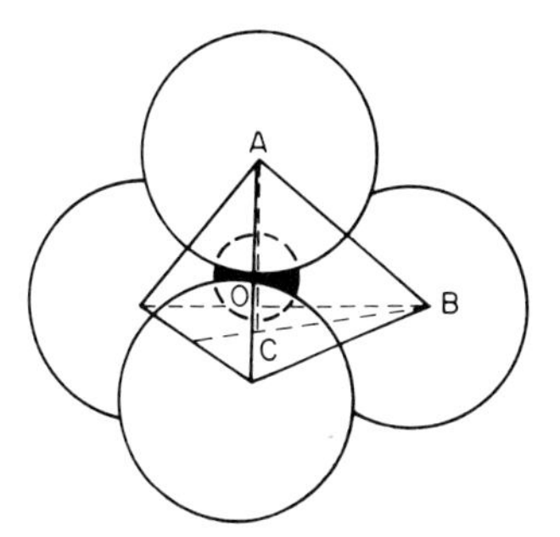

FIG. 19-5 Tetrahedral polyhedron for a cation-anion radius ratio greater than 0.255

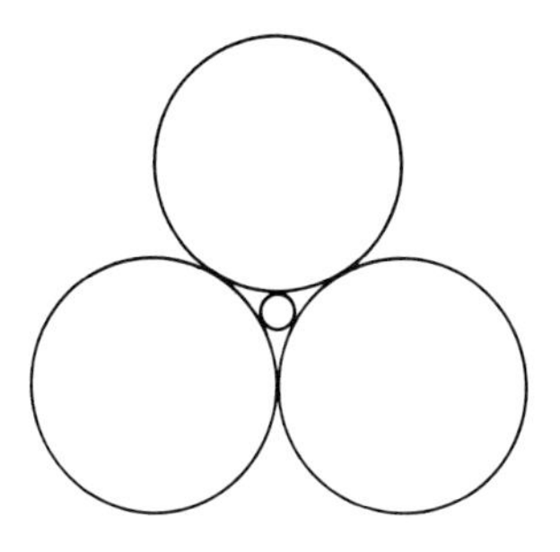

FIG. 19-6 Triangular arrangement of ions for a cation-anion radius ratio greater than 0.155

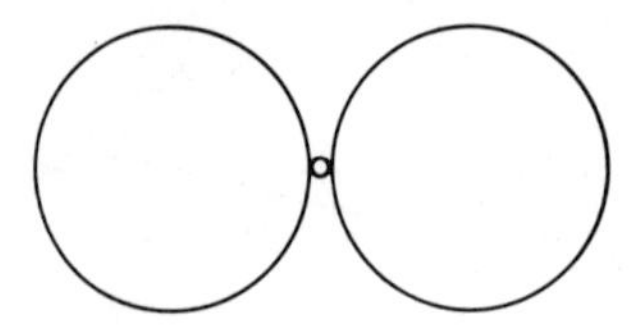

FIG. 19-7 Linear arrangement of ions for a cation-anion radius ratio smaller than 0.155

tetrahedral arrangement of anions occurs for $r_c/r_a \geq 0.225$. Still lower ratios and coordinations are shown in Figs. 19-6 and 19-7. All of these results are summarized in Table 19-2.

19-3 Linking of Polyhedra. Electrostatic Bond Strength. In the previous section we introduced the concept of a coordinated polyhedron to depict the way anions are packed about a cation. However, an isolated polyhedron has no neutrality of charge. To ensure such a neutrality within each polyhedron, its corners, i.e., its anions must be shared by other polyhedra. By how many? The answer depends on the fraction of anion charge that must be assigned to the polyhedron in order to neutralize the charge on the cation in the center. This fraction is called the *electrostatic bond strength of the cation.*[9]

TABLE 19-2 COORDINATION NUMBERS AND COORDINATED POLYHEDRA FOR CATION-ANION RADIUS RATIO, r_c/r_a

r_c/r_a	*Coordination Number*	*Coordinated Polyhedron*	*Symbolic Representation*
0–0.155	2	Line	
0.155–0.225	3	Triangle	
0.225–0.414	4	Tetrahedron	
0.414–0.732	6	Octahedron	
0.732–1	8	Cube	
1	12	Cubo-octahedron	

Consider, e.g., the structure of $Ca^{++}F_2^{-}$, Fig. 19-8. According to Table 19-1 the cation-anion radius ratio r_{Ca}/r_F is 0.73. Consequently to within 5 percent allowed by Table 19-2 the calcium ion is surrounded by eight fluorine

[9] L. Pauling, *loc. cit.*

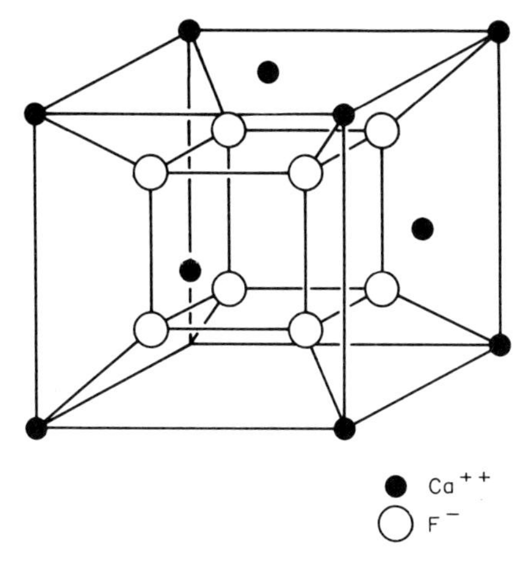

FIG. 19-8 FCC unit cell of $Ca^{2+}F_2^-$

ions placed at the corners of a cube. How many other cubes share each of these corners? The answer is four, as can be seen from the following argument: Ca^{++} is bivalent, so its charge is $+2e$ ($-e$ being the charge of one electron). This charge must be neutralized by equal contributions from the eight fluorine ions. Hence each fluorine ion contributes a fractional charge, $f = -2e/8$. However, the total charge on the fluorine ion at each corner of the cube is $-e$. Consequently the number N of cubes sharing each corner must be such that

$$Nf = -e$$

or since

$$f = -2e/8$$

$$N = 4 \quad \text{Q.E.D.}$$

How this sharing is accomplished can be seen from Fig. 19-9 in which two upper cubes a and b are sharing one corner, M, with two lower cubes, c and d. In the plan view, Fig. 19-10, these four cubes are linked with other cubes to outline the whole FCC unit cell of CaF_2. Characteristically, even though of a cubic shape, the coordinated polyhedra do not fill out the FCC lattice. There are empty spaces between them in compliance with the fourfold sharing of a common corner. To fill out the space there would have to be eight cubes at each corner.

By definition the fraction $s = f = \frac{1}{4}$ is the electrostatic bond strength of Ca^{++} in the cubic surrounding. More generally, if z is the valence of the cation and n is the coordination number, the electrostatic bond strength

$$s = z/n \tag{19-8}$$

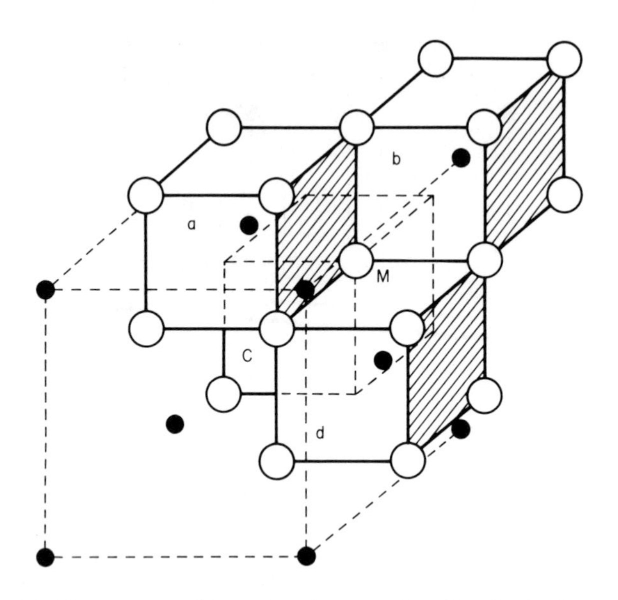

FIG. 19-9 Linking of coordinated polyhedra (small cubes) about a common corner in $Ca^{2+}F_2^-$

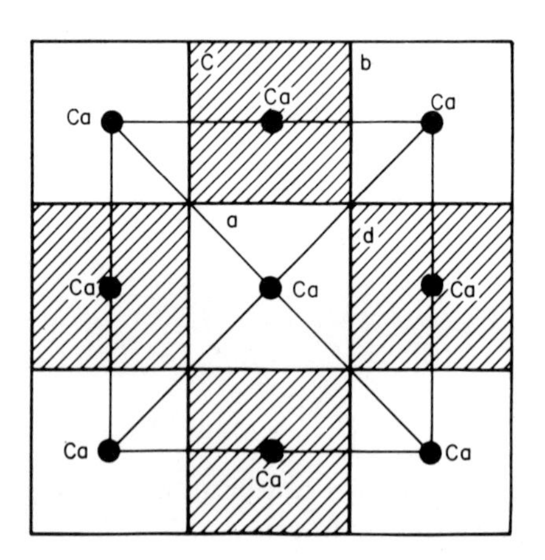

FIG. 19-10 Building of the FCC unit cell of $Ca^{2+}F_2^-$ by means of cubical coordinated polyhedra, top view. Cross-hatched cubes: lower level; open cubes: upper level

Likewise, if z' is the valence of the anion and N is the number of polyhedra sharing this anion,

$$Nz/n = z' \tag{19-9}$$

Complex Ionic Structures. The concept of coordinated polyhedra and the ensuing Eqs. (19-8) and (19-9) are of particular help in anticipating the form of crystal structures of complex ionic compounds containing two or more different cations bound to the same anion. Each cation tends to coordinate the anions according to its own bond strength, but the sum of the bond strengths about the same anion must be equal to its valency z'. Hence the number of various polyhedra sharing the same corner is limited, and so is the way they can be linked to build the crystal structure. Let $n_1 n_2 \ldots n_i$ be the coordination numbers associated with cations having valencies $z_1\ z_2 \ldots z_i$. Then the corresponding polyhedra must be grouped about an anion of valency z' in numbers $N_1 N_2 \ldots N_i$ such that

$$N_1 z_1/n_1 + N_2 z_2/n_2 \ldots + N_i z_i/n_i = z'$$

or rewriting in a more condensed form

$$\sum_i N_i z_i/n_i = z' \tag{19-10}$$

Eq. (19-10) embodies the so-called Pauling's *Electrostatic Valence Rule.*[10]

Illustrative Example

To show the usefulness of Eq. (19-10) we will predict a crystal structure for

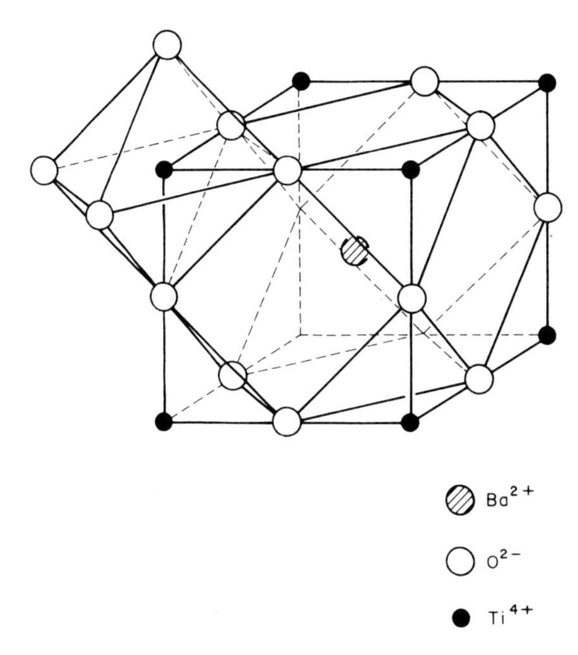

FIG. 19-11 $BaTiO_3$ Linking of two octahedra and four cubo-octahedra at a common oxygen ion. (For clarity only one octahedron and one cubo-octahedron are shown)

[10] L. Pauling, *loc. cit.*

$BaTiO_3$. Let z_1 be the valency of barium ion and z_2 be the valency of titanium ion. Using Tables 19-1 and 19-2 we have

$$r_{Ba}/r_O = 1(\pm 5\%), \text{ hence } n_1 = 12 \text{ (cubo-octahedron)}$$
$$r_{Ti}/r_O = 0.49, \quad \text{hence } n_2 = 6 \text{ (octahedron).}$$

Also

$$z_1 = 2, z_2 = 4 \quad \text{and} \quad z' = 2$$

Substitution in Eq. (19-10) yields

$$N_1 2/12 + N_2 4/6 = 2$$

or

$$N_1 + 4N_2 = 12$$

Of the three possible solutions:

$$(1) \quad N_2 = 1 \quad N_1 = 8$$

$$(2) \quad N_2 = 2 \quad N_1 = 4$$

$$(3) \quad N_2 = 3 \quad N_1 = 0,$$

only the second yields a physically acceptable configuration. This configuration is depicted in Fig. 19-11, see also Fig. 13-15.

19-4 Local Order: Crystalline and Glassy State. We saw that Pauling's Electrostatic Valence Rule has provided a clue to the way the polyhedra must be linked to establish long range order in a ceramic structure. However, this clue is not always as definitive and clear cut as, e.g., in barium titanate. Particularly, when the number of polyhedra sharing a common corner is small, there are a variety of ways they can be stacked, thereby leading to several types and several degrees of long range order: three dimensional, two dimensional and even no order at all. The flexibility of the long range order is thus in sharp contrast to the rigidity of the local order which in ceramics is maintained and preserved throughout various transformations in the shape and dimensions of the coordinated polyhedron. Silica, SiO_2 is a classical example.

Silica. According to Tables 19-1 and 19-2 the cation-anion ratio r_{Si}/r_O of 0.293 requires under ambient conditions a fourfold coordination and a tetrahedral stacking of oxygen ions about silicon, Fig. 19-12. Furthermore, the Electrostatic Valence Rule limits the number of polyhedra about each oxygen ion to two. (Problem 19-3). Suppose now we place one of the tetrahedra flat on its base BCD with its apex A upward like a pyramid, Fig. 19-13a.

Three other similarly placed pyramids can be linked to this pyramid at *B*, *C*, and *D*. At what angle? The Electrostatic Valence Rule provides no definite clue. We will see in fact that several answers are possible. We begin by distinguishing between ordered and disordered aggregations.

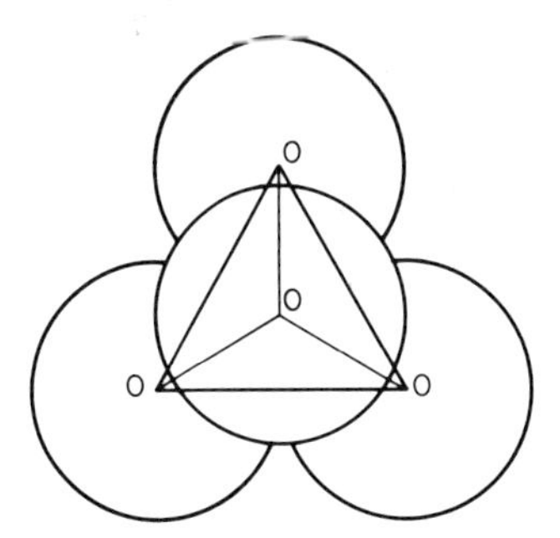

FIG. 19-12 Tetrahedral arrangement of four oxygen ions about a silicon ion (not shown) in the center

Ordered Aggregations. A twofold ordered arrangement of pyramids about a common corner requires that the included angle be the same for all corners. The simplest and most symmetric arrangement occurs when the angles are 180 degrees, i.e., when the line EE′ joining the centers of the bases passes through the corners common to any two pyramids, Fig. 19-13b. The pyramids then build a two dimensional hexagonal network. However, a less symmetric arrangement also is possible, Fig. 19-14, when the angles are comprised between 180 and 120 degrees (but are less than 120 degrees; see Problem 19-4).

We next turn to the apices *A*, Fig. 19-13a. They can be shared by an identical layer superimposed upon the first layer, but with the pyramids pointing down instead of up, Fig. 19-13b. All corners are now occupied, and there are no free apices left for the further build up in height. A two layer (neutral) structure, of course, cannot exist by itself, but in ceramics it can exist in conjunction with other layers to which it is bound by weak molecular forces akin those holding inert molecules together, Chapter 1, Section 1-8. This layered type of structure is held to be responsible for the excellent molding properties of clay minerals, as we will see in Section 19-7.

Tridymite. A layered structure of pure silica, however, can exist, if in the same layer the pyramids point alternately up and down, Fig. 19-15. By building the second layer in the form of a mirror image of the first, etc., we can construct a three dimensional hexagonal crystal of silica, called *tridymite*, in which there is an alternation of layers 1 2 1 2 . . ., not unlike that found in the hexagonal close packed structure, Chapter 1, Fig. 1-6.

Note: The more symmetrical variety of tridymite, Fig. 19-15 is called

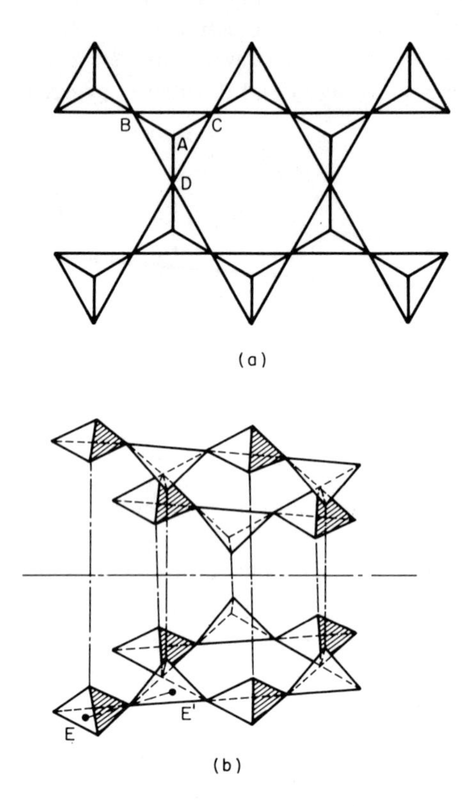

FIG. 19-13 A two dimensional layer of hexagonally linked silica tetrahedra: (a) top view; (b) perspective view

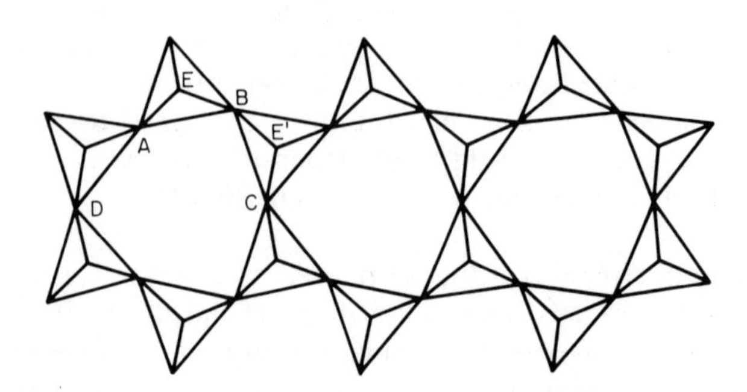

FIG. 19-14 Asymmetrical arrangement of silica tetrahedra in the two dimensional layer of Fig. 19-13

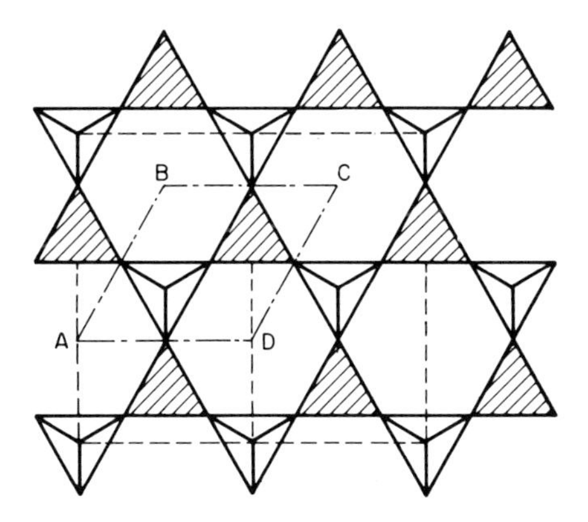

FIG. 19-15 Beta tridymite. Shaded triangles indicate tetrahedra with apices pointing down

β tridymite in distinction to α tridymite to which it reverts at a lower temperature by adopting the less symmetrical arrangement of Fig. 19-14.

Cristobalite. Instead of mirroring the first layer we can simply lift it up and turn it 60 degrees with respect to the underlying original. We can repeat the same operation with the second layer. The next repetition with the third layer reproduces the configuration of the very first layer. The 1 2 3, 1 2 3 . . ., sequence thus obtained is the same as in the FCC close packed structure, Chapter 1, Fig. 1-7. In fact a similar FCC structure results, Fig. 19-16. Yet it is not close packed. Rather it resembles the configuration of diamond, Chapter 1, Fig. 1-5, in which each carbon atom is replaced by the coordinated

FIG. 19-16 FCC cell of cristobalite. Shaded triangles indicate tetrahedra with apices pointing down

tetrahedron of silica. Nor is this resemblance unexpected considering the tetrahedral arrangement of the (covalent) bonds in the diamond variety of carbon. This cubic polymorph of silica exists near the melting point. It is called *cristobalite*.

Note: Like tridymite cristobalite reverts at a lower temperature to a less symmetrical variety based on the arrangement of Fig. 19-14.

Quartz. In this low temperature polymorph of silica there is departure from the layer structure of tridymite and cristobalite. The tetrahedra in quartz are linked to form a chain which spirals along the faces of a hexagonal prism, as indicated in the perspective view, Fig. 19-17a. This configuration is seen to be more compact, hence more dense, than the layer structure. For silica the increase in density is from about 2.3 to about 2.6 grams per square

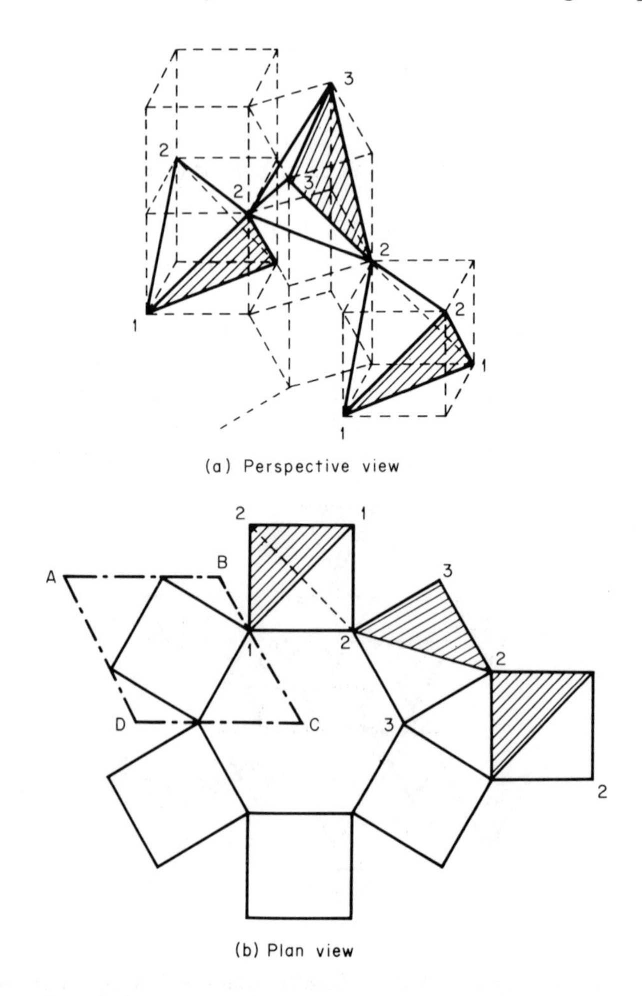

FIG. 19-17 β quartz (a) perspective view; (b) plan view

centimeter. In the β variety of quartz, two edges of each tetrahedron are parallel to the base of the prism. They are marked 1-1 and 2-2, or 2-2 and 3-3 depending on the level in the prism. Due to this parallelism the tetrahedra project horizontally as squares linked into an extended network of hexagons, Fig. 19-17b.

Before reaching room temperature β-quartz is further compacted by turning into α-quartz. The tetrahedra undergo a rotation with respect to each other as shown in the front views Fig. 19-18 b and c.[11] The horizontal projections degenerate into *trapezoids* and the network of hexagons contracts to a network of truncated triangles, Fig. 19-18a. The short and long bases of the *trapezoids* are interchanged in the horizontal projection when the directions of rotations are reversed, but the compactness of the reverse structure remains the same as that of the obverse one.

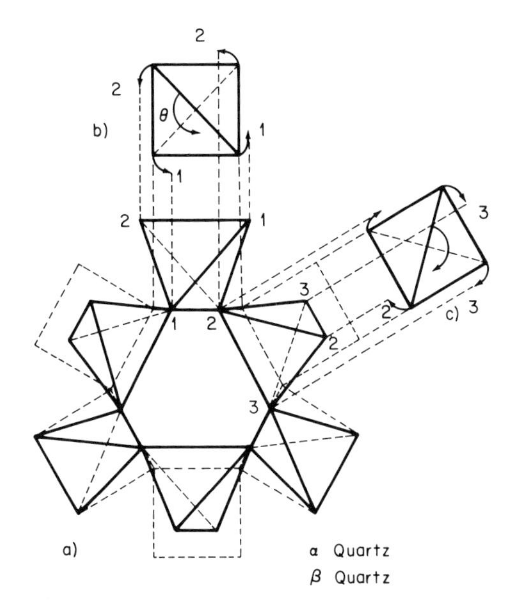

FIG. 19-18 Formation of α quartz from β quartz: rotation and compaction (a) plan view; (b) and (c) front views

Disordered Aggregations. No less than thirteen polymorphic varieties of silica have been reported to exist at atmospheric pressure,[12] even though only three—cristobalite, tridymite and quartz—involve major rearrangements of tetrahedra, see Problem 19-5. Such a proliferation of polymorphs is a vivid proof of the ease with which the long range order in silica can be modified. Yet in all these modifications the short range order of the tetrahedron remains intact. There are indications that it remains intact even

[11] Experimental data make this interpretation feasible, but they are not sufficient to make it unique, see R. B. Sosman, *Properties of Silica*, Reinhold, N.Y., 1927.

[12] Sosman, R. B. *The Phases in Silica*, Rutgers Univ. Press, N.J., 1965.

after melting,[13] notwithstanding the free and relatively random motion of molecules in the liquid state. It is therefore hardly surprising that on rapid cooling the randomness prevailing in the liquid state is carried through the solidification range conferring to silica what is called the *glassy* (disordered) *state*, Fig. 19-19. The lack of long range order accounts for the fact that bonds between adjacent tetrahedra are established in the glassy state on cooling—and broken on heating—progressively rather than simultaneously as in crystals. Consequently, the glassy state possesses a wide range of temperatures preceding melting of silica in which the material has the viscosity of molasses, between 10^4 to 10^8 poises. This circumstance renders the glassy state particularly suitable to high temperature working and shaping of ceramics, as discussed more fully in Section 19-6.

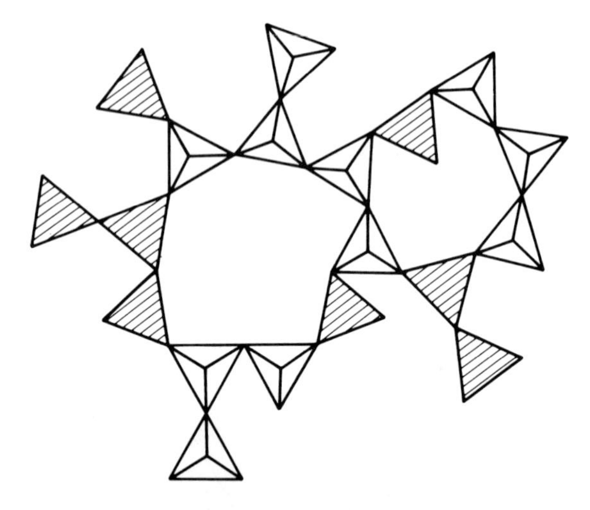

FIG. 19-19 Glassy state of SiO_2. Shaded triangles indicate tetrahedra with apices pointing down

19-5 Minerals and Ceramics. The flexibility of long range order encountered in silica is also found in other minerals. Prominent among them are *clay minerals*—silicates in which the tetrahedra built by the oxygen anions about the silicon cation are linked to other polyhedra by oxygen or hydroxyl (OH) anions grouped about cations such as Al^{+++}, Mg^{++}, Fe^{+}, etc. Examples of such aggregations will be given in Section 19-7.

As with metallic elements, minerals alone seldom possess a combination of properties suitable for current industrial processing. Only in conjunction with other elements or compounds can they be molded and cast in the desired shape and retain this shape after proper treatment. There is thus a close analogy between metallic elements and alloys on the one hand and

[13] Kingery, W. D. *Introduction to Ceramics*, John Wiley & Sons, N.Y., 1960.

minerals and ceramics on the other. Like alloys, ceramics conform to various types of phase diagrams with compounds rather than elements playing the role of components, cf. Section 18-9b. Among these components water occupies a unique and prominent position, as will be shown in Sections 19-7 and 19-8.

For the rest, the atomic size factor seems as important in ceramic as in alloy phase diagrams except that the distances of closest interatomic approach are replaced here by the shortest anion-cation distance. Thus in the examples cited in Section 18-9b the cation-anion distances in MgO and NiO differ by less than 5 percent, and both cations are octahedrally surrounded by six oxygen ions. Consequently, MgO and NiO form continuous solid solutions with Mg^{++} and Ni^{++} randomly distributed among the octahedra. On the other hand, the cation-anion distances in NaCl and RbCl differ by more than 15 percent, and as a result they give rise to a eutectic and two distinct solid phases. Finally, MgO and CaO whose cation-anion distances differ by less than 15 percent are seen to exhibit partial solid solubility.

Liquid insolubility plays a more important role in ceramics than in alloys. The region of interest is that designated by $L_1 + \alpha$ in Fig. 18-6. In this region one phase is solid, the other phase is liquid. By using a small amount of liquid it is thus possible to cement grains or grain-aggregates of the major component (or components) with a solidified layer of the minor component (or components). In many instances the minor component is in a glassy or partly glassy state, see Sections 19-7 and 19-8.

Despite this obvious analogy with alloys, it does not seem practical to classify ceramics according to various types of phase diagrams. Neither their pattern nor the kind of transformations they occasion are nearly as characteristic of the ensuing properties as in alloys. A more convenient, even though less rational, classification is adopted here based on the essential physical phenomena governing their processing. Four groups of ceramics can thus be distinguished, with no sharp dividing lines between them: (1) glasses, (2) whitewares and refractories, (3) cement and concrete, and (4) abrasives and cermets.

19-6 Glasses. As mentioned in Section 19-4 progressive reestablishment of links between tetrahedra makes it possible to work and shape silica glass below the melting point. However, in pure silica the range of working temperatures, 1700 to 1400°C, in which the viscosity varies between 10^4 and 10^8 poises is both too high and too narrow for most practical applications. To lower the range of the working temperatures we simply must lower the melting point, but to extend their range we also must prevent, or at least retard in some way, the process of linking of tetrahedra into closed loops. Both objectives can be attained by adding soda, Na_2O, to silica.

First consider the lowering of the melting point. According to Table 19-1 the cation-anion distances in Na_2O and SiO_2 differ by as much as 25 percent.

We therefore confidently expect solid insolubility with the ensuing lowering of the melting point through the formation of a eutectic. The practically important part of the phase diagram, Fig. 19-20, is between zero and 34 percent Na_2O, i.e., between pure silica and a compound conforming to the formula $Na_2O \cdot 2SiO_2$. The two compounds, $Na_2O \cdot 2SiO_2$ and SiO_2, form a eutectic melting around 800°C, i.e., more than 900°C below the melting point of pure silica.

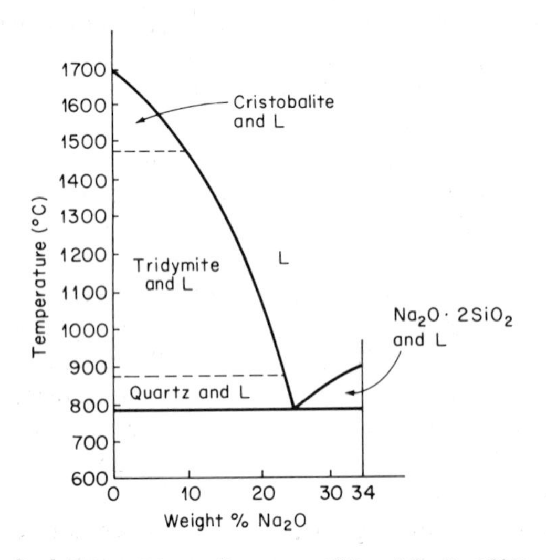

FIG. 19-20 Phase diagram. SiO_2—$Na_2O \cdot 2SiO_2$

As regards the breaking up of closed loops, the ease with which sodium can be removed (leached) from the sodium silicate glass by water indicates that the sodium ion is much more loosely bonded to oxygen ions than the silicon ion. Also the glassy state which ensues from rapid cooling is more dense than one might expect, if the loops were closed by polyhedra built about Na^+.[14] The presumption, therefore, is that the loops are not closed, but form a loose three-dimensional network. The sodium ion is pictured as being simply inserted into the open loop, in the manner schematically represented in Fig. 19-21. Thereby, not only greater density is achieved, but also neutrality of charge is maintained near the open ends of the loop.

Despite better workability, soda glass is unfit for common domestic and industrial uses because it is attacked by water. This shortcoming already had been noticed and corrected in the prehistoric times by the Phoenicians who added the less soluble CaO to the mixture. Current compositions include further correctives in the form of small additions of MgO, Al_2O_3 and K_2O.

[14] T. H. Davies, "The Physics of Glass," in *Science of Engineering Materials*, Ed., J. E. Goldman, Wiley, 1957.

In the "Pyrex" brand glass CaO, MgO, and most of Na_2O are replaced by B_2O_3, Table 19-3.

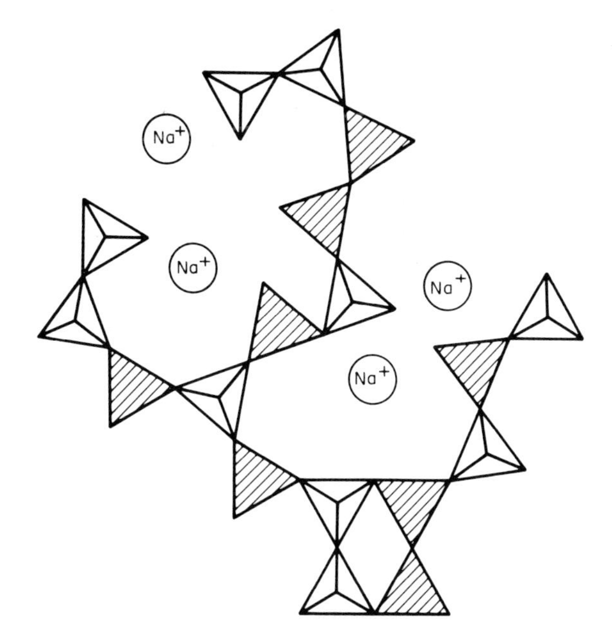

FIG. 19-21 Schematic representation of soda-silica glass

TABLE 19-3 SOME TYPICAL COMPOSITIONS OF COMMERCIAL GLASSES (WEIGHT PERCENT)

	SiO_2	Na_2O	CaO	MgO	K_2O	Al_2O_3	B_2O_3
Window Glass	72	12	11	2.5	1.5	1	
Bottle Glass	74	17	5.0	4.0			
"Pyrex" Brand	80	4				3	13

These and other varieties of glass are widely known and used for their good chemical resistance and transparency to light. Both qualities derive from the stability of configuration which characterizes the closed shell electrons as explained below:

1. Glasses are chemically resistant because closed shell electrons make it extremely difficult for the free ions, that are the active agents in chemicals, to penetrate into the glassy network.

2. The glasses are transparent to light because the same close shell electrons are too tightly bound together to *individually* interact with the relatively weak electromagnetic radiation of the visible spectrum, see Section 4-3, Chapter 4. Collectively they do interact, thereby giving rise to the electronic

polarizability $\hat{\varepsilon}_e$, as discussed in Section 13-10, Chapter 13, and the ensuing index of refraction, n.[15] In silicate glasses n varies between 1.4 and 2.1. Glasses with the higher indices of refraction of from 1.7 to 2.1 are used for optical lenses. They contain a large amount of PbO. Other ingredients endow glasses with color, translucency, and opacity.

As explained below *color* requires that the electrons respond to incoming radiation *individually* and reemit it in a more or less narrow band of the visible spectrum. The constitutive cations of glasses: Na^+, Ca^{++}, and Mg^{++}, despite their loose connections with the tetrahedral network, cannot provide such a response because all their electrons form closed shells. The same is not true of the ions of transition elements. For example, the ferrous ion Fe^{++} has four uncoupled electrons (four spin dipole moments) in the third shell, according to Table 14-2, Chapter 14. Therefore at least one of these electrons has a high probability of interacting with the visible radiation and, akin to the covalent electrons in semi-conductors, see Section 15-10, Chapter 10, it can be removed from its third subshell to some higher shell. The same law of mass action which operates in semi-conductors requires that a certain number of these electrons fall back into the third subshell. The energy recovered from such a fall is reemitted as radiation, but in a much more narrow band of the visible spectrum than the incident (white) radiation because of heat losses. Hence, the appearance of color.

The above explanation is too rough and sketchy to give more than an insight in the complex theory of color forming.[16] Yet it may provide some understanding of why ions of transition elements are used to impart color to glasses: Fe^{++}—green, Co^{++}—pink, etc., depending on the adjacent ions.

In contrast to coloring, *translucency* occurs when the individual electrons are merely set in vibration by the incident radiation. As explained in Section 4-3, Chapter 4, they then rebroadcast the incident wave lengths in all directions causing the light to be diffuse (and the glass translucent). If, in addition, there is considerable absorption of the diffuse light, the object becomes *opaque*. In accordance with the analysis carried out in Section 4-3, the diffusing (and absorbing) centers in glass must be separated from each other by distances comparable to the wave lengths of the visible spectrum. Yet there is no diffraction.

[15] The relation between n and $\hat{\varepsilon}_e$ follows from the generalization of relationship (14-17), discussed in more advanced courses of electromagnetic theory. The general formula reads

$$\hat{\mu}\hat{\varepsilon}_e v^2 = 1 \tag{19-11}$$

where v is the velocity of light in the (electronically) polarized medium. For nonmagnetic media $\hat{\mu} = \hat{\mu}_o$, hence on dividing (19-11) by (14-17) we get

$$\hat{\varepsilon}_e/\hat{\varepsilon}_o = c^2/v^2 \tag{19-12}$$

By definition,

$$n = c/v \tag{19-13}$$

Hence,

$$\hat{\varepsilon}_e/\hat{\varepsilon}_o = n^2 \tag{19-14}$$

[16] W. A. Weyl, *Coloured Glasses*, The Society of Glass Technology, Sheffield, 1951.

Among the ingredients used as opacifiers there are a number that precipitate as separate phases from the glass, e.g., mullite ($3Al_2O_3 \cdot 2SiO_2$). Others are intentionally added, e.g., TiO_2 and fluorides. Depending on their content and size they build a natural transition from glasses to whitewares and refractories to be considered in the next section.

19-7 Whitewares and Refractories. Whitewares differ from glasses in a threefold way:

a. The basic mineral is not silica but *clay mineral.*

b. The molding and shaping of the product is made at room temperature, i.e., before and not after heating, and the property involved in its shaping is plastic flow (as defined in Section 12-7, Chapter 12) rather than viscosity.

c. The establishment of primary bonds and the ensuing increase of configurational stability and rigidity occur not through increase of viscosity, but partially, on heating in the process of *drying* and totally, at much higher temperatures, in the process of firing.

Let's examine these three points in more detail:

a. *Clay Minerals.* The clay minerals have been defined in Section 19-5 as silicates made up of tetrahedra that are linked to polyhedra built about cations other than Si^{++++} by common oxygen or hydroxyl ions. More specifically, the structure of clay minerals refers to a layer structure based on the pattern of Figs. 19-13 or 19-14. For simplicity only the symmetric pattern, Fig. 19-13, will be considered. Even so, several varieties of clay minerals can be fitted into this single pattern; *kaolinite* is perhaps the best representative of the above group.

To describe the crystal structure of kaolinite we shall have to analyze in some detail how the apices A of the first silica layer in Fig. 19-13 are shared by the polyhedra built by OH^- about Al^{+++}. We begin by specifying the nature of these polyhedra.

According to Table 19-1 the r_{Al}/r_{OH} ratio is about 0.33. Yet at variance with Table 19-2 the OH^- polyhedron is not a tetrahedron but an octahedron, as though the radius of OH^- were much smaller than 1.50 Å. In silicates the radius of OH^- appears to be almost the same as that of O^{--}.

With the octahedral arrangement of OH^- about Al^{+++} Eq. (19-9) requires that each corner be shared by two octahedra. The angle between these octahedra, of course, is not specified. However, if we lay the octahedra flat on their (triangular) faces and try to build a two-dimensional layer, the only possible arrangement is that depicted in Fig. 19-22b, in which the adjacent tetrahedra have not only a common corner but also a common *edge.* Any other arrangement, e.g., the one shown in Fig. 19-22a, would cause the adjacent anions in the upper plane, e.g., at E and E', to impinge upon each other.

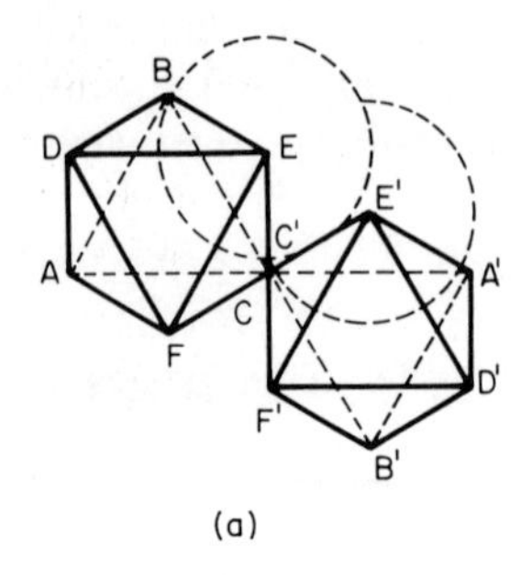

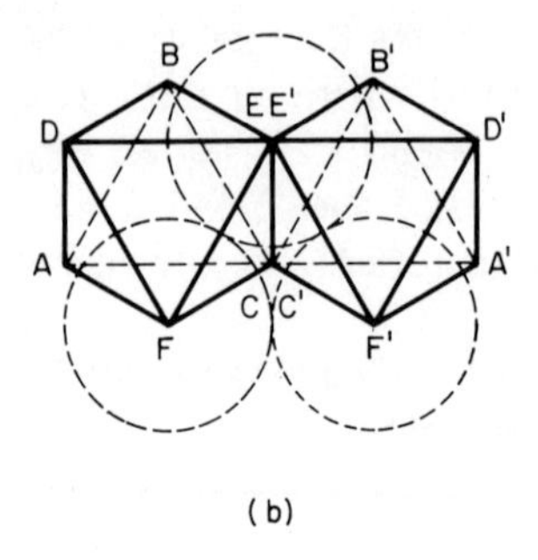

FIG. 19-22 Linking of two octahedra in a plane layer: (a) incorrect; (b) correct *ABC* and *A′B′C′* in a common lower plane; *DEF* and *D′E′F′* in a common upper plane

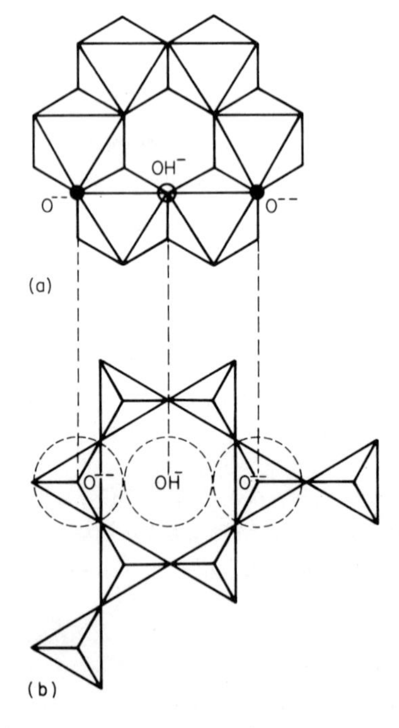

FIG. 19-23 Superpositions of layers in kaolinite: (a) aluminum octahedra layer; (b) silicon tetrahedra layer

By sharing a common edge the octahedra are seen to build a (hexagonal) close-packed layer of anions in the upper and lower planes, Fig. 19-16a. The question arises as to how this configuration can be linked with the configuration of the tetrahedra shown in Fig. 19-16b. To say it differently, which of the two ions, OH^- or O^{--}, should be shared by both layers? The answer is that only oxygen ions can be so shared, Problem 19-19. Since they are more widely spaced than the OH^- ions at the corners of the octahedra, there will be some OH^- ions left. They will fit between two oxygen ions as shown in Fig. 19-23b. Together with the surrounding six oxygen ions these hydroxyl ions build close-packed hexagons, Fig. 19-24a. So do also the OH^- ions in the upper layer.

In conclusion, the two dimensional wafer of kaolinite is made up of octahedra superimposed on tetrahedra and containing three layers of anions as follows, Fig. 19-24b:

1. one layer of O^{--} marked *DDD*...,
2. one mixed layer of O^{--} and OH^- marked *ABA*...,
3. one layer of OH^- marked *CCC*....

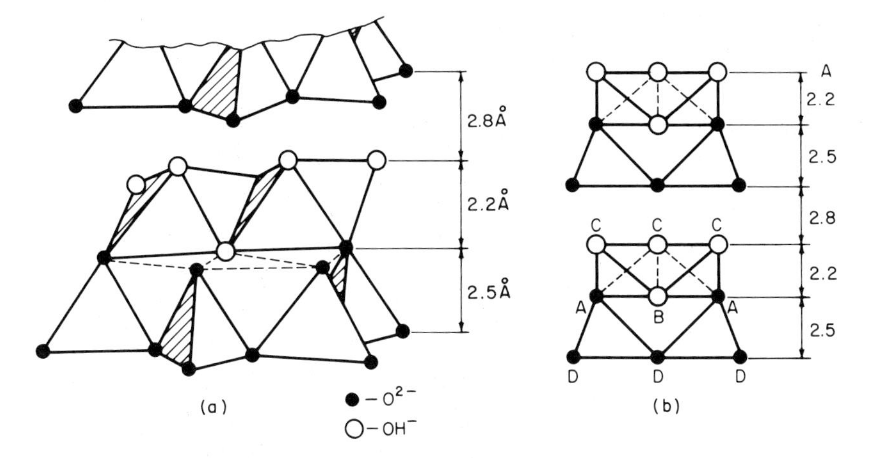

FIG. 19-24 Structure of kaolinite: (a) perspective; (b) front view (schematic)

The cations (not shown in Fig. 19-24) form two intermediate layers, to wit:

1. one layer of Si^{++++} interleaved between *DDD*... and *ABA*..., and
2. one layer of Al^{+++} interleaved between the *ABA*... and *CCC*... layers.

The crystals of kaolinite contain about 500 wafers separated from each other by a distance of 2.8 Å and held together by weak molecular bonds. Neither the shape nor the thickness of the crystals are well defined. Regular six-sided crystals are rare and all crystals are invariably small, Fig. 19-25. So are crystals of other clay minerals which differ from kaolinite in one of two respects or both:

1. an additional layer of silica tetrahedra is put atop the alumina octahedra, Fig. 19-26;
2. Si^{++++} is partially replaced by Fe^{+++} or Al^{+++} and Al^{+++} is partially replaced by Mg^{++}, Fe^{++}, etc., with the deficiency of the positive

FIG. 19-25 Well-shaped crystals of kaolinite. (Courtesy of Dr. R. J. Gibbs, Department of Geology, UCLA)

charge compensated by large cations, e.g., K^+, which, as in glasses, are loosely held and fitted between two wafers, Fig. 19-26.

The same situation exists among the unsymmetrically built layers. Clay minerals are not nearly as crystalline as other silicates, e.g., mica, whose structure resembles that of Fig. 19-26. Yet in all of them the layer structure prevails which, as we will see, has a bearing on the molding capacity of clay minerals.

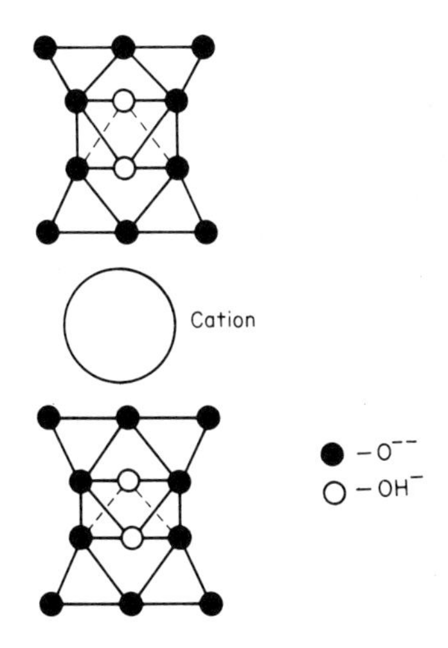

FIG. 19-26 Three-layer structure of clay mineral with large cations inserted between two wafers to compensate for charge deficiency (schematic)

b. *Molding and Shaping. Plastic Flow.* At all evidence, dry clay minerals cannot be deformed without fracturing. Only through admixture of water do they seem to acquire the property commonly and rather vaguely referred to as plasticity thanks to which they can be molded at room temperature. Even the so-called dry forming processes which must be carried out under relatively high pressure of several thousands psi require a small amount of water, from 5 to 15 percent of the volume. Considerably larger amounts of water are needed to develop plastic flow in clays: the kind of flow described in Section 12-7, Chapter 12, in which stability of shape is restored after removal of applied force. The optimum amount of water critically, but not uniquely, depends on the kind, size, and degree of perfection of the clay particles. For example, the optimum water content for pure kaolinite in the micron (10^{-4} centimeter) size can easily exceed 50 percent.[17]

If kaolinite were made up of close-packed spheres of equal size there would be 26 percent of voids in the apparent volume, Problem 19-13. These voids of necessity would have to be filled by water. In actual clay minerals the

[17] R. E. Grim, *Clay Mineralogy*, McGraw-Hill, New York, 1953.

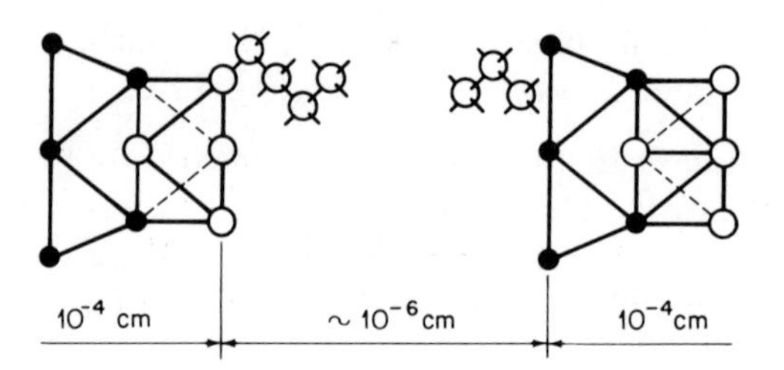

FIG. 19-27 Strings of six water molecules adhering to clay mineral platelets

particles are far from spherical. Moreover they are of different sizes. As a result, the interstices between larger particles are occupied by smaller ones, and correspondingly less water is needed to fill the remaining voids. Whatever the void fraction, apparently clay materials do not acquire their optimum plasticity until after all voids have been filled.[18] A small addition of water then suffices to produce the desired effect. The presumption, therefore, is that this effect is caused by water molecules which insert themselves between adjacent clay platelets presumably by capillary action. What follows next is at present largely a matter of speculation. There is presumption that the water molecules adhere to the platelets somewhat in the manner represented by Fig. 19-27, not singly but most likely in strings of about six (see Chapter 13, Section 13-8). Since each water molecule is known to carry an electric dipole moment of 1.87 debyes, it is as though the walls of the adjacent platelets, akin to the plates of a capacitor, were lined up with dipole moments of about 11.2 debyes, Fig. 19-28. A stable configuration ensues when the attraction between the dipole moments across the thickness r of the water layer balances the repulsion caused by the molecules impinging on each other. Knowing r we can compute the attractive force which holds the platelets together. For a value of r corresponding to about 12 percent of the water being imprisoned between the platelets the attractive force turns out to be equivalent to an outside pressure of about one atmosphere. (See Illustrative Problem, Section 19-11.) This value appears to be of the right order of magnitude for ensuring optimum plasticity to water-clay mixtures.[19] If the amount of imprisoned water rises to 35 percent, so that r is almost tripled, the attractive forces fall to less than 2 percent of their previous value, and the mixture appears to flow like a liquid.[20] Even though grossly oversimplified, the model of Fig. 19-28 seems to reasonably account for the role played by water in clay plasticity. The role is seen to be double. On the one hand, the mutual

[18] F. H. Norton, *Elements of Ceramics*, Addison-Wesley Press, 1952.

[19] F. H. Norton, *loc. cit.*, p. 79. The following quotation, even though in a different context, seems to prove our point: "A toy rubber balloon is filled with dry, pulverized clay, in which case the clay feels like a dry powder. If the balloon is slowly evacuated so that the atmosphere presses on the rubber to hold the clay particles together a remarkable change occurs; the clay in the balloon now feels just like a plastic clay-water paste."

[20] R. E. Grim, *loc. cit.*, p. 59.

attraction of the dipole moments aggregated at the two walls across the thickness of the water layer, even though weak, is sufficient to maintain the shape of the molded object when left to its own weight. On the other hand, the mobility of the unattached water molecules is great enough to overcome this weak cohesion by relatively small shearing forces. Admittedly, the role of many other factors, particularly of the kind, size, and shape of clay platelets, remains unexplained. A satisfactory theory of clay plasticity is still to be developed.

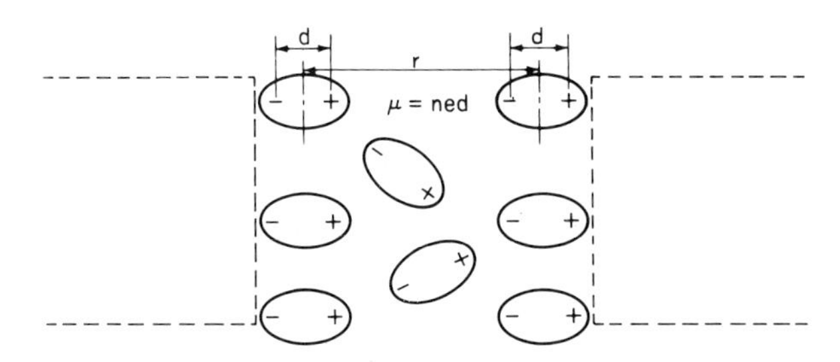

FIG. 19-28 Attraction by dipole moments of water molecules

19-8 Cement and Concrete. Despite some similarity in uses and texture, particularly as compared to common construction bricks, cement and concrete differ from whitewares and refractories in composition and mode of processing about as much as the latter differ from glasses. Here too, three major differences can be noted:

a. The basic binding material is not clay but cement, a *derivative* of clays and limestones obtained by calcination.

b. The finished product acquires cohesion and dimensional stability not at elevated temperatures in the processes of drying and firing, but at room temperature in the process of *setting* of cement-water mixtures.

c. The properties of the finished product depend less on the microstructure of the components than on the macrostructure, specifically, on the relative *ratios* of three components: (1) sand and stony aggregate, (2) cement, and (3) water.

We take up these three points one by one:

a. *Cement.* The most extensively used cementing material today is the so-called Portland cement. The name Portland is attributed to the resemblance of the calcined product first made in England in 1824 to a limestone mined on the Isle of Portland. Yet the cementing properties of calcined limestone mixed with *pozzolane*—a fine grained siliceous mineral—were already known to and utilized by Romans in surfaces as well as underwater construction. Portland cement is currently produced by a partial fusion of a mixture containing clay, limestone, and oxides of silicon, aluminum, iron, and often magnesium. When heated to about 1450°C the mass hardens to a *clinker*—a fused stony substance. The substance is crushed and, upon admixture of a few percent of gypsum, it is ground to a fine powder containing particles no larger than 10^{-3} centimeters. Structural analysis reveals the existence of four major crystalline constituents which, as we will see, play an important role in the mechanism of setting. They are listed in Table 19-4.

TABLE 19-4 MAJOR CONSTITUENTS OF PORTLAND CEMENT

Basic Chemical Formula	*Designation*	*Shorthand Notation*
$3\ CaO{\cdot}SiO_2$	Tricalcium Silicate	C_3S
$2\ CaO{\cdot}SiO_2$ (Beta)	Dicalcium Silicate	C_2S
$3\ CaO{\cdot}SiO_2$	Tricalcium Aluminate	C_3A
$4\ CaO{\cdot}Al_2O_3{\cdot}Fe_2O_3$	Tetracalcium Aluminoferrite	C_4AF

Depending on the uses (see below, Heat of Hydration) to which Portland cement is put, the above constituents figure in different proportion in the final analysis giving rise to several types of Portland cement. By way of illustration, the general purpose cement, or Portland cement type I, has the composition shown in Table 19-5, not counting the small amount of gypsum mentioned previously.

TABLE 19-5 COMPOSITION OF GENERAL PURPOSE PORTLAND CEMENT CLINKER

Constituent (Shorthand Notation)	%
C_3S	45
C_2S (Beta)	27
C_3A	11
C_4AF	8
Others and Glass	9

b. *Setting of Cement-Water Mixtures.* Like clay, cement exhibits plastic flow when mixed with water. However, the process does not stop there. With time the cement-water paste *sets*, i.e., it hardens to a rock-like consistency. The hardened mass is far from homogeneous. It contains numerous pores, and the pores are filled with water and air. Nor is its texture uniform. Rather the mass is a sort of conglomerate of a multitude of tiny particles, no longer than 100 Å, bonded together into a coherent solid. The aggregate is called the *cement gel.* The exact nature of this gel, let alone the mechanism of its formation, is still a matter of conjecture. It is not even certain whether the particles are in the crystalline or the glassy state.[21]

Heat of Hydration. Whatever the mechanism, there is little doubt that the setting of the cement paste is essentially a chemical rather than a physical process; it is accompanied by phase transformations. To a lesser or greater degree all constituents of Portland cement combine with water to form hydrated products. The reactions are largely exothermic, and to a first approximation each constituent on reacting with water evolves a specific amount of heat, called the *heat of hydration*, Table 19-6.

TABLE 19-6 HEATS OF HYDRATION OF PRINCIPAL CONSTITUENTS OF PORTLAND CEMENT

Constituents	*Heat of Hydration in* 10^5 J/kg
Tricalcium Silicate, C_3S	5
Dicalcium Silicate (Beta), C_2S	2.9
Tricalcium Aluminate, C_3A	8.4
Tetracalcium Aluminoferrite, C_4AF	4.2

According to Table 19-6 hydration of C_3A evolves the greatest amount of heat, C_3S is next and C_2S evolves the least amount of heat on hydration.

This disparity in the heats of hydration has an important bearing on the selection of the proper type of cement for use. In large concrete structures, such as dams, the heat due to hydration is not readily dissipated. To avoid excessive rise of temperature a low-heat cement, the Portland cement Type IV, is therefore recommended, in which the proportion of the low heat producing C_2S is increased at the expense of C_3A and C_3S. On the other hand, in the building of highways where rapid setting and hardening of concrete slabs is desired, Portland cement Type III, high in C_3S and C_3A and low in C_2S, is preferable. Type II, a moderately hardening cement, is intermediate between types I and IV.

Cohesive Strength. Experiment shows that the rates of setting and hardening exhibited by the four main constituents of Portland cement are commensurate with the amounts of heats of hydration.[22] So are the rates at which the cohesive strength of these components rises as can be inferred from the increase of the corresponding compressive strength with time, Fig. 19-29. According to this figure C_3S and C_3A, as well as C_4AF, acquire the major portion of their ultimate strengths in less than a month, while the full strength of C_2S is not reached even after one year. Despite the slower rate, or perhaps because of it, C_2S seems to be heading for the highest ultimate strength of all

[21] S. Brunauer, "Some Aspects of the Physics and Chemistry of Cement," *The Science of Engineering Materials*, Ed., J. E. Goldman, Wiley, 1957.

[22] S. Brunauer, *loc. cit.*

four constituents. This trend explains why cement and cemented aggregates like concrete continue to gain in strength slowly over a number of years.

Figure 19-29 also shows that the ultimate strength of Portland cement is due to hydration of C_2S and C_3S rather than to that of C_3A and C_4AF. There is at least one order of magnitude difference between the ultimate strengths of these two pairs of constituents. Hydrated C_3A and C_4AF do not appear to be much stronger than the dried products of clay-water mixtures. The presumption, therefore, is that C_3A and C_4AF too develop largely molecular bonds in the process of hydration, perhaps by the same mechanism of water adsorption as clays, whereas C_3S and C_2S acquire predominantly primary bonds in this process. This is merely presumption, since none of the hydrated products as yet have been identified, let alone isolated from the cement gel.

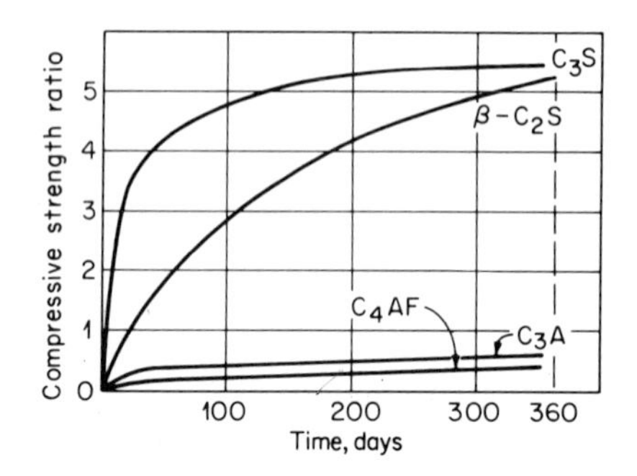

FIG. 19-29 Increase with time of the compressive strength of Portland cement constituents

Triple Function of Water. Whatever the identity of the products of hydration, it seems well established that water is not only chemically *combined* with cement in the process of hardening, but that it is also adsorbed to the surfaces of the hydrated product. Moreover, as in clays, water fills the pores, presumably by capillary action.

The amounts of water involved in these three functions are vastly different. The chemically bound water, measured by the water-cement weight ratio, w_b/c is about 80 percent of its theoretical value of 0.23 after one year of hardening, Problem 19-10. The adsorbed water-cement ratio w_a/c appears to be much smaller.[23] On the other hand, the capillary water-cement ratio w_c/c is seldom less than 0.1 and may go up as high as 0.4 to impart sufficient fluidity to the aggregate when ease of placement is paramount. All in all, the total water-cement ratio w/c may vary from about 0.4 to 0.7. Of this amount only the chemically bound water w_c is "not evaporable." The adsorbed water is partly lost on drying (and regained on moistening) thereby causing, as in

[23] S. Brunauer, *loc. cit.*

clays, shrinkage (and swelling). The capillary water is almost totally lost on drying. The pores which it leaves behind have a notable effect on the strength of cemented aggregates, as will appear below.

c. *Macrostructure of Cemented Aggregates. Concrete.* As with clay minerals, cement alone does not possess the requisite properties for current industrial applications. Compared to clay, Portland cement is too expensive as a building material, for it must be manufactured, whereas clay can be employed in its native state. In addition, pure cement-water pastes shrink too much on drying to be of practical interest. Both shortcomings have been remedied by reducing the role of Portland cement to that of a binder. In combination with water, cement welds together aggregates of crushed stone, gravel and sand into a coherent and solid mass called *concrete*—a building material that in strength and economy, to say nothing of esthetic value, competes today successfully with steel in ground construction.

Significantly concrete owes its success not so much to its microstructure, i.e., to the particular nature of its ingredients, as it does to *macrostructure*, a judicious proportioning and mixing of these ingredients, as will appear below.

However, the main reason for the tremendous expansion of concrete construction unquestionably lies in the exceptional ability of concrete to adhere to steel, as a French gardener by the name of Monnier is supposed to have discovered in 1866, when by chance or design he embedded iron rods in a concrete mix. It was later found that not only was this adhesion permanent but that it remained so in spite of temperature variation. For it turned out that concrete and iron have the same coefficient of thermal expansion. Thus a new era was ushered in building technology: the era of *reinforced* concrete.

Even though the exact nature of the bond between iron and concrete is still very much under debate, the benefits derived therefrom are beyond any doubt. As any brittle material (see Section 8-4, Chapter 4) concrete is much stronger in compression than in tension. By embedding steel bars of the right size and shape in the concrete mix and by strategically locating them in the cross section of the structural element, particularly with respect to the applied load, it is possible to utilize the full compressive strength of the concrete and to compensate for its weakness in tension by the full resistance of the supporting steel. The details of this structural symbiosis are outside the scope of this book.[24] So are the current techniques which seek to even out by *prestressing* the imbalance between compressive and tensile strength of concrete, as explained in Section 8-4.[25]

All these efforts are directed toward the design of concrete structural

[24] For more detail see e.g., L. C. Urquhart, C. E. O'Rourke, and G. Winter, *Design of Concrete Structures*, McGraw-Hill, New York, 1958.

[25] See also K. Billig, *Prestressed Concrete*, Macmillan, London, 1952.

elements rather than the building material itself. As regards the latter, the macrostructure remains the governing factor. We are thus led to consider the interplay between three basic components of this macrostructure:

1. the inert aggregate, or *aggregate* for short. Depending on the thickness of the structural element the aggregate is made up of crushed stones, gravel and sand, or gravel and sand alone;
2. *cement*, and
3. *water*.

In the design of concrete mixes, the interplay between components is reduced to the role of two ratios by weight:

1. the aggregate-cement ratio, a/c
2. the water-cement ratio, w/c.

Even though not independent, these ratios can be considered separately.

1. *Aggregate—Cement Ratio* a/c. In current mixes the tendency is to keep the a/c ratio as high as possible. The reason is fourfold: economy, dimensional stability, strength, and workability.

First, let us consider *economy*. Of all the ingredients which go into the making of concrete, cement is the most expensive. Hence the tendency is to use as much aggregate and as little cement as is structurally feasible. The same applies to maintaining *dimensional stability*, since cement is the only solid ingredient which causes overall shrinkage and swelling of the concrete.

As regards *strength*, properly selected aggregates as a rule have higher compressive strengths than hardened water-cement pastes. Hence, the higher the a/c ratio, the stronger is the concrete. The above argument remains valid even though *correctly graded* concrete mixes, when tested in compression, develop cracks often running through the aggregate rather than the cement binder. By correct grading we mean that the aggregates are made up of coarse, medium, and fine particles, e.g., crushed stone, gravel and sand, in proportions such that the medium particles fill most of the spaces between the coarse particles, and the fine particles fill most of what is left. This arrangement provides a minimum, yet sufficient, space for the cement binder to effectively weld all inert particles together. It obviously insures the maximum a/c ratio.

Finally let us consider *workability*. The ease of working and placement of concrete mixes often requires that the mass be fluid rather than plastic. In water-cement pastes this requirement is tantamount to increasing the amount of water, see Section 19-7b. However, in concrete mixes fluidity can often be increased by altering the grading of the aggregate, generally through an increased a/c ratio.[26]. Thereby the water-cement ratio is left materially unchanged to the benefit of the strength, as will appear below.

[26] For further detail see e.g., T. N. Akroyd, *Concrete Properties and Mixes*, Pergamon, 1962.

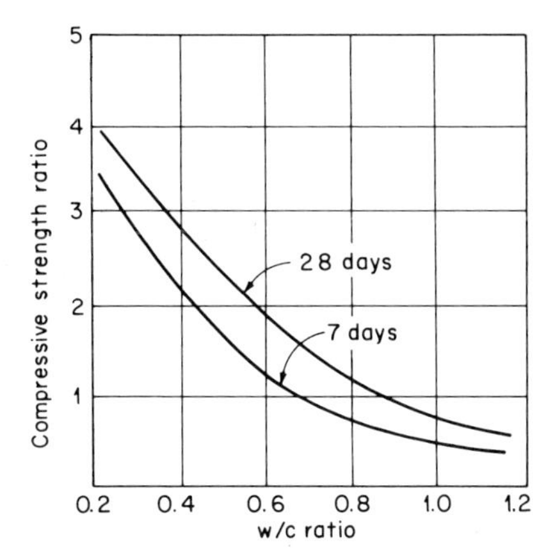

FIG. 19-30 Strength versus water-cement ratio of concrete mixes with ordinary Portland cement

2. *Water-Cement Ratio*, w/c. It was pointed out earlier that the cement binder is weaker in compression that the aggregate. Hence the design for strength of concrete mixes is predicated on the intrinsic strength of hardened water-cement pastes. According to recent work this strength decreases as the amount of *capillary* water increases. Since capillary water is lost on drying, the implication is that the decrease of strength is due to the pores left behind by water.[27] This implication is substantiated by the fact that porosity caused by entrained air during the mixing of concrete has a similar effect. Nonetheless, until some practical means has been devised to measure the degree of porosity, the water-cement ratio w/c remains the only reliable design criterion for the expected strength of concrete mixes. True, the combined and adsorbed waters w_b and w_a also are included in this ratio. However, for a given type of cement, the w_b/c and w_a/a ratios are constant, and therefore without influence on the plot of strength versus w/c, except for a shift of the abscissae, Fig. 19-30. According to the results shown in this figure—and similar results for other types of cement—*age* is the only other factor that besides the w/c ratio figures in the design of concrete mixes for strength. Both have a sound, even though for the time being qualitative, basis in the microstructure of the hardened cement pastes.

The same is not nearly as true of other factors such as additives, compacting, permeability, or resistance to corrosion, which are here not taken into consideration. Although important in design they are largely a part of the art rather than science of concrete technology.

19-9 Abrasives and Cermets. Like the prehistorical flint, Section 18-1, many high-temperature-melting natural and artificial compounds—oxides and carbides in particular—exhibit exceptional hardness and develop a sharp

[27] S. Brunauer, *loc. cit.*

TABLE 19-7

Compositions						
WC	TiC	TaC	NbC	Ni	Co	*Uses*
97–95.5					3–4.5	Machining of graphite, ceramics, boring tips, drawing dies.
85–70					15–30	Wear and shock resistant parts (cutting and blanking tools, deep drawing and swaging tools).
93		1			6	Machining of hard chilled cast iron.
	64		6	30		Heat resistant parts.

edge on being chipped. When mounted on and bonded to a flexible backing—paper or cloth—they serve as tools to cut through and abrade softer materials. Hence their name of *abrasives*. The prototype of abrasives is the sandpaper in which grains of natural flint are bonded to a paper backing by hide glue or synthetic resins. Equally ancient is the emery paper based on a black mineral—a mixture of iron oxide and aluminum oxide (corundum)—originally mined on Cape Emeri in the Grecian island of Naxos. More recent substitutes include artificial abrasives in the form of silicon carbides and aluminum oxides. They are characterized by greater consistency and hardness.[28]

However, substantial advances in the cutting and metal working techniques came only with the advent of *cermets*—metallically bonded and alloyed carbides, also called cemented carbides, and oxides. Inserts and tips made of cermets have increased manyfold the speed and life of rotary drills in the mining industry as well as the efficiency and wear resistance of cutting tools and dies in the metal working industry. Because of their exceptionally high hardness cermets have made it possible to cut and shape without cracking many refractory materials heretofore considered to be nonmachinable: glass, porcelain, and high temperature resistant brittle alloys.

The fabrication of parts made of cermets involves several steps:

1. preparation of mixtures of ceramic-metal powders, in proper proportion and grain size;
2. compacting and shaping of the unfired (green) mixture by pressing;
3. densification and conversion of the pressed product into a cohesive mass by application of heat alone or heat combined with pressure; and
4. finishing of the completed part by grinding, and more recently by

[28] *Coated Abrasives*, Behr-Manning Co., Troy, New York.

means of special machining processes: electrosparking or ultrasonic vibration.

Step three of the operation, known as *sintering*, is particularly important. Table 19-7, illustrates some typical compositions and uses of cermets.[29]

19-10 Summary. Ceramics largely owe their widespread functional and artistic role throughout the ages to the ease with which they can be shaped and hardened. In both of these treatments they tend to preserve the local order—a rigid configuration of anions around a cation, and vice-versa, called the coordinated polyhedron. The governing factor of the short range order is the *ionic radius*. Conservation of electric charge (Pauling's Electrostatic Valence Rule) presides over the linking of polyhedra. The ensuing degree of freedom explains the variety and ease of polymorphic changes, as exemplified by more than thirteen crystalline and one glassy modifications of silica. However, the rigidity of the coordinated polyhedron—of the tetrahedron—is essential to the understanding and prediction of these modifications.

The same situation occurs in other minerals, among them in *clay minerals*: a group of silicates in which tetrahedra of oxygen and hydroxyl ions built about a silicon ion are linked with polyhedra built about other cations.

Clay minerals alone seldom possess the combination of properties needed for use. Other components must be added to form the current type of ceramics. The ensuing aggregates give rise to phase diagrams similar to those of the alloys, with the atomic size factor likewise governing the extent and nature of solid and liquid solubilities. The main types of ceramics are as follows:

1. On adding various amounts of Na_2O, K_2O, CaO, MgO, Al_2O_3, etc., to SiO_2 several types of commercial *glass* are produced in which both the melting point can be lowered and the range of workability can be extended as compared to pure silica glass, and this without impairment of chemical resistance and transparency to light. Other ingredients endow glass with color, translucency, opacity, and high index of refraction (for lenses).

2. At variance with glass the basic ingredient of *whitewares* and *refractories* is a clay mineral rather than silica. The structure of *kaolinite* with alternating layers of O^{--}, Si^{++++}, ($OH^- + O^{--}$), Al^{+++} and OH^- is typical of the layer structure of all clay minerals. Typical also is the plasticity which kaolinite acquires through an admixture of water. The optimum amount of water (often as high as 50 percent of the volume) appears to be reached only after all voids (or pores) have been filled. The small additional amount of water, beyond and above the pore water, can be thought of as building molecular layers adhering to clay platelets and attracting each other by virtue of dipole moments.

[29] Adapted from P. Schwarzkopf and R. Kieffer, *Cemented Carbides*, Macmillan, New York, 1960.

3. The basic binding component of *concrete*, a building material made of coarse and fine stone *aggregates*, is cement, a derivative of clay and limestone obtained by calcination. Structural analysis of *Portland* cement reveals the presence of four major constituents: $3CaO \cdot SiO_2$, $2CaO \cdot SiO_2$(Beta), $3CaO \cdot SiO_2$ and $4CaO \cdot Al_2O_3 \cdot Fe_2O_3$ or C_3S, C_2S, C_3A and C_4AF for short. Mixed with water these constituents *set* or harden at different rates and with different heats of hydration. Their ultimate strengths also differ. Depending on the relative amounts of the above four constituents several types of Portland cement are thus available for various uses. However, the design of the *concrete* construction ultimately depends on two ratios by weight: (1) the aggregate cement-ratio, a/c, and (2) the water-cement ratio, w/c. Economy and workability are generally increased by a greater w/c ratio, whereas strength is increased by a greater a/c ratio. An important element in the design and execution of concrete constructions is *time* or the *age* of the concrete.

4. Exceptional hardness coupled with the formation of a sharp chipped edge is the basis for the use of high temperature melting natural and artificial compounds in the form of *abrasives* and *cermets*. Abrasives are made by mounting the compounds on and bonding them to a flexible backing: paper or cloth. They serve as tools to cut through or abrade softer materials. *Cermets* are metallically bonded and alloyed carbides, also called cemented carbides, and oxides. As inserts and tips they are used for high-speed cutting and machining of many refractory materials. Their mode of fabrication involves *sintering*—the densification and conversion of a pressed metal-ceramic powder into a cohesive mass by application of heat or heat and pressure. Sintering is also instrumental in the production of single phase ceramics: alumina, beryllia, magnesia, etc., and it occurs in the fabrication of whitewares and refractories.

19-11 Illustrative Problem. Compute the forces of attraction in terms of external pressure acting on platelets, Fig. 19-28.

Solution.

From the Illustrative Problem 2, Section 6-8, Chapter 6, the force of attraction f_a between two diploles moments is

$$f_a = \frac{6e^2n^2d^2}{r^4} \tag{19-15}$$

where to conform to the notations of Chapter 13 we have substituted n for z. Using Eq. (13-12) we rewrite Eq. (19-15) to read

$$f_a = \frac{6\hat{\mu}^2}{r^4} \tag{19-16}$$

The dipole moment $\hat{\mu}$ of six aggregated water molecules is 6×1.87 debyes $= 11.22 \times 10^{-18}$ electrostatic unit centimeter and the value of r for micron size platelets of kaolinite can be estimated to be of the order of 10^{-6} centimeter on the basis of the linear drying shrinkage.[29] Inserting these values in Eq. 19-16 we get

$$f_d = \frac{6 \times (11.2 \times 10^{-18})^2}{10^{-24}} = 7.5 \times 10^{-10} \text{ dynes} \qquad (19\text{-}17)$$

This force refers to an area on the platelet, which is assigned to the water molecule adhering to it. The diameter of the water molecule. being 2.76 Å (Table 6-5, Chapter 6), there follows for the stress acting on the platelet

$$\sigma = \frac{7.5 \times 10^{-10}}{2.76^2 \times 10^{-16}} = 10^6 \text{ dyne/cm}^2$$

or about one atmosphere.

If the value of r is tripled, σ falls to 1.24 percent of the above value.

References

1. W. D. Kingery, *Introduction to Ceramics*, Wiley, New York, 1960.
2. F. H. Norton, *Elements of Ceramics*, Addison-Wesley, Reading, 1952.
3. T. H. Davies, "The Physics of Glass," in *Science of Engineering Materials*, Ed., J. E. Goldman, Wiley, New York, 1957.
4. R. E. Grim, *Clay Mineralogy*, McGraw-Hill, New York, 1953.
5. S. Brunauer, "Some Aspects of the Physics and Chemistry of Cement," in *Science of Engineering Materials*, Ed., J. E. Goldman, Wiley, New York, 1957.
6. P. Schwartzkopf and R. Kieffer, *Cemented Carbides*, Macmillan, New York, 1960.

Problems

19-1 Explain why anions in the same period have generally a larger ionic radius than cations and why in the same column of the periodic table the ionic radii increase with the period.

19-2 Derive the r_c/r_a ratios of Table 19-2 from geometric arguments similar to those made for r_{Na}/r_{Cl} in Na^+Cl^+.

19-3 Prove that the number of tetrahedra sharing common corner in SiO_2 is 2.

19-4 Prove that the angle between two silica tetrahedra cannot be smaller than 120 degrees. (Hint: Consider the overlap of adjacent O^{--}).

19-5 Show that the asymmetric form of tridymite (and cristobalite) is denser than the symmetric one.

19-6 Explain the greater stability of cristobalite versus tridymite at higher temperature. Is change of density involved?

19-7 Compute the theoretical change of density from beta-tridymite to beta-quartz. Answer 22 percent.

19-8 Compute relative change of density resulting from rotation θ in the course of transformation from beta to alpha quartz.

Answer $\rho_\alpha/\rho_\beta = 0.40\delta^2$ where $\delta = \tan \theta/2$

Maximum density change is for $\delta = 1/2$, viz. 0.1.

[29] R. E. Grim, *loc. cit.*, p. 77.

19-9 Using Eq. (19-10) prove that two octahedra centered about Al^{+++} and one tetrahedron centered about Si^{++++} can share one oxygen ion, but they cannot share one OH^-.

19-10 Compute the theoretical value of w_b/c on hydration if the density of cement is 3.1, the density of the hydrated product is 3.45 gram/cubic centimeter and the original volume of cement is expanded 55 percent on hydration.

19-11 A finer grinding of the cement clinker generally promotes faster setting. Why?

19-12 Show that if cement were made of spherical close-packed grains, there would be 26 percent of voids in the apparent volume.

19-13 What would be the percentage of remaining voids in the apparent volume if the voids left by close-packing of spherical grains were filled by closely fitting smaller spherical grains.

19-14 On the basis of the solution of Problem 19-13 justify the use of a mixture of coarse and fine aggregate to improve the strength of concrete.

19-15 List some of the advantages and disadvantages of current ceramics for high temperature technology.

19-16 Ceramic-metal composites are believed to be a better solution for some of the high temperature applications than either pure metal or pure ceramic. Can you give a reason for this belief?

20 / POLYMERS

We found in Chapter 19 that the structure of ceramics can often be interpreted in terms of repeat units—the so-called coordinated polyhedra—whose aggregation, ranging from amorphous to crystalline, gave the solid its bulk properties.

In polymers the repeat unit is an aggregate of atoms—not necessarily coordinated—whose replication in the form of long chain molecules is achieved through predominantly directed covalent bonding. Included in this category are the main constituents of natural substances such as wood, wool, rubber, horn as well as synthetic products, e.g., nylon, neoprene, "Bakelite." They are conveniently grouped into fibers, elastomers (or rubbers), and plastics.

That all of them, whether nature or man-made, consist of thousands and even hundred thousands simpler units linked together by covalent bonds into giant molecules was a notion that gained slow acceptance among the chemists. They were reluctant to ascribe the "glue like" properties of polymers merely to a much larger size of their constitutive units. This reluctance may account for the rather tardy origin of synthetic polymers as compared to alloys and ceramics.[1] However, once accepted (1929) the notion of long chain molecules gave rise to a rapidly expanding and flourishing industry of plastics—so much so that some authors do not hesitate to coin the present age the age of plastics.

20-1 Polymers and the Age of Plastics. If by plastics we mean all synthetic man-made polymers, then the post-1930 period may well deserve the name of the Age of Plastics. Structurally, man-made and natural long chain molecules have much in common. The main difference lies in the way they have been processed, not in the way they are structured.

It is perhaps too early to speculate on the impact of man-made polymers on technology. However natural polymers of both vegetable and animal origin have sheltered, housed, and clothed humanity for more than 7000 years. Wood and fibers, silk and cotton, wool, hides and leather have all contributed if not to the survival, at least to the comfort and well-being of the human race from the very dawn of civilization.

Except for wood, natural polymers appear to have had less immedi-

[1] P. J. Flory, *Principles of Polymer Chemistry*, Cornell University Press, New York, 1953.

ate impact on technology than metals and ceramics. Spinning of fibers and weaving them into fabrics date from prehistoric times. Yet until about 2000 B.C. they had been a purely feminine, and presumably less-honored, occupation than metal working. So for that matter was pottery making, until it had found an artistic outlet in ceramics.

Wood was exceptional on three counts: it was the source and fuel of fire; it was an essential ingredient of iron and steel-making in the form of charcoal; and it provided—and it still provides—an excellent and cheap construction material in the form of timber. Domestic and industrial uses of wood were so extensive in antiquity that the Greek philosopher Plato (427–347 B.C.) made them directly responsible for the disappearance of forests around Athens. The growing demands for charcoal in the iron industry had an equally disastrous effect on the English forests in the 17th century, and it was the foreseeable scarcity of charcoal rather than scientific curiosity that drove the metallurgists to substitute coke for charcoal—a conversion that necessitated much more elaborate processing of coal than getting charcoal out of wood.

Nor is the epic of wood closed with this momentous technological change. Just as charcoal served the metal industry in the past, so does wood pulp serve the paper industry in the present. Paper—a Chinese invention at least 2000 years old—was rather slow in penetrating and getting acceptance in Europe over parchemin and velum. However, the inventor of the movable type in printing, Johann Gutenberg (1450), had already at his disposal a plentiful supply of paper made of rags. Subsequently the increasing use of newsprint as a mass medium of communication and indoctrination has led to the replacement of the costly handmade rag paper by the cheap machine-made wood pulp paper. By 1880 wood pulp had become the major, if not the sole ingredient of papermaking—in itself a most elaborate and scientifically controlled industrial operation. The tremendous increase in production lowered the cost of newsprint from fifteen cents a pound in 1867 to nearly one-third this value in 1880.[2] Concomitantly the economical and political power of the press rose in the same proportion. So did the importance of the paper industry, which in certain countries (Israel, Mexico) amounts almost to a monopoly.

As mentioned before, textiles played a rather minor role in the early stages of our civilization. However, their subsequent role in shaping our economic and social structure was quite remarkable. To appreciate the change we must examine the position of textile industry before and after the Industrial Revolution of the eighteenth century.

Since its inception, weaving along with spinning was a handicraft which in the making of tapestry and lacework reached a high degree of artistic perfection in the sixteenth century. Technologically, however, it had not

[2] Melvin Kranzberg and Carroll W. Pursell, Jr., Ed., *Technology in Western Civilization*, Vol. I, p. 637, Oxford University Press, New York, 1967.

advanced much since the beginning of Christian era. The preparation of fibers and the weaving of cloth remained by and large hand-made processes. Wool and linen were the main articles of ware and underwear, until the discovery of the New World and the expanding English trade with the Far East brought cotton into the picture. Cotton was much cheaper than linen and it was more suitable for making dresses and underwear than wool. The rapidly increasing demand for cotton goods brought with it the necessity for greater and faster production. It is thus that England, even though not the first country to experiment with mechanization (France made a few abortive attempts before) found itself on the road of invention and rapid improvement of textile machinery in the period covering the years 1750–1830. As a result, not only human power but also human skill were being gradually transferred to the machines. The highly prized know-how of the spinner and weaver gave way to the repetitive and monotonous task of machine tending by unskilled mill-hands. The ensuing unemployment and cheapening of the labor market met with violent opposition and hostility from the workers, culminating in the famous Luddite riots in England in 1811.[3] The textile industry was the first to introduce the factory system in which the nature and the pace of the work was determined by the machine rather than the worker. It was also the first to realize the benefits of mass production.

The credit—or blame—for these innovations is generally attributed to the cotton industry which in the span of ten years (from 1873–1882) increased its share of textile goods produced in England from 5 to almost 66 percent. The industry's present role in promoting automation in the United States appears to be similar to that which it played in England in advancing the adoption of the factory system.[4]

This short saga about the forerunners of the "Age of Plastics" could not end without mentioning rubber. The hardening of the milky sap of a Brazilian tree into an "elastic resin" was reported in 1736 by the French academician C. M. de la Condamine back from a geodetic expedition to South America. The elastic properties of the hardened resin were noted earlier but the first uses of rubber were for water-proofing garments and shoes. The exceptional elastic properties of rubber for which it is known and utilized today could not be fully exploited until rubber was "cured" of its "visco-elastic instability" by an amateur but tenacious chemist, Charles Goodyear in 1839 (see Section 20-9). Since then rubber and its synthetic progeny have put the American nation and the world on wheels as effectively as steel has put them on a canned food diet.

As with alloys and ceramics much of this success is due to a better understanding of the interplay between the configurational and statistical stabilities, as will appear from the succeeding sections.

[3] John G. Burke, *The New Technology & Human Values*, p. 5, Wadsworth Publ. Co., 1966.

[4] Melvin Kranzberg and Carroll W. Pursel, Jr., *loc. cit.*, Vol. II, pp. 95–98.

20-2 The Repeat Unit. Many components of living organisms—proteins and nucleic acids in particular—belong to the category of polymers. However our prime interest will be with materials used in engineering applications. We will see that the properties of these materials largely depend on a threefold level of aggregations: (a) between the atoms in the repeat unit (or units); (b) between the repeat units in the long chain molecules, and (c) between the long chain molecules in the bulk aggregate.

The nature of the repeat unit (or units) very often identifies the polymer by its origin, by its *monomer*. Thus a polymer deriving from the monomer ethylene becomes a polyethylene symbolized by letters PE; the monomer vinyl chloride gives rise to polyvinyl chloride, or PVC, etc., Table 20-1. According to Table 20-1 the formation of a polymer can be visualized as a process whereby the double bond between two carbon atoms in each monomer is simply converted into a single bond. As a result one directed covalent bond at each end of the repeat unit becomes available for joining up with a neighbour to the right and a neighbor to the left in a theoretically endless chain. Actually, neither is the process of polymerization as simple as suggested by the sketch, nor can the chain be extended indefinitely and arbitrarily.

The description of some frequently encountered and important polymerization reactions will help clarify this point.

a. *Addition Polymerization.* Consider, e.g., the formation of polyvinyl chloride, PVC—a basic material for making raincoats, plastic curtains, bottles, etc. The monomer

```
H       H
 \     /
  C═C
 /     \
H       Cl
```

is a gas at ordinary temperature. To change the double bond C═C into a single bond, an amount of energy exceeding the difference between the dissociation energies of C═C and C—C bonds is required, something more than 2.7 eV. Obviously, bringing together two monomers would not do the job. What is needed is an agent, an *initiator*, that has greater affinity than the monomer for the valence electrons tied up in the double bond. Such an initiator, symbolized by letter *I*, can be obtained by thermal or photochemical decomposition of organic substances containing a peroxide group (OO) (e.g., benzoyl peroxide, $[C_6H_5COO]_2$). There occurs a splitting of the molecule into two *free radicals* $R\cdot$ containing one unpaired electron marked by the dot $\cdot$. Symbolically the reaction of splitting can be written as follows:

$$I \rightarrow 2R\cdot \tag{20-1}$$

Each of the two free radicals is now able to split the double bond of the

TABLE 20-1 DERIVATION OF POLYMERS FROM MONOMERS

Monomer		*Polymer*		
Designation	*Molecule*	*Repeat Unit*	*Chain*	*Designation*
Ethylene	$H_2C{=}CH_2$	$-CH_2-CH_2-$	$-C-C-C-C-C-C-$	PE
Vinyl Chloride	$H_2C{=}CHCl$	$-CH_2-CHCl-$	$-C-C-C-C-C-C-$	PVC
Tetrafluoro-ethylene ("Teflon")	$F_2C{=}CF_2$	$-CF_2-CF_2-$	$-C-C-C-C-C-C-$	PTFE

Styrene	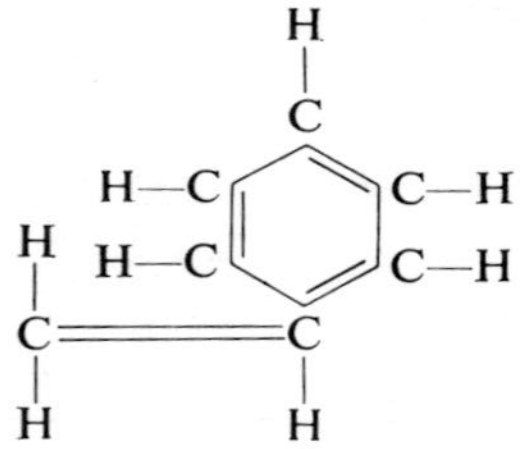	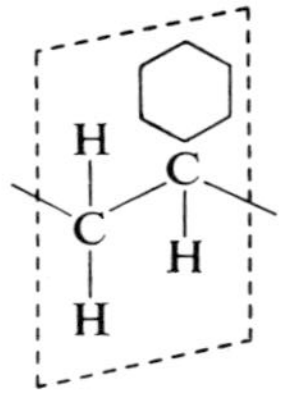	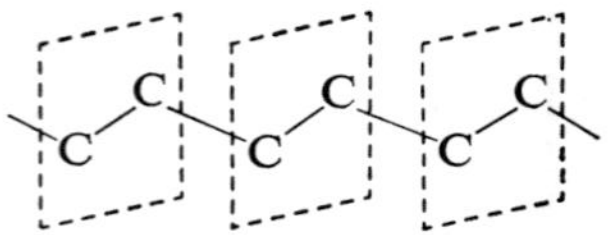	PS
Isoprene	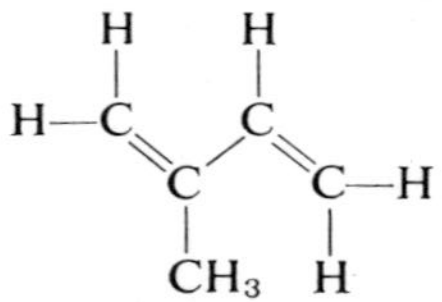	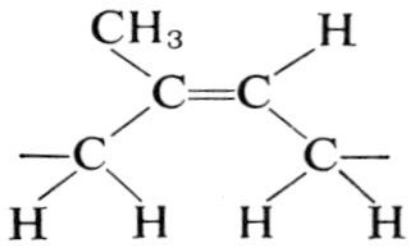	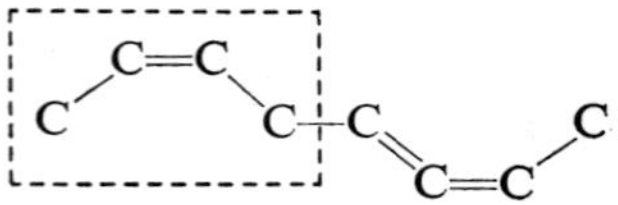	Natural Rubber (poly-*cis*-1,4-isoprene)

monomer and *initiate* growth of the polymer. The reaction yields the first link, to wit

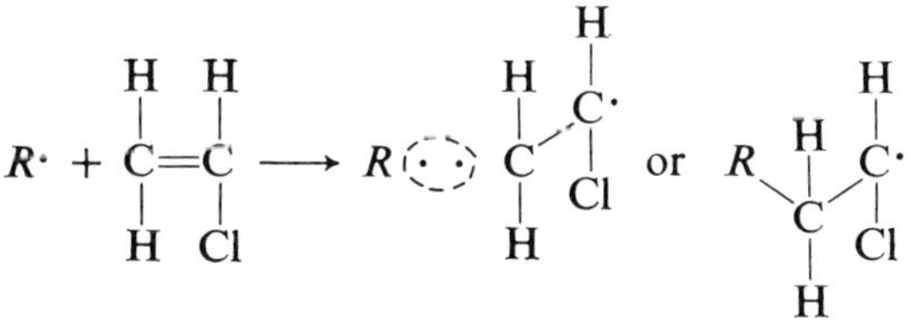

$$R\cdot + \begin{array}{c}H\ \ H\\ |\ \ \ |\\ C{=}C\\ |\ \ \ |\\ H\ \ Cl\end{array} \longrightarrow R(\cdot\ \cdot)\begin{array}{c}H\ \ \ H\\ |\ \ \ \ |\\ C - C\cdot\\ |\ \ \ \ |\\ H\ \ Cl\end{array} \text{ or } R - \begin{array}{c}H\ \ \ H\\ |\ \ \ \ |\\ C - C\cdot\\ |\ \ \ \ |\\ H\ \ Cl\end{array} \tag{20-2}$$

leaving an unpaired electron at one end. The succeeding links are now readily formed by repeating the same type of reaction.

Thus

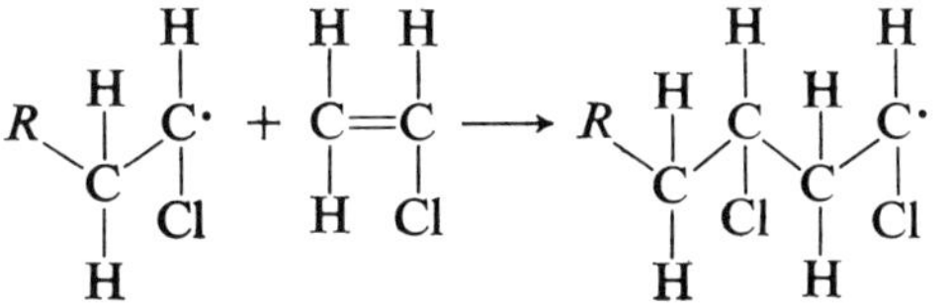

$$R - \begin{array}{c}H\ \ \ H\\ |\ \ \ \ |\\ C - C\cdot\\ |\ \ \ \ |\\ H\ \ Cl\end{array} + \begin{array}{c}H\ \ H\\ |\ \ \ |\\ C{=}C\\ |\ \ \ |\\ H\ \ Cl\end{array} \longrightarrow R - \begin{array}{c}H\ \ \ H\ \ \ H\ \ \ H\\ |\ \ \ \ |\ \ \ \ |\ \ \ \ |\\ C - C - C - C\cdot\\ |\ \ \ \ |\ \ \ \ |\ \ \ \ |\\ H\ \ Cl\ \ \ H\ \ Cl\end{array} \tag{20-3}$$

etc.

In practice this chain reaction, which is carried out in a liquid medium, propagates very quickly. It produces something like 10,000 links or repeat units, in a fraction of a second.[5] Conceivably the reaction could go until all monomers have been attached to the chains, and the open ends of the chains have been capped by the remaining free radicals $R\cdot$, thereby arresting their growth. Practically, the *termination* of polymerization is controlled by the random thermal coiling and uncoiling of the chains and the ensuing chance encounter of their chemically active open ends. There are two possibilities: (a) the two unpaired electrons, one at each end, can coalesce into a covalent bond, thereby decreasing the number of chains and making them longer; or (b) one hydrogen atom, more exactly one hydrogen free radical $H\cdot$, is transferred from one chain to the other, thereby capping its radical and leaving behind one more unpaired electron on C for the formation of a double bond.

The first mode of termination is called *coupling* or *combination*, the second, *disproportionation*. They are symbolized as shown on page 482.

The mode of polymerization described on page 482 is not restricted to the vinyl chloride monomer. Under the name of *vinyl* polymerization, it occurs in many molecules containing a C=C bond, for example in styrene, methylmetacrylate, tetrafluoroethylene, the latter two giving rise to polymers commercially known as plexiglass or lucite, and teflon. The process is variously called *addition* or *radical chain* polymerization.

[5] Sir Harry Melville, *Big Molecules*, Bell & Sons, London, 1958.

(a) coupling or combination

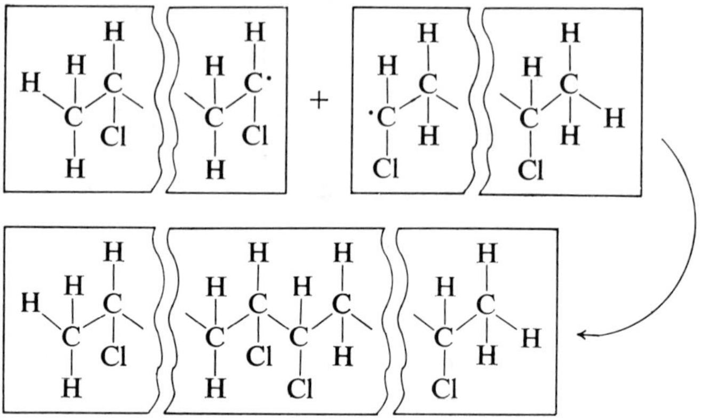

$$CH_3-CHCl\sim CH_2-\dot{C}HCl + \dot{C}HCl-CH_2\sim CHCl-CH_3 \rightarrow CH_3-CHCl\sim CH_2-CHCl-CHCl-CH_2\sim CHCl-CH_3 \qquad (20\text{-}4)$$

(b) disproportionation

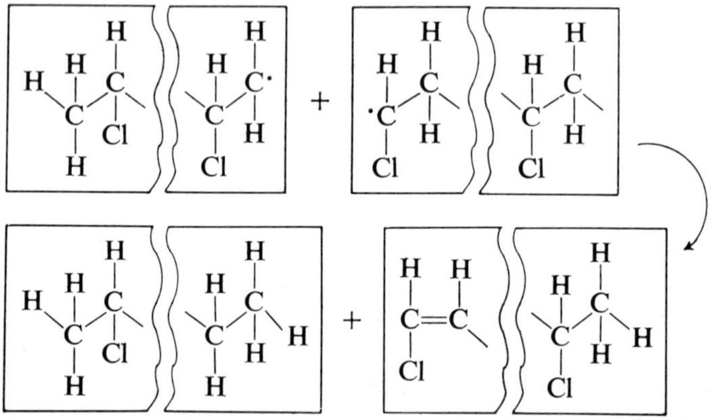

$$CH_3-CHCl\sim CHCl-\dot{C}H_2 + \dot{C}HCl-CH_2\sim CHCl-CH_2- \rightarrow CH_3-CHCl\sim CHCl-CH_3 + CHCl=CH\sim CHCl-CH_3 \qquad (20\text{-}5)$$

b. *Condensation Polymerization.* "Bakelite," the first commercial plastic, named after its Belgian inventor Baekeland around 1907, owes its origin to another equally frequent process called condensation or *stepwise* polymerization. We shall illustrate this process by having recourse to a widely used polymer known commercially as nylon 6.

The point of departure—the monomer—is an organic compound called aminocaproic acid. Its molecule consists of five repeat units $-CH_2-$ (—C— with H above and H below) to which are attached a carboxylic acid group, $HO-C(=O)-$ at one end and an amine group $-NH_2$ (—N with two H) at the other end.

The structural formula reads *in extenso*:

$$\mathrm{HO{-}\overset{\displaystyle O}{\overset{\|}{C}}{-}\underset{\underset{\displaystyle H}{|}}{\overset{\overset{\displaystyle H}{|}}{C}}{-}\underset{\underset{\displaystyle H}{|}}{\overset{\overset{\displaystyle H}{|}}{C}}{-}\underset{\underset{\displaystyle H}{|}}{\overset{\overset{\displaystyle H}{|}}{C}}{-}\underset{\underset{\displaystyle H}{|}}{\overset{\overset{\displaystyle H}{|}}{C}}{-}\underset{\underset{\displaystyle H}{|}}{\overset{\overset{\displaystyle H}{|}}{C}}{-}N\genfrac{}{}{0pt}{}{\diagup H}{\diagdown H}}$$

or in a more abbreviated form

$$\mathrm{HO{-}\overset{\displaystyle O}{\overset{\|}{C}}{-}\left\{\begin{matrix}H\\ |\\ C\\ |\\ H\end{matrix}\right\}_5{-}N\genfrac{}{}{0pt}{}{\diagup H}{\diagdown H}}$$

The polymer is produced by a stepwise coalescence of aminocaproic acid molecules with elimination (condensation) of a water molecule at each step. Thus we have

(a) step one

$$\mathrm{HO{-}\overset{\displaystyle O}{\overset{\|}{C}}{-}\left\{\begin{matrix}H\\ |\\ C\\ |\\ H\end{matrix}\right\}_5{-}N\genfrac{}{}{0pt}{}{\diagup H}{\diagdown H}\quad H{-}O{-}\overset{\displaystyle O}{\overset{\|}{C}}{-}\left\{\begin{matrix}H\\ |\\ C\\ |\\ H\end{matrix}\right\}_5{-}N\genfrac{}{}{0pt}{}{\diagup H}{\diagdown H}}$$

$$\mathrm{H_2O + HO{-}\overset{\displaystyle O}{\overset{\|}{C}}{-}\left\{\begin{matrix}H\\ |\\ C\\ |\\ H\end{matrix}\right\}_5{-}N\overset{\diagup H}{}\ {-}\overset{\displaystyle O}{\overset{\|}{C}}{-}\left\{\begin{matrix}H\\ |\\ C\\ |\\ H\end{matrix}\right\}_5{-}N\genfrac{}{}{0pt}{}{\diagup H}{\diagdown H}} \tag{20-6}$$

(b) step two

$$\mathrm{HO{-}\overset{\displaystyle O}{\overset{\|}{C}}{-}\left\{\begin{matrix}H\\ |\\ C\\ |\\ H\end{matrix}\right\}_5{-}\overset{\displaystyle H}{\overset{|}{N}}{-}\overset{\displaystyle O}{\overset{\|}{C}}{-}\left\{\begin{matrix}H\\ |\\ C\\ |\\ H\end{matrix}\right\}_5{-}N\genfrac{}{}{0pt}{}{\diagup H}{\diagdown H} + H{-}O{-}\overset{\displaystyle O}{\overset{\|}{C}}{-}\left\{\begin{matrix}H\\ |\\ C\\ |\\ H\end{matrix}\right\}_5{-}N\genfrac{}{}{0pt}{}{\diagup H}{\diagdown H}}$$

$$\mathrm{H_2O + HO{-}\overset{\displaystyle O}{\overset{\|}{C}}{-}\left\{\begin{matrix}H\\ |\\ C\\ |\\ H\end{matrix}\right\}_5{-}\overset{\displaystyle H}{\overset{|}{N}}{-}\overset{\displaystyle O}{\overset{\|}{C}}{-}\left\{\begin{matrix}H\\ |\\ C\\ |\\ H\end{matrix}\right\}_5{-}\overset{\displaystyle H}{\overset{|}{N}}{-}\overset{\displaystyle O}{\overset{\|}{C}}{-}\left\{\begin{matrix}H\\ |\\ C\\ |\\ H\end{matrix}\right\}_5{-}N\genfrac{}{}{0pt}{}{\diagup H}{\diagdown H}} \tag{20-7}$$

The same process of coalescence and condensation through elimination of a water molecule occurs in the production of other synthetic polymers: dacron, mylar, as well as silicone in which the directed covalent bonds of the chain are provided by silicone and oxygen instead of carbon. The naturally occurring polymer, cellulose, a major constituent of the vegetable kingdom, can be thought of as formed by condensation of the sugar glucose molecules according to the scheme shown below

```
                    CH2OH                                      CH2OH
  H      O———C         H          OH      O———C         OH
          H                                  H
     C            C                    C              C
OH       H  H        OH         H        H  H            H
       C————C                         C————C
   OH          OH                  OH          OH
```

Cotton, which is 95 percent cellulose, is made up of polymeric chains containing no less than 3500 repeat units.

c. *Copolymerization.* By combining two or more monomers it is possible to create a long chain molecule, called copolymer made up of a sequence of two or more kinds of repeat units. For example, the already familiar monomer vinyl chloride, Fig. 20-1 can be combined with its generic derivative

```
                     H  Cl
                     |  |
vinylidene chloride  C==C
                     |  |
                     H  Cl
```

to produce a copolymer whose repeat units are

```
     H             Cl
 H   |         H   |
 |   C         |   C
 \C/   \  and  \C/   \.
 |   Cl        |   Cl
 H             H
```

The relative ratio and the sequential arrangement of the two repeat units may vary from a random to a well ordered one. Thus, the copolymerization of styrene (S) with a monomer called methyl-methacrylate (M) is completely random, while the copolymerization of vinyl acetate (A) with a similar monomer, vinylidene cyanide (C) results in a regular alternation of the two repeat units. Symbolically we can write for the first

$$SMMSSSMSMM\ldots$$

and for the second

$$ACACAC\ldots$$

Admittedly, this variety of arrangements complicates the study of the internal structure of long chain molecules but offers a possibility for improvement of properties. Thus polymers containing 10 percent vinylidene chloride have better tensile properties than pure PVC.[6] As with alloys and ceramics copolymers are thus apt to exhibit properties unattainable in polymers made up of only one kind of repeat unit.

Understandably these possibilities increase tremendously as the number of participating species of the repeat unit grows. The amazing ability of nature to produce an almost infinite variety of proteins tailored to specific needs and functions appears to be solely due to the unlimited number of ways it can arrange and repeat about twenty amino acids.

20-3 Fibers. The virtue and versatility of large molecules is well exhibited in fibers. The fibers embody both the strength of the constitutive molecular units and the flexibility of their conformation. Yet to bring about these qualities in the filaments, we must subject the native or synthetic products to suitable mechanical and chemical treatments. The treatment of nylon is typical in this respect.[6] Chips of nylon are melted in inert atmosphere to prevent oxidation, and the liquid is forced through a series of orifices, through a spinneret, and solidified into thin filaments by a stream of cool air. During the cooling process an arrest similar to that occurring during solidification of pure liquid solid system is observed, Fig. 20-1, with the exception that the arrest appears after and not during solidification. This is due to realignment and ordering of segments of molecules into more or less parallel chains, i.e., to crystallization. Since the ordering stabilizes the system by lowering its internal energy, a certain amount of energy is liberated in the form of heat. Thereby the cooling trend is slowed down. The ordering not only renders the fibers more dense it also makes them stronger.

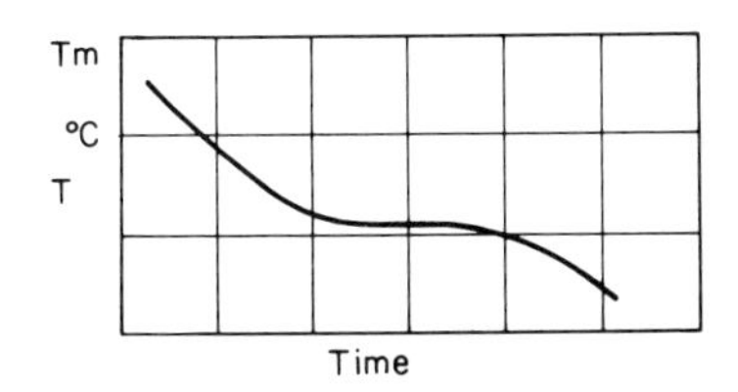

FIG. 20-1 Arrest in the cooling curve below the melting point T_m due to ordering and realignment of repeat units (crystallization) in a long chain molecule (schematic)

In nylon the most obvious manifestation of this increased strength is the resistance to abrasion on repeated rubbing. This is why nylon is used so extensively not only in the fabrication of stockings and socks, particularly at the heels where the rubbing is at its worst, but also in the manufacture of ropes, in lieu of the time honored hemp.

Another manifestation of the ordering of molecules, i.e., of crystallization, is the increase of the modulus of elasticity, amounting in nylon to as much as 140,000 psi compared to 70,000 psi for the unordered state. Yet the increase of rigidity is not without drawbacks. The ordering, by causing greater mutual attraction and alignment, deprives the molecules of the ability to coil and

[6] Sir Harry Melville, *loc. cit.*

uncoil on being pulled. As a result, nylon loses much of its extensibility. To restore this important quality, the fiber itself, rather than the molecule (see below, Elastomers), is made into a coil of fine pitch, by a procedure very much similar to that used for coiling up the ends of a ribbon in gift packages. In weaving or knitting the fiber is normally stretched, but it coils back in the finished product. This is the *crimped* nylon so popular in wearing apparel, because it provides much greater margin of fit.

The chemical treatment of fibers is no less extensive and successful. For example, to increase the crease resistance of fibers a small amount of resinous substance is incorporated in the long chain, thereby producing an effect of an "inner spring." The resinous molecule prevents the chain from collapsing and the fabric from creasing. Water- and fire-proofing are other examples of chemical treatment. The manifold variety of ways modern fabrics can be manipulated and adapted to specific uses is the best evidence of the ability of polymer technology to create "tailor made" products.

20-4 Elastomers. Most, if not all, qualities of the polymeric *fibers* can be reproduced in metallic and ceramic fibers. However, the ease with which rubbers can be stretched elastically to as much as 800 percent of their original length is unique, and it is this high elasticity that constitutes the hallmark of an important class of polymers called *elastomers.* Yet when heated beyond say 200°C they behave like viscous or visco-elastic bodies. In other words, the rubbery behavior of elastomers is very temperature sensitive.

Furthermore in the range of temperatures where high elasticity does occur, the dependence on temperature again is unique: elastomers contract instead of expanding with rising temperature for a given stress. All these manifestations can be accounted for by a model based on the free rotation and the ensuing coiling of links in a long chain molecule.[7]

20-5 Time Dependence. Cross-linking and Vulcanization. Native rubber is sticky and difficult to handle. The polymeric chains are unattached to each other, and there is nothing to prevent them from sliding past each other, akin to the molecules of a viscous liquid subjected to laminar flow, Section 12-1 Chapter 12. Actually the behavior of native rubber resembles more closely that of the visco-elastic substance analyzed in Section 12-9 of Chapter 12. When suddenly stretched a band made of native rubber resists the applied load as though it were perfectly elastic. On being kept stretched though it loses gradually its elasticity and undergoes total stress relaxation. The model used in Section 12-9 is too simple to fit a large molecule. In particular a single value of relaxation time $\theta = \eta/G$ cannot account for the observed behavior. Nonetheless, like the relaxation time η/G, the time decay of stress in polymers is strongly temperature dependent. Below the so-called glass temperature, T_g (see section 20-6) the segmental rotation

[7] F. Bueche, *Physical Properties of Polymers*, Interscience, N.Y., 1962.

of the polymeric links becomes virtually frozen; there is no stress relaxation, and the elastomer behaves like a rigid solid.

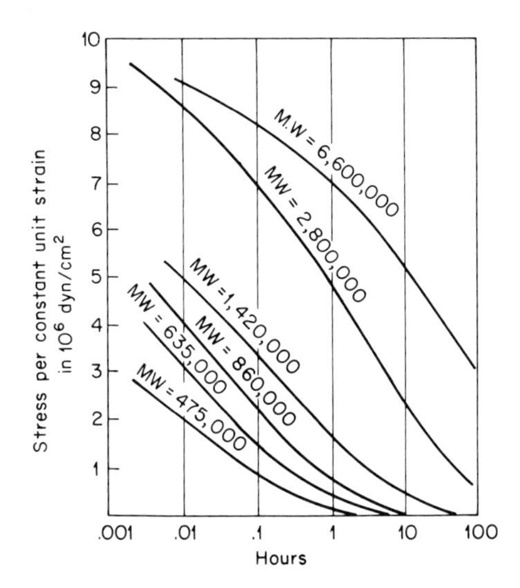

FIG. 20-2 Stress decay as a function of average molecular weight, *DP* in polyisobutelene at 30°C. (M. Mark and A. V. Tobolsky, *Physical Chemistry of High Polymeric Systems*, Interscience Publishers, Ltd., 1950, p. 340, by permission)

The time decay of stress is also dependent on the size of the molecule, on its molecular weight, as can be seen from Fig. 20-2. However, above the glass temperature, neither the size nor the entanglement of linear free molecules can make them sustain a constant stress for a long time. To support constant stress the molecules must be prevented from freely sliding past each other: they must be *cross-linked*, by bonding the *C* atoms of the backbone chains at isolated points, Fig. 20-3, and building a loose three-dimensional network. Under proper bonding conditions substantial rotational motion of the chain segments is still possible without disrupting the continuity of the network. The ensuing deformation of the elastomer will them have all the earmarks of the recoverable creep described in Section 12-11. This can be readily seen from the schematic sketch of Fig. 20-3. Under a constant force *F-F* each mesh of the network will undergo a twofold deformation:

(a) a small quasi-instantaneous (elastic) extension mainly due to C—C bond angle distortions;

(b) a large time dependent (viscous) extension due to segmental motions. Upon release of load the recovery will follow the same course in reverse: (a) a quasi-instantaneous restoration of bond angle values imposed by configurational stability, and (b) delayed re-establishment of the initial conformation of the chain links by virtue of statistical stability. The time-strain diagram resembles that of Fig. 12-6, Chapter 12. However, as with the phenomenon of stress relaxation, the recoverable creep of elastomers does not fit the simple model on which Fig. 12-6 is based. More involved models have been proposed, but their complexity defies description and analysis at this level of presentation.

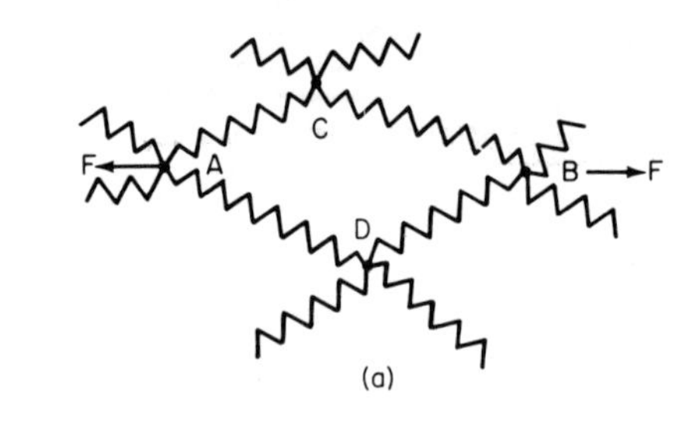

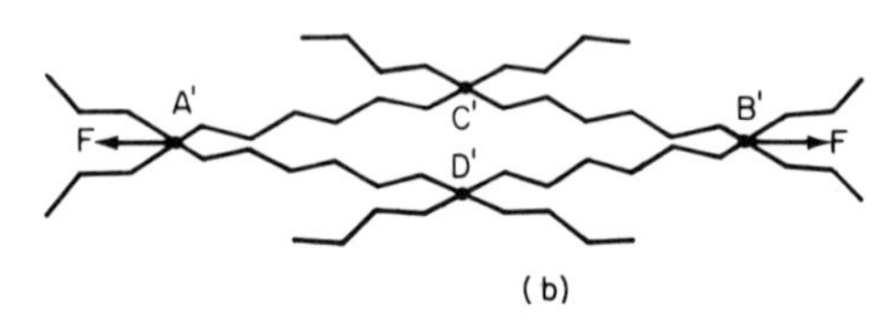

FIG. 20-3 Distortion of a cross-linked polymeric network due to creep (schematic): (a) instantaneous deformation; (b) delayed deformation

Vulcanization. An old, although by no means unique, way of building cross-links between long chain molecules, is *vulcanization*—probably the most important advance in rubber technology (made by Goodyear in 1839). Thanks to vulcanization the weak and sticky natural product is converted to the kind of rubber on which we depend so much in our daily transportation.

In the original vulcanization process, cross-linking was achieved by heating natural rubber with small amounts of sulphur (0.5–5 parts per 100 parts of rubber by weight). In the course of the ensuing reaction some sulphur molecules form bridges from one polymeric chain to the other in the manner schematized by Fig. 20-4, thereby tying the two molecules at isolated points. To preserve high elasticity, so valuable in rubbers, it is essential that there be only a limited number of such bridges. Increasing this number leads to a rapid loss of not only ductility but also strength, the latter due to the incidence of brittleness and crack formation, Fig. 20-5 (cf. Chapter 8).

Carbon Black. Even though capable of sustaining stress, vulcanized rubber is not particularly abrasion resistant, an essential quality in tires. Moreover, it is subject to oxidation with the ensuing loss of strength.

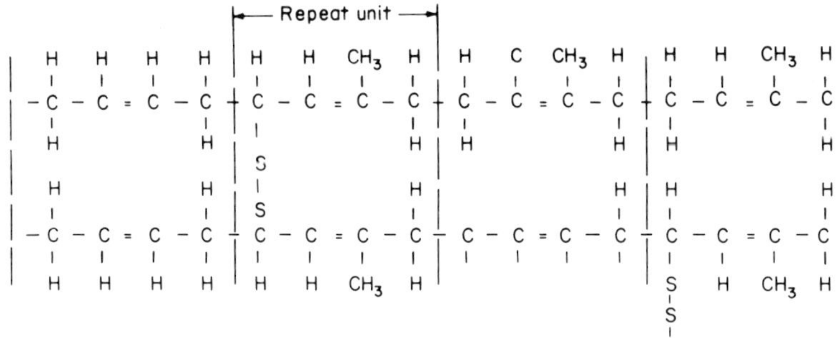

```
                  |←— Repeat unit ——→|
 H   H   H   H  | H   H  CH3  H  | H   C  CH3  H  | H   H  CH3  H
 |   |   |   |  | |   |   |   |  | |   |   |   |  | |   |   |   |
-C - C = C - C  + C - C = C - C  + C - C = C - C  + C - C = C - C
 |           |    |           |    |           |    |           |
 H           H    |           H    H           H    H           H
                  S
 H           H    |           H                H    H           H
 |           |    S           |                |    |           |
-C - C = C - C  + C - C = C - C  + C - C = C - C  + C - C = C - C
 |   |   |   |    |   |   |   |    |   |   |   |    |   |   |   |
 H   H   H   H    H   H  CH3  H                     S   H  CH3  H
                                                    |
                                                    S
                                                    |
```

FIG. 20-4 Crosslinking of molecules of natural rubber by vulcanization

Both shortcomings can be materially improved by incorporating finely divided carbon into the body—the so-called *carbon black*, obtained by decomposition of hydrocarbons. Apparently more than simple lubrication is involved in this process, since concomitant with the resistance to wear and abrasion, the tensile strength of natural rubber also substantially increases with the incorporation of moderate amounts (up to 20 percent in volume) of carbon black.

20-6 Glassy Transition. Regardless of their atomic configuration and molecular conformation all linear polymers lose their rigidity above a certain temperature and manifest a more or less rubbery behavior. Conversely, below this temperature even elastomers become rigid and brittle like glass. From the point of view of molecular conformation of the repeat units, the

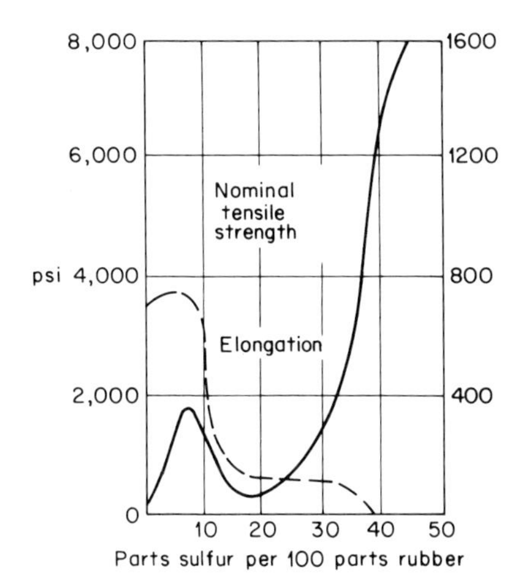

FIG. 20-5 Effect of degree of vulcanization on mechanical properties of rubber (Billmeyer, Jr., F. W., *Textbook of Polymer Science*, Interscience, 1962, p. 538, by permission)

glassy state sets in when the probability of overcoming rotational barriers by thermal agitation becomes so negligible as to practically exclude rotation. Despite its statistical character, this condition occurs at a rather well-defined temperature, T_g for a given polymer. The reason is that even though loss of rotational freedom is statistically distributed among the molecules, the molecule which momentarily loses its freedom of rotation impedes the rotation of the neighbors. As a result the whole polymer manifests a rather sudden incidence of rigidity and brittleness. The same kind of cooperation exists when the rotational freedom of the molecule is restored on heating, and it accounts for an equally sudden appearance of rubber elasticity at the temperature T_g. Below this temperature failing to induce deformation by rotation and uncoiling of links, the external force now is opposed by the much greater resistance offered by the C—C bonds between the repeat units. This resistance causes the polymer to behave like a rigid body endowed with a modulus of elasticity of the order of 10^{11} dynes/square centimeter (see Section 6-5, Chapter 6). Since the C—C bond of the polymeric backbone is little influenced by either the degree of crystallinity of the molecule or the nature of side groups, all polymers possess about the same modulus of elasticity below their *glassy* temperature T_g—a fact evidenced in Fig. 20-6 by the convergence of all curves toward a common upper limit. Above the glassy temperature, there is a marked decrease of the modulus of elasticity due to incipient rotational freedom. Because of the ensuing visco-elastic behavior, the trends become time dependent and so do the elastic moduli (see Section 12-11, Chapter 12). In Fig. 20-6 the degree of crystallinity and cross-linking appear as governing factors for the trends observed. Other factors principally affect the location of the glass temperature, T_g. We shall single out the degree of polymerization, *DP*, and the structure of the monomer.

A higher degree of polymerization entails a higher glass temperature. To see this in a qualitative way consider the role of terminal links, or ends, of a long chain molecule. Being restrained on one side only, these links possess a greater degree of freedom than the intermediate links. They can therefore be

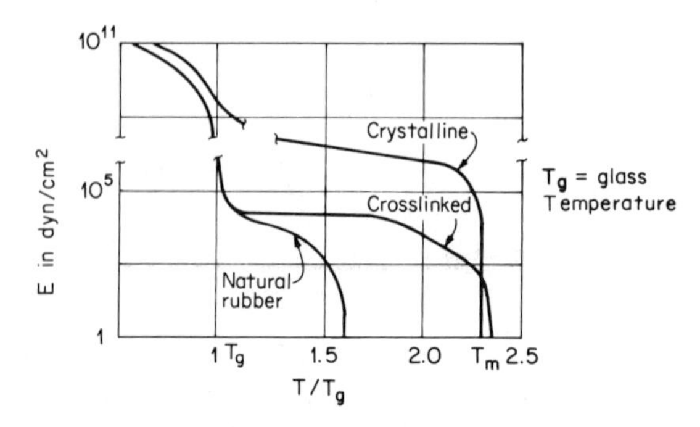

FIG. 20-6 Effect of relative temperature on modulus of elasticity (schematic)

visualized as initiating the glass-rubber transition process. To spread the process to the intermediate links, additional thermal energy, through increase of temperature, must be provided. Longer molecules have a smaller proportion of terminal links, and hence larger amounts of extra energy per link, and higher temperatures must be attained for the rubber-glass transition. The glass temperature levels off at very high molecular weights, as does the melting point, presumably because chain folding somehow restricts the chain length.

The structure of the monomer affects T_g by the nature of the side groups, by their number and bulkiness. Thus, in the relatively bulky polystyrene, rotation of links already ceases at 70°C (or higher), whereas the same result in the relatively smooth polybutadiene cannot be achieved until the temperature has been lowered to −85°C. By and large the melting point, when it exists, follows the same trend. From the practical point of view, low values of T_g are desirable in elastomers and high values of T_g are sought in those plastics (Section 20-7) whose main function is to provide three-dimensional rigidity.

20-7 Plastics. In current parlance, the word plastics has come to signify almost all products manufactured from or with polymeric materials, including adhesives and coatings. Here we specifically consider a category of plastics that differ from fibers and elastomers by their ability to be molded or otherwise processed into solid articles of any desired shape.

Not only do these articles constitute a major portion of products manufactured by the plastic industry[8] but they also represent a sizable fraction of parts utilized in the automotive, electrical appliance, and communication (telephone, radio, TV) industries. Nor is their share in the fabrication of household goods to be minimized. Plastics possess a combination of properties which makes them preferable to other materials. They are less brittle than glass, yet they can be made equally transparent and smooth, thereby finding extensive application in photography where they successfully replace glass plates. Their high dielectric strength (Section 13-13, Chapter 13) singles them out for electric insulation, as does their chemical inertness for corrosion resistance. The ease with which they can be mass-produced contributes greatly to their popularity as wrappers and bags. Yet it is in the creation of plastics, such as "Teflon," with properties unmatched by any other material, that plastic technology holds out the greatest promises for the future.

[8] Plastics, as understood here, can be estimated to represent more than 50 percent of all goods manufactured from polymeric materials (ref., H. R. Simonds and J. M. Church, *A Concise Guide to Plastics*, Reinhold, New York, 1963). Their total production for 1967 amounted to 14.47 billion pounds according to *The Western Plastics*, Part II, January 1968.

Thermosetting and Thermoplastic Materials. In the course of fabrication the plastics can solidify in a twofold manner:

1. The long chain molecules can develop covalent bridges through their branch chains or cross-links and form a continuous three-dimensional network, not unlike glasses, Chapter 19, Section 19-6.
2. They can remain essentially linear and unattached to each other.

The first mode of solidification produces materials that cannot be resoftened by raising the temperature. Rather, the three-dimensional network is broken up, and the original structure cannot be re-established on cooling. Presumably because of this irreversibility these materials are called *thermosetting* materials.

In contrast, the second mode of solidification gives rise to materials that can be resoftened and remolded by application of heat and pressure. They preserve their plasticity at high temperature. Hence they are named *thermoplastic* materials.

Both kinds of plastics find wide industrial and practical applications. As a rule thermosetting materials are stronger and harder. Typical thermosetting materials are phenolic resins, amino resins and epoxy resins. Among thermoplastic materials we can cite polyethylene, polystyrene, methyl methacrylite ("Plexiglass,"), and vinylidene chlorides.

20-8 Composite Materials. That a combination of materials can produce properties unattainable in each of them separately, has been pointed out previously in connection with alloys and ceramics. Polymers are no exception to the rule, and Nature has provided striking examples of its application. In wood vessels made of flexible cellulose fibers are cemented together by lignin, a harder polymeric material. The whole acquires rigidity and increase of strength in axial direction, thereby conferring to the composite a characteristic directionality of properties known as orthotropy.

A similar situation is encountered in the structure of bone. Here a strong but brittle precipitate containing tiny crystals of hydroxide apatite (calcium fluor or chlorine phosphate) is embedded in a softer but tougher matrix of collagen, a polymeric substance consisting mainly of polypeptide. Like wood, the bone has a fibrous structure which accounts for the directionality of its mechanical properties.

Bone is an example of a composite in which the more brittle component is also the more rigid, i.e., possesses a higher modulus of elasticity. If the two components deform as a unit, the same amount of strain causes the more rigid component to take on a higher stress, in accordance with Hooke's law. If, moreover, the harder component is made up of many fibers, an accidental fracture of one of them puts locally a somewhat higher stress on the rest without greatly affecting the matrix. Consequently a crack initiated by the fracture of the fiber fails to propagate in the surrounding matrix for want of the necessary stress level. Therein lies the crack arresting ability of a polymeric matrix, bonding thin high-strength ceramic fibers.

Coupled with this ability is also the capability of an adhering matrix to smooth out local stress concentration caused in an embedded bundle of fibers by the fracture of one of them. To see this more clearly consider Fig. 20-7. The pull exerted on the two parts of the broken fiber is now causing shearing strains between the matrix and the end portions of each part. However the matrix adheres to the fiber over the whole length. Consequently the shearing strain gradually fades and the fiber continues to support the pull at some distance away from the break. Since the breaks are statistically distributed among the fibers, the diminution of strength at a given section due to the failure of a fiber is also statistically accounted for. Put another way, each section is statistically subjected to the same stress.

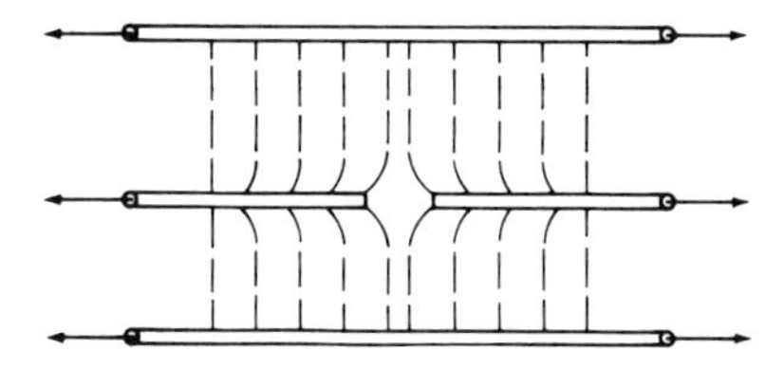

FIG. 20-7 Crack arresting action of a resin matrix in a composite material

The ensuing tensile strength, even though smaller than the fracture stress of a single fiber, is much larger than the (combined) strength of the loose bundle, attaining as much as 80 percent of the fracture stress of a single fiber.[9]

The above results specifically refer to glass fibers impregnated with epoxy resins (polymers containing a characteristic epoxide group C—C (bridged by O) in the repeat unit). However considerations of Chapter 8 suggest that replacement of glass fiber by ceramic filaments of much higher modulus of elasticity is apt to greatly improve the resistance of the *composite*. Moreover it will also increase its rigidity—an essential prerequisite for use in compression because of inherent danger of buckling. Therein lies the great promise of composite materials for the future.

20-9 Summary. Almost all substances of the vegetable and animal kingdom—wood, wool, bone, proteins—and a goodly number of man-made materials—"Bakelite," neoprene, nylon, "Teflon," silicones—belong to the category of *polymers*. These are aggregates of long chain molecules, often containing 10,000 repeat units and more, built from simpler molecules,

[9] R. B. McKee, Jr., and G. Sines, "Statistical model of the Tensile Fracture of Parallel Fiber Composite," *A.S.M.E. Annual Meeting, Rubbers and Plastics*, Paper 68-WA/RP-7, New York, 1968.

monomers, by linking the latter together. In *addition polymerization* the links are established by splitting a double bond C=C into a single bond and two unpaired electrons ·C—C·. To set the process going an *initiator* must be added. The process is terminated by either *combining* (coupling) two chains or by a reaction called *disproportionation*.

In *condensation polymerization* bonds are established through direct linking of reactive groups in adjacent monomers with elimination of a small molecule (water) in the process.

The range and variety of properties can be increased by linking dissimilar monomers in *copolymerization*.

Partial crystallinity is sought in fibers, because the ensuing order and stability increases their strength and modulus of elasticity. A typical example is nylon. The various treatments which nylon and other fibers can undergo account for the "tailor-made" characteristics of many industrial fabrics.

At variance with fibers amorphous state is needed in elastomers to endow them with the high elasticity characteristic of rubber.

To sustain a load for a sufficient length of time (i.e., to prevent total stress relaxation) natural rubber is vulcanized: its long chain molecules are *cross-linked* at intervals with sulphur atoms. In addition *carbon black* must be incorporated to prevent excessive wear and oxidation on rubbing, this is particularly important in tires.

All polymers, even elastomers, become rigid and brittle below the glassy transition temperature T_g, at which rotational motion is frozen. The glassy temperature is affected by the degree of crystallinity, cross-linking, *DP* (degree of polymerization) and nature and number of the side groups (substituents of H).

In contrast to fibers and elastomers, polymers referred to here as *plastics* can be plastically deformed and shaped, as well as molded, in the course of solidification by application of heat and pressure. Depending on whether in this process the long chain molecules become interconnected by cross-links and side chains or remain largely unattached to each other, we distinguish between *thermosetting* and *thermoplastic* materials. Unlike the former, the latter can be resoftened and reshaped by a renewed application of heat and pressure.

From the engineering point of view it appears more promising to use plastics as a binder for high strength but brittle ceramic fibers. The *composite* material made of a bundle of such fibers imbedded in the plastic, e.g., in epoxy resin, has a much higher strength than the loose bundle and a much greater rigidity than any plastic material conceivably can have.

References

Introductory

1. K. F. O'Driscoll, *The Nature and Chemistry of High Polymers*, Reinhold, New York, 1964.

2. M. Gordon, *High Polymers*, Iliffe, London, 1963.
3. G. C. East and D. Margerison, *Introduction to Polymer Chemistry*, Pergamon, London, 1967.
4. Sir Harry Melville, *Big Molecules*, Bell & Sons, London, 1950.

Advanced

5. Paul J. Flory, *Principles of Polymer Chemistry*, Cornell U.P., New York, 1953.
6. F. W. Billmeyer, Jr., *Textbook of Polymer Science*, Interscience, New York, 1962.
7. F. Bueche, *Physical Properties of Polymers*, Interscience, New York, 1962.

Problems

20-1 Show the steps of polymerization leading from the vinylidene chloride $CH_2{=}CCl_2$ to polyvinylidene chloride.

20-2 Show the steps of (condensation) polymerization leading from the

```
              H²
              |
monomer HO—C—C=O to the polyester
                 |
                OH
```

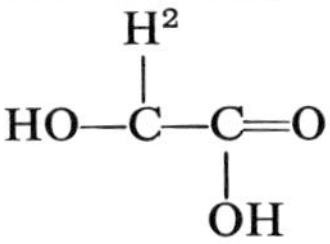

```
      H2          H2    O           H2    O           O  OH
      |           |     ‖           ‖     ‖           ‖  |
HO—C—C—O—C—C—O—C—C—O—C—C—O—C—C—O—C—CH2
      ‖     ‖           ‖     ‖           ‖
      O     O           H2    O           H2
```

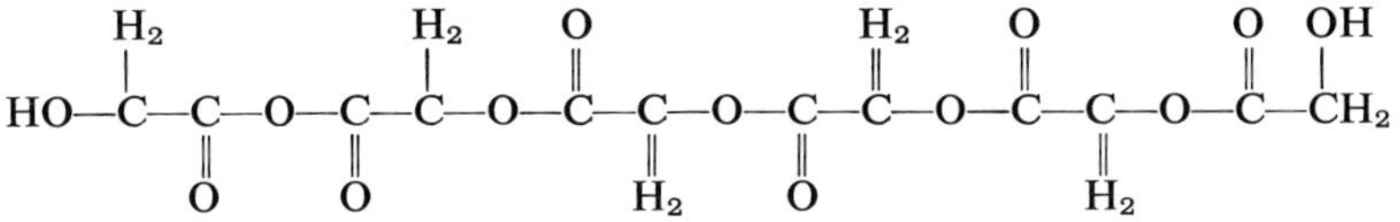

20-3 If thermal agitation were the only factor influencing copolymerization, what would be the probability of obtaining a polymer of the type $ACACAC\ldots$?

20-4 Assume the energy U per repeat unit of the polyethylene lattice can be represented by formula

$$U = \frac{K}{r}$$

where r is the C—C bond length $= 1.54$ Å.

Knowing that the energy of dissociation of the C—C bond is 83 kilogram calorie/mole, obtained the value of the bulk modulus B in the glassy state, from the relation $B = \left(\frac{\partial^2 u}{\partial v^2}\right)$, where u is the energy per unit volume.

Note: Polyethylene builds an orthogonal unit cell having the dimensions $7.41 \times 4.94 \times 2.55$ Å^3 and containing four CH_2 repeat units.

20-5 Assuming that the stress applied to a noncross-linked elastomer relaxes to half its value in one hour, compute the coefficient of viscosity η on the assumption that the elastomer behaves like a Newtonian liquid. (See Chapter 12.) Assume a modulus of elasticity of 10^5 dynes/square centimeter.

20-6 The probability dP of finding the end of a glass fiber at a distance α from its origin is taken to be

$$dP = \frac{1}{b\sqrt{\pi}}\, e^{-x^2/\alpha^2 dx}$$

where b is the standard deviation.

Assuming fibers of length $3b$ and strength f obtain the most probable fractional loss of strength per fiber.

21/ THE EFFECT OF ENVIRONMENT ON MATERIALS

21-1 Introduction to Corrosion. Corrosion refers to the oxidation of a metal in the presence of water or another liquid electrolyte. The liquid is important in that it provides a path for the ion transfer associated with the chemical reaction while an electron current flows through the material being corroded. For example, if we consider the formation of $Fe(OH)_2$ we can write

$$\begin{aligned} &\text{anode } Fe \rightarrow Fe^{++} + 2e \\ &\text{cathode } 2H_2O \rightarrow 2H^+ + 2OH^- \\ &2H^+ + 2e \rightarrow H_2 \end{aligned} \tag{21-1}$$

with the implication that the Fe^{++} cations or the OH^- anions or both diffuse through the liquid from the region where they are formed to some other place where they combine to form the ferrous hydroxide. In the iron there is a corresponding electron current from the anodic to the cathodic regions. Since corrosion involves an electron flow, nonconductors such as polymers cannot corrode although they can oxidize as will be discussed later.

The requirement of a liquid electrolyte does not necessarily mean that corrosion can take place only on materials immersed in an electrolyte. For example, there may be sufficient water vapor in the atmosphere to form thin layers of adsorbed moisture on exposed surfaces. In addition, there are a variety of contaminants in the atmosphere than can cause such layers to become effective electrolytes. With the exception of gold, metals are thermodynamically unstable in their usual service environments. That is, the free energy of the metal plus environment is decreased if the metal is oxidized. The only reason that metallic materials are suitable for engineering use is that under appropriate conditions, surface films form which slow down the oxidation reaction.

Primarily we are concerned about corrosion because it is a process which often limits the service life of a structure or component, or conversely, in order to obtain a reasonable service life we may have to utilize more expensive materials or special protective measures. Typical corrosion rates for a variety of materials in various environments are shown in Table 21-1. The values listed there give the average rate of removal of material from the surface but quite often the attack is nonuniform—pitting may occur under some conditions which will lead to a much shorter useful life. Also the effect of corrosion processes on mechanical properties of metallic materials may be quite pronounced. Drastic reductions in fatigue strength, toughness, or tensile strength may occur in environments that cause only very modest corrosion rates.

In order to be able to make rational decisions regarding the importance of corrosion, it is necessary to have a basic understanding of the mechanisms by which it occurs. Although corrosion is generally an undesirable process, there are also commercial processes which utilize corrosion in a beneficial manner. Electrolytic plating, etching to form printing plates or printed circuits, and electrochemical machining are all examples where advantage is taken of the chemical reactions involved in corrosion.

21-2 Standard Electrode Potentials. In order to understand how corrosion occurs it is convenient to review the concept of standard electrode potentials. Consider what happens when a piece of metal is immersed in pure water. There is a tendency for metal ions to leave the metal and enter into solution. Since the metal ions carry a positive charge, as a result of their dissolution, the metal becomes negatively charged with respect to the solution. Even at very low solute concentrations, the solution tendency is overcome by the electrostatic attraction between the positive ions and the metal, so that an equilibrium ion concentration is established in the water.

Suppose now a second kind of metal is immersed in the water. It too will very slightly dissolve until an equilibrium ion concentration is reached. In general however, different metals have different solution tendencies so that different potentials with respect to the solution are developed on each metal. These potentials cannot be measured separately, but the potential difference between the two electrodes can be measured by a potentiometer.[1] The metal with the greater solution tendency will have lost more ions and will therefore be the negative electrode.

Since potentials can only be measured between electrodes, the hydrogen electrode is chosen as a standard or reference electrode. This electrode consists of an inert metal (usually platinum) over which is bubbled hydrogen gas at 1 atmosphere (see Fig. 21.1). By definition, in a solution containing a 1 molar concentration of H^+ ion the single electrode potential E^o for the reaction

$$H_2 \rightarrow 2H^+ + 2e \quad E^o = 0 \tag{21-2}$$

is taken as zero.[2] With respect to this electrode, the oxidation potentials of the other metals at 25°C are listed in the Electromotive Series shown in

[1] Because of the internal impedance of the cell, the expected emf will only be measured when there is no current flowing so that generally a potentiometric measurement is required.

[2] Actually the solution should have unit activity of the hydrogen ion but we will assume that this corresponds to a one molar solution.

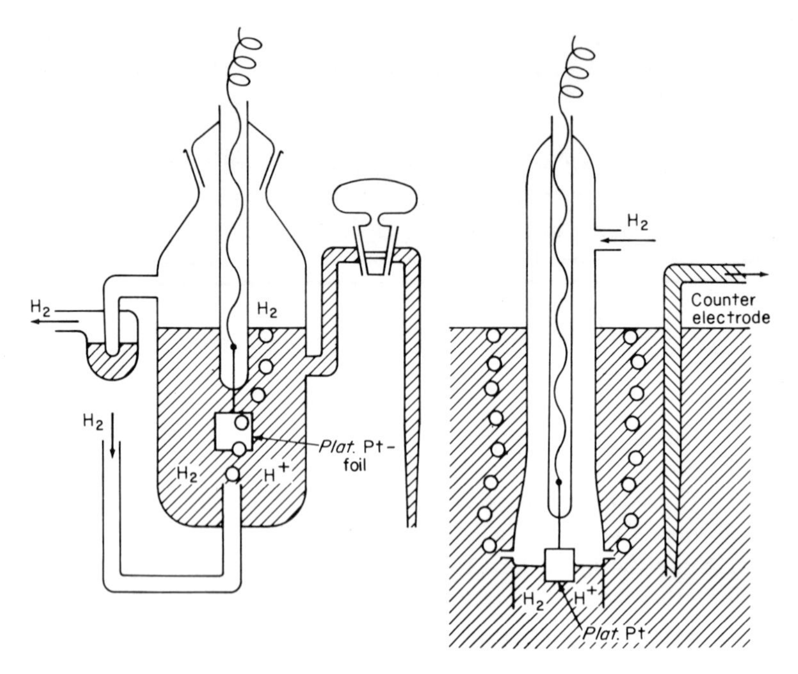

FIG. 21-1 Schematic diagram showing two possible constructions of a hydrogen electrode. In both cases the electrode is designed to prevent mixing of the solution surrounding the hydrogen electrode with that surrounding the other electrode making up the cell. (From D. Veter, *Electrochemical Kinetics*, Springer, New York, 1967, by permission)

Table II. For example, for $Cu \rightarrow Cu^{++} + 2e$, $E^o = 0.337$ volts. This means that the emf for the cell shown in Fig. 21-2 will be 0.337 volts with the hydrogen electrode negative.

As has already been mentioned, at equilibrium, the solution tendency of a metal is just balanced by electrostatic attraction forces. The solution tendency of a metal is affected, however, by the presence of similar metallic ions already in solution. If a copper bar is immersed in a concentrated solution of Cu_2Cl fewer additional ions will go into solution than if the bar were immersed in pure water. Therefore, the potential difference observed between dissimilar metals immersed in a solution depends on the nature and concentration of the ions already in solution and the standard oxidation potentials are determined using solution which are one molar in the ions of the electrode.

Returning to Fig. 21-2 there are several features worth noting. Some method is required to prevent copper ions from coming directly in contact with the hydrogen electrode if the correct cell potential is to be measured. Otherwise the reaction $C^{++} + 2e \rightarrow Cu$ could occur directly on the hydrogen electrode rather than at the copper electrode. Then there would be no tendency for electron flow in the external circuit and thus no cell voltage

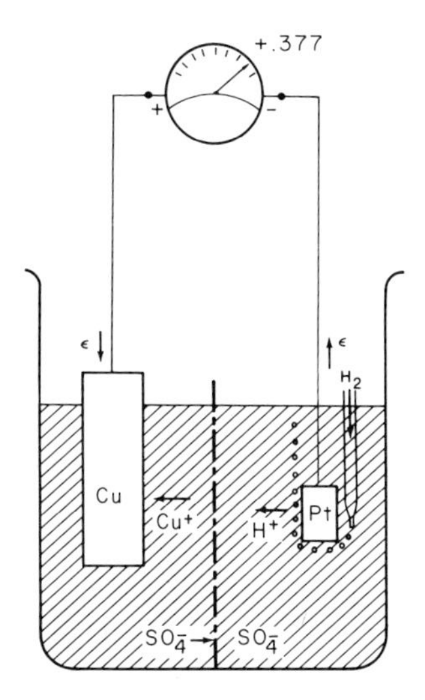

FIG. 21-2 Schematic diagram of an electrochemical cell containing a copper electrode and a hydrogen electrode each surrounded by an electrolyte 1 molar in the corresponding ions

indicated. Either a semipermeable diaphram or an appropriate cell geometry as in Fig. 21-1 can be used to prevent convection of copper ion. Copper has a lower solution tendency than hydrogen so the copper electrode is the cathode and is positive (reduction occurs here and electrons are taken from the external circuit).

The standard oxidation potential for iron is -0.44 volts. This means that since iron is above hydrogen in the electromotive series, if the copper electrode of Fig. 21-2 were replaced with an iron bar and the cupric ion in solution by ferrous ion, the iron electrode would be the anode and would tend to dissolve or corrode. This illustrates the principle that corrosion always takes place at the anode which supplies electrons to the external circuit and is the negative electrode during corrosion.

The cell voltage is independent of the actual metal used for the hydrogen electrode as long as the metal is inert (does not enter into the chemical reaction). In this case since we are talking about a standard hydrogen electrode, the solution surrounding it is a concentrated acid and the choice of metals is limited. In general, however, if iron is in electrical contact in an acid solution with a metal which is below it in the electromotive series, we would expect the iron to corrode and hydrogen gas to be formed at the cathode. Note that if the surface area of the anodic regions is small compared to the cathodic portion, the entire corrosion reaction is concentrated on a small area with the possibility of a rapid deterioration. For example, the use of steel bolts in a copper sheet could lead to rapid failure of the bolts while the reverse situation, copper bolts in a steel sheet, might give quite satisfactory service. Even if no dissimilar metal were present, the iron itself is not perfectly homogeneous so that the regions of the bar with slightly greater solution tendency would be anodic and corrode. For example, in steel, carbides may be cathodic and ferrite anodic. Even in single phase metals there are invariably local differences in composition, work-hardening, surface conditions, temperature, or adjacent solution concentration which cause local anodic regions to develop.

If a cell consisting of iron and copper electrodes is made as shown in Fig. 21-3, the iron electrode has the greater solution tendency so that it will be anodic and corrode if a current is allowed to flow in the external circuit. The cathode reaction at the copper electrode could either involve the formation of hydrogen gas or the plating out of metallic copper. Since the latter reaction gives the greater cell emf it is more likely. In this case the cell emf is calculated from the equations.

$$\begin{array}{ll} \text{Anode Fe} \rightarrow \text{Fe}^{++} + 2e & -E^o = 0.440 \text{ v} \\ \text{Cathode Cu}^{++} + 2e \rightarrow \text{Cu} & E^o = 0.337 \text{ v} \\ \hline & E_T = 0.777 \text{ v} \end{array}$$

If the value of $E_T = E^o$ (cathode) $- E^o$ (anode) is positive, then the cathode and anode have been properly chosen. If E_T is negative, the reactions and the polarities are actually reversed. In the above example, the choice is obvious; however, when we consider the effect of concentration, it is not always obvious initially which electrode is the anode.

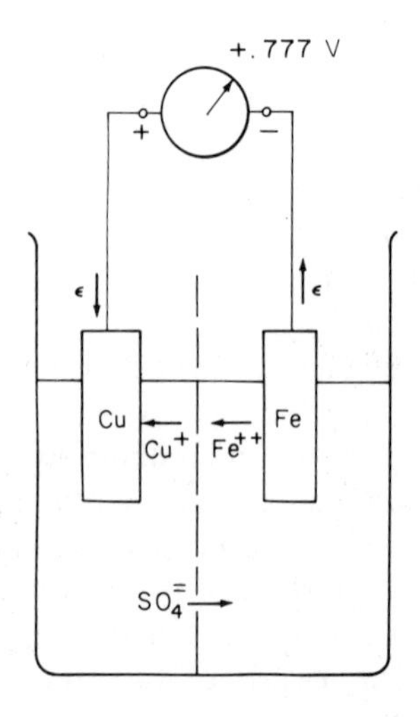

FIG. 21-3 Iron-Copper Corrosion Cell. If the electrodes are surrounded by solutions one molar in the corresponding metal ions, the cell emf is 0.777 v. On closing the external circuit a current will flow from the copper to the iron, and the iron will corrode

The magnitude of the cell emf is important for two reasons in corrosion considerations. First of all, if an electrochemical cell exists so that a particular metallic material is anodic then it can be expected that corrosion may occur. Secondly, in a general way, the larger the magnitude of the cell emf, the greater the corrosion rate. It should be appreciated, however, that there are many important exceptions to this latter statement.

21-3 The Effect of Concentration. Usually we deal with solutions that are not 1 molar and so it is important to determine what effect solution concentration has on cell potential. In general the more concentrated the solution is in the ions produced by anodic oxidation, the less will be the solution tendency of the ions and the more positive the single electrode potential. If the cell emf is reduced to zero because of this effect, no current will flow when electrical contact is made between electrodes and corrosion will not occur.

Consider a single electrode oxidation reaction of the type

$$M \rightarrow M^{n+} + ne$$

Associated with this reaction is a free energy change. If this single electrode is operated under standard conditions and is connected to a standard hydrogen electrode, the resulting free energy increase per mole of ions formed is ΔG^o. If the ions are formed in a solution that is not 1 molar, the free energy change differs from the standard value. This change occurs for the same reasons that the free energy of mixing of a crystal or gas depends on concentration. It can be shown that for dilute solutions[3]

$$\Delta G_A = \Delta G_A{}^0 + RT \ln C_A \qquad (21\text{-}3)$$

where C_A is the concentration of the anode ions in solution (in molar units) and R is the gas constant. Suppose that we define a thermodynamic system to be an electrochemical cell consisting of the anode, the surrounding solution, a standard hydrogen electrode and the external electrical circuit. In the external circuit there is a very large capacitor for storing electrical energy as shown in Fig. 21-4. If the solution process occurs reversibly, there is no free energy

[3] The reasoning involved is, very briefly, for a perfect gas, the work done during an isothermal expansion from pressure P_1 to pressure P_2 is $-RT \ln (P_2/P_1)$ and the corresponding free energy change of the gas is $RT \ln (P_2/P_1)$. If we take the free energy of the gas as G_A at 1 atmosphere, it follows that at some other pressure

$$G = G^0 + RT \ln P$$

For a mixture of perfect gases at a total pressure of 1 atmosphere, the partial pressure of each gas is equal to its concentration so

$$G_A = G_A{}^0 + RT \ln C_A$$

In many respects dilute solutions of ions in water are similar to perfect gases, and we can write a similar equation for the free energy of the solute where we now take as the standard state a concentration of 1 molar. An ion, on going from the metal to a solution, has an additional free energy change $\Delta G_A{}^0$ due to its change in state, so Eq. (21-3) results.

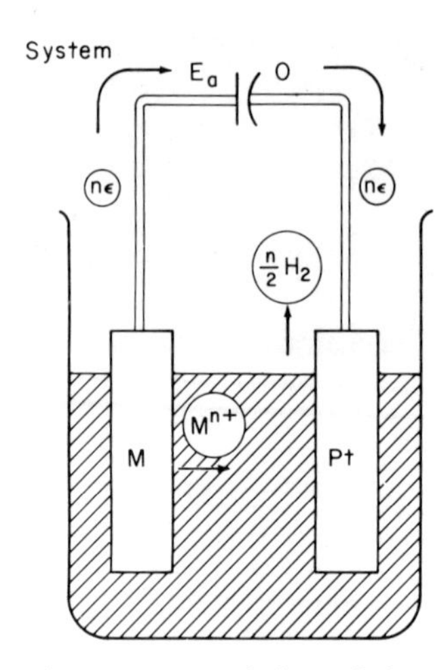

FIG. 21-4 A thermodynamic system consisting of the cell shown above with a capacitor connected between the electrodes. The cell electrolyte has a concentration of metal ions around the metal anode, the cathode is a standard hydrogen electrode. When one additional metal ion goes into solution there is a change in the chemical free energy of the system equal to $\Delta G_0/n + kT \ln C_A$ and a corresponding change in the electrical energy of the capacitor $n\epsilon E_A$

change in the system since no external work is done. Associated with one metal ion going into solution, n electrons are removed from the cathode side of the capacitor and n electrons are gained on the anode side. The electrical work done on the capacitor in this process is $-nE_Ae$ per ion or $-nN_oeE_A$ per mole of ions where N_o is Avogadro's number. N_oe is the Faraday constant F ($F = 9.65 \times 10^4$ coulombs/mole). The electrical work done must be just equal to the chemical free energy decrease ($-\Delta G$) resulting from the anodic dissolution process. Therefore,

$$-nFE_A = -\Delta G^o - RT \ln C_A$$

but $\Delta G^o/nF = E_A{}^o$ so

$$E_A = E_A{}^o + \frac{RT}{nF} \ln C_A$$

In general, there may be several ions formed and several reactants as in the equation

$$aA + bB \rightarrow ne + dD + hH \tag{21-4}$$

where A, B, D and H may be elements, compounds or ions. In this case

$$E_A = E_A{}^o + \frac{RT}{nF} \ln \left[\frac{(C_D)^d(C_H)^h}{(C_A)^a(C_B)^b}\right] \tag{21-5a}$$

If A, B, D or H are pure elements or compounds, their concentration as a solid is unity. Also the concentration of water may be taken as unity. For gases, the concentration may be taken equal to the partial pressure of the gas in the surrounding atmosphere.[3] In order that E_A be in volts it is necessary that R be in joules/°K mole. Eq. (21-5a) is known as the Nernst equation. Converting to base 10 and evaluating at 25°C we have

$$E_A = E_A{}^o + \frac{0.059}{n} \log \frac{(C_D)^d (C_F)^f}{(C_A)^a (C_B)^b} \qquad (21\text{-}5b)$$

A similar equation can be written for the cathode reaction taking care to write the reaction in the same form as Eq. (21-4) with the electrons on the right hand side.

21-4 Corrosion of Metals in Acid Solutions. As an example of the application of the Nernst equation, suppose that an iron piece is immersed in water at 25°C and we wish to know if corrosion will take place. Assume that the reactions at the anodic and cathodic regions are

$$\text{Anode} \quad Fe \rightarrow Fe^{++} + 2e \qquad E_A{}^o = -0.440$$

$$\text{Cathode} \quad H_2 \rightarrow 2e + 2H^+ \qquad E_C{}^o = 0$$

and from (21-5b) we can write

$$E_A = E_A{}^o + (0.059/2) \log C_{Fe^{++}} \text{ anode potential}$$

$$E_C = 0 + (0.059/2) \log (C_{H^+}{}^2/P_{H_2}) \text{ cathode potential.}$$

In the above equation P_{H_2} is the gas pressure in a bubble of hydrogen evolved at the cathode which is normally 1 atmosphere. The values of $C_{Fe^{++}}$ and C_{H^+} can be determined from the following considerations. The maximum concentration of the Fe^{++} ion in otherwise pure water is limited by the low solubility of the corrosion product $Fe(OH)_2$ (1.5×10^{-3} gram/liter or 1.67×10^{-5} Mole). This value is probably a good approximation to the ferrous ion concentration at the anode. The hydrogen ion concentration is determined from the relation $C_{H^+} \times C_{OH^-} = 10^{-14}$. For $Fe(OH)_2$ in solution, the hydroxyl ion concentration is twice the ferrous ion concentration so

$$C_{H^+} = 10^{-14}/(2 \times 1.67 \times 10^{-5}) = 3 \times 10^{-10}$$

Substituting appropriate values we find $E_A = -0.581$ volts, $E_C = -0.561$ volts, and the emf $E_2 = E_C - E_A$ 0.02 volts. Since this value is positive, the reaction proceeds as assumed and corrosion should occur. Actually the experimentally measured corrosion rate of iron in deaerated water is quite slow (less than 5×10^{-4} centimeter/year) owing partly to the very small driving voltage (0.02 volt). If the hydrogen ion concentration is increased by making the solution acidic, the corrosion rate and the cell emf increase.

Under most conditions, metals above hydrogen in the electromotive series will corrode when placed in pure water with hydrogen formed at the cathode although the corrosion rate may be very low for metals near hydrogen in the series. As a general rule metals corrode more rapidly in acidic solutions for the reasons just discussed.[4]

21-5 The Effect of Dissolved Oxygen. Water can dissolve a small but significant amount of oxygen at normal temperature and pressure. Much of the corrosion that occurs is directly related to the presence of this dissolved oxygen. In aqueous solutions containing dissolved oxygen, instead of hydrogen being formed at the cathode as discussed in the previous section, the following reaction can take place:

$$O_2 \text{ (dissolved)} + 2H_2O + 4e \rightarrow 4OH^- \quad (E_C{}^o = 0.40 \text{ v})$$

In the atmosphere, the partial pressure of O_2 is about 0.2 atmosphere so if the water is saturated with air, the partial pressure of oxygen in the water can be taken as 0.2 atmosphere also. For a neutral solution saturated with air the oxygen cathode potential is from the Nernst equation, $E_C = 0.40 - (0.059/4) \log (10^{-28}/0.2) = 0.808$ volt and the cell emf for an iron anode in equilibrium with $Fe(OH)_2$ is $E = 1.389$ volts. This value is much higher than for the corresponding cell with a hydrogen electrode so that in aerated neutral solutions it is not surprising that the corrosion is primarily due to the oxygen cathode reaction.

Figure 21-5 shows the effect of dissolved oxygen concentration on the corrosion rate. The maximum in corrosion rate indicated in this figure is due to the phenomena of passivation. At sufficiently oxidizing conditions (high cell emf) an impermeable oxide film is developed through which the metal ions must diffuse in order to react with oxygen. Because of the low solid state diffusion rates, the corrosion process is slowed down drastically when a film forms.

Because of the large oxygen cathode potential (0.808 volt) metals well below hydrogen in the electromotive series can corrode by this mechanism. For example copper and even silver can corrode in aerated water.

Under most service conditions involving corrosion, the concentration of metal ions in solution which could be involved in a cathode reaction is quite low. Therefore the sort of cathode reaction discussed in conjunction with Fig. 21-3 is quite unlikely. Instead hydrogen and oxygen cathodes account for most of the corrosion. For either of these two cathode reactions, the cell emf depends very little on the differences in the materials forming the cathode and anode areas. The cell emf may depend primarily on concentration differences in the electrolyte at the cathode and anode. For example, the oxygen cathode potential becomes more positive as the oxygen concentration is increased. Therefore, in a solution where there are variations in the oxygen

[4] Compare, for example, the corrosion rates listed in Table 21-1 for sulfuric acid and water.

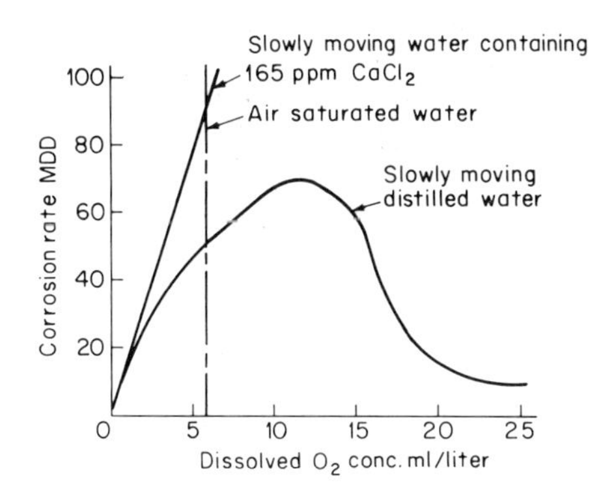

FIG. 21-5 Effect of dissolved oxygen on the corrosion rate of mild steel in slowly moving water at 25°C. [Uhlig, Tradis, and Stein, *J. Electrochemical Soc.*, **102**, 59 (1955).] A maximum in the corrosion rate for distilled water is observed because beyond a certain oxygen concentration, the corrosion rate is no longer limited by oxygen diffusion. A high oxygen concentration is developed at the anode which causes a continuous oxide film to be developed. This results in a large *IR* drop for the corrison current which must flow through it, thus drastically limiting the corrosion rate. In the presence of chloride ion, a stable film does not develop

concentration, the maximum cell emf for any given anode reaction will be obtained if the cathodes are located in regions of high oxygen concentration. Corrosion occurs at areas which are relatively deficient in oxygen as would be expected below sediment or rust deposits or under barnacles or other marine growth. Examples of various oxygen corrosion cells are shown in Fig. 21-6. This type of corrosion may very well lead to pitting since if corrosion products build up locally, the oxygen content under this porous layer will be depleted owing to difficult diffusion. This oxygen depletion will cause the breakdown of any protective oxide film and enhance further local corrosion.

The location of the cathodes could also be determined by a region of low hydroxyl ion concentration as this would cause a more positive cathode potential. In a similar manner, a hydrogen cathode reaction would be favored in a region of high hydrogen ion concentration. Therefore, in a tank containing an acid solution, one might expect corrosion to be occurring in the regions where the pH was highest.

If the electrolyte is uniform in concentration, local hydrogen or oxygen cathodes may be determined by non-homogeneities in the corroding material. In a two phase alloy, one phase will invariably be more noble than the other and thus may serve as the cathode. The cell emf is not affected by the relative position of the cathode metal in the electromotive series as it is simply serving as a vehicle for electron transfer at the cathode where hydrogen gas or hydroxyl ions are being formed.

The type of corroding material does, however, determine the anode potential and therefore affects the overall cell emf. Even small micro-

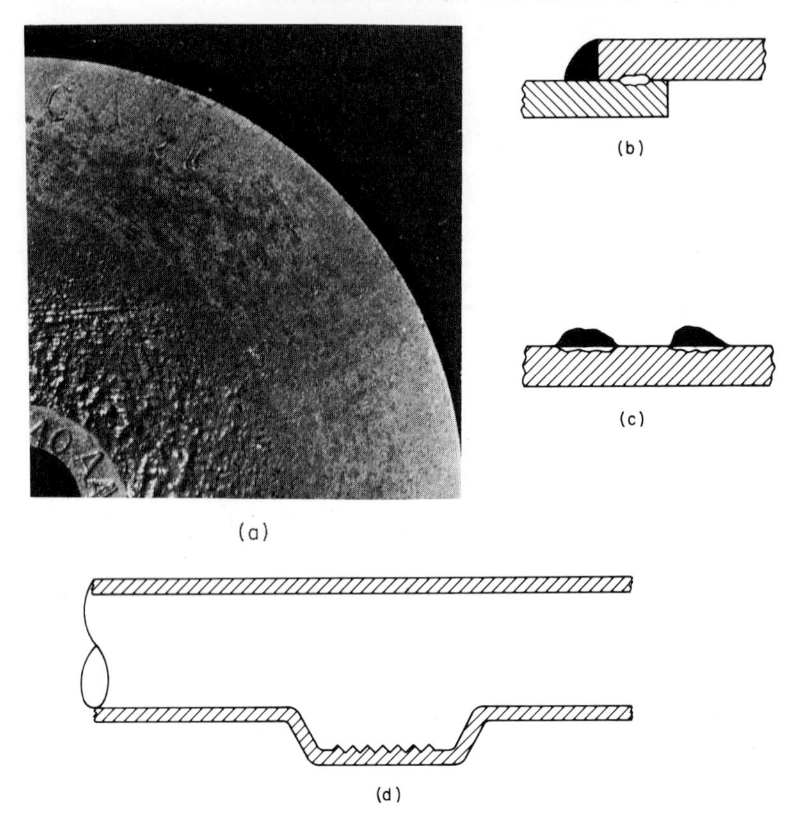

FIG. 21-6 Examples of differential aeration cells: (a) more oxygen is available to the outer faster moving portion of a rotating cast iron disk, so corrosion occurs on the center portion. (From F. L. LaQue and H. R. Copson, *Corrosion Resistance of Metals and Alloys*, second edition, Reinhold, New York, 1963, by permission); (b) corrosion occurs in the overlapped portion of a welded joint where the oxygen concentration is deficient; (c) under barnacles or sediment deposits, the oxygen concentration is reduced and corrosion occurs; (d) a blind hole in a pipe line contains stagnant solution which is depleted in oxygen and leads to pitting

structural differences in a nominally single phase material can determine the location of cathodes and anodes assuming that the position of the material on the electromotive series is such that a corrosion potential is developed against a hydrogen or oxygen cathode. Sometimes, for reasons to be considered later, corrosion may occur more rapidly if cathodes and anodes are close together even though this has no effect on cell emf. Therefore, two phase alloys may corrode more rapidly then single phase alloys, and cold worked single phase alloys may corrode more rapidly than single phase alloys.

21-6 Factors Influencing the Corrosion Rate. The rate at which a corrosion reaction takes place is directly proportional to the electric current flowing from cathode to anode. The reason for this is that for each cation going into solution at the anode or for each anion formed at the cathode there is a fixed number of electrons traveling from the anode to the cathode through the metallic external circuit. We can express the result in terms of J_C, the number of moles of cations leaving the anode per unit area per unit time or in terms of J_A, the number of moles of anions leaving the cathode per unit area per unit time.

$$J_C = I/A_A n_C F \tag{21-6a}$$

$$J_A = I/A_C n_A F \tag{21-6b}$$

where I is the current in the external circuit, A_A is the surface area of the anode and n is the number of moles of electrons transferred in the electrode reaction. Similar definitions apply for Eq. (21-6b).

In the cell shown in Fig. 21-7a a variable resistance is inserted in the external circuit connecting cathode and anode. The cell voltage can now be measured as a function of the current flowing in this circuit. Under actual service conditions the anode and cathodes cannot be physically separated from each other since they are usually both located on the same component. In this case the corrosion current cannot be directly measured. Nevertheless it is possible at least in principle to calculate the current and thus obtain a corrosion rate. By analogy with an electrical circuit containing a battery we can write as shown in Fig. 21-7b,

$$I = E/(R_l + R_A + R_C) \tag{21-7a}$$

where $R_A + R_C$ is the internal resistance of the cell and R_l is the electron resistance in the metallic circuit connecting the two electrodes. The external resistance depends on the particular materials and geometry involved in the external circuit and on possible contact resistances. In most practical situations involving corrosion, R_l is small compared to $R_A + R_C$ so that the cell can be considered almost as a short circuited battery with a negligible voltage between cathode and anode. In this case, for a given cell emf, the corrosion rate depends on $R_A + R_C$.

The cell voltage is measured between the electrodes and therefore across R_l. This voltage is from Eq. (21-7) and Fig. 21-7b.

$$V = IR_l = E\left(\frac{R_l}{R_A + R_c + R_l}\right) \tag{21-7b}$$

A corrosion current will flow through the cell unless R_l is infinite (open circuit conditions) causing V to be less than the cell emf. This decrease in voltage $(E - V)$ is referred to as the polarization of the cell and is equal to $I(R_A + R_C)$. In most cases R_A and R_C are strongly dependent on the actual operating conditions of the cell. Several factors go into determining the polarization and these are discussed below.

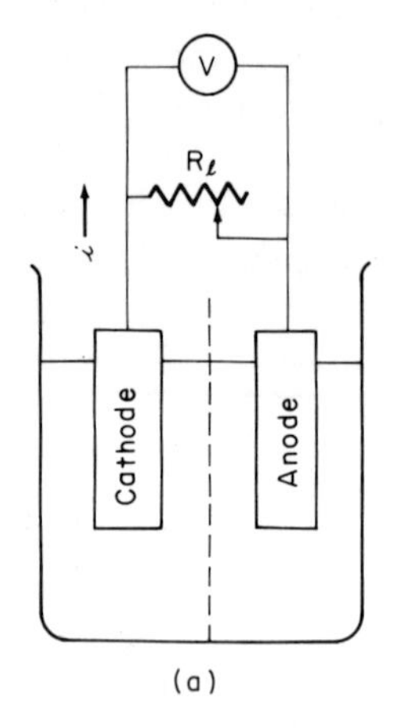

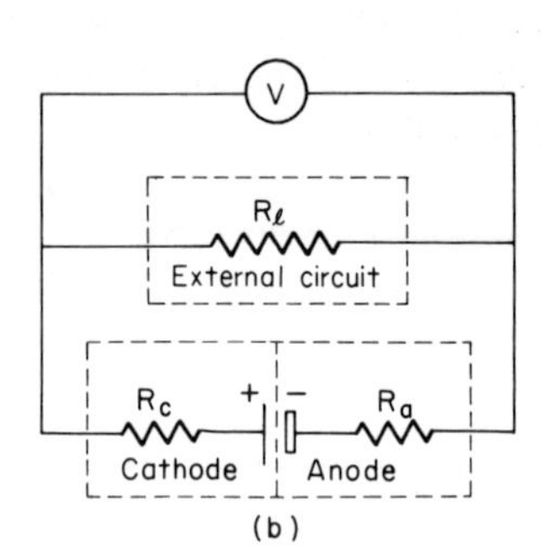

FIG. 21-7 (a) A corrosion cell with a variable external resistance R_l is shown. Depending on the magnitude of this resistance, the corrosion current can be varied over a wide range; (b) The equivalent electrical circuit of the cell shown in part A. The battery emf corresponds to the corrosion potential. The current flow is limited primarily by the cathode and anode internal impedances R_C and R_A. In addition there is the impedance R in the metallic part of the circuit

(1) *Concentration Polarization.* At the anode (in the cell of Fig. 21-2 for example) cations are produced. These ions diffuse through the electrolyte away from the anode. In a similar manner, at a hydrogen cathode, hydrogen ions diffuse to the cathode and at an oxygen cathode dissolved oxygen diffuses to the cathode and hydroxyl ion away from the cathode. In order for these diffusion fluxes to occur at a finite rate there must be a concentration gradient near the electrode. This implies that at the electrodes the ion concentrations are altered from their values in the bulk solution.

The magnitude of the change in concentration at the electrode depends on the corrosion current and the diffusivity of the ions or dissolved gases in solution. In general we can write for the diffusion rate

$$J = -D dc/dx \tag{21-8}$$

where J is related to the corrosion current by Eq. (21-6a or 21-6b), depending on the electrode. The concentration change is always in such a direction that on using the Nernst equation, the cell voltage is reduced so that some of the voltage drop at the cathode and anode can be attributed to concentration polarization.

Diffusivities are known for many ions in water (typical values at 20°C are about 1×10^{-5} square centimeters/second) so that for any given cell geometry and electrolyte, it is possible in principle using Eq. (21-8) to calculate the concentration change at the electrode as a function of the corrosion rate.

The problem is complicated by the presence of convective mixing in addition to pure diffusion. Using Eq. (21-5) the voltage change as a function of the concentration change can be obtained, and from Eq. (21-6) the voltage change as a function of corrosion current is obtained.

There are many instances where the diffusion of oxygen to the cathode is the rate controlling factor in corrosion. That is, the polarization of the cathode due to the local depletion of oxygen is almost equal to the cell emf. Thus, for example, in most instances when steel is subject to corrosion while immersed in rivers, lakes, or sea water, changes in the composition or heat-treatment of the steel have little effect on its corrosion rate. The rate is simply determined by the diffusion kinetics of the oxygen. If under such conditions a plain carbon steel screw is used in an alloy steel part, the alloy steel being more noble than carbon steel will act as the cathode and the steel screw will be the anode. Now the overall corrosion rate is limited by the rate at which oxygen can diffuse to the entire part but the corrosion is concentrated at the steel screw.

(2) *Activation Polarization.* When a single electrode is initially immersed in an electrolyte, after a short initial reaction, a dynamic equilibrium is established. Ions leave the solution and plate on the metal at precisely the same rate as ions leave the metal and go into solution. The magnitude of these two fluxes depends on the energy barrier to solution or deposition of an ion in much the same way that the diffusivity depends on an activation energy. If the potential on the electrode is altered the solution tendency is no longer exactly counterbalanced by electrostatic forces and the equilibrium is upset. One of the fluxes is increased while the other is decreased as shown in Fig. 21-8. If a cell has an emf associated with it, this implies that the open circuit potentials of the cathode and anode are different. When the electrodes are connected together through a resistance R_l which is small compared to R_A and R_C, it follows from Eq. (21-7b) that V is small. This is simply another way of saying that the anode and cathode potentials must become almost identical and therefore both are changed from their equilibrium values. This is shown schematically in Fig. 21-9 where it is seen that as the cell current increases, the two electrode potentials approach each other. In microscopic terms, this means the more each electrode potential is altered from its equilibrium (open circuit) value, the greater the effect on the energy barrier and the greater the net ion flux.

When, as shown in Fig. 21-8b, an ion goes from the electrolyte to the electrode under nonequilibrium conditions, its free energy decreases by ΔG_i and there is an associated voltage drop ΔE since $\Delta G_i = ne\Delta E$ where ne is the charge associated with the ion. It is this voltage drop ΔE that corresponds to the change in electrode voltage with current shown in Fig. 21-9. If the net flux is such that ions leave the electrode (anodic reaction) then an ion on dissolution has a lower energy and similar remarks can be made. Therefore,

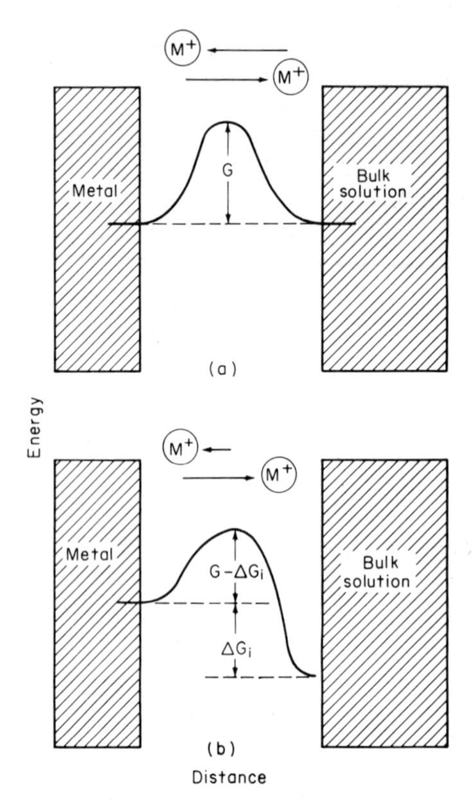

FIG. 21-8 (a) The free energy of a metal ion as a function of position, for an electrode in equilibrium with the electrolyte surrounding it. The free energy of the ion is identical in the metal and in the solution but there is a free energy barrier G on going from one state to another; (b) by increasing the potential of the metal with respect to the solution, a metal ion now has a lower free energy in the solution so more ions leave the metal than return and a net flux occurs. The magnitude of the flux depends on the magnitude of the energy barrier $G - \Delta G_i$ and on the thermal energy of the atoms

at both electrodes in a cell, in order for there to be net ion fluxes, the potential of the electrode must be altered from its equilibrium value, and we say there are overvoltages associated with the electrode reactions. The magnitude of these overvoltages depends very strongly on the particular reaction involved and the surface condition of the electrode. Fortunately, from the standpoint of preventing corrosion, the overvoltage associated with the two common cathode reactions, the hydrogen and the oxygen cathode are both quite high. Although the specific nature of the cathode material has no effect on the emf for these reactions, the material does strongly affect the activation energy for the reaction and thus the net flux for any given polarization. Platinum cathodes cause a relatively low activation energy for these reactions (platinum

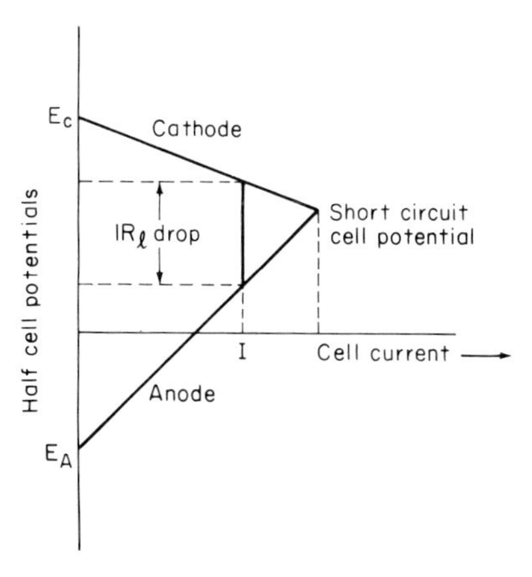

FIG. 21-9 At open circuit conditions (no corrosion) the anode and cathode are at potentials E_A and E_C respectively with respect to a hydrogen electrode. If a corrosion current exists the two voltages are displaced from their equilibrium values due to the *IR* drops at the cathode and anode. At short circuit conditions the two voltages become identical. It is this short circuit voltage which may be either positive or negative depending on the polarization characteristics of the electrodes which would normally be measured on a corroding piece of metal

is a good catalyst) and are thus used for measuring equilibrium values where polarization would lead to erroneous results. The dissolution of zinc in acid solutions is a good example of the importance of activation polarization. High purity zinc is attacked only relatively slowly while the impure or mossy zinc which contains iron and copper in dilute solid solution, dissolves quite rapidly after a short induction period. These impurities being below zinc in the emf series after being anodically dissolved, redeposit on the zinc surface and catalyze the cathode reaction since the hydrogen overvoltage is much less for these elements than for zinc. As a result, the overvoltage on the cathode regions is reduced and the corrosion rate increased as shown in Fig. 21-10.

(3) *IR Voltage Drop.* In an active corrosion cell, an ion current exists in the electrolyte between the electrodes. Just as in a metallic circuit, there must be a potential gradient for this current to exist. In this case, the potential of the solution varies between anode and cathode. As a result, the potential of an ion changes as it moves between electrodes and there is a corresponding *IR* voltage drop. In general, concentrated electrolytes have lower electrical resistivities than dilute solutions since there are more charge carriers per unit volume. The reasoning is entirely analogous to that discussed for solid conductors in a previous chapter. Usually, if the electrolyte is moderately concentrated in a solute that ionizes strongly, i.e., sea water (resistivity is about 14 ohm centimeters), the *IR* drop is quite small. The *IR* drop may

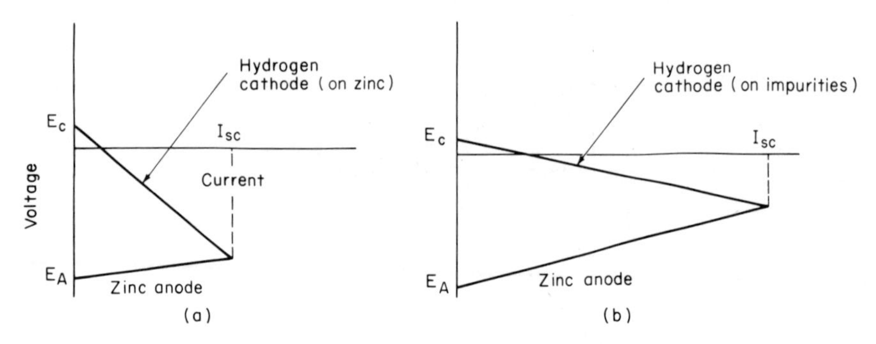

FIG. 21-10 Current voltage diagrams for the corrosion of zinc: (a) Pure zinc is corroding with a relatively low corrosion current I_{sc} since there is a large overpotential associated with the hydrogen cathode reaction on zinc; (b) once copper or iron plate out on the zinc surface, the cathode overpotential is reduced and the corrosion current I_{sc} is increased

also occur due to the formation of an insulating film on the anode. Corrosion products often have a very high electrical resistance and thus if an adherent continuous film is formed it can be quite effective in reducing further corrosion to a minimum. The corrosion resistance of active metals and alloys such as aluminum, titanium, and stainless steel is based on this phenomenon. If the service conditions are such that a film is thermodynamically stable the metal is said to be in the passive state.

21-7 Corrosion Prevention. From a knowledge of corrosion processes it is possible to develop several general methods for eliminating or minimizing corrosion. Perhaps the most obvious procedure would be to use metallic materials sufficiently noble so that under the particular service conditions encountered there would be no driving emf for corrosion. Economically, this is not a feasible solution under most conditions so other procedures must be resorted to. One possibility is to cover the exposed surface with some protective coating. It is possible to use an insulating layer or to plate the surface with a sufficiently noble metal. If such a coating is to be effective, it must be continuous or else considerable pitting could take place at pin holes. As already mentioned, some metals naturally form oxide films that inhibit further corrosion. The oxides of Al, Ti and Cr are all quite high in resistance and form continuous adherent films under appropriate conditions. This accounts for the excellent corrosion resistance of these materials or, in the case of Cr particularly, for alloys containing significant quantities of these elements. In order to extend the applicability of corrosion inhibition by film formation, metallic materials are often given chemical treatments designed to form optimum film characteristics. Aluminum, for example, is anodized which involves making it the anode in a sulfuric acid solution. The resultant oxide film is exceptionally thick and adherent and will prevent corrosion under

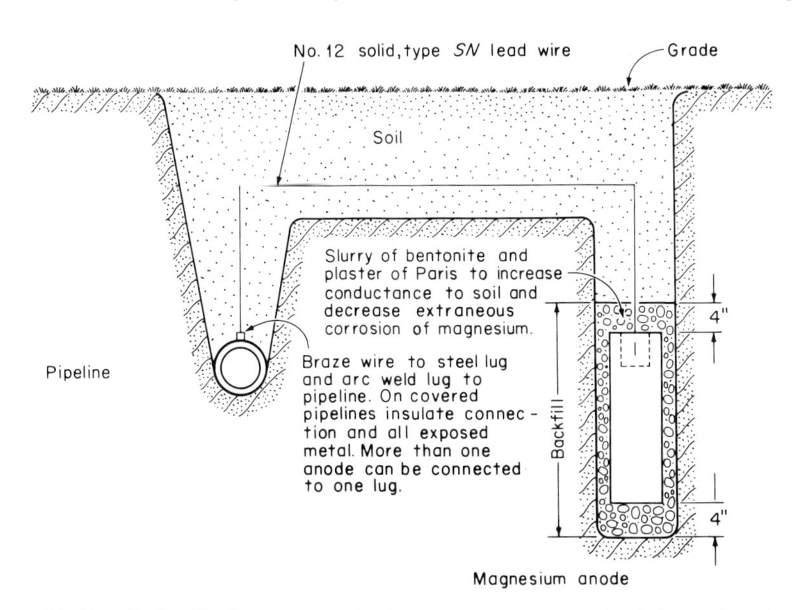

FIG. 21-11 Cathodically protected pipe employing a sacrificial anode. (From H. H. Uhlig, *Corrosion and Corrosion Control*, Wiley, New York, 1963, by permission)

conditions where a naturally occurring film is inadequate. In a similar manner zinc is often dipped in a solution containing CrO_3^+ ions as these form a protective surface film. Chemical treatments which form protective films are called passivation treatments as the surface becomes passive against further corrosion.

Instead of mechanically protecting the surface with an insulating or a noble metal layer, it is possible to utilize a procedure called cathodic protection. This involves electrically coupling the structure which is to be protected to a sacrificial anode of a more active metal, commonly zinc or magnesium. In this case, depending on the electrolyte, the entire structure acts as either a hydrogen or oxygen cathode while the active metal becomes the anode. The coupling can be accomplished by plating as in the case of galvanized steel which is plated with zinc. Galvanized steel has an advantage as compared to tin plate in that scratches or pin holes are of no consequence. On the other hand, the zinc will corrode at some finite rate and once it is gone, the steel has only a short life. Another procedure is to use separate and renewable rods of the sacrificial anode material which are then electrically connected to the structure. This procedure is often used for protection of hot water heaters, ships hulls, and buried pipe lines. (See Fig. 21-11.) Of course the cathodically protected structure and the sacrificial anode must be in an ionically conducting medium. In the case of a pipe line, corrosion is a serious problem only if the soil is wet in which case ionic conduction in the soil is possible. Actually very few long distance pipe lines would be economically feasible if it were not for cathodic protection. In order to minimize the number and corrosion rate of the anodes, the pipe is covered with a protective organic coating prior to laying. In this way the area accessible to corrosion is limited to the coating defects and the corresponding cathodic protection current required is greatly reduced. This means that the anodes can be spaced quite far apart without causing too large an *IR* voltage drop in the pipe and surrounding soil.

In order to use cathodic protection to prevent corrosion it is simply necessary to maintain the protected structure at a sufficiently negative potential with respect to the surrounding electrolyte so that anodic reactions are inhibited. This can be accomplished by the use of a sacrificial anode or by using an inert anode and a direct current power supply to maintain the necessary voltage on the structure. Since the potentials involved are on the order of 1 volt the power requirements are quite nominal.

For metals which depend on the development of oxide films for corrosion prevention, anodic protection is sometimes feasible. If these metals are in environments which are only moderately oxidizing, a continuous film may not be developed, and pitting may take place. By making such a material even more anodic (impressing a positive voltage on it) a stable continuous film is developed with a resulting low corrosion rate.

Another procedure used for corrosion prevention is to alter the solution in contact with the structure so as to minimize the corrosion effects. For example, boiler feed water may be deaerated prior to using so as to minimize the possibility of oxygen cathodes being formed in the boiler. On the other hand, a stainless steel part is more likely to show pitting attack on a stagnant solution depleted of oxygen than in a rapidly flowing electrolyte. This follows because of local breakdown of the passive film under non-oxidizing conditions, particularly if chloride ions are present.[5] For a closed cycle heat exchanger it may be feasible to add ions to the water, which will form passive films on the metal surfaces.

21-8 Conditions for Oxidation. Oxidation differs from corrosion in that it is a process which takes place without the presence of a liquid electrolyte or a metallic cathode. A clean metallic surface can react directly with an atmosphere as shown in Eq. (21-9) if the resulting free energy change ΔG is negative

$$aMe + bO_2 \rightarrow Me_aO_{2b} \qquad \Delta G < 0 \tag{21-9}$$

Although oxygen is the most commonly encountered oxidizing gas, SO_2 and H_2S from fuels and chlorine or other gases encountered in specific situations can cause similar reactions. A classical example is the tarnishing of silver by

[5] The importance of chloride ions in preventing passivation in iron is shown in Fig. 21-5.

the hydrogen sulfide in the atmosphere. Of more engineering consequence is the presence of SO_2 in the combustion chambers of jet engines. ΔG depends on the temperature and partial pressure of the reactant gas but with the exception of the noble metals, under most conditions $\Delta G \ll 0$ and the initial reaction on a clean metal surface proceeds quite rapidly even at room temperature. Fortunately, however, the reaction often will quickly slow down due to the necessity for ion diffusion through the oxide film that is formed. If a dense, adherent film forms which prevents direct contact between the metal and the atmosphere, the oxidation rate will become very slow as the film thickens. It is primarily for this reason that oxidation is usually only of concern at elevated temperatures. Typical data showing the change in film thickness with time during oxidation at 400°C in air are shown in Fig. 21-12.

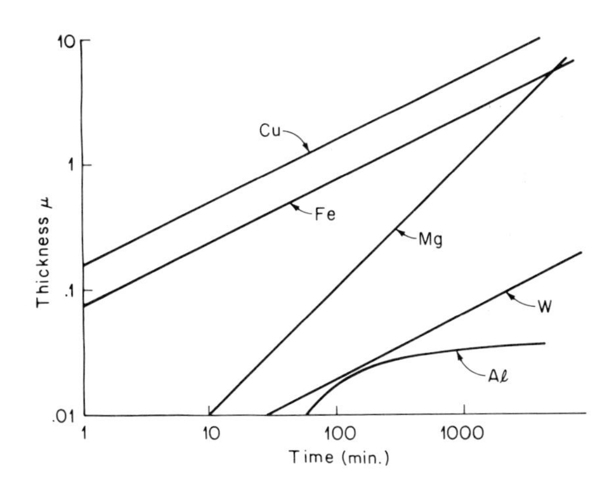

FIG. 21-12 Typical oxidation rates at 400°C of various metals in dry air or oxygen at 0.2 atm. are shown as a function of time. Copper, iron, and tungsten show parabolic oxidation rates, magnesium a linear rate, and aluminum has a complex time dependence

In considering the oxidation resistance of metals we are primarily concerned with oxidation rate and this is usually controlled by diffusional processes. Thus, the observed oxidation resistance of the metal might be quite high even though there is a large driving force for oxidation. Pilling and Bedworth[6] showed that metals could be divided into two classes depending on the relative volumes of the oxide and metal. If the volume of the oxidation product is greater than that of the metal from which it forms, it seems reasonable that a dense film might be produced which would limit the

[6] N. Pilling and R. Bedworth, *J. Inst. Metals*, **29**, 534 (1923).

oxidation rate. From Eq. (21-9) the ratio of the oxide volume to the metal volume is

$$\frac{V_{ox}}{V_{met}} = \frac{M_{ox}}{M_{met}} \frac{\rho_{met}}{\rho_{ox}} \frac{1}{a}$$

where M is a molecular weight and ρ a density.

For the very light metals, sodium, potassium, magnesium, and calcium this ratio is less than one while for aluminum, berylium, and the heavier metals the ratio is greater than one. Of course, it may be for one reason or another that even if the Pilling-Bedworth ratio is favorable, an adherent, dense oxide film is not maintained. There is inevitably some misfit between the atomic planes of oxide and of the metal so that residual stresses build up in the oxide film unless it is able to plastically deform. This means that the film eventually spalls off and a new film starts growing leading to a discontinuous increase in the local oxidation rate.

21-9 Oxidation Kinetics. In order for oxidation to take place through a film, there must be diffusion of oxygen ions or metals ions and electron or hole motion as indicated in Fig 21-13. Electrical conductivity is required because at the film-gas interface, electrons are taken on by the oxygen atoms while at the film-metal interface they are released by the metal atoms. The oxide film replaces both the liquid electrolyte and the metallic conduction path present during corrosion.

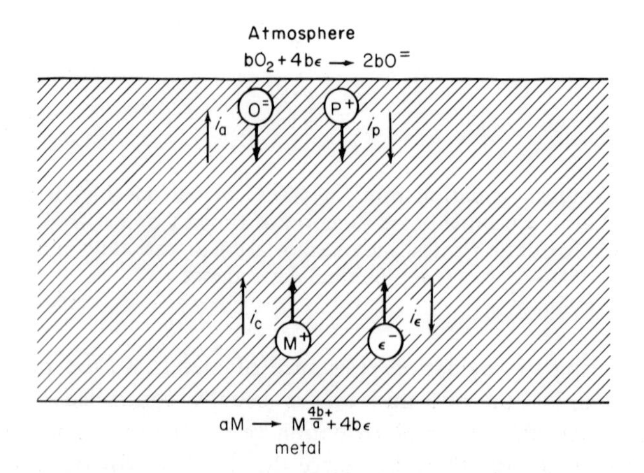

FIG. 21-13 The various diffusion and corresponding electric currents existing in an oxide film during oxidation. At the atmosphere-oxide interface, anions are formed which diffuse toward the metal. As electrons are required for the dissociation reaction taking place at this interface, holes may also be created which diffuse toward the metal. At the metal oxide interface cations and electrons are formed which diffuse through the film

If the oxidation process is diffusion limited, to a first approximation, the concentration difference ΔC of the diffusing ions between the inner and outer surfaces of the oxide film remains constant as the film thickness y increases. For example, at the outer surface there is an oxygen excess while at the inner oxide surface there is an oxygen deficiency. If the diffusivity D of the ions in the film remains independent of time and position, the diffusion flux is simply

$$J = -D\frac{\delta c}{\delta y} = -D\frac{\Delta c}{y}$$

The instantaneous growth rate dy/dt is proportional to the flux if J_{O_2} moles of oxygen react according to Eq. (21-9) per second, per unit area, the corresponding increase in film thickness is

$$\frac{dy}{dt} = \frac{J_{O_2}M_{ox}}{b\rho_{ox}} = \frac{K}{y} \tag{21-10a}$$

where K is a proportionality constant. Thus

$$y = (2Kt)^{1/2} \tag{21.10b}$$

and a parabolic thickening law with respect to time should be observed. Once the film becomes thick enough so that it no longer adheres to the metal surface this law breaks down. Further, for very thin films up to about one hundred atomic layers thick, other factors may limit the growth rate so at both the thin and thick film limits this equation is not applicable.

In a manner analogous to corrosion, we can describe the instantaneous oxidation rate in terms of the electron current in the film. By a reasoning entirely analogous to that used in obtaining Eq. (21-5) it follows that the emf driving the electron and ion currents is $\Delta G/n$. From the reactions shown in Fig. 21-13, it follows that $n = 4b$. Using resistances to limit the electron, hole, cation, and anion currents, the oxidation process is described by the equivalent electrical circuit shown in Fig. 21-14a. The corresponding current which defines the oxidation rate is given by Eq. (21-11) where R_i is a resistance equivalent to R_A and R_C in parallel and R_e is a resistance equivalent to R_C and R_ϵ in parallel.

$$I = \frac{E}{R_i + R_e} = \frac{(\Delta G/Fn)}{R_i + R_e} \tag{21-11}$$

The flux J is related to I by Eq. (21-6) so on combination of Eq. (21-6) and Eq. (21-10a) we have

$$I = \frac{dy}{dt} FAn \frac{\rho_{ox}}{M_{ox}} \tag{21-12}$$

On combining Eq. (21-11) and Eq. (21-12) we have

$$\frac{dy}{dt} = \frac{\Delta G}{F^2A(R_i + R_e)n^2}\left(\frac{M_{ox}}{\rho_{ox}}\right) \tag{21-13}$$

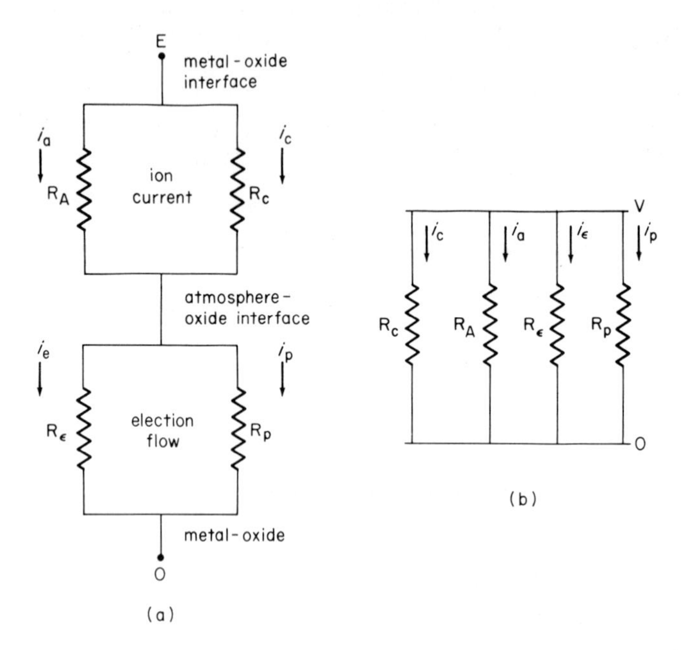

FIG. 21-14 Equivalent circuits for oxide films: (a) during oxidation it is necessary that there be both an ionic current and an electronic current to maintain charge neutrality in the film. The two flows are in series as shown, (b) during an electrical conductivity experiment with an oxide, current can be conducted either by electronic motion or ionic diffusion. Ionic motion leads to a shift in the position of the oxide but to no additional oxide formation. Therefore the electronic and ionic flows have independent parallel paths as shown

Of the parameters in Eq. (21-13) $(R_i + R_e)$ is the only one for which experimental data is not readily available. It is possible to relate $R_i + R_e$ to the conductivity of the oxide however. The ionic resistance depends on the charge carried by the diffusing ions and their diffusivity. In a normal conductivity measurement on a defect semiconductor, the ionic and electronic currents would be in parallel whereas during oxidation they are in series. The fraction of the current in a conductivity measurement carried by anions can be represented by N_a, by the cations by N_c, and by the holes or electrons N_e. The sum of these three transport numbers must add to one.

$$N_a + N_c + N_e = 1$$

Considering the three current flows as occurring through three resistors in parallel as shown in Fig. 21-14b, we can write

$$\frac{1}{R} = \frac{1}{R_a} + \frac{1}{R_c} + \frac{1}{R_e} = \frac{A}{y\kappa N_a} + \frac{A}{y\kappa N_c} + \frac{A}{y\kappa N_e} \quad \text{and} \quad R = \frac{y}{A\kappa}$$

where κ is the conductivity. On solving this equation for $R_i + R_e$ we obtain

$$R_i + R_e = \frac{y}{A\kappa}\left(\frac{1}{N_a + N_c} + \frac{1}{N_e}\right) = \frac{y}{A\kappa}\frac{1}{N_e(N_c + N_a)} \tag{21-14}$$

Substituting Eq. (21-14) into Eq. (21-13) we have

$$\frac{dy}{dt} = \frac{\Delta G \kappa N_e(N_c + N_a)}{n^2F^2y}\left(\frac{M_{ox}}{\rho_{ox}}\right) \tag{21-15}$$

and from Eq. (21-10a)

$$K = \frac{\Delta G \kappa V_e(N_c + N_a)}{n^2F^2}\left(\frac{M_{ox}}{\rho_{ox}}\right) \tag{21-16}$$

In order to evaluate Eq. (21-16) it is necessary to know the transport numbers in addition to the oxide conductivity. Usually this experimental data is not available. Also, it may well be that due to differences in stoichiometry the conductivity measured on a bulk oxide sample may be different than that in a thin film. Nevertheless if the conductivity is low, the film growth rate will be correspondingly low. There are then two conditions for metallic materials to fulfill for good oxidation resistance: (1) The oxide film must be continuous and adherent, and (2) to minimize the conductivity it must not be a defect-containing lattice. Aluminum and chromium oxides fulfill these conditions quite well and correspondingly these metals are known for their oxidation resistance. In most oxides, the metal ions are considerably more mobile than the anions owing to their smaller size.[7] In this case the oxide film grows by metal ions diffusing through the oxide to the outer surface.

As an example of the evaluation of oxidation rates, consider the formation of Cu_2O at 1000°C in an atmosphere where the partial pressure of O_2 is 1.5×10^{-2} atmospheres. Under these conditions Cu_2O forms a defect lattice which is a p type semiconductor due to the presence of a small number of Cu^{++} ions. $\rho_{ox} = 6.0$ grams/cm^3 and $\kappa = 6.4\ \Omega^{-1}\ \text{cm}^{-1}$. Due to the relatively high electronic conductivity $N_e \approx 1$ and diffusion data indicate that $N_c + N_a = 5.10^{-4}$ for this temperature and pressure. From thermodynamic data on the heat of formation of Cu_2O it is known that $\Delta G = -13{,}660$ calories/gram mole $= -57{,}000$ joules/gram mole of Cu_2O. Substituting these values into Eq. (21-16)

$$K = \frac{-57{,}100 \times 6.4 \times 1 \times 5 \times 10^{-4} \times 143}{2(96.5 \times 10^3)^2 6} = 2.3 \times 10^{-8}\ \text{cm}^2/\text{sec}$$

This result agrees reasonably well with the experimental value of 5.4×10^{-8} square centimeter/second.

[7] Since the relative mobility of the cations and anions also depends on the concentrations of cations and anion vacancies, no completely general statement about relative diffusion rates can be made.

21-10 Oxidation in Polymer Materials. Polymer materials may also have their properties altered as a result of oxidation type reactions. In this case no oxide scale is formed because oxygen diffuses in the polymer quite rapidly and the reaction occurs throughout the bulk of the polymer. The oxidation rate is limited by the rate at which the chemical reaction can take place. At high temperatures polymers oxidize quite rapidly because of the lack of a protective scale so they are rarely used at temperatures greater than 300°C. Oxidation leads to a variety of changes in the polymer structure. Depending on the particular polymer, cross-linking, scission, polymerization, or depolymerization may occur. The actual chemical reactions in most instances are not known but free radicals are formed which cause the subsequent reactions to occur. Although the properties of the resulting polymer are generally degraded, in some cases the oxidation reaction is utilized. Paints harden due to an oxygen caused polymerization and the same is true of a variety of polymer adhesives and sealants such as silicone rubber that are available on the market.

21-11 Radiation Damage. Practically all properties of solids can be altered by high energy radiation over a sufficient length of time. Although radiation damage is of importance in a variety of fields, most of the interest has originated from the practical problem of building nuclear reactors that work reliably over long periods of time. The structural elements, various controls, fuel, and moderator are subjected to neutron, gamma, and fission fragment radiation. Typical flux levels in a reactor may be on the order of 10^{12} neutrons/square centimeter second so that over a period of time a significant fraction of the atoms in the solid may be affected by the various radiations present.

The gamma radiation causes damage primarily by pair production in which part of the photon energy is converted to the production of an electron and positron pair. These particles may have considerable kinetic energy, and subsequent impacts with atoms in the solid can cause much the same sort of damage as neutron radiation.

The neutrons emitted on fissioning a U^{235} atom have energies ranging from 0.5 to 10 million electron volts with an average of 1.5 million electron volts. In a reactor, it is necessary to slow down those high energy neutrons before they will react with the fuel to cause a continuing fission process. The graphite or other moderator material slows down the fast neutrons by a repeated collision process so that the neutron energy spectrum in a reactor goes all the way from 10 million to 0.03 electron volts. This later value is typical of a particle in thermal equilibrium with its environment.

There are basically three ways in which high energy radiation can affect solids. In crystalline materials, the most important factor to consider is the displacement of an atom resulting from impact by a neutron or other particle. Such collisions result in the formation of vacancies and interstitials or more complex defect groups, which can significantly affect various properties of the solid. In Fig. 21-15a the effect of radiation on the yield strength of copper and on the electrical conductivity of germanium is shown. As is typical of experiments performed in reactors the exposure is reported in terms of *nvt* units which is the integrated thermal neutron flux per square centimeter. The fast neutrons are not counted in this unit and since the proportion of fast to slow neutrons differs from one position to another and one reactor to another, the unit is somewhat approximate.

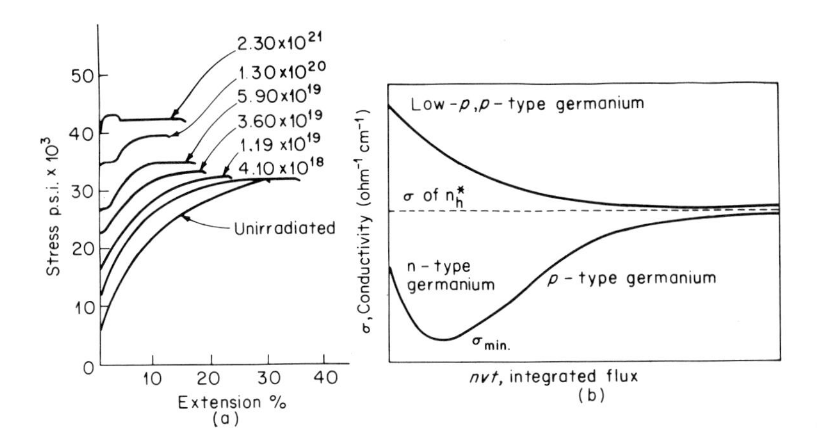

FIG. 21-15 The effects of neutron radiation: (a) variation in the stress strain curve of polycrystalline copper (irradiated at 80°C. and tested at 20°C., dose indicated in *nvt* units) (From M. J. Makin in *Radiation Effects*, edited by W. F. Sheely, Gordon and Beach, New York, 1967, permission granted); (b) schematic diagram of the conductivity of germanium as a function of radiation dose (From Douglas S. Billington and James H. Crawford, Jr., *Radiation Damage in Solids*, Princeton University Press, Princeton, 1961, by permission)

In polymer materials, the ionizing properties of the radiation are most important as changes in the electronic structure of the atoms result in the formation of free radicals and broken bonds. In this case a variety of units describing the extent to which the radiation will cause ionization in various media may be used. In Fig. 21-16 the effect on the elastic modulus of a polymer to exposure in a nuclear reactor is shown. For such exposure, the ionizing radiation is primarily caused by reactions between the neutrons and polymer material. A third possibility for damage is that an atom may capture a neutron and the resulting nuclear reaction results in the production of an isotope of a different element. In this way an impurity atom is introduced into the solid.

This problem is of considerable importance in uranium fuel elements since some of the fission products lead to rare gas formation which causes swelling,

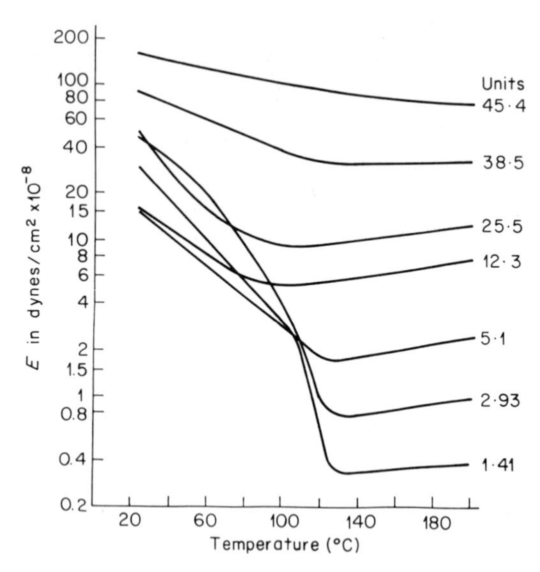

FIG. 21-16 The effect of neutron radiation (*nvt* units) on the elastic modulus of polyethylene. (From Charlesby and N. H. Hancock, *Proc. Roy. Soc., London*, **A 218,** 245 (1953) by permission)

cracking, and general dimensional instability in the fuel elements while in service. We will not consider this problem further however.

In a collision between a neutron and an atom it can be shown that the maximum energy (E_p) that can be transferred to an atom by a neutron collision is

$$E_p = \frac{4E_n Mm}{(M + m)^2} \approx \frac{4E_n}{M}$$

where E_n is the neutron energy, m the neutron mass and M the atomic mass. The approximation follows because usually $M \gg m$. For an energetic neutron of about 1 million electron volts, the energy transfer is ≈ 40 thousand electron volts which is much greater than the binding energy of an atom (≈ 2 electron volts). As a result of the collision between an energetic neutron and an atom (primary knock-on) the atom is displaced from its position in the solid often by a distance on the order of 100 Å. As a result of the large energy imparted to the atom, it may be able to knock additional atoms out of their positions before it is finally slowed down and stopped. Since the neutron will have lost only a relatively small portion of its energy as a result of the collision, it will proceed on through the solid and collide with other atoms leaving a track of damage through the solid until it is finally slowed down enough so that it is captured by an atom in some type of neutron reaction.

The mean free path L_d between displacement collisions is given by an expression

$$L_d = (N_a \sigma_d)^{-1}$$

where N_a is the number of atoms per unit volume and σ_d is the displacement cross-section of an atom for a high energy neutron. σ_d is in units of square centimeters and in effect measures the apparent cross-sectional area of an atom in so far as the probability of a nuclear collision is concerned. For most atoms σ_d is in the range $2 - 4 \times 10^{-24}$ square centimeter while N_a is about $0.5 - 1 \times 10^{23}$ cm^{-3} so L_d is typically about 0.2 centimeter. This means that if a neutron is moving through a thick solid it will undergo more than one primary knock-on but that they are quite far apart from each other so that the resulting damage is associated with separated small regions.

In metals, the most important effect of radiation damage is probably on their mechanical properties. Basically the radiation introduces large numbers of vacancies and interstitials into the lattice. These defects are quite mobile in most metals at room temperature and above, so that there may be considerable rearrangement of the defects into various sorts of aggregations. In any case these small regions distort the surrounding lattice and set up high elastic stress fields. In this respect the effect is very similar to precipitation hardening; the yield stress is increased because of the radiation induced defects and dislocations. The longer the exposure the greater the defect concentration and the greater the stress increase. At temperatures somewhat below the recrystallization temperature of the metals, the radiation damage anneals out.

Associated with the increased strength caused by radiation there is usually a decreased ductility which may lead to problems of brittle fracture. This is particularly true in bcc metals where the dislocations interact strongly with the tetragonal distortion produced by interstitials. The effect of radiation on the transition temperature of a steel is shown in Fig. 21-17.

The effects of radiation damage on the electrical properties of semiconductors are particularly noticeable because of the sensitivity of semiconductors to small changes in the number of conduction electrons or holes. The various defects created by the radiation affect both the mobility and the charge carrier density of semi-conductors. The mobility is decreased because of the increased scattering of conduction electrons. The number of charge carriers is altered because of the influence of the defects on the electronic energy levels. Just as an impurity atom can cause a local energy level slightly above the valence band or slightly below the conduction band, vacancies or interstitials resulting from the radiation can cause similar energy levels. This is not surprising since a vacancy can be crudely considered as an impurity atom of zero valence. Thus it would be expected to cause one or more holes while an interstitial should cause an extra conduction electron. Actually the problem is somewhat more complicated than this and the

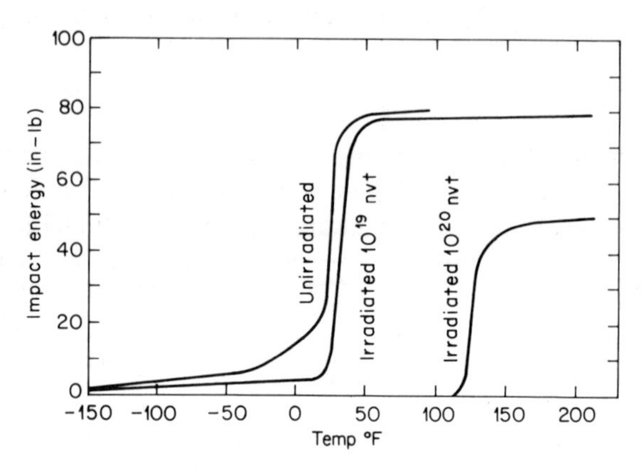

FIG. 21-17 The effect of neutron radiation on the impact energy of a carbon-silicon steel. Irradiation causes a large increase in the transition temperature. (From J. C. Wilson and R. G. Berggren, Proc. ASTM 55, 689 (1955), by permission)

defects present are not isolated vacancies and interstitials. However, various donor and acceptor states are produced by radiation and these do affect the conductivity. For example in Fig. 21-15b it can be seen that *n* type germanium goes through a minimum in conductivity. This is because the majority of the radiation induced defects are holes so that initially the conductivity decreases rapidly as the holes cancel out the free electrons initially present. The conductivity rises once the material is converted to *p* type germanium due to the excess of holes. The conductivity of the initially *p* type germanium decreases; however, the primary effect of the radiation is to decrease the mobility of the holes already present.

21-12 Radiation Damage in Polymers. Polymer materials are more susceptible to radiation damage than metals because of the possibility of new molecular configurations resulting from the broken bonds caused by the radiation. Not only does this lead to the possibility of relatively greater changes in properties but also these changes can be accomplished by much less energetic radiation. Much data has been collected on the radiation damage caused by ultraviolet light and these observations are certainly substantiated by everyday experience with the deterioration of some plastics on exposure to sunlight. Photons in the ultraviolet ranges, or, of course, more energetic particles have sufficient energy so that on interaction with a molecule a valence electron is promoted into a higher energy level, that is to an excited state. The excited electron may remain bound to the parent nucleus and the excess energy is eventually dissipated by various electronic interactions so that the electron falls back to its original stable state and the only net effect is a heating of the polymer. A second possibility is that the covalent bond between two atoms may be broken and the valence electron is ejected from the atom leaving behind one or two radicals. If the radicals capture a free electron and reunite there is again no effect, but it is possible that some other sort of chemical reaction involving other nearby atoms will take place resulting in cross-linking or chain scission. Quite often, in addition to the property changes caused by the change in the polymer structure, hydrogen, carbon dioxide or hydrocarbon gases are products of the chemical reactions involved and these gases can cause serious distortion of the polymer. As would be expected from a knowledge of polymer structure, if radiation causes cross-linking, in polymers which are initially linear there is an increase in strength, toughness, elastic modulus, and viscosity and a decrease in crystallinity. With large radiation doses the polymer may become quite hard and brittle. On the other hand, if chain scission predominates, the polymer is gradually degraded and eventually becomes quite weak. At the present time it is not possible to predict from first principles if cross-linking or scission will predominate in any given polymer, but a number have been investigated and some results are shown in Table 21-3, and Fig. 21-18 and 21-19.

Empirically it is observed that in polymers containing benzene rings, radiation effects are much less pronounced than in similar polymers with different side groups. For example, in polystyrene 1400–1600 electron volts of ionizing radiation is absorbed by the polymer for each broken bond whereas the actual energy required for bond breaking is only on the order of 5 electron volts. This means that most of the absorption processes do no involve bond breaking. In polyethylene, however, only 40–60 electron volts are absorbed per broken bond. It is believed that the reason for this is that an excited electron in a benzene ring can easily dissipate energy by resonance in the ring

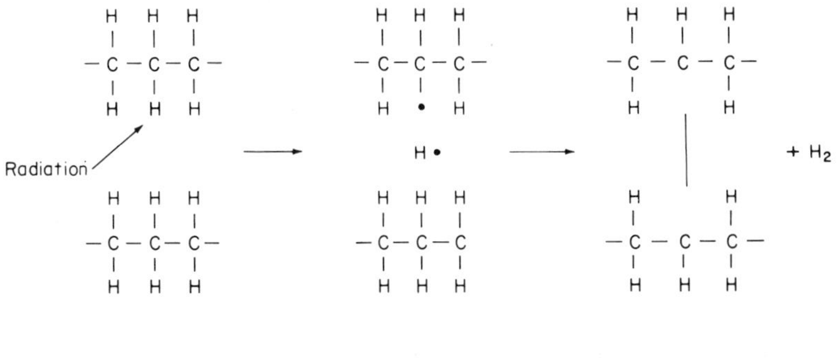

FIG. 21-18 Radiation induced chemical reaction that could cause crosslinking in polyethylene: (a) radiation causes the formation of a radical and a hydrogen atom; (b) the hydrogen atom reacts with a neighboring polymer chain to produce a second radical and molecular hydrogen; (c) the two neighboring radicals react to cause crosslinking with a carbon double bond

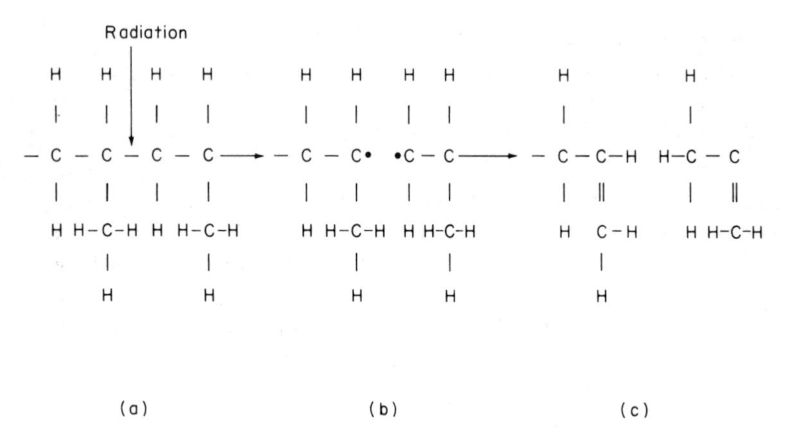

FIG. 21-19 A scission reaction which could occur in polypropylene is shown. In (a) the chain is severed by the incident radiation. In (b) the radicals react with neighboring methyl groups to form a stable unsaturated polymer

so that there is less tendency for it to be ejected. The design implications for the use of polymer materials in radiation fields are obvious.

The occurrence of cross-linking is usually attributed to the formation of polymer radicals at adjacent sites on neighboring chains. If radicals were produced at random sites, close pairs would not occur often enough to account for the observed degree of cross-linking and it seems probable that the initially ejected hydrogen atom may remove a neighboring hydrogen atom forming molecular hydrogen as indicated in Fig. 21-18. The two chains then combine to form a cross-link. A scission reaction might occur as shown in Fig. 21-19.

The study of radiation effects in polymers is complicated by the fact that small amounts of impurities may alter the reactions considerably so that polymers which are nominally similar but made by different processes may show considerably different behavior. The presence of oxygen in many polymers inhibits cross-linking and promotes scission. This may result simply from the oxygen molecule reacting with the radicals produced by radiation before cross-linking or recombination can occur. In any case, since many polymers are permeable to oxygen, the extent of the radiation effects depend not only on the total dose but also on the exposure time and temperature.

21-13 Summary. Materials are affected by their environment in a variety of ways. Chemical reactions with the oxygen present either in air or dissolved in water are from a technological standpoint the most important. Nearly all metallic materials will corrode in water or oxidize in air although the reaction rates differ by many orders of magnitude for different materials. Corrosion and oxidation are similar in that a motion of both electrons and ions is involved. Some metallic materials form adherent dense

TABLE 21-1 CORROSION RATE RANGES EXPRESSED IN MILS PENETRATION PER YEAR (MPY)

Metal	*Acid Solutions*			*Alkaline Solutions*	*Neutral Solutions*		*Air*
	Non-oxidizing		*Oxidizing*				
	Sulfuric, 5%	*Acetic 5%*	*Nitric, 5%*	*Sodium Hydroxide, 5%*	*Fresh Water*	*Sea Water*	*Normal Outdoor Urban Exposure*
Aluminum	8–100	0.5–5	15–80	13,000	0.1	1–50	0–0.5
Zinc	High	600–800	High	15–200	0.5–10*	0.5–10*	0–0.5
Tin	2–500*	2–500*	100–400	5–20	0–0.5	0.1	0–0.2
Lead	0–2	10–150*	100–6000	5–500*	0.1–2	0.2–15	0–0.2
Iron	15–400*	10–400	1000–10,000	0–0.2	0.1–10*	0.1–10*	1–8
Silicon Iron	0–5	0–0.2	0–20	0–10	0–0.2	0–3	0–0.2
Stainless Steel	0–100†	0–0.5	0–2	0–0.2	0–0.2	0–200†	0–0.2
Copper Alloys	2–50*	2–15*	150–1500	2–5	0–1	0.2–15*	0–0.2
Nickel Alloys	2–35*	2–10*	0.1–1500	0–0.2	0–0.2	0–1	0–0.2
Titanium	10–100	<0.1	<0.1–1	<0.2	<0.1	<0.1	<0.1
Molybdenum	0–0.2	<0.1	High	<0.1	<0.1	<0.1	<0.1
Zirconium	<0.5	<0.1	<0.1	<0.1	<0.1	<0.1	<0.1
Tantalum	<0.1	<0.1	<0.1	<1	<0.1	<0.1	<0.1
Silver	0–1	<0.1	High	<0.1	<0.1	<0.1	<0.1
Platinum	<0.1	<0.1	<0.1	<0.1	<0.1	<0.1	<0.1
Gold	<0.1	<0.1	<0.1	<0.1	<0.1	<0.1	<0.1

* Aeration leads to the higher rates in the range.
† Aeration leads to passivity; scarcity of dissolved air leads to activity.
Note: The corrosion rate ranges for the solutions are based on temperatures up to 212°F.
Source: F. L. LaQue and H. R. Copson, *Corrosion Resistance of Metals and Alloys*, Second Ed., Reinhold, New York, 1963, by permission.

films of the corrosion or oxidation product which drastically limit further chemical reaction.

Because of the large variation in rate proper material selection is important. In addition, a knowledge of the corrosion process can be put to use to devise techniques such as cathode or anodic protection. More recently, the effect

TABLE 21-2 ELECTROMOTIVE FORCE SERIES*

Electrode Reaction	E° (*Volts*) *at* 25°C
$Li = Li^+ + \epsilon^-$	−3.05
$K = K^+ + \epsilon^-$	−2.93
$Ca = Ca^{++} + 2\epsilon^-$	−2.87
$Na = Na^+ + \epsilon^-$	−2.71
$Mg = Mg^{++} + 2\epsilon^-$	−2.37
$Be = Be^{++} + 2\epsilon^-$	−1.85
$U = U^{+++} + 3\epsilon^-$	−1.80
$Hf = Hf^{++++} + 4\epsilon^-$	−1.70
$Al = Al^{+++} + 3\epsilon^-$	−1.66
$Ti = Ti^{++} + 2\epsilon^-$	−1.63
$Zr = Zr^{++++} + 4\epsilon^-$	−1.53
$Mn = Mn^{++} + 2\epsilon^-$	−1.18
$Nb = Nb^{+++} + 3\epsilon^-$	ca −1.1
$Zn = Zn^{++} + 2\epsilon^-$	−0.763
$Cr = Cr^{+++} + 3\epsilon^-$	−0.74
$Ga = Ga^{+++} + 3\epsilon^-$	−0.53
$Fe = Fe^{++} + 2\epsilon^-$	−0.440
$Cd = Cd^{++} + 2\epsilon^-$	−0.403
$In = In^{+++} + 3\epsilon^-$	−0.342
$Tl = Tl^+ + \epsilon^-$	−0.336
$Co = Co^{++} + 2\epsilon^-$	−0.277
$Ni = Ni^{++} + 2\epsilon^-$	−0.250
$Mo = Mo^{+++} + 3\epsilon^-$	ca −0.2
$Sn = Sn^{++} + 2\epsilon^-$	−0.136
$Pb = Pb^{++} + 2\epsilon^-$	−0.126
$Fe = Fe^{+++} + 3\epsilon^-$	−0.036
$H_2 = 2H^{++} + 2\epsilon^-$	0.000
$Cu = Cu^{++} + 2\epsilon^-$	0.337
$Cu = Cu^+ + \epsilon^-$	0.521
$2Hg = Hg_2^{++} + 2\epsilon^-$	0.789
$Hg = Hg^{++} + 2\epsilon^-$	0.854
$Pd = Pd^{++} + 2\epsilon^-$	0.987
$Ag = Ag^+ + \epsilon^-$	0.899
$Pt = Pt^{++} + 2\epsilon^-$	ca1.2
$Au = Au^{+++} + 3\epsilon^-$	1.50
$Au = Au^+ + \epsilon^-$	1.68

* The standard oxidation potentials are listed for electrodes in contact with solutions of unit activity ≈ 1 molar in the cation involved.

of various radiations on materials has become an important consideration. Both polymer and metallic materials may have their properties drastically changed by neutron or gamma radiation.

TABLE 21-3 EFFECT OF HIGH ENERGY ELECTRONS ON POLYMERS*

Polymers Becoming Cross-linked	*Polymers Becoming Degraded*
Polyacrylic esters	Polymethyl methacrylate
Polyacrylic acid	Polymethacrylic acid
Polyacrylamide	Polymethacrylamide
Polyvinyl alkyl ethers	Polyvinyl chloride
Polyvinyl methyl ketone	Polyvinylidence chloride
Polystyrene	Polytetafluorethylene
Polyesters	Polychlorotrifluoroethylene
Nylon	Cellulose
Polyethylene	Polyisobutylene
Polymethylene	Poly-α-methylstyrene
Polypropylene	
Chlorinated polyethylene	
Chlorosulfonated polyethylene	
Natural rubber	
GR-S	
Butadience-acrylonitrile copolymers	
Styrene-acrylonitrile copolymers	
Neoprene-W	
Neoprene-GN	
Polydimethysiloxanes	

* Source: Frank A. Bovey, *The Effects of Ionizing Radiation on Natural and Synthetic High Polymers*, Interscience, New York, 1958, by permission.

References

Introductory

1. Herbert H. Uhlig, *Corrosion and Corrosion Control*, Wiley, New York, 1963.
2. J. Hartley Bowen, Jr., and Dominick V. Rosato, "Radiation," in *Environmental Effects on Polymeric Materials*, Vol. 1, Dominick V. Rosato and Robert T. Schwartz, Eds., Interscience Publishers, New York, 1968.
3. Jere H. Brophy, Robert M. Rose, and John Wulff, *The Structure and Properties of Materials*, Vol. II, Wiley, New York, 1964. (See Ch. 9, "Oxidation" and Ch. 10, "Aqueous Corrosion.")
4. Ulick R. Evans, *Introduction to Metallic Corrosion*, St. Martins, New York, 1963.
5. J. S. Scully, *The Fundamental of Corrosion*, Pergamon, New York, 1966.

Advanced

1. Karl Hauffe, "The Mechanism of Oxidation of Metals and Alloys at High Temperature," in *Progress in Materials Science*, Vol. 4, Chalmers, Ed., Pergamon, New York, 1953.
2. Karl Hauffe, *Oxidation of Metals*, Plenum, New York, 1965.

3. Carl Wagner, "Diffusion and High Temperature Oxidation of Metals," in *Atom Movements*, John H. Hollomon, Ed., American Society for Metals, Metals Park, 1951.
4. O. Kubaschewski and B. E. Hopkins, *Oxidation of Metals and Alloys*, Sec. Ed., Butterworths, London, 1962.
5. Robert B. Fox, "Photodegradation of High Polymers," in *Progress in Polymer Science*, Vol. 1, A. D. Jenkins, Ed., Pergamon, New York, 1967.
6. Frank A. Bovey, *Effects of Ionizing Radiation on Natural and Synthetic High Polymers*, Interscience, New York, 1958.
7. Douglass S. Billington and James H. Crawford, Jr., *Radiation Damage in Solids*, Princeton U.P., Princeton, 1961.

Problems

21-1 A capacitor consists of two parallel copper plates each 0.01 centimeter thick and separated by an air gap of 0.2 centimeter. If the lower plate is just submerged in water, what fraction of it would have to dissolve as single valent ions to create a potential of 1 volt across the capacitor?

21-2 In the refining of copper, steel scrap is often used to precipitate copper out of acid solution. If the solution initially has a concentration of 0.01 mole, what fraction of it would precipitate on the introduction of an excess of iron? Assume the iron goes into solution as ferrous ion.

21-3 Suppose that the rate at which oxygen can diffuse to a sheet of iron is the limiting factor in determining the corrosion rate. Suppose the diffusivity of oxygen in water is 1.5×10^{-5} square centimeters/second and that it diffuses through a distance of 1 centimeter to the sheet. If the oxygen concentration 1 centimeter away is 1 millimeter oxygen/liter water, what is the corrosion rate of the sheet in mils per year?

21-4 Explain why magnesium has a linear oxidation rate.

21-5 Explain why rubber may become brittle after long exposure to air.

21-6 Give a plausible explanation for the fact that at low radiation levels and low temperatures, increasing radiation decreases the elastic modulus of polyethylene while the reverse is true at high temperatures. (See Fig. 21-14.)

21-7 The properties of polyethylene are often improved in commercial practice by irradiation. Assume that a dose of 10^7 rads (1 rad = 100 ergs/gram) are necessary to cross-link polyethylene for heat shrinkable packing. What is the minimum current required by a 2×10^6 electron volt electron beam accelerator to produce 200 pounds of product per hour? Assume the entire electron beam is absorbed in the polyethylene.

INDEX